199

GREENBOOK GUIDE

Devoted Exclusively to

HALLMARK

KEEPSAKE ORNAMENTS

MAGIC ORNAMENTS

MINIATURE ORNAMENTS

&

EASTER/SPRING ORNAMENTS

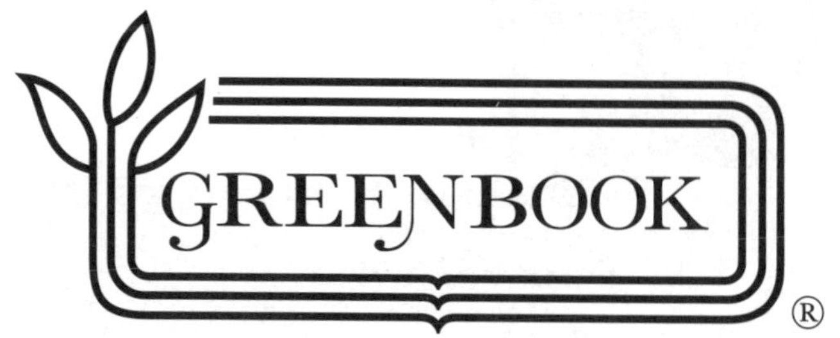

The Most Respected Guides To Popular Collectibles
& Their After Market Values
2000 Sunset, PO Box 645
Pacific Grove, CA 93950
(831) 656-9000
FAX (831) 656-9004

Printed in Canada.

ISBN 0-923628-60-6

GREENBOOK TRUMARKET™ PRICES are compiled from trades and information provided by retailers, dealers and collectors. Manufacturers verify factual information only and are not consulted or involved in any way in determining our TRUMARKET™ Secondary Market Prices.

Table Of Contents

The GREENBOOK GUIDE TO HALLMARK KEEPSAKE ORNAMENTS contains line drawings of each ornament issued prior to 1990 and black and white photos of ornaments issued from 1990 on. In addition, specific factual information is included next to each piece, as well as the GREENBOOK Trumarket Prices for each Keepsake, Magic, Miniature and Easter/Spring ornament.

Factual information includes the ornament Title, Description, Hallmark Stock Number, and Material. Size, and the name of the Artist are included when available. If the ornament is part of a Series or Collection, the name of the Series (and position in the Series) or Collection is included. Specific Edition Limits are provided, as well as information on Special Effects – Light, Motion, Music and Sound – when they apply. The original Suggested Retail Price (SRP) is also included.

Secondary Market Prices, as reported by retailers and collectors, are included as well. Because there are so many factors based on individual judgements, and because prices can vary depending on time of year or section of the country, GREENBOOK Trumarket Prices **are never an absolute number.** Use them as a benchmark. All GREENBOOK Trumarket Prices are for ornaments MINT IN BOX (MIB).

Ornaments are listed in four major categories: Keepsake, Magic, Miniature and Easter/Spring. Within each category, ornaments are listed chronologically by year of issue. Within each year, ornaments are listed alphabetically. If the ornament is part of a Series or Collection, it is listed under the name of the Series or Collection. For example, the 1995 Keepsake ornament *"Town Church,"* which is part of the NOSTALGIC HOUSES & SHOPS SERIES, would be found in the Keepsake section, in the year 1995, under NOSTALGIC HOUSES & SHOPS.

The following symbols are used throughout the ARTCHARTS:

- (pen) = artist's name
- (bulb) = lighted
- (note) = plays tune
- (arrows) = motion
- (switch) = on/off switch
- (sound waves) = makes sound

PAGE LAYOUT

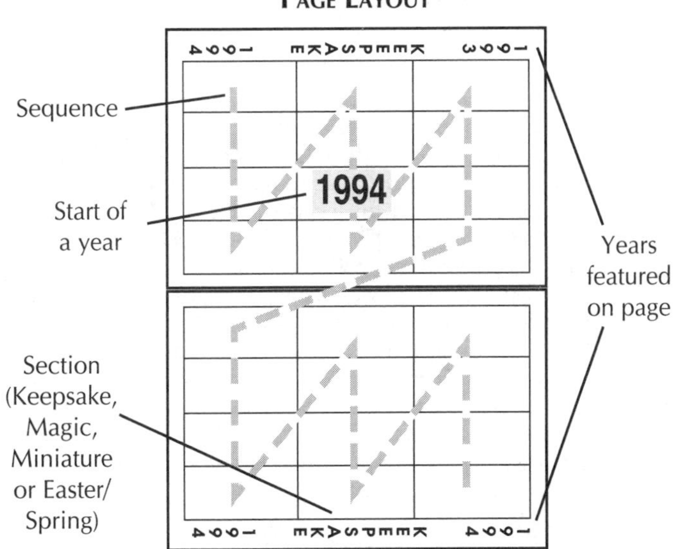

SAMPLE ARTCHART LISTING

Position in Series

Name of Series

Photo

Title of Ornament

Descriptive Information

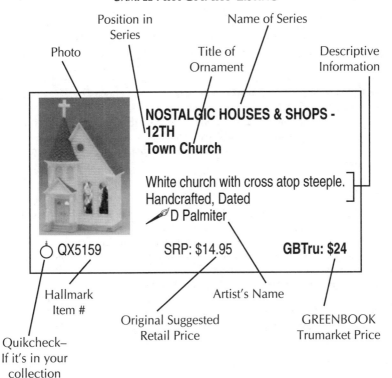

NOSTALGIC HOUSES & SHOPS - 12TH
Town Church

White church with cross atop steeple.
Handcrafted, Dated
D Palmiter

QX5159 SRP: $14.95 **GBTru: $24**

Hallmark Item #

Artist's Name

Original Suggested Retail Price

GREENBOOK Trumarket Price

Quikcheck– If it's in your collection

HISTORY OF HALLMARK

1973

The first selection of 1973 ornaments was featured in a *Winter Seasons* Hallmark retailer catalog. The contents page of that catalog contains product listings for *Hanukkah, Christmas Counter, Christmas Party, Sewn Products* and *New Year Products.* Where is the new 1973 line of Hallmark Christmas ornaments shown? They're tucked under the *Sewn Products* heading! The ornaments are officially called *Tree Trimmers.* The original 1973 ornament offering consisted of 6 ball ornaments and 12 yarn ornaments. Two different *Betsey Clark* ball ornaments make Betsey the first ever licensed character offered on a Hallmark ornament. The 1973 *First Edition Betsey Clark* ball is the first series ever offered. It stands to reason that these early ornaments have some of the lowest production numbers ever, making them hard to find, particularly the ball ornaments. Of the six 1973 ball Ornaments, *Santa with Elves,* the *Manger Scene, Elves* and *Christmas Is Love,* are the most difficult to find. Remember, ball ornaments break and over the years many have been lost. Poor storage conditions often lead to spots on the ornament. (Always check the bottom of the ball ornaments to insure they are in mint condition.)

1974

In 1974 a separate Hallmark retailer catalog for *Christmas Tree Trimmers* is produced. Because of their immediate popularity in 1973, glass ball ornaments are offered in 1974 in new sizes. The new, smaller sized ball ornaments are sold in sets of two or four. Licensed *Norman Rockwell* designs are added and *Betsey Clark* ornaments are back. *Raggedy Ann and Raggedy Andy* appear for the first time. *Currier & Ives* reproductions are used on ball ornaments. *The Snow Goose, Angel,* and *Norman Rockwell Santa* ball ornaments all are produced in low numbers, making them hard-to-find. Six yarn ornaments are offered in 1974. Yarn ornaments are "improved" and made larger. Boxes for ball ornaments are constructed of a plastic sleeve with cardboard top and bottom, held together by a gold-elastic cord. Retailers displayed boxed ornaments on a simple shelving unit. Yarn ornaments are sold in sealed polybags and were never boxed. A sample of each yarn ornament hung above the boxed ornaments on the display shelf below.

1975

The first ornament premiere takes place in 1975. Hallmark retailers are encouraged to set up a preview department on June 16th and expand the display to a total department on September 8th. Dated, unbreakable satin ball ornaments are introduced. "Nostalgia" and "Adorable" ornaments are the first hard-plastic handcrafted ornaments. *Raggedy Ann and Raggedy Andy* are used on ball ornaments, as Adorable ornaments, and are the first and only property yarn ornaments. The word plastic is used to describe ornaments — "injection-molded plastic" to be precise. "Plastic" is never again mentioned in catalogs as the material Handcrafted ornaments are made of. The line now contains 32 ornaments.

1976

"Twirl-Abouts," "Tree Treats" and "Yesteryears" ornaments are added. "Twirl-Abouts" are the first ornaments to feature movement. The *Bicentennial Charmers* commemorative ball ornament is the first ornament to be issued in a commemorative box. Two other ball ornaments are also designed to celebrate the Bicentennial. The caption *Baby's First Christmas,* makes its first appearance on a ball ornament. The satin ball ornament *Rudolph and Santa* introduces Rudolph to the Hallmark line. This hard-to-find ball ornament commands high secondary market prices today. Four tree skirts are offered that coordinate with the party theme designs for the year. Salt and Pepper Shakers and Napkin Rings make their first appearance.

1977

Peanuts ball ornaments debut in the 1977 line in distinctive doghouse-shaped boxes. 1977 is the only year Hallmark uses this unusual, and now hard-to-find packaging. The number of ornaments in the line jumps with 48 new designs added and approximately half the line dated. The dated feature of the ornaments is emphasized as an "important consideration for collectors." (Hallmark already knows we exist!) Ball ornament packaging is changed to a cardboard box with windows cut on all four sides — and a separate cardboard end piece on top and bottom. The caption, *Our First Christmas* debuts. Other new ball ornament captions include: *Granddaughter, Grandson, Grandmother, Mother, Love,* and *New Home.* Chrome and gold colored ball ornaments are introduced. The *Beauty of America* collection marks another first with four landscape designs. This group is hard to find, again because of low production numbers on these ornaments. The second collection of four ball ornaments offered in 1977, *Christmas Expressions,* is also difficult to find. The "Tiffany," metal, and acrylic ornaments make their first appearance. The 1977 *Betsey Clark Series* ball ornament is shown in the retailer catalog with the notation next to it, "Numerous requests bring this exclusive property back for 1977." Hallmark had intended to cancel this series, but because of collector demand they decided to issue it at the last minute. Retailers were notified of this decision in August, and this resulted in much lower production than usual. Only 24,360 of the 1977 *Betsey Clark Series* ball ornament were produced! The *Grandma Moses* ball ornament is introduced. Although *Grandma Moses* was repeated in 1978, this is one of the most rare Hallmark ornaments today. Disney ball ornaments are introduced, a first for this popular license with Hallmark. The metal *Snowflake Collection* is the only group of ornaments offered in a mailable box. Sewn fabric ornaments make their first appearance in the Keepsake line. A new dimensional, corrugated cardboard tree-shaped freestanding ornament display is also introduced and offered to retailers for several years that follow. A counter-top display is also available. Topped with a star, this pyramid-shaped tree design holds eight ball ornaments. Stocking Hangers, a Tree Topper, and a Table Top Decoration are offered in 1977 — all firsts.

1978

This is the year that is best known for the series that never quite happened. The ball ornament, *The Quail,* is introduced as the first design for an annual series of *Game Bird* dated ornaments. (Although a dated Cardinal ornament appeared in 1979, it doesn't seem it was intended as a follow-up.) The *Panorama Ball* ornament, showing the little boy who's fallen on the ice, is also announced as the first in a series (no name was

1978 continued

given to this one) of dated ornaments. *Animal Home* was announced as the first in a series of *Christmas Critters Homes* that never continued. None of these announced series ever came to be. In 1978, seventy-percent of the line is priced at $3.50 or less. (Doesn't that kill you?) The *25th Christmas Together* caption debuts. The *Cardinal* is the first clip-on ornament. *Schneeberg Bell* takes its name from the last name of the Hallmark artist who designed it. Schneeberg was an incredibly talented artist who worked in a collage format, and his designs can be found on several older jigsaw puzzles, as well as ball ornaments. The *Little Trimmers Collection* is introduced — this is the first time ornaments have been sold separately and packaged together as a group of four. The *Mouse in Thimble* later becomes the first in the *Thimble* series. *Spencer Sparrow* makes his first appearance in the line. *Reindeer Chimes* is the first metal chime ornament offered. Individual ornament display stands, a curved-brass hanger on a wood base — identical to the ones sold today — are available for collectors to purchase. Ball ornaments are now available in a new color — ecru. A new showcase retailer-display-system is added that closely resembles the ones we see today. It's a series of niches, each holding an ornament, with signing and caption identifiers. Available to Hallmark retailers in 4 foot or 8 foot systems, it's designed to hold all 54 ornaments in the 1978 line.

1979

The first consumer ornament brochure makes its debut with *Santa's Motorcar,* the First Edition of the *Here Comes Santa* series featured on the cover. More firsts in 1979 include two new captions, *Teacher* and *Special Friend.* The first handcrafted *Baby's First Christmas* ornament is introduced. *Winnie the Pooh* arrives on a ball ornament. Research by Hallmark reveals that 40% of purchasers consider themselves Hallmark ornament collectors. New boxes with artwork inside, behind the ornament, are introduced. The see-through lid allows the illustration or photo used to compliment the ornament. Examples of these boxes can be found on the *Baby's First Christmas* (handcrafted) and the *Here Comes Santa* ornaments. Ball ornament packaging is changed to a one-piece cardboard box with windows cut on all four sides. The removable (and easily lost and damaged) separate top and bottom pieces have been replaced by flap closures. The *Black Angel* ball ornament is the first ornament in the line to feature an African-American subject. The second *Little Trimmers* group appears and the new designs are again sold grouped together — this time as a set of three — or individually. *A Christmas Salute* later becomes the Second Edition in the *Thimble* series. *Christmas Eve Surprise* is the first "shadowbox" ornament. The *Drummer Boy* panorama ball was introduced as the second in a series of "scene-in-a-ball" ornaments. (Remember the 1978 boy on ice *Panorama* ball was supposed to have been the first in this series. Could *Ready for Christmas* have been intended as the second in the never-materialized *Christmas Critters Homes* series?) *Ice Hockey Holiday,* the Snoopy "scene-in-a-ball" ornament is later designated the First Edition in the *Snoopy and Friends* panorama ball series, but was not designated a series the year it came out. The First Edition *Bellringer* series debuted in 1979, but was originally called *The Bellswinger* series. Production was low on the first *Bellringer,* especially when compared to other first edition series ornaments. This is the last year the ornament line was called "The Tree Trimmer Collection."

1980

The name "Keepsake Ornaments" debuts! It's a new decade and the ornament line is growing by leaps and bounds. There are now 80 designs, a 30% increase over 1979. New ball ornament captions include: *Son, Daughter, Grandparents, Dad Mother & Dad, Grandfather,* and *Black Baby's First Christmas.* New licensed properties include the Muppets. New ornament formats include: "Frosted Images;" "Cameo Keepsakes" such as Betsey Clark and Norman Rockwell; the first flocked ornament, *Merry Redbird;* and the first tin ornament, *Santa's Flight.* Special Edition ornaments, *Checking it Twice,* and *Heavenly Minstrel* are introduced to Hallmark retailers as "larger than traditional ornament designs that will not display in the Keepsake Ornament display, but should be placed with special collectible and Christmas items." Because of their size, Hallmark felt consumers might not accept these two Special Edition pieces, and used each in a table top design as well. Cameo-style ornaments are introduced and featured on the new *Norman Rockwell* Cameo series. The 1980 *Betsey Clark* cameo was originally intended to be a first in series ornament. In 1980, 55% of those who buy ornaments consider themselves collectors. (Our numbers are growing!) And, they buy two or more ornaments when making a purchase. (No surprise there!) The size of the retail ornament display has grown to 12 feet. The new, second ornament brochure cover features *Santa's Express,* the Second Edition in the *Here Comes Santa* series and "encourages customers to collect by design and theme." Two ornaments produced using a new process — decoform — are shown in the Hallmark retailer catalog but are never available for sale outside the Kansas City area. They are *Holiday Dove* and the harder-to-find *Christmas Kitten. A Cool Yule* is introduced but not designated as a First in Series ornament in the retailer catalog or on the box. This leaves collectors scrambling to find the first edition in 1981, when the Second in Series *Frosty Friends* is introduced and is finally marked as a series ornament. (A *Spot of Christmas Cheer* could have been the third edition in the *Christmas Critters Homes* series. *A Christmas Vigil* could well have been the third edition in a "phantom" panorama ball series.)

1981

Several new commemoratives debut in 1981, including *Godchild* and *50 Years Together.* A Baby's First for *Baby Boy* and *Baby Girl,* along with the first photoholder ornaments are introduced in 1981. The number of true believers continues to grow. Hallmark research shows 67% of ornament buyers now consider themselves collectors and 75% of that number have been collecting more than 3 years. The new consumer ornament brochure features the Third Edition of *Here Comes Santa, Rooftop Deliveries.* The *Drummer Boy* is the first all-wood ornament in the line. *Mr. and Mrs. Claus* Adorables return as a boxed set, each originally introduced in 1975 and sold separately. Today, the single ornaments from 1975 command much higher secondary market prices than the pair that are packaged together, even though the ornaments are identical. *Muppets* handcrafted ornaments are added to the line. The *Traditional Black Santa* ball ornament is the first time an African-American Santa appears on an ornament. The *Ice Fairy* is the only all-white ornament Hallmark has ever produced. Plush, stuffed ornaments debut. Trimmers, unboxed ornaments, are sold for the first time, but are not shown in the Hallmark retailer catalog.

1982

It's the first time Keepsake Ornaments and Christmas decorations — Trimmer ornaments, stocking Hangers, etc. — are shown in the same Hallmark retailer catalog. The consumer brochure tradition continues, with the cover featuring the Fourth Edition of *Here Comes Santa, Jolly Trolley.* Series ornaments are identified for the first time on the ornament itself. A Christmas tree symbol with an edition number to indicate the series position or the number of the position of the ornament in the series is now stamped on the ornaments — an important first for collectors! Glass and satin ball ornaments are now available in a wide range of colors. Cloisonné and embroidered ornaments are introduced for the first time. Ball ornament packages are redesigned to feature a larger front opening on the box to show more of each ornament design. Hallmark store ceiling-decor signs feature three ornaments — *Cycling Santa, Jolly Trolley,* and *The Spirit of Christmas.* These signs are popular with collectors today. (Could *Pinecone Home* have been another *Christmas Critters Home* series ornament?) The *Angel Chime* ornament marks the first time an ornament is included in the Keepsake line that originally was marketed under another division of Hallmark, as an Ambassador ornament. The *Angel Chime* was available in very limited quantities and is extremely rare today. The *Musical Angel* is the first of many Donna Lee angel ornaments that are collector favorites. Three classic-shaped musical ornaments are offered in the Hallmark Gift selection for Christmas 1982. Each came with a display stand. The first Hallmark promotional ornament, a brass winter-scene is offered for $3.95 with any Hallmark purchase. An *Angel Tree Topper* and a *Miss Piggy Stocking Hanger* are designed and shown in the Hallmark retailer catalog but are never produced for retail sales.

1983

The expanded ornament line includes 117 ornaments and accessories. A larger collectors brochure is produced. It features 16 pages and Hallmark notes to retailers, "it's mailable." New shapes and materials add variety to the line. These include blown glass bells, teardrop-shape ball ornaments, and porcelain enamel. A new crown-cap on satin ball ornaments references back to Hallmark's Gold Crown logo. A peek-in ball ornament, *Christmas Wonderland,* is clear glass and features artwork with a different scene on both the inside and outside of the ornament. While Hallmark applied for a patent on this "bandless" decorating process, *Christmas Wonderland* is the only ornament ever produced in this manner, making it rare and unusual. Hallmark said the ability and technology to create another ornament like this has been lost. New captions on ornaments in 1983 include: *Grandchild's First Christmas, Baby's Second Christmas, Child's Third Christmas,* and *10th Christmas Together.* The hinged *Old-Fashioned Santa* is the first "posable" ornament. The new *Porcelain Bear* series marks the first porcelain ornament series. In 1983, 75% of all ornament buyers now consider themselves collectors — a 42% increase since 1978! Three new classic-shaped musical ornaments are available as part of the "Hallmark Musical Collection." Each came with an acrylic stand. Also included in this musical offering is the *Twelve Days of Christmas* ornament (no stand). A Hallmark designed and illustrated paperback book of The Night Before Christmas is given away as a promotion — free with any ornament purchase. A five-foot tall stuffable Santa is offered by Hallmark stores as a promotional giveaway for the Open House festivities.

1984

Lighted Ornaments are introduced in 1984, forever changing the possibilities of ornament collecting. To showcase this clever first, a store display in the shape of a house allows shoppers to "create the magic" themselves by pushing a button to light the ornament. A separate ornament brochure is added for the 10 new Lighted Ornament designs. New "wooden" tree-shaped store-displays are offered for the Keepsake Ornament line. Smaller ball ornaments, both in satin and blown glass, are available in response to consumer requests. A new decorating process for ball ornaments prints the design directly on the ball, eliminating the plastic band. New "mouse in Santa hat" caps on ball ornaments are added to *Grandchild's First Christmas, Baby's 1st Christmas* (boy and girl), and *Child's 3rd Christmas* ornaments. New commemorative captions for 1984 include *Gratitude* and *Baby-sitter. Katybeth* is introduced to the line for the first time and quickly becomes a favorite with many collectors. Fabric photoholders are also a first this year. *Marathon Santa* and *Uncle Sam* promote the Olympics and Election Day themes. A new acrylic process used in the *Old Fashioned Rocking Horse* ornaments combines an etched brass horse inside an acrylic ornament. The first porcelain Limited Edition ornament, *Classical Angel,* is produced in an edition size of 24,700. The first *Snoopy and Woodstock* handcrafted ornament appears. Three musical ornaments are added to the line. The clip-on *Chickadee* is the first porcelain bird ornament offered. *Three Kittens in a Mitten* is the first ornament produced based on a Nursery Rhyme. What is probably collectors all-time least-favorite series, *Art Masterpiece,* begins. Ornament Rings — a set of three connecting ring display stands are offered for sale for the first time and quickly become a favorite of collectors, and still sell quickly on the secondary market today. The Open House promotion is a ceramic *Snow Couple* Salt and Pepper Shaker set, available for $2.95. Customers can have their picture taken with a five-foot tall Santa that is later raffled off by Hallmark stores.

1985

A new caption for *Niece* is added. New property ornaments include Rainbow Brite, Hugga Bunch, and Fraggle Rock. Ornaments grouped in decorative "themes" (but sold separately) such as "The Heirloom Christmas Collection" and "The Country Christmas Collection" are introduced. The *Night Before Christmas* ornament is the only time a "flip-chart" has been used. *Children in the Shoe* continues the Nursery Rhyme subjects. The Special Edition, *The Spirit of Santa Claus,* is larger than most ornaments in the line and is the first two-piece Special Edition. *Chris Mouse* debuts as the first Lighted Series. *Katybeth* is the first Lighted property ornament and a lighted *Baby's First Christmas* is added to the line. For the first time, some lighted ornaments are dated. The first Hallmark Christmas record album is offered at the Hallmark Open House.

1986

With the growing popularity of the Keepsake Ornament line, Hallmark details the evolution of an ornament for retailers. It takes two years from start to finish to make a Keepsake Ornament. The design process starts with market research to determine what designs ornament buyers want. Hallmark designers then continue to research and work with ideas and sketches. It can take up to 75 different steps from the time an artist begins work on a design until it is completed. A new "Collectors Courier"

1986 continued

newsletter is available at Hallmark stores as a giveaway. This Courier predates the official newsletter of the Collector's Club. Two ornament themes are added, "Christmas Medley Collection" and "Country Treasures Collection." A *Statue of Liberty* ornament is produced to celebrate the 100th Anniversary of the famous monument in New York harbor. *Paddington Bear* and *Heathcliff* ornaments are introduced for the first time. New captions for 1986 are *Husband* and *Brother.* A country-look 4-pack ball ornament set, *Mary Emmerling,* debuts and is the first time a multi-pack of ornaments has been offered in several years. The *Sweetheart* caption debuts. The first handcrafted *Sweetheart* gazebo ornament is sought-after by collectors of the *Nostalgic Houses and Shops* ornament series to use in their displays. Nursery Rhymes are back with *Wynken, Blynken, and Nod.* The Limited Edition porcelain *Unicorn* ornament is the hottest thing going in the fall of 1986. Collectors are searching everywhere for it. Lighted ornaments are now designated "Light and Motion" ornaments as 3 new innovations are unveiled: motion, changing scenes and a hologram. *First Christmas Together* and *Friendship* commemoratives are added to the Light and Motion line. A large retailer-display ornament duplicates the new *Village Express* Light and Motion ornament. Exclusive Open House products include four ornaments, the *Coca-Cola Santa* ball ornament (another first in licensed properties), *Old-Fashioned Santa, Santa and His Reindeer,* and *Santa's Panda Pal.* In 1985 Hallmark offers two promotional ornaments that are a tie-in with "Santa Claus The Movie." Unfortunately, the ornaments are no more successful than the movie. A Christmas theme tree featuring Hallmark ornaments valued at $500.00 is given away by stores as an Open House prize! The second Hallmark Open House record/tape is offered. *On the Right Track* is available as a Gold Crown Exclusive ornament.

1987

The Hallmark Keepsake Ornament Collectors Club is introduced in 1987 and forever changes how we collect, what we collect, and who we collect it with! The size of the ornament line has now grown to 140 ornaments. The 1987 ornament brochure is the first to show both the Keepsake and Keepsake Magic ornaments together. *Christmas is Gentle* is the first Limited Edition ornament to be hand-numbered. "Artist's Favorites" Ornaments are introduced and each ornament and package carries the signature of the creator. The first handcrafted *Dad* ornament is added to the line. *Holiday Greetings* is the first ornament that is designed specifically to be used as a gift for business associates. New properties are *Jammie Pies* and *Dr. Suess' The Grinch's Christmas. Bright Christmas Dreams* is the first Crayola ornament and predates the Crayola series by two years. The collection format is continued with the "Old Fashioned Collection" of five nostalgic ornaments. *In a Nutshell,* the first hinged-open/close ornament, is included in that group. The "Christmas Pizzazz Collection" includes many innovations, such as the croaking *Mistletoad.* Two other unusual designs in the Pizzazz selections are *Doc Holiday,* a Santa on a spring-horse, and *Christmas Fun Puzzle,* a jointed-ball ornament that allows the collector to rotate the ornament and change the design. The *Goldfinch* is the first porcelain bird ornament that is designed to hang on the tree, rather than clip-on. The Lighted line is renamed "Magic" and the ornament prices are lowered in response to consumer influence. Blinking lights on the *Good Cheer Blimp* are a first in the Magic line. The first lighted photoholder, *Memories are Forever* is added to the line. *North Pole Power and Light* is offered as a promotional Open House ornament.

1988

A new caption *Five Years Together* appears for the first time on an ornament. *Child's Third Christmas* features a bouncy-ball made of a new rubberlike material. The *Daughter* gingerbread baker ornament strikes a chord with ornament buyers. It's an immediate hit and sells out before Christmas. A Crayola crayon makes a second appearance and is featured on the *Teacher* ornament. A larger-than-usual Special Edition ornament, *The Wonderful Santacycle* is offered and is reminiscent of the 1982 *Cycling Santa.* New licenses include Hershey's KISSES and OREO Cookies. In fact, Hallmark artists must have been hungry in 1988 because nine ornaments are food-related — *Sweet Star, Teeny Taster, Filled with Fudge, A KISS From Santa* and *OREO Chocolate Sandwich Cookies.* Food themes continue in the Artist's Favorites group with *Merry-Mint Unicorn, Little Jack Horner, Midnight Snack,* and *Very Strawberry,* all representing tasty ideas. Three new ornaments meet the continuing demand from collectors for more tin ornaments. One of the three, the tin *Americana Drum,* commemorates the 1988 election year, as does the handcrafted *Uncle Sam Nutcracker.* The first *Feliz Navidad* ornament is introduced in 1988. Life-style ornaments were offered for the first time with eight Santa ornaments depicting various hobbies and pastimes. *Mary's Angels,* a new 1988 series is based on the drawings of Mary Hamilton. No Hallmark ornament collector would want to be without the Fifth Edition of the *Nostalgic Houses and Shops* series - *Hall Bro's* represents an old-time card and gift shop and features an early Hallmark logo above the door. The Magic *Kringle's Toy Shop* is offered as a special promotional ornament. It's the first time a lighted *First Christmas Together* ornament is offered. The Miniature Ornament line is introduced and includes ornaments in a variety of materials. Four Miniature Series debut. Three captioned, dated Miniature ornaments are included: *Baby's First Christmas, Mother,* and *First Christmas Together. Sneaker Mouse* and *Jolly St. Nick* replicate all-time favorite ornaments from the Keepsake line. *Joyous Heart* is all wood and features letters that turn. This Miniature Ornament is particularly hard to find today. The Collector's Club offers Limited Edition ornaments for the first time. The Miniature Ornament, *Hold On Tight* is available as the first early-renewal bonus ornament for Charter Members.

1989

The *Children's Age Collection* of five ornaments makes its first appearance. Each ornament is a teddy bear holding a candy cane number from one to five to commemorate one year of a child's first five Christmases. This group also includes the new captions for *Child's Fourth Christmas* and *Child's Fifth Christmas.* A handcrafted *Brother* ornament is offered and is a new caption for 1989. The first shipment of the 1989 *Teacher* ornament is released with the caption placed upside-down on the ornament. This is quickly corrected on the remaining pieces. The life-style Santa ornaments continue with eight new offerings. The Peanuts ball ornament is particularly special this year for it commemorates the 25th Anniversary of *A Charlie Brown Christmas.* Three new hinged-nutshell ornaments make up the "Nutshell Trio" collection. After the popularity of previous Crayola ornaments, the *Crayola* series begins in 1989. A new ball ornament series, *The Gift Bringers* starts and Hallmark announces in advance that the series will be limited to five years. This is the first time Hallmark has announced the number of ornaments in a series at its introduction. Music is added to two Magic ornaments. Flickering light is another new innovation. *Rudolph the Red-Nosed Reindeer* makes his first appearance in years as a Hallmark

1989 continued

Magic ornament. The size of the Miniature Ornament line increases by 40%. *Santa's Magic Ride* is the first Special Edition Miniature Ornament. *Strollin' Snowman* and *Merry Seal* are the first porcelain Miniature Ornaments. A personalized Collector's Club ornament, *Visit From Santa* is offered for the first time. The Open House Promotion for 1989 was the "Christmas Carousel Horse Collection." The Carousel Horses mark the beginning of a continuing tradition of Open House collections available during a multi-week Christmas promotion.

1990

New ornaments for *Mom-to-Be* and *Dad-to-Be* are introduced and prove immediately popular. New captions for 1990 acrylic ornaments include *Across the Miles, Child Care Giver,* and *Jesus Loves Me.* The lifestyles ornaments continue with six Polar Penguin ornaments — backpacking baby, driving a tiny red-sports car and other active 90's activities. Both the *Snoopy and Woodstock* and the *Peanuts* ball ornament boxes carry a special slogan, "40 Years of Happiness" celebrating the 40th Anniversary of Peanuts. Garfield makes his first appearance in the Hallmark line. A Special Edition Collection based on Dickens characters begins with the first in the collection, *Mr. Ashbourne.* The new ornament series *Heart of Christmas* is the first series to feature an open/closed hinged design. The 1990 *Rocking Horse* series ornament is a big hit — probably because of its distinctive colors and becomes hard to find in the stores, resulting in higher secondary market prices. *Fabulous Decade* is introduced as a series that will continue through, and celebrate the final decade of the 20th Century. Collectors are really pleased to find an off/on switch feature is added to Magic ornaments. Because of production problems, *Children's Express,* one of several popular light and motion train ornaments Hallmark has offered over the years, isn't easy to find in retail stores during the Christmas season. 1990 sees the popular *Frosty Friends* in a collection of miniature ornaments designed to be displayed on a wreath in the "Little Frosty Friends" collection for the annual Open House promotion. The Miniature Ornament line sees many firsts in 1990. New captions include *Grandchild's First Christmas* and *Teacher.* "Artist's Favorites" are added to the Miniature line. The "Precious Edition" Miniature ornament makes its debut with *Cloisonné Poinsettia.*

1991

A new caption, *A Child's Christmas* is introduced for preschool children. The first silver-plate *Baby's First Christmas* is offered. Four commemoratives appear as handcrafted ornaments for the first time — *Grandson's First Christmas, Granddaughter's First Christmas, Godchild,* and *Sister.* The *Mother* ornament uses mixed-media, combining fine porcelain with tin. Anniversary Photoholders are available in brass and chrome finishes. The *Gift of Joy* offers the unusual combination of brass, copper, and chrome in a revolving design. Three collections of ornaments debut in 1991. The porcelain "A Christmas Carol Collection" represents five characters from the popular Dickens tale. The "Winnie-the-Pooh Collection" offers the five famous Pooh characters and *Christopher Robin* from the A.A. Milne story. (This is the only time to date *Christopher Robin* has been offered by Hallmark.) Seven "Tender Touches Collection" ornaments are introduced and reflect the popularity of the *Tender Touches* figurine collection from Hallmark. Collectors fond of the early "Nostalgia Ring" ornaments are pleased to find three new designs in the 1991 line that hark back to those earlier days at Hallmark. Three new tin ornaments titled *Jolly Wollies* appeal to collectors and bring back memories of old tobacco tins. These three tin ornaments also represent a new format for tin designs because they open as boxes and can also be hung on the tree. *Wee Three Kings,* a new hinged-nutshell ornament is introduced and is the most rare of all the nutshell ornaments. The first *Mary Engelbreit* ball ornament is added to the line. 1991 is the year of the *Corvette,* the First Edition of the *Classic American Car* Series. The *Corvette* immediately becomes one of the most popular new series in years and rises quickly on the secondary market. *Santa's Antique Car,* 13th in the *Here Comes Santa* series is a hard-to-find ornament.

The Magic ornament line doubled in size in 1991 and included the first Special Edition ornament, *Santa Special* and features the sound of a real train engine. The big news in Magic ornaments was the introduction of the first Star Trek ornament, the *Starship Enterprise.* The *Enterprise* began what is now a tradition of Hallmark Star Trek ornaments. This popular 25th Anniversary Star Trek ornament continues to rise in price each year on the secondary market. The lighted movie theatre ornament, *It's A Wonderful Life* is sought after by collectors for use with the *Nostalgic Houses and Shops* ornament displays. The *Tiny Tea Party Set* made its debut in 1991 and marked the first time a group of Miniature Ornaments had been designed to be sold as a set. *Mom* made its first appearance as a mini in 1991. The *Silver Santa* "Precious Edition" is the first silver-plated mini ornament. Again, two Keepsake ornaments familiar to collectors appear in the Miniature line, *Heavenly Minstrel* and *Wee Toymaker.* The first *Feliz Navidad* miniature ornament was introduced. It's the Fifth Year Anniversary of the Collector's Club and to celebrate Hallmark issues a *Charter Member Ornament — Five Years Together.* This special Club ornament also is the first and only red acrylic ornament ever produced. There are several other firsts in Collector's Club Ornaments for 1991. *Galloping Into Christmas* is the first tin Club ornament. *Beary Artistic* is the first lighted Club Ornament. *Hidden Treasure/Li'l Keeper* is a combined ornament. *Hidden Treasure* is hinged and opens to reveal the *Li'l Keeper* Miniature Ornament inside. *Santa's Premiere,* a hand-painted fine porcelain bell/ornament, is the first-ever Gold Crown Exclusive ornament designed specifically for the Ornament Premiere. The 1991 Open House promotion is the "Claus & Co. R.R. Collection" and the *Locomotive* quickly becomes the hard-to-find piece. To commemorate Operation Desert Storm, Hallmark produces the *Flag of Liberty* ornament in honor of the American Armed Forces. A portion of the sale of each *Flag of Liberty* ornament was donated by Hallmark to the American Red Cross. Other big news in 1991 is the introduction of Keepsake Easter Ornaments. The original eleven ornaments include captions for "Baby's First Easter," "Daughter," "Son," and "Grandchild." The first porcelain ornament in this collection is *Lily Egg. Full of Love* becomes hard to find and is the most popular of the 1991 Easter selection.

1992

Two fun new commemorative photoholders are announced for the family pet in 1992 — *Special Dog* and *Special Cat.* The *Special Dog* photoholder is featured in pre-Christmas advertising and sells out well before the holiday. An elaborate *Baby's First Christmas* ornament is offered for the first time in porcelain. "Maxine" represents the *Spirit of Christmas Stress* and is the first ornament introduced from the popular Hallmark "SHOEBOX GREETINGS." *Cheerful Santa* is the first African-American handcrafted Santa. *Please Pause Here* is unusual in that it's a clip-on ornament and represents the first COCA COLA handcrafted Santa in the line. Always trying out new ideas, Hallmark

1992 continued

offers *A Santa-Full!* which shows Santa with a see-through tummy-full of cookies, and it's a hit with ornament buyers! One more *Winnie-the-Pooh* ornament is offered, answering last year's question of *Where's Owl?* Three interacting ornament sets are introduced for the first time. Each "Hang-Together" consists of two-parts designed to be hung side-by-side on the tree. Trains are always popular, and the four-piece *Christmas Skyline* Collection (sold separately) and the three-piece *Silver Star Train* set (sold as a set) are introduced. *Mother Goose* features moveable action and predates the official *Mother Goose* storybook series by a year. *Lily*, a charming and sleepy little angel — the Fifth Edition of *Mary's Angels* — truly becomes a sleeper ornament, disappears from shelves and rises in price on the secondary market.

"Voice" is added to the Magic Ornament line in 1992. Ornament buyers can add a personalized message to *Santa's Answering Machine*. Star Trek fans are wished holiday greetings by Mr. Spock from the second Star Trek ornament, the *Shuttlecraft Galileo*. The *Baby's First Christmas* Magic ornament is in high demand and sold-out at stores before Christmas. "Grandma" is a new caption in the Miniature Ornament line. *Friendly Tin Soldier* is the first Miniature tin ornament. *COCA-COLA Santa* is the first time this popular license appears as a Miniature ornament. *Sew, Sew Tiny* is the second set of mini-mice designed to be sold as a group. The new First Edition *Night Before Christmas* tin house represents a departure for series ornaments. The tin house contains the first Miniature Ornament, and will be followed for the next four years by a new Miniature Ornament designed to be displayed inside the house. The Limited Edition Club Members Only *Christmas Treasures* is the first time a group of Miniature Ornaments is offered as a set through the club. *O Christmas Tree* is the second porcelain bell ornament designed specifically as a Gold Crown Ornament Premiere special. *Santa and His Reindeer* is a hit as the Christmas-time Open House promotion for 1992. It's the second year for the Hallmark Keepsake Easter collection. The line now includes 20 ornaments. Two series begin, *Egg in Sports* and *Easter Parade*. *Crayola Bunny* makes an appearance as the first licensed property Easter ornament, *Joy Bearer* is sought-after by collectors.

1993

It's the 20th Anniversary of Hallmark Keepsake Ornaments! To celebrate, Hallmark offers 20th Anniversary Editions of three popular series, *Frosty Friends, Nostalgic Houses and Shops*, and *Here Comes Santa*. A fourth Anniversary Edition, *Glowing Pewter Wreath*, features Christmas motifs. The new commemorative *Sister to Sister* is a big hit and sells out before Christmas. Other new captions for 1993 include the *Our Family* photoholder and *Our Christmas Together*. New property characters in 1993 include *Looney Tunes*, the *Pink Panther, Superman* and *Lou Rankin*. Hershey's Cocoa makes its first appearance. The *New Home* ornament is a hit and this dated key-shaped ornament sells out quickly. Two ornaments with a religious theme, *He Is Born* and *Star of Wonder* sell out before Christmas and are sought-after on the secondary market. A special ornament designed by the winner of the Hallmark Collector's Club Convention costume contest, *Look for the Wonder*, is featured. A group of "Holiday Fliers" ornaments continues the tin ornament tradition. The charming and fun *Room For One More* is a delightful hit with collectors. For the second year, three new "Hang-Togethers" ornament sets are offered. The Special Edition *Julianne and Teddy* ornament is the first of three ornaments featuring old-fashioned dolls with teddy bears.

1993 continued

The First Edition *Holiday BARBIE* ornament is offered as a Special Issue ornament and starts a frenzy of BARBIE-buying on the Hallmark secondary market. Personalized Ornaments are offered for the first time. A new collection of "Showcase Ornaments" is available to Gold Crown Stores. Showcase ornaments feature materials not usually associated with Hallmark ornaments, such as fine bisque porcelain, and silver-plate. The first *Winnie-the-Pooh* Magic ornament debuts in 1993 and Pooh speaks to us for the first time. *Messages of Christmas* continues the recorder-ornament feature, allowing consumers to record their own personalized message. Star Trek continues in the 1993 Magic line with *Star Trek, the Next Generation.* The first tin Miniature Ornament series, *On The Road,* debuts in 1993. Miniature "Precious Edition" ornaments include both the *Cloisonné Snowflake* and the popular *Crystal Angel.* The first Collector's Club bottle cap ornament, *Forty Winks* is offered. To celebrate the 20th Anniversary of Hallmark ornaments, club members could purchase the ornament *Trimmed with Memories,* a Christmas tree that's trimmed with tiny replicas of older series ornaments. *You're Always Welcome,* the first "Tender Touch" Premiere Event Ornament is offered. *The Bearingers of Victoria Circle* is the 1993 Reach promotion special offer. The Easter Ornament line expands. The first-ever Easter Ornament set, *Maypole Stroll* is offered.

1994

BARBIE is back! The Second Edition *Holiday BARBIE* flies off the shelves and Hallmark introduces the First in Series *Nostalgia BARBIE* ornament too! A new caption for 1994 is *Grandpa.* Occupation ornaments are added to the line. "Looney Tunes" return. The *Flintstones* are added along with *Batman, LEGO,* and *Beatrix Potter* licensed ornaments. A special "Wizard of Oz Collection" is available. The *Beatles Gift Set* causes a stir among collectors. The First Edition *Murray Champion* is a hit and reflects the demand for the "Kiddie Car Classics" pedal-cars by Hallmark. Lifestyle ornaments continue to be offered with more designs than ever. "Maxine" appears for the first time as a lighted ornament, and more "SHOEBOX GREETING" designs are added to the Keepsake collection. For the third year, three "Hang-Together" ornament sets are available. Personalized ornaments return again. A Special Edition Magic Ornament, *Gingerbread Fantasy* is priced at $44.00 but is so popular with buyers, it proves hard to find at the retail level. The *Klingon Bird of Prey* is the fourth Special Issue Star Trek ornament. The "Lion King Collection" of ornaments ties in with the blockbuster Disney movie of the same name. The Lion King light and music ornament is recalled due to problems with the music. The ornament is redesigned and ships back into Hallmark stores with light only at a lower retail price of $20.00. *Noah's Ark* in the Miniature Ornament line is issued as the first in a Special Edition that will continue with pairs of Noah's animals available in upcoming years. *Baking Tiny Treats,* the fourth in the unannounced series of tiny mice engaged in human activities, proves immediately popular. "Tiny Toons" make their first appearance as Miniature Ornaments. The 1994 Collector's Club members-only ornament, *On Cloud Nine,* is the last Donna Lee angel. The "Sarah Plain and Tall Collection," based on the popular Hallmark Hall of Fame television movie, is offered as the Open House promotion. A special "Tender Touch" ornament, *Eager for Christmas* is designed for the 1994 Ornament Premiere weekend. The 1994 Easter ornaments add *Peanuts* and a *Tender Touch* ornament to the line, as well as a new *Crayola* ornament. *Tilling Time* is offered as a first-time Club Exclusive Easter ornament.

1995

Special Issue Ornaments are big in 1995. BARBIE's back and is going to continue to be popular with both the *BARBIE* and *Holiday BARBIE* series going strong! Star Trek ornaments increase in number with characters from the popular series being added for the first time. A boxed set of three Miniature Ornaments, *The Ships of Star Trek* is introduced. Hallmark continues to appeal to the male ornament collector, following the 1994 introduction of *Baseball Heroes* with the new *Football Legends* and *Hoop Stars.* Hallmark has a "Pocahontas Collection" of character ornaments from the Disney movie of the same name. The new *All-American Truck* series is going to be popular. A fun group of accessories for the ever-popular *Nostalgic Houses and Shops* series is introduced for the first time. Collectors will undoubtedly buy several sets to decorate their "tiny towns." It's the 15th Anniversary of the Rocking Horse series and Hallmark is celebrating by releasing an *Anniversary Edition Rocking Horse* ornament in pewter. New licensed characters and properties for 1995 include Popeye, Andrew Brownsword, Marjolein Bastin, PEZ, Dudley the Dragon, The Magic Schoolbus, Thomas The Tank Train Engine - No.1 and Wheel of Fortune. The 1996 Olympics are celebrated with the acrylic ornament, *The Olympic Spirit.* Lifestyles ornaments continue to be popular and there are more than ever in the line. New "SHOEBOX GREETINGS" characters have been added to the ornament line. Showcase Ornaments return with a first, *The Fireman,* from the new series, *Turn of the Century Parade.* The popular artwork of Marjolein Bastian is featured in a Showcase Collection titled "Nature' s Sketchbook." Personalized Ornaments continue. The elaborate *Victorian Toy Box* is the new Special Edition Magic Ornament for 1995. Five new Miniature Ornament series debut in 1995. A tiny *Murray Champion* and *Alice in Wonderland* are new Miniature Ornament properties. The new Miniature *Clothespin Soldier* series replicates the familiar Keepsake series of the same name. A first in the Miniature line are the two Lighted Miniature Ornaments, each powered by a tiny battery (included). The familiar Moustershire figurines have been translated to a set of three Miniature Ornaments and a tiny Moustershire Cottage. Collector's Club members are thrilled at the new *Brunette Debut - 1959 BARBIE* ornament and the *1958 Ford Edsel* ornament - each designed to complement existing series. The Open House promotion celebrates the 30th Anniversary of a *Charlie Brown Christmas.* A third Tender Touch ornament, *Wish List,* is designed especially for the Ornament Premiere. Easter 1995 brings the First Edition *Springtime BARBIE* ornament. *Peanuts* is difficult to find as this cute ornament of Snoopy wearing Bunny ears flies off the shelves. Looney Tunes' *Bugs Bunny* makes his first appearance as an Easter ornament.

1996

The first ever Collector's Club series debuts with the *1988 Happy Holidays BARBIE Doll* ornament, which complements the on-going *Holiday BARBIE* series. The Collector's Club *1937 Steelcraft Auburn* by Murray complements the on-going *Kiddie Car Ornament* series, and the Members Only Club *Wizard of Oz* ornament complements previous issue *Wizard of Oz* ornaments. Another first in 1996 is the *Bashful Mistletoe* three-piece Merry Miniature set designed exclusively for the July Ornament Premiere. *A Tender Touch* is again offered during the Ornament Premiere. The Atlanta Summer Olympics are celebrated in "The Olympic Spirit Collection" of figurines and Keepsake Ornaments. A third Disney collection is designed for "The Hunchback of Notre Dame." A special *101 Dalmatians* ornament will be available during the Christmas-time Open House festivities. Collectors who purchase the

1996 continued

101 Dalmatians ornament will be rewarded with an additional 101 Gold Crown points on their Gold Crown account. To celebrate 30 years of Star Trek, a set of two ornaments on a display base is offered. New Star Trek characters include *Commander Riker* and *Mr. Spock*. Another Star Trek ship, the *U.S.S, Voyager* is available. A new sports series, *At the Ballpark* debuts with *Nolan Ryan*. All sports series ornaments will be packed with a classic trading card in the ornament box. To celebrate the 50th Anniversary of *It's A Wonderful Life*, a special Anniversary Edition ornament will be offered at select Gold Crown stores in November. In addition to *Nolan Ryan*, four new exciting series debut: *Lionel 700E Hudson Steam Locomotive, Native American BARBIE, Madame Alexander Cinderella*, and *Christy–All God's Children*. The popular *Peanuts Gang* series ends in 1996 along with the long-running and always popular *Rocking Horse*. To commemorate the end of the *Rocking Horse* series, a special gold-plated miniature *Rocking Horse* ornament is available only at the Hallmark Artist on Tour events held during the fall of 1996. The success of the *NFL Helmets* in 1995, brings back the NFL Collection, this time with 30 teams represented on a Keepsake *Number One Fan* ornament. Personalized ornaments are discontinued in 1996. Showcase ornaments return with a new series for 1996 — *Pansy* is the first in the *Language of Flowers* series. Popular artist Marjolein Bastian has designed three Showcase ornaments. Linda Sickman again designs three Folk Art ornaments — each features details in copper. Two new *Cookie Jar Friends* ornaments are fun additions to the Showcase collection. *Freedom 7* is the first in the new Journeys Into Space Magic Ornament series. The first Magic *Star Wars* ornament is introduced, along with a boxed set of three miniature *Star Wars* ornaments. The *Jetsons* debut as a Magic ornament. The *Wizard of Oz* Magic ornament continues this popular on-going collection. *Father Time* is the first Magic ornament to feature an actual clock. Three miniature ornament collections that feature a background scene are introduced for 1996. The *Nutcracker Ballet* includes a stage, along with the *Little Ballerina* ornament, the first of five, in the only new miniature series. *O Holy Night* features a manger background, along with three dated display pieces: Mary, Jesus, and Joseph. In celebration of the 60th Anniversary of "Gone With The Wind," a miniature *Tara, Rhett* and *Scarlett* are available as a set. The Precious Edition Miniature Ornament harks back to the popular *Crystal Angel*. This new 1996 version is called *Sparkling Crystal Angel* and features an angel made of silver plate and green lead crystal. Little Looney Tunes Loveables feature *Baby Tweety* and *Baby Sylvester*, continuing this popular miniature ornament collection. Both *Winnie the Pooh* with *Tigger* and *Woodstock* debut as Miniature Ornaments. The *Nature's Angels* series ends in 1996, as well as *March of the Teddie Bears* and the 5th and final in *The Night Before Christmas* series. *Wonder Woman* debuts in the 1996 Keepsake line. Keepsake Looney Tune ornaments include *Marvin the Martian, Foghorn Leghorn and Henery Hawk, Olive Oyl and Swee' Pea, Yogi Bear and Boo Boo. A Tree for Snoopy* complements the miniature *Woodstock* ornament. *Hershey's, Coke*, the *Wizard of Oz Witch of the West*, and *Pez* all return in 1996. Marjolein Bastian has her first Keepsake ornament, *Christmas Snowman*. Angels and religious subjects are prevalent in 1996. A new ornament designation, Collector's Choice, picked by Clara Johnson Scroggins debuts. An adorable *Beatrix Potter Baby's First Christmas* ornament is another 1996 first.

1997

The 1997 Dreambook is redesigned and is more beautiful than ever. The Magic and Showcase Ornaments are no longer featured in separate sections of the book but are displayed alongside the Keepsake Ornaments. A new ornament display, with electricity throughout, is designed for stores so the light/music/voice/motion ornaments can be sprinkled from one end of the fixture to the other. Club members receive the Dreambook with the early March mailing of the Collector's Courier. Later in March Hallmark holds a first time ever Sneak-a-Peak event at Gold Crown stores to preview the new 1997 line, and everyone is invited! Collectors view a video of select ornaments, receive the new Dreambook, and get a free commemorative lapel pin for attending the event. The July Ornament Premiere again offers collector exclusives. For the second time, a limited Premiere exclusive three-piece set of Merry Miniatures is available. This year it's *Snowbear Season.* Once again, the popular Hallmark studio artist, Ed Seale, has designed a "Tender Touches" ornament, *The Perfect Tree* just for the Premiere. New series ornaments, property ornaments, Special Issue ornaments, and Disney ornaments dominate the 1997 Keepsake line.

Four collections showcase Disney, including Mickey & Co., Classic Movies, New Releases, and Winnie-The-Pooh. In 1932, Walt Disney and J.C. Hall produced the first Hallmark products featuring Disney characters. In 1997 four new collections of Keepsake Ornaments have been designed using Disney's lovable creations. The Mickey & Co. collection includes two new series: Mickey's Holiday Parade Series, *Bandleader Mickey* and Hallmark Archives Series, *Donald's Surprising Gift.* The nostalgic Mickey & Co. collection shows the Disney characters as they were created in the 1930's, with their original pie-shaped eyes. A new *Cinderella* series debuts. A special two-piece ornament set celebrates *Snow White's* 60th anniversary. It's the fourth time Hallmark has produced ornaments that tie-in with the annual summer Disney movie release, and this year's ornaments feature characters from Hercules. Other Hallmark ornaments celebrate recent Disney movies, including The Little Mermaid, Aladdin, The Lion King, 101 Dalmatians, and The Hunchback of Notre Dame.

Sci-fi fans find more Star Trek and Star Wars ornaments in 1997. A *Star Wars* series debuts with *Luke Skywalker.* The light and voice *Darth Vader* ornament is sure to be popular. *Yoda* and a Miniature ornament set of *C-3PO* and *R2-D2* complete the collection. Star Trek ornaments include *Commander Data* and *Dr. Leonard McCoy.* The unofficial series of Star Trek ships continues in 1997 with the *U.S.S. Defiant.*

A Special Issue *1997 Corvette* and *Miniature 1997 Corvette* debut in September. Airplanes are featured in a series for the first time with *The Flight at Kitty Hawk,* 1st in *The Sky's the Limit* series.

The Hallmark Sports Collection expands with the introduction of *Wayne Gretzky,* 1st in the *Hockey Greats* series and Jeff Gordon, 1st in the *Stock Car Champions* series. The "NFL Collection" returns this year with football blimp ornaments sporting one of 30 team logos. For the first time basketball fans can hang an ornament plaque with their their favorite team logo on the tree as Hallmark honors 10 of the NBA's top teams.

Two famous movie legends appear as 1st in series ornaments - *Marilyn Monroe* and *Scarlett O'Hara,* both sculpted by Hallmark artist Patricia Andrews.

1997 continued

BARBIE returns and although it's the 5th in series, this *Holiday BARBIE* ornament is also a stunning first! *Holiday BARBIE* is a brunette for the very first time, and her dress is a knock-out! *Wedding Day BARBIE* is the 4th in the *BARBIE* series. A *BARBIE and Ken Wedding Day* set is also designed to complement this series. It's Ken's first appearance as a Hallmark ornament. The *Holiday Traditions BARBIE Doll,* a new 1st-in-series is exclusive to Hallmark. This doll is part of the new BARBIE "Holiday Homecoming Collection" that includes a limited edition figurine and plate, as well as a matching ornament. The new BARBIE "Victorian Christmas Collection" includes a limited edition plate, matching ornament, and a set of three greeting cards, all featuring the now retired 1994, 1995, and 1996 Hallmark exclusive Christmas BARBIE dolls.

Two Special Issue Ornaments from a collection entitled "Thomas Kinkade, A Painter of Light" arrive in November. Of these, *Victorian Christmas* is a 1st in the new T*homas Kinkade* series.

Popular culture is reflected in many 1997 ornaments. *Howdy Doody, The Lone Ranger, Mr. Potato Head, Michigan J. Frog,* and *The Incredible Hulk* all make their first appearance in the Keepsake line. The *Lincoln Memorial* brings history to the Christmas tree. *Miss Gulch* continues the popular Wizard of Oz collection that began in 1994. Lifestyles and Occupation ornaments include everything from The *Boy Scouts of America* to firemen to teachers. The Ethnic and Religious collections are expanded to include a diversity of culture and religion.

Four new Miniature Ornament series debut, including the sure-to-be popular *Antique Tractors.* Collectors Classics Miniature ornaments include *Casablanca* and a new mini-set of four *Wizard of Oz* ornaments.

Series retiring in 1997 include the popular *Chris Mouse,* as well as *Christmas Visitors, Turn-of-the Century Parade, Baseball Heroes,* and *Mother Goose.* All of the original four 1988 Miniature Ornament series are now over, with the announcement of the retirement of the Old English Village, and miniature *Rocking Horse* series. The Miniature Ornament series *Santa's Little Big Top,* also retires in 1997.

It's the 175th anniversary of Clement C. Moore's *The Night Before Christmas* and the The Hallmark Keepsake Ornament Collector's Club offers four ornaments based on this classic story. Club Edition ornaments include the 2nd-in-Club-series *1989 Holiday BARBIE* and another *Kiddie Car Classic* both designed to complement the on-going Keepsake series. A club exclusive "Tender Touches" ornament, *Farmer's Market,* is designed to go with the 1997 Springtime collection.

In 1997, Easter Ornaments are renamed "Springtime" Ornaments. 1997 Springtime Ornaments include two new series. The 1st in the *Children's Collection Series* is *Rapunzel BARBIE.* The first in the *Sidewalk Cruisers* series is the green Velocipede trike. Marjolein Bastin's artwork makes its Springtime debut with *Garden Bunnies, Nature's Sketchbook.* The *Springtime BARBIE* series ends, along with *Apple Blossom Lane, Garden Club,* and *Springtime Bonnets.* For the first time, Hallmark produces a brochure for Springtime Ornaments. The "Spring Pictorial Review" pictures all Easter Ornaments produced from their introduction in 1991 to 1997. The brochure spurs collector's interest and results in an increase in secondary market sales of the Springtime Ornaments.

1998

1998 begins the 25th year that Hallmark has produced ornaments to help us celebrate holidays and special moments in our lives. A special collection has been created to commemorate this anniversary year. Included in this collection are adaptations of favorite designs from earlier years. These include selected archival master pieces, special issues of cherished characters, a new grouping of meticulously blown glass ornaments, and the ongoing creativity demonstrated by a wide range of themes and styles. These new items, once again, allow collectors to choose the best way to express holiday spirit, tradition, and the true meaning of Christmas.

Hallmark has introduced us to more than100 different series during this 25 year period. These series have focused on many different themes. From the early Betsey Clark ball ornament series that numbered 13 to the current 20th edition of the Here Comes Santa series, collectors have enjoyed continuity of each theme as it has expanded over many years. In 1998 ten new series were introduced to add to the excitement.

Special issues debuted in 1993. They continue to be among the most sought after ornaments in the collection. Licensed properties mirror and reflect trends in the culture. They include pop culture icons, Hollywood legends, sports celebrities, cars, and a hold-on-to-childhood love affair with Disney favorites. Whether you enjoy munching on chocolate, opening a brand new box of crayons; remembering how you carried your lunch to school, your favorite television programs or dolls and toys you once played with– all these memories and experiences have found their way into favorite Hallmark ornaments.

The first glass ornaments were introduced in Europe over a century ago. Decorated glass balls were part of the first collection ever produced by Hallmark. Today, Hallmark brings the splendor of hand blown, finely detailed, hand painted glass ornaments back into the spotlight. Three of the ornaments are inspired by cherished favorites in the Keepsake collection. The *Gifts For A King* are a beautiful beginning to the celebration that marks the spirit and meaning of Christmas. The ball ornaments featuring the poinsettias take us back to the earlier days of decorative tree trim. The child in us all will love the candy and sugarplum house ornaments.

Every wish, hope and dream can be found in the selection and artistry of the Hallmark introductions. Many ornaments are not restricted to holiday themes and the addition of Spring ornaments brings greater dimension to decorating our homes and lives. Collectors are able to enjoy multi-cultural themes, satisfy their interests in sports through the sports collections, and are able to extend the ornament year to other holidays as well.

The Hallmark Collector's Club has more than a quarter of a million active members. It is the largest of its kind in the nation. In August of this year, club members will gather at a convention to celebrate the 25th Anniversary of their favorite collectibles. The fellowship they share is just one of the benefits they enjoy. For many club members, ornaments have become a passionate hobby that adds enthusiasm to their way of life. The newsletter keeps members supplied with product information and special releases available only to club members: adding to the exclusivity. A special treat is in store for collectors who join the club in 1998.

It is the collector's enthusiasm that inspires creativity and brings the excitement of discovery and recognition to us all. Each year Hallmark strives to make the new collection outshine the ones that came before. Their attention to quality and craftsmanship attest to their success. This 1998 collection showcases Hallmark's leadership in the industry. Over 3,073 ornaments have been introduced since 1973 and each one has a story, a memory and a dream.

PATRICIA ANDREWS

Hallmark Keepsake Ornament studio artist Patricia Andrews enjoys designing ornaments that convey the innocent, playful emotions that many people associate with childhood. Perhaps that's why her popular BARBIE™ Hallmark Keepsake Ornaments look as if they could come to life.

As a charter member of the National Hallmark Keepsake Ornament Collector's Club, Patricia admits she's an avid collector. "I receive a sample of each ornament I create," she says, "but I don't want to stop there, so I go out shopping for more Hallmark Keepsake Ornaments just like everyone else."

Patricia began her Hallmark career as an engraver when she joined the company in 1976. She is married to Dill Rhodus, who also creates Hallmark Keepsake Ornaments.

Hallmark Keepsake Ornament Artist Since: 1987

(I actually started on May 1, 1987– the same day the Hallmark Keepsake Ornament Collector's Club started!)

What I like best about sculpting Hallmark Keepsake Ornaments: I work in a family atmosphere on a fun product that's appreciated by so many people. What could be better?

Hallmark Keepsake Ornament Milestones: Before I started sculpting the Holiday BARBIE™ Hallmark Keepsake Ornaments, I was completely unknown. Now I'm known as the "Barbie Lady" and I'm married to "Joe Montana!" (Patricia's husband, Dill, sculpted the 1995 Joe Montana Hallmark Keepsake Ornament).

Activities I Enjoy (besides being a Hallmark Keepsake Ornament Artist):

Gardening (we have four acres) and making "honey-do" lists for my husband.

Favorite Childhood Memory: Attending high school in Bermuda.

The Last Good Movie I Saw: "Courage Under Fire."

Most Prized Possession: My 1961 BARBIE® doll.

Person I Admire Most: Martin Luther King, Jr.

NINA AUBÉ

Nina joined Hallmark in 1981 as a specialty artist for gift products. She sat right next to John "Collin" Francis and, watching as he sculpted Merry Miniatures® figurines, she decided to create some three-dimensional art. Those creations earned her the opportunity to begin sculpting Merry Miniatures®, and she's sculpted more than 100 to date.

Since joining the Hallmark Keepsake Ornament studio full time, she remains inspired by how much collectors care. "Collectors clearly express that Hallmark Keepsake Ornaments aren't just tree decorations," Nina says. "They are about honoring memories that mean something to people."

Hallmark Keepsake Ornament Artist Since: 1994

What I like best about sculpting Hallmark Keepsake Ornaments: I actually get to sculpt for a living! I worked primarily as a two-dimensional artist for many years, but working three-dimensionally truly is where my artistic passion lies. Having the freedom to sculpt my own ideas makes it all the more fun.

Hallmark Keepsake Ornament Milestones: Attending my first Artists On Tour (AOT) event in Atlanta and discovering that collectors actually like my work! I had sculpted a lot of Merry Miniatures® figurines on a free-lance basis for a number of years, but the Atlanta AOT really was the first time my name was associated directly with characters that I'd developed. It was a wonderful feeling to find out that people really appreciate and collect my work.

Activities I Enjoy (besides being a Hallmark Keepsake Ornament Artist): I collect a little bit of everything including Hallmark Keepsake Ornaments! I keep my eyes open for dolls and toys from my childhood, especially "Liddle Kiddles," which were made by Mattel in the 1960's. I love going to flea markets, antique malls and toy shows to hunt for new treasures to add to my collections. I also enjoy traveling—exploring new territories and re-visiting old favorites—gardening, going to the movies, dining out with friends and family, reading, long walks and playing with my pets.

Favorite Childhood Memory: I have lots of fun memories of teasing and playing tricks on my big sisters. I was a bit of a practical jokester. Still am, actually! I also remember playing a game that my sisters and I invented. We called it, "Draw in the Dark." We'd pick a subject to draw, such as a dog, then turn out the lights and try to draw it in the dark. Then we'd turn the lights on and crack up over our silly-looking creations.

The Last Good Movie I Saw: "As Good As It Gets."

Most Prized Possession: My cockatiel, Opie. But I don't really consider him a possession—he's my little buddy. He's a very sweet and affectionate pet; loves to have his head scratched. As soon as I get home, he insists on riding around the house on my shoulder. As far as inanimate possessions, several years ago I discovered a doll at a flea market that is very dear to my heart. It's a baby "Liddle Kiddle" doll named "Liddle Diddle" that was my absolute favorite as a child. She was my BARBIE® doll's "baby." Just holding her again brought back great memories. I also have several family heirlooms that mean a lot to me. My mother's Shirley Temple doll; my grandmother's glass ornament collection, my great grandfather's old writing desk; and my great-great-grandmother's locket.

Person I Admire Most: I admire honest people who live lives consistent with their personal beliefs and values.

KATRINA BRICKER

For Katrina Bricker, the old adage, "You learn something new every day," never has been more true. That's because this year, Katrina celebrates her third year as a Hallmark Keepsake Ornament studio artist.

Recruited by Hallmark straight out of college, Katrina worked in Hallmark's Specialty department for about a year before she was asked to interview for a position in the Hallmark Keepsake Ornament studio.

"My life changed in the blink of an eye," Katrina says. "I spent the next year asking a lot of questions, observing and learning. I'm still asking a lot of questions, observing and learning. I don't think I'll ever be done with that." Katrina says she already has gained a wealth of knowledge from the other artists. "They are masters at what they do," she says.

Hallmark Keepsake Ornament Artist Since: 1995

What I like best about sculpting Hallmark Keepsake Ornaments: When I am creating Hallmark Keepsake Ornaments, I am doing something that I truly love to do. In essence, this is my dream job! In high school, I discovered how much I enjoyed sculpting, but I really had no idea where I would be able to use my talent. I heard about the Hallmark Keepsake Ornament studio when I was in college, and it became my employment goal. I'm really blessed to have been given this opportunity.

Hallmark Keepsake Ornament Milestones: Sculpting ornaments that are based on licensed properties has been a milestone for me. It was an incredible learning experience to work with the people at other companies, such as Disney. They showed me how to inject more personality into my ornaments. That experience has changed how I develop my own creations and has encouraged me to uncover the personality in each ornament.

Activities I Enjoy (besides being a Hallmark Keepsake Ornament Artist): I really enjoy horseback riding. In fact, I've been a horse fanatic since I was a little girl—I guess you never really grow up! I also have a large collection of horse figurines.

Favorite Childhood Memory: My family! My grandparents, in particular, are prominent in my childhood memories. One set of grandparents would take us to the zoo from time to time, while the other would take us fishing and on nature walks. I have so many wonderful childhood memories. I never could single out just one.

The Last Good Movie I Saw: I would have to say "Jane Eyre." It's my absolute favorite book, and the recent movie was wonderfully done.

Most Prized Possession: I love my cocker spaniel, Molly. (I guess she's not really a "possession," but she's prized!) I rescued her a few months after I moved to Kansas City. She was matted, dirty, severely underweight and had heart worms. We got through all that, though, and now she's doing great. My husband and I couldn't imagine life without her.

Person I Admire Most: I'd have to choose seven people—my two parents, my four grandparents and of course, my husband, Paul! They have shown me the importance of family and commitment.

ROBERT CHAD

Since joining the Hallmark Keepsake Ornament studio in 1987, Robert Chad has successfully applied his talents to many subjects. But his favorites are cartoon characters such as LOONEY TUNES™ and SPIDER MAN™.

"Cartoons are an important part of Americana," he says. "They are one of the few things that connect baby boomers with younger generations. In fact, I've found that older cartoon characters are reemerging and becoming popular again."

A self-proclaimed "tube head," Chad remembers cartoons being a big part of his life when he was a child. After watching TV, he would try to mimic the animation with his pencil. That mimicking eventually led him to become an artist.

Hallmark Keepsake Ornament Artist Since: 1987

What I like best about sculpting Hallmark Keepsake Ornaments: I don't like to admit it, but I love the idea that—after I'm gone—my ornaments will live on. They may even be passed down through families for generations. That's incredible to me.

Hallmark Keepsake Ornament Milestones: Finally getting the chance to sculpt Marvin the Martian after waiting for nine years!

Activities I Enjoy (besides being a Hallmark Keepsake Ornament Artist): Traveling, being an artist, listening to music and watching movies.

Favorite Childhood Memory: In Junior High School, after being totally underestimated (I was overweight), I hit a grand-slam homerun to right field.

The Last Good Movie I Saw: "Smoke."

Most Prized Possession: Two Cecil Forbes etchings, one of Ann Hathaway's Cottage.

Person I Admire Most: Salvador Dali. He was lucky to be able to build a life around his own imagination.

KEN CROW

Who wouldn't love to be an adult and a child at the same time? Hallmark Keepsake Ornament studio artist Ken Crow has one of those special jobs where he can, indeed, be both!

"I think as a kid would think to come up with my ideas," Ken says. During his first glimpse of the Hallmark Keepsake Ornament Studio many years ago, he says he "got the same chills, the same feelings as a kid first entering Disneyland."

After working as a Hallmark Keepsake Ornament studio artist for 14 years, Ken declares, "The magic and excitement haven't faded a bit!"

A native of Long Beach, California, Ken joined Hallmark in 1979. He worked as an artist in several Hallmark departments before coming to the Hallmark Keepsake Ornament Studio.

Hallmark Keepsake Ornament Artist Since: 1984

What I like best about sculpting Hallmark Keepsake Ornaments: Having people enjoy my talents. I enjoy being able to create something and have people tell me how much they like it.

Hallmark Keepsake Ornament Milestones: I was visiting my Dad in Southern California, and we saw a Hallmark commercial for the Santa and eight reindeer ornament collection I created. The reason this was a milestone was because my Dad didn't have much interest in my artistry up to that point. But when he saw the commercial, he looked over and said, "Ken, I'm proud of you." At that moment, I felt great! It truly was a proud moment of acceptance between father and son.

Activities I Enjoy (besides being a Hallmark Keepsake Ornament Artist): Puppetry. I especially love marionettes and hand puppets. If I wasn't a Hallmark Keepsake Ornament artist, and if I could make a living at it, I would be Gepetto.

Favorite Childhood Memory: As a child, being at the Main Street at Disneyland. The Seven Dwarfs walked out of the castle and Grumpy stepped on my foot. I felt as if I had come in contact with a real cartoon character. It was magical.

The Last Good Movie I Saw: "Babe," "Toy Story," and "The Adventures of Pinocchio."

Most Prized Possession: I have a ventriloquist dummy named Jerry Mahoney. My folks gave it to me as a child.

Person I Admire Most: Either my wife or my dad. But my entire family is so special it's hard to single out any individual. They are all great!

JOANNE ESCHRICH

Even when she was a little girl, Joanne Eschrich remembers wanting to paint, draw and sculpt. "My favorite moments in elementary school were when the art teacher would come into our classroom, pushing her cart full of paint tubes and clay," she recalls. "I couldn't wait to use color or shape to create characters and scenes that were fun and full of life."

Joanne says she still feels that same creative impulse today. "I like to put lots of life and animation into the Hallmark Keepsake Ornaments I create," she says. "It's even fun to imag-

ine that, after I've completed an ornament, it might somehow come to life!"

Growing up outside of Boston, Joanne was inspired by the city and the ocean. But she pulled up her saltwater roots and headed for Kansas City—and Hallmark—right after she graduated from Southeastern Massachusettes University with a degree in illustration.

"I told my family that I'd stay at Hallmark just long enough to gain a little experience—that was 15 years ago!" she says, smiling. She put her talents to work designing specialty gift products, paper partyware and greeting cards before she joined the Hallmark Keepsake Ornament studio.

Hallmark Keepsake Ornament Artist Since: 1996

What I like best about sculpting Hallmark Keepsake Ornaments: I really enjoy the personal contact that we get to have with collectors. When I was designing gift wrap or partyware for Hallmark, I learned whether certain designs were popular with the general public, but there was no opportunity for one-on-one feedback from the people who bought the products. With Hallmark Keepsake Ornaments, I get to hear collectors tell me why they like an ornament or what an ornament reminds them of. It's wonderful!

Hallmark Keepsake Ornament Milestones: The first time I sculpted a human figure! Before I joined the Hallmark Keepsake Ornament studio, I'd always sculpted or drawn animals for children's products. Working on the 1997 Disney ornaments gave me my first opportunity to sculpt human faces and forms. I'm delighted at how the ornaments turned out.

Activities I Enjoy (besides being a Hallmark Keepsake Ornament Artist): Traveling with my family, dining out with friends and shopping with my best friend, Cindy.

Favorite Childhood Memory: I grew up on a farm with three sisters and two brothers, and I have wonderful memories of cold-weather fun. We made igloos and snowmen, went ice skating on the pond and skidded our sleds down the driveways.

The Last Good Movie I Saw: "Waiting for Guffman"—it's hilarious!

Most Prized Possession: I don't exactly consider them possessions, but my two little daughters—Jamie and Anna—are the light of my life.

Person I Admire Most: My sister, Laurie. She's presently battling cancer. Her strength, optimism and faith never cease to amaze me.

JOHN "COLLIN" FRANCIS

John "Collin" Francis draws inspiration for his designs from many sources. "I listen to my family, friends, and to the suggestions of Hallmark Keepsake Ornament Collector's Club members. Sometimes, just driving down the street will give me an idea for a fun ornament," he says.

John also relies on his love of animals, the outdoors and his native Wyoming. Ornament collectors everywhere share in that fun through John's Hallmark Keepsake Ornament creations.

Hallmark Keepsake Ornament Artist Since: 1986

What I like best about sculpting Hallmark Keepsake Ornaments: The most interesting hobby I can think of is sculpting three-dimensional things. So I feel lucky to come to work every day and do something that I consider to be an enjoyable hobby.

Hallmark Keepsake Ornament Milestones: In the early 1980's, I was with a small group of people beginning to sculpt ornaments for Hallmark. One person from our group was chosen to sculpt Merry Miniatures® for the Specialty department– that was me. After a while, a vice president decided I should be sent to Trim-a-Home, or what is now known as the Hallmark Keepsake Ornament studio. It was the biggest breakthrough in my 31 years with Hallmark.

Activities I Enjoy (besides being a Hallmark Keepsake Ornament Artist): I love to feed the birds. I have five feeders in my backyard that I fill every morning. The possum who lives under my deck really takes advantage of this situation. I'm also starting to do watercolor painting again. I used to do it a long time ago, and I've enjoyed getting back into my old hobby.

Favorite Childhood Memory: The time that touched me the most was after my grandfather passed away. My father was away from home for five or six months to settle grandfather's estate in Washington. When he finally returned home, I saw him standing in the kitchen and ran to him. I still remember hugging him tightly—it was very emotional.

The Last Good Movie I Saw: I'm crazy for old movies. The best movie I've seen is called "Laura"– it's a murder mystery.

Most Prized Possession: I wouldn't call her a possession, but my wife. She's such a wonderful person. I could never replace all the things she does every day. I'm very lucky.

Person I Admire Most: In addition to my dad and mom, I admire an instructor of mine—Gary Coulter—at Hastings College in Hastings, Nebraska. He had such an enthusiasm for three-dimensional objects, and he truly valued the artistic approach to coming up with new ones. It was fun to be around him. He touched all of his students. He is presently head of the art department at Fort Hays State College in Hays, Kansas.

TAMMY HADDIX

Tammy Haddix came to Hallmark directly from the Kansas City Art Institute, where she was recruited by a Hallmark representative during a campus visit. Since joining Hallmark, she has worked primarily on two-dimensional artwork for products such as gift wrap, albums, books and partyware.

"I've always been interested in sculpting," Tammy says, "and I had done some lapel pins, salt and pepper shakers and picture frames. This led to some special assignments for the Hallmark Keepsake Ornament studio."

When she was young, Tammy says that she drew all over the walls in her closet. "My mom still hasn't painted over those drawings," she recalls. "I drew on any flat surface, even underneath the countertop on the bathroom vanity!"

Hallmark Keepsake Ornament Artist Since: 1996

What I like best about sculpting Hallmark Keepsake Ornaments: Being able to put life and emotion into the pieces I sculpt. Bringing characters to life is what I love to do!

Hallmark Keepsake Ornament Milestones: Right before I started at the Hallmark Keepsake Ornament Studio, I had a son, Zachary. He definitely influences my sculpting– I see his face in several of my pieces! My first real milestone with Hallmark Keepsake Ornaments was my very first local club tour to Little Rock, Arkansas. I was the guest speaker, which I had never done before. It ended up being a lot of fun, because the collectors did their best to make me feel at home. It was my first chance to meet some collectors– what friendly people they are!

Activities I Enjoy (besides being a Hallmark Keepsake Ornament Artist): Gardening, antiquing and spending time with my son, my husband and our families.

Favorite Childhood Memory: I remember the first time I realized that I wanted to work at Hallmark– I was 5 years old. My mom took me to a Hallmark store, and as I looked around at all the cards, I told her that's what I wanted to do someday—I wanted to be an artist! Dreams do come true!

The Last Good Movie I Saw: "Contact" on video because with a one-year-old, you just don't go to the movies.

Most Prized Possession: I'd have to say my home, which my husband Rick, and I had built especially for us. We take a lot of pride in it and in the gardens which we add to every year.

Person I Admire Most: My mom. She's the one who never let me say "I can't".

KRISTINA KLINE

Originally from Iowa, Kristina Kline was a student at the Kansas City Art Institute when she first met two members of the Hallmark Keepsake Ornament team. Jack Benson, Hallmark Keepsake Ornament studio manager, and Robert Chad, studio artist, were at the school teaching a sculpting class for promising young artists. The raggedy teddy bear and cat that Kris sculpted gave her the opportunity to intern at the Hallmark Keepsake Ornament Studio in the summer of 1995. She's been there ever since!

"Everyone at the Hallmark Keepsake Ornament studio is like a family," says Kris. "When I came as an intern, people were willing to share their ideas and their tools. They were there to help."

Hallmark Keepsake Ornament Artist Since: 1995

What I like best about sculpting Hallmark Keepsake Ornaments: It's a way for me to put myself into my work. It's fun to create a fantasy of characters down to the last detail.

Hallmark Keepsake Ornament Milestones: My recent promotion to Artist II was definitely a big milestone in my career. Also, creating Sweet Memories—this year's eight-piece set of blown glass candy ornaments—was fun and quite a challenge for me. Not only was I working with a new material, but it was also a whole new way of thinking.

Activities I Enjoy (besides being a Hallmark Keepsake Ornament Artist): I enjoy quiet times at home, going to the movies, baking and sewing—especially sewing stuffed animals.

Favorite Childhood Memory: When I was a young girl, my calico cat ran away. She was gone for six months, and I'd just about given up all hope. Then one day after school, I desperately called out for her. Suddenly, I heard meowing behind me and she was there! It's the first time I remember laughing and crying at the same time. I was so happy!

The Last Good Movie I Saw: "Men In Black", and "Anastasia". The "Star Wars" trilogy is also a timeless classic– the new footage made it even more of a treat.

Most Prized Possession: I treasure my family and friends. I also value a quilt that my mom made and a bow-front chest of drawers that my parents refinished for me. But my most prized possession is a Hallmark pin of a leprechaun holding a clover balloon. My dad gave it to me. He picked it out himself, which is what makes it so special.

Person I Admire Most: My mom and dad because of all they've done for me. My brother and sister-in-law are also very important to me. But above all, Jesus Christ is the most important influence in my life.

TRACY LARSEN

Clara Johnson Scroggins, noted ornament authority, was right when she said that one of Tracy Larsen's 1997 designs would be among the year's most popular ornaments. Not a bad start for a debuting Hallmark Keepsake Ornament artist.

The ornament Scroggins was referring to commemorates the 50th anniversary of the television program, "It's Howdy Doody™ Time!" Tracy says: "Of all the designs I created for the 1997 collection, it's the one of which I'm most proud."

Tracy was born the same year that Howdy Doody went off the air. But that didn't limit his portrayal of the memorable marionette. "The other artists gave my design the 'thumbs up,' " say Larsen. "That really boosted my confidence."

Tracy grew up at the foot of Ben Lomond Mountain in the northern part of Utah. "I miss the mountains," he says. "I hope to incorporate more of their beauty in future ornament designs."

Hallmark Keepsake Ornament Artist Since: 1995

("But I'd worked at Hallmark since 1987 as a greeting card artist.)

What I like best about sculpting Hallmark Keepsake Ornaments: I enjoy the appreciation that collectors show for the work we do. It's fun to witness the excitement and anticipation that each new ornament line inspires, first when the Dream Book is released and then when the line actually premieres in stores.

Hallmark Keepsake Ornament Milestones: That would have to be the Howdy Doody™ anniversary ornament—it's probably my most significant contribution. It was only the second ornament that I sculpted as a Hallmark Keepsake Ornament artist, and I'm so pleased by how well it was received by collectors and by my coworkers.

Activities I Enjoy (besides being a Hallmark Keepsake Ornament Artist): I have four children whom I love to spend time with (and who take up the majority of my leisure time). I'm also involved extensively in my church's youth activities and choirs. When I find time, I like to paint, play sports, coach Little League and browse through collectible stores.

Favorite Childhood Memory: I was 9 years old. My baseball team was playing the best team in the league. It was the bottom of the ninth inning, the score was tied 8 to 8, and the most-feared Little League pitcher, Randy Anderson (he looked a lot like Randy Johnson from Seattle) was on the mound. I was the first batter. I smacked a fast ball over the center fielder's head and won the game with my first-ever home run! Later on that season, I hit two grand slams in one game.

The Last Good Movie I Saw: I don't get to many movies. But we took the children to see Disney's "Hercules," and we all enjoyed it.

Most Prized Possession: My family. In terms of material things, I value some paintings that I created as a student during my senior year at Brigham Young University. I also have some old family photos and mementos that are meaningful.

Person I Admire Most: Jesus Christ, without whom, I believe, nothing else would really matter.

JOYCE LYLE

Joyce Lyle's oldest brother, Jerold, was an artist who helped to develop her love of beautiful art. But Joyce did not imagine she would become an artist when she was growing up in Tulsa, Oklahoma.

"I first studied physical education at Oklahoma State University, but later took up art education in hopes of teaching," Joyce recalls. She married before finishing school and soon was raising five children—a daughter and four sons—who kept her and her husband more than busy.

Joyce first worked at Hallmark for two years beginning in 1979, then stepped back from full-time work to become a free-lance artist for the company. She joined Hallmark Keepsake Ornaments in 1984. "At that time, I had never sculpted anything and didn't know I could," Joyce says. "My job was to paint duplicate ornaments that other artists had sculpted, and paint flat artwork for ball or brass ornaments– plus other jobs that needed doing. But it was only a few years before ornaments that I had sculpted began appearing in Hallmark's line."

Hallmark Keepsake Ornament Artist Since: 1984

What I like best about sculpting Hallmark Keepsake Ornaments: I enjoy the variety of ornaments we design and the opportunity to express myself in my work. Also, I love working with and learning from the creative, fun, crazy people here at Hallmark Keepsake Ornaments! Top that off with being able to meet and talk with collectors who buy our work because they love it—it's great!

Hallmark Keepsake Ornament Milestones: It was great to see the very first ornament that I sculpted hanging in stores and watching people actually buy it! It was a Brother ornament in the 1989 line– a puppy in a tennis shoe. It was an appropriate beginning since I have six brothers and four sons!

Activities I Enjoy (besides being a Hallmark Keepsake Ornament Artist): I love to sing. My husband, Tom, and I are in our church's choral and handbell choirs, and have been in several community choirs. I direct a children's choir of five and six year olds– really fun! We've traveled quite a bit with the handbell choir, including trips to Tulsa, Oklahoma and Estes Park, Colorado for national festivals. Most of all, we love to spend time with our family, especially with our children and grandchildren. We've tried to be there through the years of sports, plays and other activities, and we wouldn't trade those times for anything.

Favorite Childhood Memory: Christmas with my family was always great fun. We didn't have a lot of money—not with seven children, mom and dad—but we always had fun trying to get gifts for everyone and keeping them secret. In the summers, I often spent time in Wagoner, Oklahoma with cousins. We never really did anything very special—just things that kids do to occupy themselves on hot summer days—but I have great memories of those times.

The Last Good Movie I Saw: I love "The Sound of Music," "The Music Man," "While You Were Sleeping," "Sleepless In Seattle," and "Titanic".

Most Prized Possession: The material possessions I prize are things my children have made or that Tom has given me. Pictures of my family and my three grandchildren top the list. I have some wonderful cross stitchings that my daughter made, things my boys made in shop in junior high school, a beautiful four-poster bed that Tom surprised me with last year and a few antiques I enjoy. But much more than things, I prize my relationships with my family and friends, and the memories of times spent together.

Person I Admire Most: My Mom. She was a remarkable lady!

LYNN NORTON

A cherished family tradition of model building and his own outstanding technical abilities have brought Lynn a rewarding 31-year career at Hallmark. He worked for 21 years as an engraver, becoming a Hallmark Keepsake Ornament technical artist in 1987.

"It all began with my great-grandfather, who hand crafted a large-scale model of a train engine for my uncle when he was a boy," Lynn explains. Lynn was bitten by the model bug at age 8. Since then, he's had life-long romance with planes, trains and automobiles.

His model-building expertise served him well when sculpting Hallmark Keepsake Ornaments depicting the ships of STAR TREK®, STAR TREK®: THE NEXT GENERATION and STAR WARS™.

Hallmark Keepsake Ornament Artist Since: 1987

What I like best about sculpting Hallmark Keepsake Ornaments: Working with so many creative personalities. There are laughs and surprises around every corner, every day of the year.

Hallmark Keepsake Ornament Milestones: Being asked to sculpt my first ornament, the 1991 Starship Enterprise, and having it be so popular and successful.

Activities I Enjoy (besides being a Hallmark Keepsake Ornament Artist): Restoring old things that have been discarded or overlooked. I like to surround myself with old stuff that looks and feels as good as it was when it was new.

Favorite Childhood Memory: Sitting on my great-grandfather's knee, just before he retired, and pulling the throttle of his locomotive in the old rail yards of Kansas City. He let me run it for hours.

The Last Good Movie I Saw: "Titanic."

Most Prized Possession: My ornament, the Enterprise "D" from STAR TREK®: THE NEXT GENERATION™ signed by Patrick Stewart (Captain Picard).

Person I Admire Most: I've been influenced by so many people. For years I kept a diary of favorite quotations. It's interesting to recall what was going on in my life based on the quotations I enjoyed at a particular time. I think the person I've collected the most quotations from is Robin Williams. Comedians are like modern sages. They just wrap their wisdom in humor.

DON PALMITER

Don Palmiter has been a Hallmark Keepsake Ornament studio artist for 11 years, but he's been with Hallmark 31 years. A Kansas City native, he joined the company right out of high school and spent several years as a Hallmark engraver.

Don says, "After joining the Hallmark Keepsake Ornament staff, I worked for three years solely on collectible figurines, including the Hometown American and Mary and Friends groups."

Don, who is designing the entire Classic American Cars Hallmark Keepsake Ornament series, has a lifelong affection for classic automobiles.

"I've owned quite a selection of cars," he says. "Among them have been a 1962 Corvair, a 1963 Rolls Royce Silver Cloud and a 1968 Corvette."

Don also serves as the primary design and research consultant for Kiddie Car Classics, a nostalgic collection of scale-model sidewalk transportation such as scooters, tricycles and handcars. He worked with pedal-car authorities and other collectors to select the items that will be sculpted for each of these popular collections- and he sculpts most of them himself.

Hallmark Keepsake Ornament Artist Since: 1987

What I like best about sculpting Hallmark Keepsake Ornaments: I enjoy making things that other people enjoy collecting—things that bring them pleasure and good memories. Hallmark Keepsake Ornaments are about excellence in design but, at a deeper level, they are about memories. So I have fun dipping into my own memories and interests to create ornaments.

Hallmark Keepsake Ornament Milestones: The Classic American Cars series! I invested lots of time and effort into convincing my colleagues that Hallmark Keepsake Ornaments based on classic cars would be popular with collectors. Because I love cars so much, I stuck with the idea until I got the green light. The first in the series debuted eight years ago, and it's been great to see it take off, and lead me into other ornaments and collectibles based on transportation.

Activities I Enjoy (besides being a Hallmark Keepsake Ornament Artist): Most of all, I enjoy spending time with my family, and I like working in my yard. I also enjoy interior decorating, going to antique malls (I look for items to add to my various collections) and traveling. Participating in church activities and spending time with friends are important too.

Favorite Childhood Memory: A family vacation to Colorado and seeing real mountains for the very first time!

The Last Good Movie I Saw: I really enjoyed "Titanic."

Most Prized Possession: I don't think any single possession is more important to me than others, although I do have a variety of possessions that I prize highly. Among those would be an art glass collection, a large antique crystal collection and more that 30 pieces of Guiseppe Armani sculpture.

Person I Admire Most: I admire a lot of people, but by far the one I admire most is Karol, my wife of 30 years. She's put up with me! She's also been my best supporter.

SHARON PIKE

Sharon Pike is back in the swing of things. After a four-year hiatus, she returned two years ago to what she calls the "greatest job there is"—working as a sculptor in the Hallmark Keepsake Ornament Studio.

Sharon began her Hallmark career in process art and later worked in greeting cards, gifts, books and soft-sculpted animals.

Her love of animals—and of sculpting them—is evident in the Hallmark Keepsake Ornaments she has created. From furry to feathered, Sharon loves them all!

Hallmark Keepsake Ornament Artist Since: 1983

What I like best about sculpting Hallmark Keepsake Ornaments: Everything about this job is fun! I love sculpting little animals and just having the opportunity to express myself artistically. I even get to use my sense of humor in my work—for that I consider myself lucky!

Hallmark Keepsake Ornament Milestones: The most recent milestone was when I finally returned to work here in the Hallmark Keepsake Ornament studio after a four-year "break" during which I was nursing a badly broken arm. I'm so glad to be back!

Activities I Enjoy (besides being a Hallmark Keepsake Ornament Artist): I enjoy just about anything that's artsy. I love art shows, painting and going to the theater. I also make jewelry.

Favorite Childhood Memory: I think my favorite childhood memory must be when I got my first bike. It was blue, it came as a Christmas gift, and it was so nice. (My brother got a red bike the following year, which made me momentarily envious.) We lived in North Carolina at the time, which is a state that doesn't suffer from sub-zero weather in late December, so I actually could go outside and ride my new bike on Christmas day.

The Last Good Movie I Saw: "Titanic." I also like science fiction movies. Actually, I love science fiction anything!

Most Prized Possession: My kitty. She's a girl, her names is C.C., she's a calico, and she's my companion. And Skunk– I must mention him. He's another of my kitties who died last year at age 17, but I still think of him as a part of my household. Actually, Skunk inspired a lot of my ornaments.

Person I Admire Most: I admire artists—especially the great masters from centuries past. I think I admire all artistic people, in general. Here in the Hallmark Keepsake Ornament studio, I'm an admirer of Robert Chad. He does great work, he's good moral support, and we share the same sense of humor!

DILL RHODUS

Dill Rhodus, who grew up in Kansas City, Mo., joined Hallmark more than 31 years ago as an apprentice engraver. During the next several years, he honed his skills and was promoted to the position of senior artistic engraver.

In the years he has been designing Hallmark Keepsake Ornaments, Dill has created a diversity of ornament styles– from professional athletes to STARWARS™ characters.

"I'm an avid baseball fan, so you can imagine my excitement when I was given the opportunity to sculpt Hank Aaron," Dill says. "The challenge was to capture his distinctive style."

Another big challenge for Dill was sculpting New York Jets quarterback Joe Namath, third in the Football Legends series. Dill says he watched videos and studied many photos to capture Namath's unique body language.

Another sports-themed ornament by Dill, Jackie Robinson, commemorates 50 years since the legend integrated Major League Baseball.

Dill is married to Patricia Andrews, another Hallmark Keepsake Ornament Artist.

Hallmark Keepsake Ornament Artist Since: 1986

What I like best about sculpting Hallmark Keepsake Ornaments: The wide range of subjects that I get to work on! I sculpt everything from cute cats to ornaments based on real people.

Hallmark Keepsake Ornament Milestones: It would have to be getting my baseball and football ornaments into the Hallmark Keepsake Ornament line—and then seeing the overwhelming response from collectors. When the Joe Montana ornaments (the first in the Football Legends series in the San Francisco '49er uniform and the complement to the series that portrayed Montana as a Kansas City Chief) that I sculpted debuted with the 1995 line, many people were surprised at how popular they were. But I wasn't surprised!

Activities I Enjoy (besides being a Hallmark Keepsake Ornament Artist): I enjoy coaching my daughter's soccer team. When my older children, Andrea and Shawn were younger, I coached soccer for them and now I'm back at it for Elizabeth. And I LOVE to play golf—it's truly one of my passions. I like to work in the yard too. Trish and I have four acres, and she's really the gardener. I guess you might say I'm the caretaker—I take care of the lawn and the trees and I enjoy it.

Favorite Childhood Memory: I have two—going fishing with my dad and playing Little League baseball. I had such a good time playing Little League that it's tough to pick out one game that's more memorable than others, but I do remember a Little League season that was my favorite. My dad coached my team when I was 9 years old. He was a great dad and a great coach, and he made that season the best one of all.

The Last Good Movie I Saw: "Contact." I was fascinated by how that movie dealt with the tension between religion and science—faith and facts—and how those two can come together. And Jodie Foster's performance was great.

Most Prized Possession: I don't know if you'd call them "possessions," but there's nothing I value more than my family.

Person I Admire Most: I really admire my mom and dad. They built the mold out of which I live my life. I was born to them rather late in their lives, and now that I have children of my own, I can see more clearly how much they gave—and, sometimes, how much they gave up—for me.

Anita Marra Rogers

For Anita Marra Rogers, becoming a Hallmark Keepsake Ornament studio artist was a case of love at first sight. Even though it happened 11 years ago, she remembers it as if it were yesterday.

"I stepped into the Hallmark Keepsake Ornament Studio, looked around and thought, 'This is what I want to do,' " she recalls.

Anita began working as a part-time Hallmark artist in the fall of 1984, moving to full time three years later. Her love for animals is demonstrated in Hallmark Keepsake Ornaments such as the Puppy Love series, while her talent for portraying people is showcased in the recent STAR TREK® ornaments.

Hallmark Keepsake Ornament Artist Since: 1987

What I like best about sculpting Hallmark Keepsake Ornaments: The opportunity to express myself through my work.

Hallmark Keepsake Ornament Milestones: The Beatles Gift Set for 1994. By sculpting The Beatles, I was able to demonstrate that I could do realistic likenesses of people, and I've been doing them ever since.

Activities I Enjoy (besides being a Hallmark Keepsake Ornament Artist): I enjoy collecting Hallmark Keepsake Ornaments as well as Longaberger Baskets and Pottery. I also enjoy mind-boggling puzzles of which I have quite an assortment. I love baking, traveling and spending time with my family.

Favorite Childhood Memory: The big snowstorm on my birthday when school was canceled and I got to play in the snow all day.

The Last Good Movie I Saw: "Willie Wonka and the Chocolate Factory." I enjoyed it as a kid, and I still enjoy it as an adult. Willie Wonka is a fun movie the whole family can enjoy.

Most Prized Possession: The first sculpture I did of a deer and bunny that gave me the incentive to keep on sculpting and to try for a job making Hallmark Keepsake Ornaments.

Person I Admire Most: Actually, the two people I admire most are my parents for always supporting and encouraging me in my artistic endeavors.

Ed Seale

Whether building his first boat—a wooden catamaran—or creating a Hallmark Keepsake Ornament, Hallmark Keepsake Ornament studio artist Ed Seale loves working with his hands.

Ed, born in Toronto, grew up in the wooded countryside of southern Ontario. His early interests led him to seasonal work—eight years as a carpenter in Canada during summers and as a boat builder in Florida during winters. Although he enjoyed this work, his heart directed him to art, and, eventually to Hallmark—where he put his experience to work.

"I like to combine different artistic elements," Ed says. "For example, I'll sculpt a whimsical animal in a scene where you would normally expect to find a person. I think it makes the ornament more appealing."

At Hallmark, Ed is noted for drawing on past experiences, future trends and his own intuition to create some of the most memorable Hallmark Keepsake Ornaments, including several in the highly prized Frosty Friends series.

Hallmark Keepsake Ornament Artist Since: 1980

What I like best about sculpting Hallmark Keepsake Ornaments: Working with this great group of people—they're like extended family—and being in on the creative process from concept through the finished ornament is very satisfying! But connecting with collectors is most rewarding of all. When someone tells you that they really like your work and that a particular ornament has a special personal meaning to them—it leaves you with a wonderful feeling!

Hallmark Keepsake Ornament Milestones: Discovering how much I like sculpting little animals and how, sometimes, they can represent us better (and with more whimsy and appeal) than we can represent ourselves was a milestone. Eventually, it led me to start the Tender Touches Collection.

Activities I Enjoy (besides being a Hallmark Keepsake Ornament Artist)**:** Sailing my catamaran, photography, being a new grandfather, travel, and I'm an incurable do-it-yourselfer around the house.

Favorite Childhood Memory: I have indelible memories of country Christmases in Canada—the one-room schoolhouse where our teacher would start getting us ready for "The Christmas Concert" many weeks before Christmas, the excitement of the big night of the concert at the community hall, my parents coming to see and hear us perform, a surprise visit from Santa in the middle of the activities ("Ho! Ho! Ho!), and candy for us all! Then, eventually, Christmas morning finally arrived and how magical it looked when my two brothers and I came downstairs– because after we kids had gone to sleep, mother had rearranged things, added more decoration, put out presents and filled the stockings. It's a childhood memory undimmed by time. P.S. We always had a white Christmas!

The Last Good Movie I Saw: "Ulee's Gold."

Most Prized Possession: My memories—without question.

Person I Admire Most: Charles Kuralt. He was a gentle journalist who traveled to and reported from every corner of America and the world. He had a way of being genuinely interested wherever he was and in whoever he was with. He was a thoughtful man who made you feel that, despite our problems, all was pretty well with the world. I admire him and I miss him.

LINDA SICKMAN

When she first started creating Hallmark Keepsake Ornaments, Linda Sickman never dreamed how popular ornament collecting would become. But that was 22 years ago. Since then, she has created more than 300 designs that have become cherished treasures for thousands of collectors.

Linda gained much popularity for the Rocking Horse series, which rode into the sunset in 1996 after 16 glorious years. Collectors might be surprised to learn that Linda originally hadn't planned to create and entire series of rocking horses.

"In the beginning, I planned to do one horse," Linda explains. "But after I carved it, I couldn't decide how to paint it. So I submitted several different designs. Hallmark liked them all, so my rocking horses became a series."

Although the Rocking Horse series has ended, many of Linda's other ornament creations still are available to delight collectors. Her Folk Art Americana Collection, for example, includes Hallmark Keepsake Ornaments that are individually painted to recreate the look of hand-carved wood. She also is known for her pressed tin creations, especially her Tin Locomotive and Yuletide Central tin train ornaments.

Hallmark Keepsake Ornament Artist Since: 1976

What I like best about sculpting Hallmark Keepsake Ornaments: First of all, I love the people I work with. We really have fun! And I love the artistic aspect of sculpting Hallmark Keepsake Ornaments because it gives me the opportunity to immerse myself in a fantasy world and express what I see there.

Hallmark Keepsake Ornament Milestones: The opportunity to do this kind of work—to express myself in my own designs—is in itself a milestone. I probably wouldn't appreciate all of the ongoing artistic milestones here with Hallmark Keepsake Ornaments as much as I do if it hadn't been for an earlier career milestone. When I first joined hallmark 35 years ago, I worked in process art and then in lettering—in those positions, I added finish work to original designs done by other artists. Then a lady named Ruth Moorhead who worked in the Specialty group hired me to do her finished artwork. I did that for one day, and then she gave me the opportunity to create my own designs. Every artist needs someone like Ruth to say, "I have confidence in you and your talent. Ruth still has my gratitude.

Activities I Enjoy (besides being a Hallmark Keepsake Ornament Artist): I'm an ornament collector, and I have small collections of tin toys and nutcrackers. I also enjoy the symphony and the theater.

Favorite Childhood Memory: I could be wrong, but it seems to me that the winters of my childhood came with a lot more snow than the winters of my adulthood! I remember going out to my dad's farm, and we'd hook the sled to the back of the tractor so he could pull us around. And I remember making snow angels.

The Last Good Movie I Saw: I really liked "Shine"—fantastic!

Most Prized Possession: My family and friends aren't possessions but there's nothing I value more.

Person I Admire Most: Mother Theresa

Bob Siedler

Bob Siedler became a Hallmark Keepsake Ornament studio artist through the little-known "noon doodle" method. "I was working in Hallmark's sales promotion department as a graphic artist," Bob explains. "On my lunch hours, I started making clay roughs and called them my 'noon doodles." Eventually, I completed a group of small figurines that I showed to the Hallmark Keepsake Ornament art director."

Those clay roughs eventually helped land Bob a job in the Hallmark Keepsake Ornament Studio, where he has been working since 1982.

Bob thrives on variety. "Each year, we create a completely new line of ornaments," he says. Each one is different, so every assignment presents new challenges."

Bob says he meets the constant challenge of coming up with fresh ideas by observing people. "For me, watching people's behavior provides enough information to supply me with a lifetime of ideas," he says.

Hallmark Keepsake Ornament Artist Since: 1982

What I like best about sculpting Hallmark Keepsake Ornaments: Each ornament is a new challenge.

Hallmark Keepsake Ornament Milestones: In 1984, "Santa Mouse" took me from being a duplicate artist toward being a designer.

Activities I Enjoy (besides being a Hallmark Keepsake Ornament Artist): Golf and snow skiing.

Favorite Childhood Memory: I'll always remember the first Christmas present I received other than underwear and socks. It was a microscope. I still have it.

The Last Good Movie I Saw: I don't go to the movies. I haven't seen a movie in years.

Most Prized Possession: The microscope.

Person I Admire Most: My parents. They raised 4 children through some pretty tough times.

Sue Tague

Sue Tague's career has grown along with Hallmark. A native of Long Island, New York, Sue attended Syracuse University where she majored in illustration and earned a degree in fine arts. Her first stop on the career ladder was Hallmark. Little did she know that it probably also would be her last!

"I intended to stay at Hallmark for one year just to get some experience," Sue says. "That was 32 years ago!"

During the first 10 years of her Hallmark career, Sue designed greeting cards. When the company expanded into three-dimensional products, so did Sue. She worked as a designer, sculpting pewter and porcelain figurines for Little Gallery and creating licensed characters for Kid Biz.

Hallmark Keepsake Ornament Artist Since: 1994

Although I joined the Hallmark Keepsake Ornament studio just four years ago, I've helped to create Hallmark Keepsake Ornaments and other collectibles for many years. In fact, I designed one of the first ball ornaments that Hallmark ever made. I also contributed to some of the earliest series, including the Thimble series that began back in 1978, and I've worked on lots of Merry Miniatures® through the years.

What I like best about sculpting Hallmark Keepsake Ornaments: I really love to sculpt! I've painted, I've drawn...sculpting really is my favorite form of artistic expression.

Hallmark Keepsake Ornament Milestones: A number of years ago, employees here at Hallmark created a new kind of wax especially for sculpting. For me, the development of that wax was a milestone. Before I had that wax, the process I used for sculpting an ornament was complicated and much more time consuming. The Hallmark wax gave me freedom to sculpt in the way I'd always wanted.

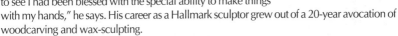

Activities I Enjoy (besides being a Hallmark Keepsake Ornament Artist)**:** I love to make dolls and puppets. I designed the Family of Bears plush toys (mom, poppa and baby) that were the very first ever market by Hallmark under the Heartline brand name– I guess I tend to get in on the beginning of things here at Hallmark! Quite honestly, if someone told me that I could go home for the afternoon and do whatever I wanted, I think I'd do almost the same thing that I do while I'm here!

Favorite Childhood Memory: When I think about my childhood, I think about the beach. I still miss it.

The Last Good Movie I Saw: "As Good As It Gets".

Most Prized Possession: They're not possessions, but I prize my kids more than anything. My son is in the Merchant Marines, and he's at sea off the Alaskan coast. My daughter is a senior at the University of Kansas.

Person I Admire Most: I admire people who believe deeply in something and follow through on their beliefs.

Duane Unruh

As a Hallmark Keepsake Ornament senior designer, Duane Unruh is enjoying a fourth championship season! After a successful 24-year career as a high school athletic coach, Duane started a second career as a Hallmark artist.

"When I was growing up, my whole life centered around sports. My father was a college and high school coach for 40 years, and I followed in his footsteps," Duane says.

As a child growing up in rural Kansas, Duane began to notice he had a special gift. "I was a child during the Depression and made many of my own toys out of necessity. Even then I began to see I had been blessed with the special ability to make things with my hands," he says. His career as a Hallmark sculptor grew out of a 20-year avocation of woodcarving and wax-sculpting.

Hallmark Keepsake Ornament Artist Since: 1984

What I like best about sculpting Hallmark Keepsake Ornaments: I enjoy the entire process—doing the research, starting the modeling, determining the gesture and expression, and detailing the finished figure.

Hallmark Keepsake Ornament Milestones: Sculpting Lighting the Flame, the Hallmark Keepsake Magic Ornament which commemorated the Centennial Olympic Games in Atlanta. Because of my background in sports and coaching, it's near and dear to my heart. I also enjoyed sculpting the NFL Collection.

Activities I Enjoy (besides being a Hallmark Keepsake Ornament Artist): Going to my 76 acres of wooded land and working with my tractor-loader and mower.

Favorite Childhood Memory: Receiving a new basketball for Christmas when I was 7 years old.

The Last Good Movie I Saw: "Titanic".

Most Prized Possession: My dog, Amber.

Person I Admire Most: My wife, Barbara. We've been married 44 years.

LaDene Votruba

As one of the Hallmark Keepsake Ornament studio artists, LaDene Votruba doesn't have any trouble generating new designs. She frequents her large home library, scans and collects magazines, and always remains alert to new ideas during her travels.

"Many of the things I identify with in my life are reflected in my work." She says. "As ornaments, they continue to represent life's treasured moments."

LaDene says she feels a special affinity for the Beatrix Potter designs she has sculpted over the past several years. "I can really relate to Beatrix Potter's artwork," she explains. "It's similar to my own styling."

LaDene was raised on a farm near Wilson, Kansas, and she is of Czechoslovakian descent. She joined the Hallmark Keepsake Ornament Studio in 1983 after ten years in other creative positions at Hallmark.

Hallmark Keepsake Ornament Artist Since: 1983

What I like best about sculpting Hallmark Keepsake Ornaments: I enjoy expressing my feelings about Christmas, Easter and springtime. Hopefully those feelings will touch our collectors too.

Hallmark Keepsake Ornament Milestones: The Gift Bringers Hallmark Keepsake Ornament ball collector's series, the 1996 Beatrix Potter™ Peter Rabbit™ first-in-the-series ornament and the 1997 second-in-the-series Beatrix Potter™ Jemima Puddle-duck™.

Activities I Enjoy (besides being a Hallmark Keepsake Ornament Artist): I like antiquing, reading, going to the movies, enjoying music, history, walking in the country (particularly my family's farm in Kansas) shopping, and making jewelry.

Favorite Childhood Memory: I always fondly remember the Christmases, birthdays and other holidays when we had big family dinners and all my favorite relatives came over, or we visited them at their homes. Another favorite remembrance is the Christmas when I received a horse as a Christmas present.

The Last Good Movie I Saw: There have been several: "Midnight in the Garden of Good and Evil", "Kundun", "Titanic", "Great Expectations", "Good Will Hunting", and "As Good As It Gets".

Most Prized Possession: My family heirloom antiques.

Person I Admire Most: I really can't name just one. I admire Walt Disney for all he did for generations of children and adults (children at heart!); Harry Truman for his honesty; Audrey Hepburn (I always wanted to be her!); Christopher Reeve for his positive attitude and determination in the face of adversity (a true "superman"!); and Jimmy Stewart, an all-American "everyman"—a real gentleman.

Nello Williams

As an illustrator in Tucson, Arizona, one of Nello William's favorite pastimes was to make Christmas ornaments, which he would give as gifts to friends and family. Little did he know that his hobby would one day lead to a career as a Hallmark Keepsake Ornament studio artist.

While in Tucson, Nello interviewed for a position with Hallmark's card division. "I showed my illustration portfolio in hopes of getting a job as a card artist," he explains.

But it wasn't Nello's drawings that caught the interviewer's eye. Instead, it was one of his handmade Christmas ornaments, which Nello just happened to have with him.

"The interviewer evidently saw potential in that ornament," says Nello. "She put me on a track that led to an internship at the Hallmark Keepsake Ornament studio."

There, Nello was given the opportunity to prove his talents. Two of the ornament designs he sculpted during that internship were featured in the 1997 Hallmark Keepsake Ornament Collection. "I guess you could say they got me the job." Nello says.

Hallmark Keepsake Ornament Artist Since: 1995

What I like best about sculpting Hallmark Keepsake Ornaments: I like the feeling or creating something that didn't exist before. You start with nothing but an idea, and end up with a product you can actually hold in your hand and be proud of.

Hallmark Keepsake Ornament Milestones: Being put on the Disney team was certainly a milestone for me. As a kid, I wanted to be a Disney animator. But when I grew up, I discovered that I'm a better sculptor. So now I get to put my childhood dreams into three-dimensional form!

Activities I Enjoy (besides being a Hallmark Keepsake Ornament Artist): I'm a musician, so I really enjoy playing the guitar and keyboard, writing songs and composing music. I also like to collect Buck Rogers and Flash Gordon-type space memorabilia—my electric guitar is covered with Buck Rogers-style images!

Favorite Childhood Memory: I grew up in a small town in the Arizona valley, where I would spend hours roaming my parent's property. My brother and I would daydream some of the best adventures to pass our time. The freedom I felt then really helped to develop my imagination.

The Last Good Movie I Saw: "Anastasia." One of my all-time favorite movies was "Shadow Lands" starring Anthony Hopkins. I'm also a big fan of Disney movies, especially "Mary Poppins" and "Who Framed Roger Rabbit?"

Most Prized Possession: I truly value my friendships and my relationship with my family. With regards to a material possession, my most prized would have to be my musical instruments. They're worth more than my car!

Person I Admire Most: My mom. She was always my biggest fan. The best of what I am today is due to my mom's teachings.

1973

Elves

Elves playing in snow.
Glass Ball, 3.50"

XHD1035 SRP: $2.50 **GBTru: $70**

Yarn Blue Girl

Girl caroler in blue dress.
Yarn, 4.50"

XHD852 SRP: $1.25 **GBTru: $18**

Betsey Clark

Musicians.
Glass Ball, 3.25"

XHD1002 SRP: $2.50 **GBTru: $95**

Manger Scene

Nativity scene.
Glass Ball, 3.25"

XHD1022 SRP: $2.50 GBTru: **$68**

Yarn Boy Caroler

Boy caroler.
Yarn, 4.50"

XHD832 SRP: $1.25 **GBTru: $22**

BETSEY CLARK - 1ST Christmas 1973

Girl with lamb & girl with deer.
Glass Ball, 3.25", Dated

XHD1102 SRP: $2.50 **GBTru: $88**

Santa With Elves

Santa with elves.
Glass Ball, 3.25"

XHD1015 SRP: $2.50 **GBTru: $65**

Yarn Choir Boy

Choir boy.
Yarn, 4.50"

XHD805 SRP: $1.25 **GBTru: $24**

Christmas Is Love

Two angels playing mandolins.
Glass Ball, 3.25"

XHD1062 SRP: $2.50 **GBTru: $68**

Yarn Angel

Angel.
Yarn, 4.50"

XHD785 SRP: $1.25 **GBTru: $24**

Yarn Elf

Elf.
Yarn, 4.50"

XHD792 SRP: $1.25 **GBTru: $22**

1974

Yarn Green Girl
Girl caroler in green dress.
Yarn, 4.50"

XHD845 | SRP: $1.25 | **GBTru: $22**

Yarn Mrs. Santa
Mrs. Claus.
Yarn, 4.50"

XHD752 | SRP: $1.25 | **GBTru: $22**

Angel
Angel.
Glass Ball, 3.25"

QX1101 | SRP: $2.50 | **GBTru: $68**

Yarn Little Girl
Girl dressed in pink.
Yarn, 4.50"

XHD825 | SRP: $1.25 | **GBTru: $22**

Yarn Mrs. Snowman
Mrs. Snowman.
Yarn, 4.50"

XHD772 | SRP: $1.25 | **GBTru: $20**

BETSEY CLARK - 2ND Musicians
Choir and orchestra of children.
Glass Ball, 3.25", Dated

QX1081 | SRP: $2.50 | **GBTru: $69**

Yarn Mr. Santa
Santa Claus.
Yarn, 4.50"

XHD745 | SRP: $1.25 | **GBTru: $24**

Yarn Soldier
Soldier.
Yarn, 4.50"

XHD812 | SRP: $1.00 | **GBTru: $18**

Buttons & Bo
Buttons & Bo, Set/2.
Glass Balls, 2.25"

QX1131 | SRP: $3.50 | **GBTru: $48**

Yarn Mr. Snowman
Snowman.
Yarn, 4.50"

XHD765 | SRP: $1.25 | **GBTru: $20**

Charmers
Girl w/tree, carolers, and girl w/bird.
Glass Ball, 3.25", Dated

QX1091 | SRP: $2.50 | **GBTru: $40**

Currier & Ives

Colonial winter scenes, Set/2.
Glass Balls, 2.25"

QX1121 SRP: $3.50 **GBTru: $46**

Raggedy Ann & Raggedy Andy

Raggedy Ann & Andy scenes, Set/4.
Glass Balls, 1.75"

QX1141 SRP: $4.50 **GBTru: $70**

Yarn Mrs. Santa

Mrs. Santa.
Yarn, 4.75"

QX1001 SRP: $1.50 **GBTru: $18**

Little Miracles

Boy and his rabbit, Set/4.
Glass Balls, 1.75"

QX1151 SRP: $4.50 **GBTru: $46**

Snowgoose

Snowgoose.
Glass Ball, 3.25"

QX1071 SRP: $2.50 **GBTru: $68**

Yarn Santa

Santa.
Yarn, 4.75"

QX1051 SRP: $1.50 **GBTru: $20**

Norman Rockwell

Santa/dollhouse & Santa w/kids in pj's.
Glass Ball, 3.25"

QX1111 SRP: $2.50 **GBTru: $62**

Yarn Angel

Angel.
Yarn, 4.75"

QX1031 SRP: $1.50 **GBTru: $22**

Yarn Snowman

Snowman.
Yarn, 4.75"

QX1041 SRP: $1.50 **GBTru: $18**

Norman Rockwell

Father/son/Christmas tree & postman.
Glass Ball, 3.25", Dated

QX1061 SRP: $2.50 **GBTru: $65**

Yarn Elf

Elf.
Yarn, 4.75"

QX1011 SRP: $1.50 **GBTru: $22**

Yarn Soldier

Soldier.
Yarn, 4.75"

QX1021 SRP: $1.50 **GBTru: $20**

1975

ADORABLE
Raggedy Andy

Raggedy Andy with gift.
Handcrafted, 6.50"
D Lee

QX1601 SRP: $2.50 **GBTru: $280**

Betsey Clark

Skaters & girl w/stock'g cap, Set/2.
Satin Balls, 2.50", Dated

QX1671 SRP: $3.50 **GBTru: $25**

ADORABLE
Betsey Clark

Betsey Clark holding star.
Handcrafted, 3.50"
D Lee

QX1571 SRP: $2.50 **GBTru: $225**

ADORABLE
Raggedy Ann

Raggedy Ann with bird.
Handcrafted, 3.50"
D Lee

QX1591 SRP: $2.50 **GBTru: $265**

Betsey Clark

Child praying.
Satin Ball, 3.00", Dated

QX1631 SRP: $2.50 **GBTru: $32**

ADORABLE
Drummer Boy

Drummer boy.
Handcrafted, 3.50"
D Lee

QX1611 SRP: $2.50 **GBTru: $210**

ADORABLE
Santa

Santa with kitten.
Handcrafted, 3.50"
D Lee
(Re-issued '81 w/Mrs. Santa as boxed set - QX4485, SRP $12, GBTru $135.)

QX1551 SRP: $2.50 **GBTru: $220**

BETSEY CLARK - 3RD
Caroling Trio

Girls singing.
Glass Ball, 3.75", Dated

QX1331 SRP: $3.00 **GBTru: $49**

ADORABLE
Mrs. Santa

Mrs. Santa with kittens.
Handcrafted, 3.50"
D Lee
(Re-issued '81 w/Santa as boxed set - QX4485, SRP $12, GBTru $135.)

QX1561 SRP: $2.50 **GBTru: $210**

Betsey Clark

Children w/animals & birds, Set/4.
Satin Balls, 2.00", Dated

QX1681 SRP: $4.50 **GBTru: $30**

Buttons & Bo

Christmas activities, Set/4.
Glass Balls, 1.75", Dated

QX1391 SRP: $5.00 **GBTru: $42**

Charmers

Girl surrounded by ornaments.
Glass Ball, 3.50", Dated

QX1351 SRP: $3.00 **GBTru: $38**

Marty Links

Girl kissing boy under mistletoe.
Glass Ball, 3.25", Dated

QX1361 SRP: $3.00 **GBTru: $28**

NOSTALGIA
Joy

"JOY" with manger baby.
Handcrafted, 3.25"
L Sickman

QX1321 SRP: $3.50 **GBTru: $158**

Currier & Ives

Farm scene.
Satin Ball, 3.00"

QX1641 SRP: $2.50 **GBTru: $30**

Norman Rockwell

Santa by fireplace.
Satin Ball, 3.00"

QX1661 SRP: $2.50 **GBTru: $42**

NOSTALGIA
Locomotive

Locomotive [see 1976: QX2221].
Handcrafted, 3.25", Dated

QX1271 SRP: $3.50 **GBTru: $100**

Currier & Ives

Skaters & old mill, Set/2.
Glass Balls, 2.25"

QX1371 SRP: $4.00 **GBTru: $15**

Norman Rockwell

Boys sleeping with Santa watching.
Glass Ball, 3.25", Dated

QX1341 SRP: $3.00 **GBTru: $46**

NOSTALGIA
Peace On Earth

"Peace…" [see 1976:QX2231].
Handcrafted, 3.25", Dated
L Sickman

QX1311 SRP: $3.50 **GBTru: $130**

Little Miracles

Angel with animals, Set/4.
Glass Balls, 1.75", Dated

QX1401 SRP: $5.00 **GBTru: $38**

NOSTALGIA
Drummer Boy

Drummer boy.
Handcrafted, 3.25"
L Sickman

QX1301 SRP: $3.50 **GBTru: $125**

NOSTALGIA
Rocking Horse

Rocking horse.
Handcrafted, 3.25"
L Sickman

QX1281 SRP: $3.50 **GBTru: $124**

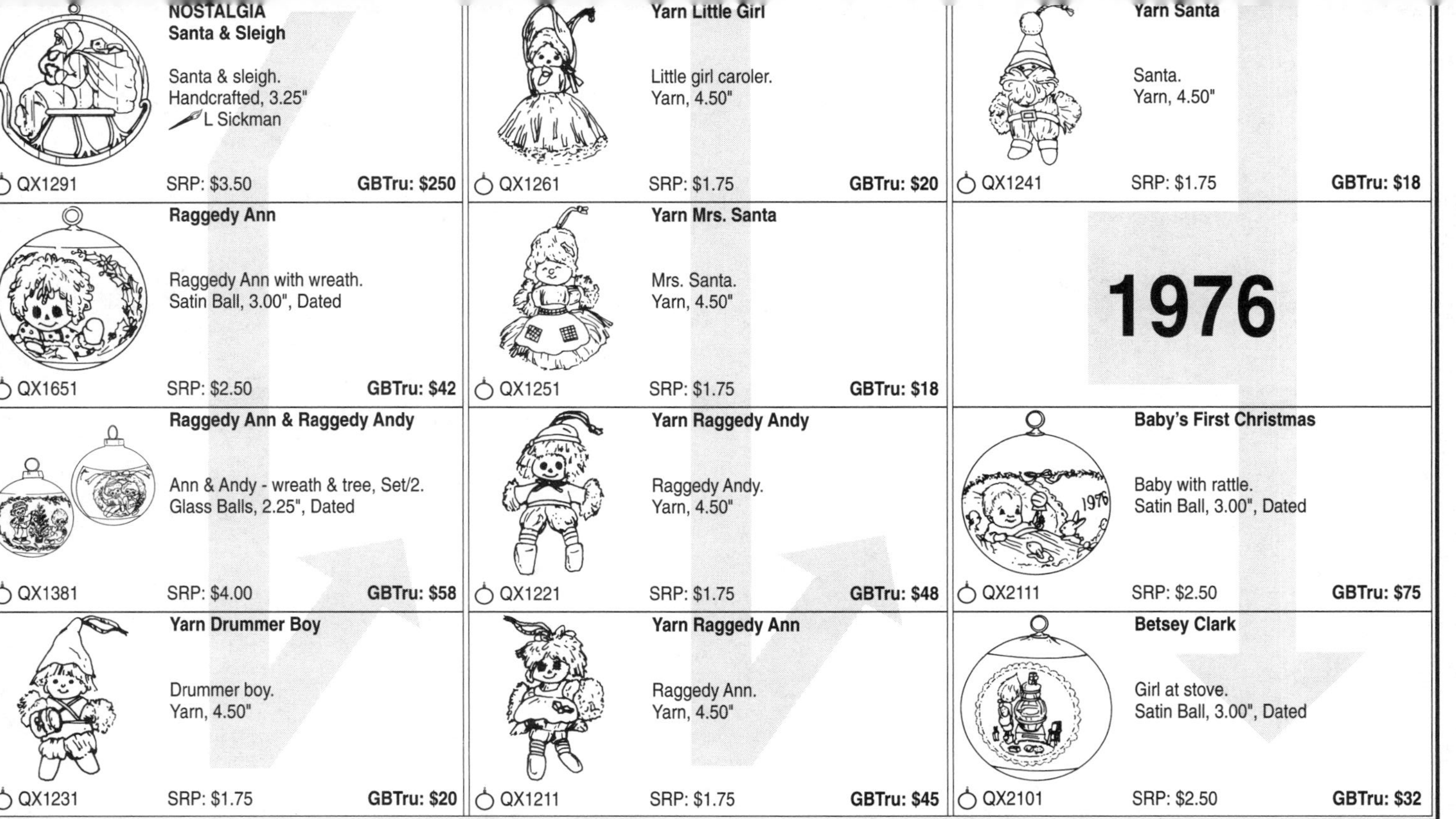

NOSTALGIA
Santa & Sleigh

Santa & sleigh.
Handcrafted, 3.25"
L Sickman

QX1291 SRP: $3.50 **GBTru: $250**

Raggedy Ann

Raggedy Ann with wreath.
Satin Ball, 3.00", Dated

QX1651 SRP: $2.50 **GBTru: $42**

Raggedy Ann & Raggedy Andy

Ann & Andy - wreath & tree, Set/2.
Glass Balls, 2.25", Dated

QX1381 SRP: $4.00 **GBTru: $58**

Yarn Drummer Boy

Drummer boy.
Yarn, 4.50"

QX1231 SRP: $1.75 **GBTru: $20**

Yarn Little Girl

Little girl caroler.
Yarn, 4.50"

QX1261 SRP: $1.75 **GBTru: $20**

Yarn Mrs. Santa

Mrs. Santa.
Yarn, 4.50"

QX1251 SRP: $1.75 **GBTru: $18**

Yarn Raggedy Andy

Raggedy Andy.
Yarn, 4.50"

QX1221 SRP: $1.75 **GBTru: $48**

Yarn Raggedy Ann

Raggedy Ann.
Yarn, 4.50"

QX1211 SRP: $1.75 **GBTru: $45**

Yarn Santa

Santa.
Yarn, 4.50"

QX1241 SRP: $1.75 **GBTru: $18**

1976

Baby's First Christmas

Baby with rattle.
Satin Ball, 3.00", Dated

QX2111 SRP: $2.50 **GBTru: $75**

Betsey Clark

Girl at stove.
Satin Ball, 3.00", Dated

QX2101 SRP: $2.50 **GBTru: $32**

Betsey Clark

3 scenes; duet, ski'g, caroling, Set/3.
Satin Balls, 2.00", Dated

QX2181 SRP: $4.50 **GBTru: $29**

BETSEY CLARK - 4TH
Christmas 1976

Two girls in bonnets & winter scene.
Glass Ball, 3.25", Dated

QX1951 SRP: $3.00 **GBTru: $78**

BICENTENNIAL
Colonial Children

Children in colonial clothing, Set/2.
Glass Balls, 2.25", Dated

QX2081 SRP: $4.00 **GBTru: $38**

Bicentennial '76 Commemorative

Girl dressed in 1776 outfit.
Satin Ball, 3.00", Dated

QX2031 SRP: $2.50 **GBTru: $25**

Bicentennial Charmers

Charmers in colonial clothing.
Glass Ball, 3.25", Dated

QX1981 SRP: $3.00 **GBTru: $34**

Cardinals

Cardinals.
Glass Ball, 2.62", Dated

QX2051 SRP: $2.25 **GBTru: $42**

Charmers

Boy/pool & girl/campfire, Set/2.
Satin Balls, 2.50", Dated

QX2151 SRP: $3.50 **GBTru: $42**

Chickadees

Chickadees on branch.
Glass Ball, 2.62", Dated

QX2041 SRP: $2.25 **GBTru: $40**

Currier & Ives

Winter village scene.
Satin Ball, 3.00", Dated

QX2091 SRP: $2.50 **GBTru: $32**

Currier & Ives

Winter snow scene.
Glass Ball, 3.25", Dated

QX1971 SRP: $3.00 **GBTru: $36**

Happy The Snowman

Snowman, Set/2.
Satin Balls, 2.50"

QX2161 SRP: $3.50 **GBTru: $36**

Marty Links

Girl by fireplace & tree, Set/2.
Glass Balls, 2.50", Dated

QX2071 SRP: $4.00 **GBTru: $29**

Norman Rockwell

Santa feeding reindeer.
Glass Ball, 3.25", Dated

QX1961 SRP: $3.00 **GBTru: $48**

Rudolph & Santa

Rudolph and Santa.
Satin Ball, 2.50", Dated

QX2131 SRP: $2.50 **GBTru: $88**

TREE TREATS
Shepherd

Shepherd with lamb.
Handcrafted, 3.00", Dated

QX1751 SRP: $3.00 **GBTru: $120**

NOSTALGIA
Locomotive

Locomotive [see 1975: QX1271].
Handcrafted, 3.25", Dated
L Sickman

QX2221 SRP: $4.00 **GBTru: $148**

TREE TREATS
Angel

Angel with snowflake.
Handcrafted, 3.00", Dated

QX1761 SRP: $3.00 **GBTru: $120**

TWIRL-ABOUT
Angel

Angel in tree.
Handcrafted, 4.00", Dated
L Sickman

QX1711 SRP: $4.50 **GBTru: $130**

NOSTALGIA
Peace On Earth

Village scene [see 1975: QX1311].
Handcrafted, 3.25", Dated
L Sickman

QX2231 SRP: $4.00 **GBTru: $129**

TREE TREATS
Reindeer

Reindeer.
Handcrafted, 3.00", Dated

QX1781 SRP: $3.00 **GBTru: $115**

TWIRL-ABOUT
Partridge

Partridge in wreath.
Handcrafted, 3.75", Dated
L Sickman

QX1741 SRP: $4.50 **GBTru: $120**

Raggedy Ann

Raggedy Ann at fireplace.
Satin Ball, 2.50", Dated

QX2121 SRP: $2.50 **GBTru: $48**

TREE TREATS
Santa

Santa.
Handcrafted, 3.00", Dated

QX1771 SRP: $3.00 **GBTru: $185**

TWIRL-ABOUT
Santa

Santa in wreath.
Handcrafted, 3.50"
L Sickman

QX1721 SRP: $4.50 **GBTru: $89**

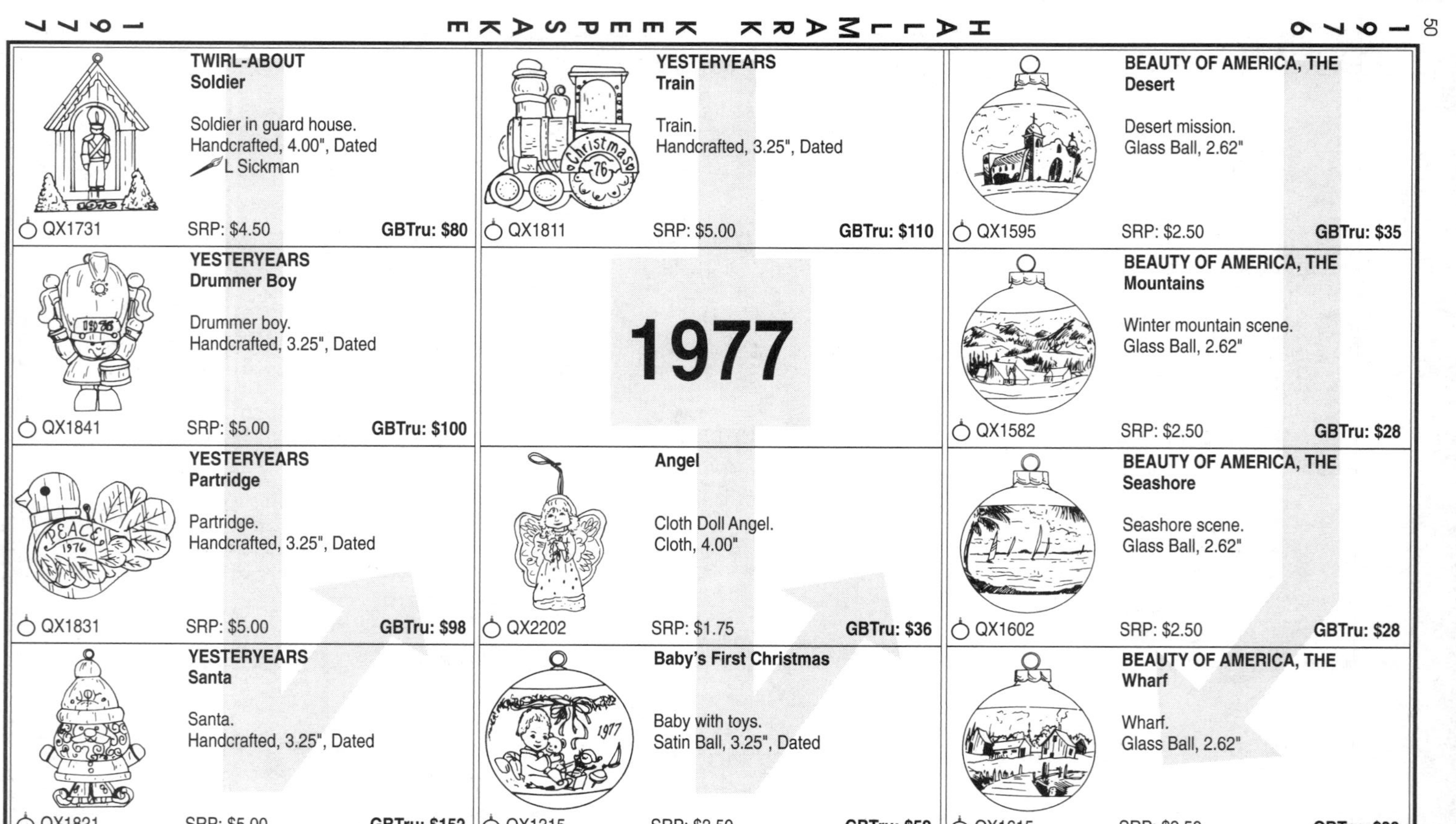

TWIRL-ABOUT
Soldier

Soldier in guard house.
Handcrafted, 4.00", Dated
L Sickman

QX1731 SRP: $4.50 **GBTru: $80**

YESTERYEARS
Train

Train.
Handcrafted, 3.25", Dated

QX1811 SRP: $5.00 **GBTru: $110**

BEAUTY OF AMERICA, THE
Desert

Desert mission.
Glass Ball, 2.62"

QX1595 SRP: $2.50 **GBTru: $35**

YESTERYEARS
Drummer Boy

Drummer boy.
Handcrafted, 3.25", Dated

QX1841 SRP: $5.00 **GBTru: $100**

BEAUTY OF AMERICA, THE
Mountains

Winter mountain scene.
Glass Ball, 2.62"

QX1582 SRP: $2.50 **GBTru: $28**

YESTERYEARS
Partridge

Partridge.
Handcrafted, 3.25", Dated

QX1831 SRP: $5.00 **GBTru: $98**

Angel

Cloth Doll Angel.
Cloth, 4.00"

QX2202 SRP: $1.75 **GBTru: $36**

BEAUTY OF AMERICA, THE
Seashore

Seashore scene.
Glass Ball, 2.62"

QX1602 SRP: $2.50 **GBTru: $28**

YESTERYEARS
Santa

Santa.
Handcrafted, 3.25", Dated

QX1821 SRP: $5.00 **GBTru: $152**

Baby's First Christmas

Baby with toys.
Satin Ball, 3.25", Dated

QX1315 SRP: $3.50 **GBTru: $52**

BEAUTY OF AMERICA, THE
Wharf

Wharf.
Glass Ball, 2.62"

QX1615 SRP: $2.50 **GBTru: $28**

BETSEY CLARK - 5TH
Truest Joys Of Christmas

Three carolers/little girl with bird.
Glass Ball, 3.25", Dated

QX2642 SRP: $3.50 **GBTru: $425**

CHRISTMAS EXPRESSIONS
Ornaments

Ornaments: caption M.F. Ames.
Glass Ball, 3.25"

QX1555 SRP: $3.50 **GBTru: $34**

COLORS OF CHRISTMAS
Candle

"Stained glass" candle.
Acrylic, 3.25", Dated

QX2035 SRP: $3.50 **GBTru: $42**

Charmers

Four children caroling.
Glass Ball, 3.25", Dated

QX1535 SRP: $3.50 **GBTru: $38**

CHRISTMAS EXPRESSIONS
Wreath

Wreath/caption: T. Malloy.
Glass Ball, 3.25"

QX1562 SRP: $3.50 **GBTru: $32**

COLORS OF CHRISTMAS
Joy

"Stained glass" joy.
Acrylic, 3.25", Dated

QX2015 SRP: $3.50 **GBTru: $45**

CHRISTMAS EXPRESSIONS
Bell

Bell/caption, H.W. Longfellow.
Glass Ball, 3.25"

QX1542 SRP: $3.50 **GBTru: $32**

Christmas Mouse

Mr. & Mrs. Mouse around tree.
Satin Ball, 3.25"

QX1342 SRP: $3.50 **GBTru: $54**

COLORS OF CHRISTMAS
Wreath

"Stained glass" wreath.
Acrylic, 3.25", Dated

QX2022 SRP: $3.50 **GBTru: $44**

CHRISTMAS EXPRESSIONS
Mandolin

Mandolin/horns: caption R.L. Stevenson.
Glass Ball, 3.25"

QX1575 SRP: $3.50 **GBTru: $34**

COLORS OF CHRISTMAS
Bell

"Stained glass" bell.
Acrylic, 3.25"
L Sickman

QX2002 SRP: $3.50 **GBTru: $42**

Currier & Ives

Scenes: grist mill & horse sleighs.
Satin Ball, 3.25", Dated

QX1302 SRP: $3.50 **GBTru: $28**

DISNEY
#1 Merry Christmas #2 Happy Holidays

Mickey/Minnie - Donald/sleigh, Set/2.
Satin Balls, 2.25"

QX1375 SRP: $4.00 **GBTru: $36**

DISNEY
Merry Christmas 1977

Mickey with Donald and Goofy.
Satin Ball, 3.25", Dated

QX1335 SRP: $3.50 **GBTru: $40**

First Christmas Together

Two cardinals on branch.
Satin Ball, 3.25", Dated

QX1322 SRP: $3.50 **GBTru: $54**

For Your New Home

Holiday decorated house.
Glass Ball, 3.25", Dated

QX2635 SRP: $3.50 **GBTru: $35**

Granddaughter

Girl on skates.
Satin Ball, 3.25"

QX2082 SRP: $3.50 **GBTru: $125**

Grandma Moses

New England village scenes.
Glass Ball, 3.25"

QX1502 SRP: $3.50 **GBTru: $120**

Grandmother

Basket of flowers.
Glass Ball, 3.25"

QX2602 SRP: $3.50 **GBTru: $50**

Grandson

Santa with toys.
Satin Ball, 3.50"

QX2095 SRP: $3.50 **GBTru: $125**

HOLIDAY HIGHLIGHTS
Drummer Boy

Drummer boy.
Acrylic, 3.25"

QX3122 SRP: $3.50 **GBTru: $52**

HOLIDAY HIGHLIGHTS
Joy

"JOY".
Acrylic, 3.25", Dated

QX3102 SRP: $3.50 **GBTru: $36**

HOLIDAY HIGHLIGHTS
Peace On Earth

Village scene.
Acrylic, 3.25", Dated

QX3115 SRP: $3.50 **GBTru: $48**

HOLIDAY HIGHLIGHTS
Star

Star with beams.
Acrylic, 3.25"

QX3135 SRP: $3.50 **GBTru: $42**

Love

Stained glass.
Glass Ball, 3.25", Dated

QX2622 SRP: $3.50 **GBTru: $28**

NOSTALGIA
Antique Car

Antique car.
Handcrafted, 3.25", Dated
L Sickman

QX1802 SRP: $5.00 **GBTru: $54**

PEANUTS
Peanuts

Charlie/Lucy and
Snoopy/"Santa" Woodstock.
Satin Ball, 3.25", Dated

QX1355 SRP: $3.50 **GBTru: $49**

Mother

Pink roses and green holly.
Glass Ball, 3.25"

QX2615 SRP: $3.50 **GBTru: $32**

NOSTALGIA
Nativity

Holy Family.
Handcrafted, 3.25"

QX1815 SRP: $5.00 **GBTru: $135**

PEANUTS
Peanuts

Snoopy-sled/gang-snowman, Set/2.
Glass Balls, 2.25"

QX1635 SRP: $4.00 **GBTru: $60**

Norman Rockwell

Four favorite Christmas activities.
Glass Ball, 3.25", Dated

QX1515 SRP: $3.50 **GBTru: $45**

NOSTALGIA
Toys

Toys.
Handcrafted, 3.25", Dated
L Sickman

QX1835 SRP: $5.00 **GBTru: $115**

Rabbit

Rabbit and bird.
Satin Ball, 2.62"

QX1395 SRP: $2.50 **GBTru: $65**

NOSTALGIA
Angel

Flying angel.
Handcrafted, 3.25"
D Lee

QX1822 SRP: $5.00 **GBTru: $80**

PEANUTS
Peanuts

Charlie Brown/Sally and
Schroeder/Lucy.
Glass Ball, 2.62"

QX1622 SRP: $2.50 **GBTru: $49**

Santa

Cloth Doll Santa.
Cloth, 4.00"

QX2215 SRP: $1.75 **GBTru: $36**

Snowflake Collection

Snowflakes, Set/4.
Chrome Plated, 2.13"
L Sickman

QX2102 SRP: $5.00 **GBTru: $79**

TWIRL-ABOUT
Della Robia Wreath

Girl kneeling in wreath.
Handcrafted, 3.56", Dated
D Lee

QX1935 SRP: $4.50 **GBTru: $90**

YESTERYEARS
House

Christmas house.
Handcrafted, 3.75", Dated

QX1702 SRP: $6.00 **GBTru: $105**

Squirrel

Squirrel with food.
Satin Ball, 2.62"

QX1382 SRP: $2.50 **GBTru: $100**

TWIRL-ABOUT
Snowman

Snowman in snowflake.
Handcrafted, 3.75", Dated
L Sickman

QX1902 SRP: $4.50 **GBTru: $40**

YESTERYEARS
Jack-In-The-Box

Jack-in-the-Box.
Handcrafted, 4.00", Dated

QX1715 SRP: $6.00 **GBTru: $90**

Stained Glass

Stained glass "Merry Christmas".
Glass Ball, 3.25", Dated

QX1522 SRP: $3.50 **GBTru: $38**

TWIRL-ABOUT
Weather House

Boy/girl/weather house.
Handcrafted, 4.00", Dated

QX1915 SRP: $6.00 **GBTru: $79**

YESTERYEARS
Reindeer

Reindeer on wheels.
Handcrafted, 4.25", Dated

QX1735 SRP: $6.00 **GBTru: $100**

TWIRL-ABOUT
Bellringer

Boy ringing bell.
Handcrafted, 3.75"

QX1922 SRP: $6.00 **GBTru: $50**

YESTERYEARS
Angel

Smiling angel.
Handcrafted, 3.50", Dated

QX1722 SRP: $6.00 **GBTru: $92**

1978

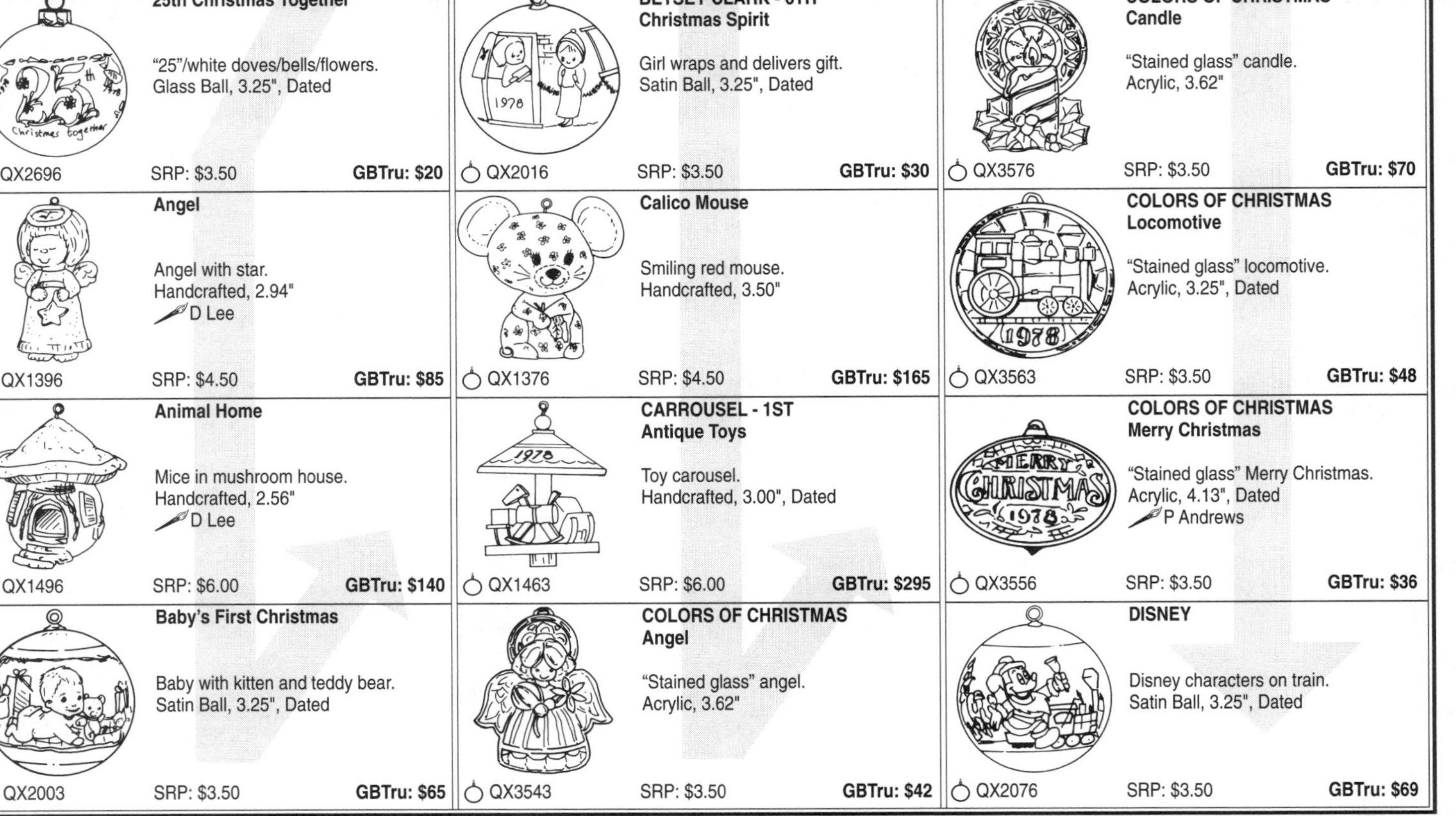

25th Christmas Together

"25"/white doves/bells/flowers.
Glass Ball, 3.25", Dated

QX2696 | SRP: $3.50 | **GBTru: $20**

Angel

Angel with star.
Handcrafted, 2.94"
D Lee

QX1396 | SRP: $4.50 | **GBTru: $85**

Animal Home

Mice in mushroom house.
Handcrafted, 2.56"
D Lee

QX1496 | SRP: $6.00 | **GBTru: $140**

Baby's First Christmas

Baby with kitten and teddy bear.
Satin Ball, 3.25", Dated

QX2003 | SRP: $3.50 | **GBTru: $65**

BETSEY CLARK - 6TH
Christmas Spirit

Girl wraps and delivers gift.
Satin Ball, 3.25", Dated

QX2016 | SRP: $3.50 | **GBTru: $30**

Calico Mouse

Smiling red mouse.
Handcrafted, 3.50"

QX1376 | SRP: $4.50 | **GBTru: $165**

CARROUSEL - 1ST
Antique Toys

Toy carousel.
Handcrafted, 3.00", Dated

QX1463 | SRP: $6.00 | **GBTru: $295**

COLORS OF CHRISTMAS
Angel

"Stained glass" angel.
Acrylic, 3.62"

QX3543 | SRP: $3.50 | **GBTru: $42**

COLORS OF CHRISTMAS
Candle

"Stained glass" candle.
Acrylic, 3.62"

QX3576 | SRP: $3.50 | **GBTru: $70**

COLORS OF CHRISTMAS
Locomotive

"Stained glass" locomotive.
Acrylic, 3.25", Dated

QX3563 | SRP: $3.50 | **GBTru: $48**

COLORS OF CHRISTMAS
Merry Christmas

"Stained glass" Merry Christmas.
Acrylic, 4.13", Dated
P Andrews

QX3556 | SRP: $3.50 | **GBTru: $36**

DISNEY

Disney characters on train.
Satin Ball, 3.25", Dated

QX2076 | SRP: $3.50 | **GBTru: $69**

Drummer Boy

Drummer boy at manger.
Glass Ball, 3.25", Dated

QX2523 SRP: $3.50 **GBTru: $28**

First Christmas Together

Folk art design: birds/flowers/greens.
Satin Ball, 3.25", Dated

QX2183 SRP: $3.50 **GBTru: $30**

For Your New Home

Window with wreath and lit candle.
Satin Ball, 3.25", Dated

QX2176 SRP: $3.50 **GBTru: $28**

Granddaughter

Girl decorating tree.
Satin Ball, 3.25"

QX2163 SRP: $3.50 **GBTru: $35**

Grandmother

Red roses with holly leaves.
Satin Ball, 3.25"

QX2676 SRP: $3.50 **GBTru: $32**

Grandson

Raccoons enjoying winter fun.
Satin Ball, 3.25"

QX2156 SRP: $3.50 **GBTru: $34**

Hallmark's Antique Card Collection Design

Antique card replica.
Satin Ball, 3.25"

QX2203 SRP: $3.50 **GBTru: $40**

HOLIDAY CHIMES
Reindeer Chimes

Reindeer suspended from snowflake.
Chrome Pltd, 5.50"
L Sickman

QX3203 SRP: $4.50 **GBTru: $44**

HOLIDAY HIGHLIGHTS
Dove

Dove.
Acrylic, 3.00"

QX3103 SRP: $3.50 **GBTru: $99**

HOLIDAY HIGHLIGHTS
Nativity

Nativity.
Acrylic, 3.00"

QX3096 SRP: $3.50 **GBTru: $75**

HOLIDAY HIGHLIGHTS
Santa

Santa.
Acrylic, 3.00"

QX3076 SRP: $3.50 **GBTru: $64**

HOLIDAY HIGHLIGHTS
Snowflake

Snowflake.
Acrylic, 3.00", Dated

QX3083 SRP: $3.50 **GBTru: $44**

Holly And Poinsettia

Poinsettia.
Handcrafted, 3.50"
L Sickman

QX1476 SRP: $6.00 **GBTru: $70**

LITTLE TRIMMERS
Drummer Boy

Drummer boy.
Handcrafted, 2.12"

QX1363 SRP: $2.50 **GBTru: $75**

Love

Heart with birds and poinsettias.
Glass Ball, 3.25", Dated

QX2683 SRP: $3.50 **GBTru: $35**

Joan Walsh Anglund

Children caroling and decorating tree.
Satin Ball, 3.25", Dated
JW Anglund

QX2216 SRP: $3.50 **GBTru: $40**

LITTLE TRIMMERS
Little Trimmer Collection

Mini Mouse, Santa, angel, drummer boy boxed set.
Handcrafted, 1.75"-2.25"

QX1323 SRP: $9.00 **GBTru: $325**

Merry Christmas (Santa)

Santa with reindeer.
Satin Ball, 3.25", Dated

QX2023 SRP: $3.50 **GBTru: $35**

Joy

"JOY" stained glass look.
Glass Ball, 3.25"

QX2543 SRP: $3.50 **GBTru: $29**

LITTLE TRIMMERS
Praying Angel

Angel praying.
Handcrafted, 2.00"
D Lee

QX1343 SRP: $2.50 **GBTru: $74**

Mother

Blue flowers with snowflakes.
Glass Ball, 3.25", Dated

QX2663 SRP: $3.50 **GBTru: $20**

Joy

"Bread dough" J-O-Y with elf.
Handcrafted, 4.25"

QX1383 SRP: $4.50 **GBTru: $75**

LITTLE TRIMMERS
Santa
QX1307, QX1327,QX1356 also pkg'd as Trimmer set/3, QX1599
Santa waving.
Handcrafted, 2.25"

QX1356 SRP: $2.50 **GBTru: $45**

Nativity

Old world nativity.
Glass Ball, 3.25"

QX2536 SRP: $3.50 **GBTru: $48**

Panorama Ball

Peek-in View - Fallen skater.
Handcrafted, 3.62", Dated

○ QX1456 SRP: $6.00 **GBTru: $110**

PEANUTS
Peanuts

Snoopy and Woodstock with tree.
Satin Ball, 2.62", Dated

○ QX2043 SRP: $2.50 **GBTru: $55**

PEANUTS
Peanuts

Peanuts gang singing.
Satin Ball, 3.25", Dated

○ QX2056 SRP: $3.50 **GBTru: $70**

PEANUTS
Peanuts

Snoopy/fireplace & Snoopy/toy store.
Satin Ball, 3.25", Dated

○ QX2063 SRP: $3.50 **GBTru: $60**

PEANUTS
Peanuts

Charlie Brown wrapped in lights.
Satin Ball, 2.62"

○ QX2036 SRP: $2.50 **GBTru: $60**

Quail, The

Quail.
Glass Ball, 3.25", Dated

○ QX2516 SRP: $3.50 **GBTru: $32**

Red Cardinal

Cardinal (clip-on).
Handcrafted, 4.00"
D Unruh

○ QX1443 SRP: $4.50 **GBTru: $165**

Rocking Horse

Polka-dot rocking horse.
Handcrafted, 3.50", Dated

○ QX1483 SRP: $6.00 **GBTru: $80**

Schneeberg Bell

Wood carving collage bell.
Handcrafted, 4.00", Dated

○ QX1523 SRP: $8.00 **GBTru: $160**

Skating Raccoon

Raccoon skating.
Handcrafted, 2.75"
D Lee

○ QX1423 SRP: $6.00 **GBTru: $72**

Spencer Sparrow

Spencer sparrow on wreath.
Satin Ball, 3.25", Dated

○ QX2196 SRP: $3.50 **GBTru: $42**

THIMBLE - 1ST
Mouse In A Thimble
Little Trimmers
Mouse in thimble.
Handcrafted, 1.75"

○ QX1336 SRP: $2.50 **GBTru: $225**

TWIRL-ABOUT
Angels

Angels decorating tree.
Handcrafted, 3.87", Dated

QX1503 SRP: $8.00 **GBTru: $330**

TWIRL-ABOUT
Dove

Dove in snowflake.
Handcrafted, 3.56", Dated
L Sickman

QX1903 SRP: $4.50 **GBTru: $58**

Yarn Green Boy

Boy dressed in green.
Yarn, 4.50"

QX1231 SRP: $2.00 **GBTru: $22**

Yarn Green Girl

Girl dressed in green.
Yarn, 4.50"

QX1261 SRP: $2.00 **GBTru: $18**

Yarn Mr. Claus

Mr. Claus.
Yarn, 4.50"

QX3403 SRP: $2.00 **GBTru: $18**

Yarn Mrs. Claus

Mrs. Claus.
Yarn, 4.50"

QX1251 SRP: $2.00 **GBTru: $16**

Yesterday's Toys

Old-fashioned toys.
Glass Ball, 3.25", Dated

QX2503 SRP: $3.50 **GBTru: $32**

1979

Baby's First Christmas

Tree surrounded by toys.
Satin Ball, 3.25", Dated

QX2087 SRP: $3.50 **GBTru: $20**

Baby's First Christmas

Knitted stocking with toys.
Handcrafted, 4.00", Dated

QX1547 SRP: $8.00 **GBTru: $125**

Behold The Star

Three Kings/shepherds following star.
Satin Ball, 3.25"

QX2559 SRP: $3.50 **GBTru: $32**

BELLRINGERS, THE - 1ST
Bellswinger, The

Elf swinging on bell clapper.
Porc/Hndcr, 4.00", Dated

QX1479 SRP: $10.00 **GBTru: $300**

BETSEY CLARK - 7TH
Holiday Fun

Children reading with tree on sled.
Satin Ball, 3.25", Dated

QX2019 SRP: $3.50 **GBTru: $38**

Christmas Collage

"Seasons Greetings"
Christmas collage.
Glass Ball, 3.25", Dated

QX2579 SRP: $3.50 **GBTru: $18**

Christmas Treat, A

Teddy climbing up candy cane.
Handcrafted, 4.75"
(Re-issued in '80, SRP $5.50.)

QX1347 SRP: $5.00 **GBTru: $65**

Black Angel

Angel/2 scenes.
Glass Ball, 3.25", Dated
T Blackshear

QX2079 SRP: $3.50 **GBTru: $16**

Christmas Eve Surprise

Shadow box/Santa
descends chimney.
Handcrafted, 4.25", Dated

QX1579 SRP: $6.50 **GBTru: $48**

COLORS OF CHRISTMAS
Holiday Wreath

"Stained Glass" wreath.
Acrylic, 3.50", Dated

QX3539 SRP: $3.50 **GBTru: $36**

CARROUSEL - 2ND
Christmas Carrousel

Angel musicians.
Handcrafted, 3.50", Dated

QX1467 SRP: $6.50 **GBTru: $175**

CHRISTMAS IS FOR CHILDREN
Christmas Is For Children

Girl on swing with kitten.
Handcrafted, 4.25"

QX1359 SRP: $5.00 **GBTru: $80**

COLORS OF CHRISTMAS
Partridge In A Pear Tree

"Stained Glass" Partridge.
Acrylic, 3.25", Dated

QX3519 SRP: $3.50 **GBTru: $35**

Christmas Chickadees

Chickadees enjoying holly berries.
Glass Ball, 3.25", Dated

QX2047 SRP: $3.50 **GBTru: $22**

Christmas Traditions

Traditional Christmas items.
Glass Ball, 3.25", Dated
L Sickman

QX2539 SRP: $3.50 **GBTru: $28**

COLORS OF CHRISTMAS
Star Over Bethlehem

"Stained Glass" Shepherds.
Acrylic, 3.50"
L Sickman

QX3527 SRP: $3.50 **GBTru: $52**

COLORS OF CHRISTMAS
Words Of Christmas

Message in “stained glass” design.
Acrylic, 3.75"

QX3507 SRP: $3.50 **GBTru: $55**

DISNEY
Winnie-The-Pooh

Winnie-the-Pooh with honey jar.
Satin Ball, 3.25", Dated

QX2067 SRP: $3.50 **GBTru: $30**

Downhill Run, The

Squirrel and rabbit on toboggan.
Handcrafted, 3.00"
D Lee

QX1459 SRP: $6.50 **GBTru: $135**

Drummer Boy, The

Panorama /boy drums for lamb/ duck.
Handcrafted, 3.25"

QX1439 SRP: $8.00 **GBTru: $105**

Friendship

Skaters and sleigh scenes.
Glass Ball, 3.25", Dated

QX2039 SRP: $3.50 **GBTru: $18**

Granddaughter

Girl feeding birds and animals.
Satin Ball, 3.25", Dated

QX2119 SRP: $3.50 **GBTru: $20**

Grandmother

Birds and basket of flowers.
Glass Ball, 3.25", Dated

QX2527 SRP: $3.50 **GBTru: $14**

HERE COMES SANTA - 1ST
Santa's Motorcar

Santa in car.
Handcrafted, 3.50", Dated

QX1559 SRP: $9.00 **GBTru: $640**

HOLIDAY CHIMES
Star Chimes

Star chime mobile.
Chrome Pltd, 4.00", Dated
L Sickman

QX1379 SRP: $4.50 **GBTru: $45**

HOLIDAY HIGHLIGHTS
Christmas Angel

Etched design flying angel.
Acrylic, 4.25", Dated

QX3007 SRP: $3.50 **GBTru: $84**

HOLIDAY HIGHLIGHTS
Christmas Cheer

Bird on holly branch.
Acrylic, 3.50", Dated

QX3039 SRP: $3.50 **GBTru: $45**

HOLIDAY HIGHLIGHTS
Christmas Tree

Christmas tree.
Acrylic, 4.50", Dated

QX3027 SRP: $3.50 **GBTru: $64**

HOLIDAY HIGHLIGHTS
Love

Heart.
Acrylic, 3.50", Dated

QX3047 SRP: $3.50 **GBTru: $82**

Light Of Christmas, The

Art deco candle design.
Glass Ball, 3.25", Dated

QX2567 SRP: $3.50 **GBTru: $18**

Mary Hamilton

Choir of angels.
Satin Ball, 3.25", Dated

QX2547 SRP: $3.50 **GBTru: $20**

HOLIDAY HIGHLIGHTS
Snowflake

Snowflake.
Acrylic, 3.50", Dated

QX3019 SRP: $3.50 **GBTru: $36**

LITTLE TRIMMERS
Angel Delight
QX1307, QX1327,QX1356 also pkg'd as Trimmer set/3, QX1599
Angel in nutshell.
Handcrafted, 1.75"

QX1307 SRP: $3.00 **GBTru: $90**

Mother

White poinsettias.
Glass Ball, 3.25"

QX2519 SRP: $3.50 **GBTru: $16**

Holiday Scrimshaw

Ivory angel.
Handcrafted, 3.50", Dated

QX1527 SRP: $4.00 **GBTru: $198**

LITTLE TRIMMERS
Matchless Christmas, A
QX1307, QX1327,QX1356 also pkg'd as Trimmer set/3, QX1599
Mouse/matchbox bed.
Handcrafted, 2.50"

QX1327 SRP: $4.00 **GBTru: $58**

New Home

Town scene.
Satin Ball, 3.25", Dated

QX2127 SRP: $3.50 **GBTru: $28**

Joan Walsh Anglund

Children w/gifts & hanging stockings.
Satin Ball, 3.25", Dated
JW Anglund

QX2059 SRP: $3.50 **GBTru: $29**

Love

Snowflakes and holly w/Gothic script.
Glass Ball, 3.25", Dated

QX2587 SRP: $3.50 **GBTru: $25**

Night Before Christmas

Santa scenes from poem.
Satin Ball, 3.25", Dated

QX2147 SRP: $3.50 **GBTru: $35**

Our 25th Anniversary

Satin ribbons, bells, & rings.
Glass Ball, 3.25", Dated

QX2507 SRP: $3.50 **GBTru: $20**

PEANUTS
Time To Trim

Snoopy with Woodstock.
Satin Ball, 3.25", Dated

QX2027 SRP: $3.50 **GBTru: $35**

SEWN TRIMMERS
Rocking Horse, The

Quilted rocking horse.
Fabric, 4.50"

QX3407 SRP: $2.00 **GBTru: $15**

Our First Christmas Together

Poinsettias & greenery.
Glass Ball, 3.25", Dated

QX2099 SRP: $3.50 **GBTru: $52**

Ready For Christmas

Birdhouse with Mr. & Mrs. Redbird.
Handcrafted, 3.00", Dated
D Lee

QX1339 SRP: $6.50 **GBTru: $125**

SEWN TRIMMERS
Stuffed Full Stocking

Quilted stocking.
Fabric, 4.50"

QX3419 SRP: $2.00 **GBTru: $16**

Outdoor Fun

Girl on swing.
Handcrafted, 3.00"
L Sickman

QX1507 SRP: $8.00 **GBTru: $110**

SEWN TRIMMERS
Angel Music

Quilted angel.
Fabric, 4.50"

QX3439 SRP: $2.00 **GBTru: $18**

Skating Snowman, The

Snowman on metal skates.
Handcrafted, 4.25"
D Lee

QX1399 SRP: $5.00 **GBTru: $60**

PEANUTS
Grandson

Snoopy and Woodstock on sleigh.
Satin Ball, 3.25", Dated

QX2107 SRP: $3.50 **GBTru: $25**

SEWN TRIMMERS
Merry Santa

Quilted Santa.
Fabric, 4.50"

QX3427 SRP: $2.00 **GBTru: $16**

SNOOPY & FRIENDS - 1ST
Ice-Hockey Holiday

Snoopy/Woodstock play'g ice hockey.
Handcrafted, 3.25", Dated

QX1419 SRP: $8.00 **GBTru: $80**

1980

Spencer Sparrow

Sparrow swinging on garland.
Satin Ball, 3.25", Dated

QX2007 SRP: $3.50 **GBTru: $22**

TWIRL-ABOUT
Santa's Here

Santa twirls in snowflake.
Handcrafted, 4.00", Dated
L Sickman

QX1387 SRP: $5.00 **GBTru: $60**

Baby's First Christmas

Santa talking to baby.
Satin Ball, 3.25", Dated

QX2001 SRP: $4.00 **GBTru: $20**

Teacher

Raccoon writing on blackboard.
Satin Ball, 3.25", Dated

QX2139 SRP: $3.50 **GBTru: $10**

Baby's First Christmas

Shadow box tree with baby toys.
Handcrafted, 3.90", Dated
L Sickman

QX1561 SRP: $12.00 **GBTru: $39**

THIMBLE - 2ND
Christmas Salute, A

Soldier thimble.
Handcrafted, 2.25"
(Re-issued in '80, SRP $4.00.)

QX1319 SRP: $3.00 **GBTru: $160**

25th Christmas Together

"25" framed with flowers & garland.
Glass Ball, 3.25", Dated

QX2061 SRP: $4.00 **GBTru: $14**

Beauty Of Friendship

Friendship caption with garland.
Acrylic, 3.25", Dated

QX3034 SRP: $4.00 **GBTru: $38**

TWIRL-ABOUT
Christmas Heart

Doves in heart.
Handcrafted, 3.50", Dated
L Sickman

QX1407 SRP: $6.50 **GBTru: $80**

Animals' Christmas,The

Rabbit & bird trim tree.
Handcrafted, 2.50"
D Lee

QX1501 SRP: $8.00 **GBTru: $48**

BELLRINGERS, THE - 2ND
Bellringers,The

Bell with two angels.
Porc/Hndcr, 2.12", Dated

QX1574 SRP: $15.00 **GBTru: $70**

Betsey Clark

Angel praying.
Cameo, 3.37", Dated

QX3074 SRP: $6.50 **GBTru: $35**

BETSEY CLARK - 8TH
Joy-In-The-Air

Children on sled.
Glass Ball, 3.25", Dated

QX2154 SRP: $4.00 **GBTru: $28**

Betsey Clark's Christmas

Shadowbox - child in snow scene.
Handcrafted, 4.00", Dated

QX1494 SRP: $7.50 **GBTru: $25**

Black Baby's First Christmas

Baby/toys/nested birds in tree.
Satin Ball, 3.25", Dated

QX2294 SRP: $4.00 **GBTru: $16**

Caroling Bear

Bear/bird sing carols.
Handcrafted, 3.20", Dated
D Lee

QX1401 SRP: $7.50 **GBTru: $130**

CARROUSEL - 3RD
Merry Carousel

Santa and reindeer.
Handcrafted, 3.12", Dated

QX1414 SRP: $7.50 **GBTru: $130**

Checking It Twice

Special Edition
Elfin Santa with list.
Handcrafted, 6"
T Blackshear

QX1584 SRP: $20.00 **GBTru: $145**

Christmas At Home

Yule log burning in fireplace.
Glass Ball, 3.25", Dated

QX2101 SRP: $4.00 **GBTru: $24**

Christmas Cardinals

Birds perched on holly.
Glass Ball, 3.25", Dated

QX2241 SRP: $4.00 **GBTru: $24**

Christmas Choir

Children in choir robes/church.
Glass Ball, 3.25", Dated

QX2281 SRP: $4.00 **GBTru: $68**

Christmas Love

Schneeberg collage of love.
Glass Ball, 3.25", Dated

QX2074 SRP: $4.00 **GBTru: $24**

Christmas Time

Stagecoach journey.
Satin Ball, 3.25", Dated

QX2261 SRP: $4.00 **GBTru: $22**

Christmas Vigil, A

Boy/dog peek out window (panorama).
Handcrafted, 3.81"
D Lee

QX1441 SRP: $9.00 **GBTru: $92**

COLORS OF CHRISTMAS
Joy

Stained glass "JOY".
Acrylic, 4.00", Dated

QX3501 SRP: $4.00 **GBTru: $18**

Dad

"DAD" on red plaid.
Glass Ball, 3.25", Dated

QX2141 SRP: $4.00 **GBTru: $15**

Daughter

Kittens at play and napping.
Glass Ball, 3.25", Dated

QX2121 SRP: $4.00 **GBTru: $32**

DISNEY
Disney

Mickey & Minnie skate/Santa Mickey.
Satin Ball, 3.25", Dated

QX2181 SRP: $4.00 **GBTru: $25**

Drummer Boy

Drummer boy.
Handcrafted, 3.00", Dated
D Lee

QX1474 SRP: $5.50 **GBTru: $75**

Elfin Antics

Elves link hands to ring bell.
Handcrafted, 4.50"

QX1421 SRP: $9.00 **GBTru: $170**

First Christmas Together

Couple on moonlight sleigh ride.
Glass Ball, 3.25", Dated

QX2054 SRP: $4.00 **GBTru: $20**

First Christmas Together

Heart-shaped with caption.
Acrylic, 3.50", Dated

QX3054 SRP: $4.00 **GBTru: $39**

Friendship

Lace and ribbon/caption.
Glass Ball, 3.25", Dated

QX2081 SRP: $4.00 **GBTru: $15**

FROSTED IMAGES
Dove

Dove.
Acrylic, 2.00"

QX3081 SRP: $4.00 **GBTru: $30**

FROSTED IMAGES
Drummer Boy

Drummer boy.
Acrylic, 2.00"

QX3094 SRP: $4.00 **GBTru: $20**

FROSTED IMAGES
Santa

Santa.
Acrylic, 2.00"

QX3101 SRP: $4.00 **GBTru: $20**

FROSTY FRIENDS - 1ST
Cool Yule, A

Eskimo w/polar bear reading on ice.
Handcrafted, 3.00", Dated

QX1374 SRP: $6.50 **GBTru: $625**

Granddaughter

Little girl sleeping under quilt.
Satin Ball, 3.25", Dated

QX2021 SRP: $4.00 **GBTru: $18**

Grandfather

Covered bridge/farm wagon.
Glass Ball, 3.25", Dated

QX2314 SRP: $4.00 **GBTru: $12**

Grandmother

Caption/date in flwr/bird/animal frame.
Glass Ball, 3.25", Dated

QX2041 SRP: $4.00 **GBTru: $14**

Grandparents

Currier & Ives home in woods.
Glass Ball, 3.25", Dated

QX2134 SRP: $4.00 **GBTru: $20**

Grandson

Snowman with sled and tree.
Satin Ball, 3.25", Dated

QX2014 SRP: $4.00 **GBTru: $26**

Happy Christmas

Koala/pear tree/partridge.
Satin Ball, 3.25", Dated

QX2221 SRP: $4.00 **GBTru: $24**

Heavenly Minstrel

Special Edition
Winged angel with lute.
Handcrafted, 6.25"
D Lee

QX1567 SRP: $15.00 **GBTru: $295**

Heavenly Nap, A

Angel sleeping on the moon.
Handcrafted, 3.50"
D Lee

QX1394 SRP: $6.50 **GBTru: $44**

HERE COMES SANTA - 2ND
Santa's Express

Santa in locomotive.
Handcrafted, 3.00", Dated

QX1434 SRP: $12.00 **GBTru: $165**

HOLIDAY CHIMES
Santa Mobile

Santa in sleigh flying over homes.
Chrome Pltd, 3.87"

QX1361 SRP: $5.50 **GBTru: $38**

HOLIDAY CHIMES
Snowflake Chimes

Snowflake mobile.
Chrome Pltd, 1.90"
L Sickman

QX1654 SRP: $5.50 **GBTru: $25**

Jolly Santa

Santa ice skating.
Glass Ball, 3.25", Dated

QX2274 SRP: $4.00 **GBTru: $20**

LITTLE TRIMMERS
Merry Redbird

Flocked redbird.
Handcrafted, 1.87"

QX1601 SRP: $3.50 **GBTru: $36**

HOLIDAY HIGHLIGHTS
Three Wise Men

Three Wise Men.
Acrylic, 4.00", Dated

QX3001 SRP: $4.00 **GBTru: $25**

LITTLE TRIMMERS
Christmas Owl

Owl sitting on log.
Handcrafted, 2.00"

QX1314 SRP: $4.00 **GBTru: $38**

LITTLE TRIMMERS
Swingin' On A Star

Mouse sitting on star.
Handcrafted, 2.12"

QX1301 SRP: $4.00 **GBTru: $62**

HOLIDAY HIGHLIGHTS
Wreath

Wreath.
Acrylic, 3.25", Dated

QX3014 SRP: $4.00 **GBTru: $69**

LITTLE TRIMMERS
Christmas Teddy

Teddy bear w/heart.
Handcrafted, 1.25"

QX1354 SRP: $2.50 **GBTru: $100**

Love

Love caption.
Acrylic, 4.00", Dated

QX3021 SRP: $4.00 **GBTru: $52**

Joan Walsh Anglund

Three girls ice skating.
Satin Ball, 3.25", Dated
JW Anglund

QX2174 SRP: $4.00 **GBTru: $18**

LITTLE TRIMMERS
Clothespin Soldier

Wooden soldier.
Handcrafted, 3.00"

QX1341 SRP: $3.50 **GBTru: $35**

Marty Links

Girl leading boy & friends in song.
Satin Ball, 3.25", Dated

QX2214 SRP: $4.00 **GBTru: $14**

Mary Hamilton

Children hang stockings by fireplace.
Glass Ball, 3.25", Dated

QX2194 SRP: $4.00 **GBTru: $15**

MUPPETS
Merry Christmas 1980

Muppets singing Christmas songs.
Satin Ball, 3.25", Dated

QX2201 SRP: $4.00 **GBTru: $30**

Santa 1980

Santa on "1980".
Handcrafted, 4.12", Dated

QX1461 SRP: $5.50 **GBTru: $85**

Mother

Poinsettias circle ornament.
Satin Ball, 3.25", Dated

QX2034 SRP: $4.00 **GBTru: $14**

Nativity

Nativity scene.
Glass Ball, 3.25", Dated

QX2254 SRP: $4.00 **GBTru: $32**

Santa's Flight

Santa in hot air balloon.
Tin, 4.00", Dated
L Sickman

QX1381 SRP: $5.50 **GBTru: $105**

Mother

Heart with caption.
Acrylic, 3.50", Dated

QX3041 SRP: $4.00 **GBTru: $29**

NORMAN ROCKWELL - 1ST
Santa's Visitors

Santa w/two children.
Cameo, 3.37", Dated

QX3061 SRP: $6.50 **GBTru: $152**

Santa's Workshop

Santa with toys/checks list.
Satin Ball, 3.25", Dated

QX2234 SRP: $4.00 **GBTru: $18**

Mother and Dad

Holly with red berries circle ornament.
Glass Ball, 3.25", Dated

QX2301 SRP: $4.00 **GBTru: $15**

PEANUTS
Peanuts

Snoopy singing "12 Days of...".
Satin Ball, 3.25", Dated

QX2161 SRP: $4.00 **GBTru: $30**

SNOOPY & FRIENDS - 2ND
Ski Holiday

Snoopy skis/Woodstock rides bowl.
Handcrafted, 3.25", Dated
J Francis

QX1541 SRP: $9.00 **GBTru: $90**

Snowflake Swing, The

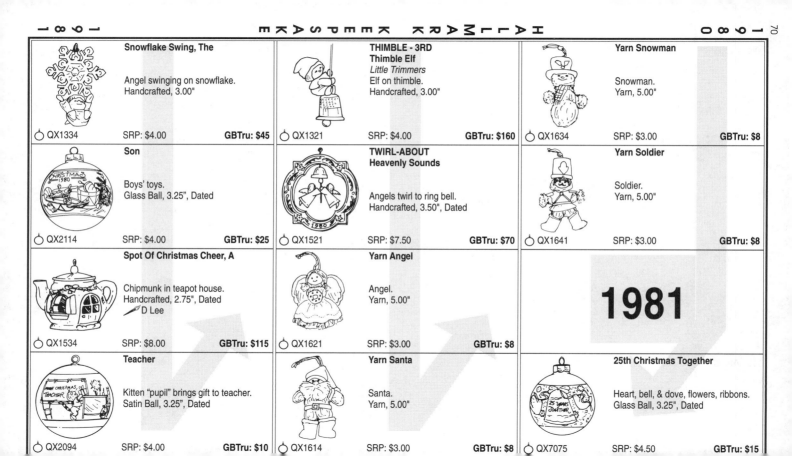

Angel swinging on snowflake.
Handcrafted, 3.00"

QX1334 SRP: $4.00 **GBTru: $45**

Son

Boys' toys.
Glass Ball, 3.25", Dated

QX2114 SRP: $4.00 **GBTru: $25**

Spot Of Christmas Cheer, A

Chipmunk in teapot house.
Handcrafted, 2.75", Dated
D Lee

QX1534 SRP: $8.00 **GBTru: $115**

Teacher

Kitten "pupil" brings gift to teacher.
Satin Ball, 3.25", Dated

QX2094 SRP: $4.00 **GBTru: $10**

THIMBLE - 3RD
Thimble Elf
Little Trimmers
Elf on thimble.
Handcrafted, 3.00"

QX1321 SRP: $4.00 **GBTru: $160**

TWIRL-ABOUT
Heavenly Sounds

Angels twirl to ring bell.
Handcrafted, 3.50", Dated

QX1521 SRP: $7.50 **GBTru: $70**

Yarn Angel

Angel.
Yarn, 5.00"

QX1621 SRP: $3.00 **GBTru: $8**

Yarn Santa

Santa.
Yarn, 5.00"

QX1614 SRP: $3.00 **GBTru: $8**

Yarn Snowman

Snowman.
Yarn, 5.00"

QX1634 SRP: $3.00 **GBTru: $8**

Yarn Soldier

Soldier.
Yarn, 5.00"

QX1641 SRP: $3.00 **GBTru: $8**

1981

25th Christmas Together

Heart, bell, & dove, flowers, ribbons.
Glass Ball, 3.25", Dated

QX7075 SRP: $4.50 **GBTru: $15**

25th Christmas Together

Bells with bows and holly.
Acrylic, 4.50", Dated

QX5042 SRP: $5.50 **GBTru: $18**

50th Christmas

"50 Years Together".
Glass Ball, 3.25", Dated

QX7082 SRP: $4.50 **GBTru: $14**

Baby's 1st Christmas

Wreath photoholder.
Acrylic, 4.00", Dated

QX5162 SRP: $5.50 **GBTru: $24**

Baby's 1st Christmas

Gifts and toy.
Cameo, 3.37", Dated

QX5135 SRP: $8.50 **GBTru: $14**

Baby's 1st Christmas

Old-fashioned wicker carriage.
Handcrafted, 3.75", Dated

QX4402 SRP: $13.00 **GBTru: $58**

Baby's 1st Christmas - Black

Baby w/teddy playing peek-a-boo.
Satin Ball, 3.25", Dated

QX6022 SRP: $4.50 **GBTru: $18**

Baby's 1st Christmas - Boy

Baby with teddy.
Satin Ball, 3.25", Dated

QX6015 SRP: $4.50 **GBTru: $20**

Baby's 1st Christmas - Girl

Baby with teddy.
Satin Ball, 3.25", Dated

QX6002 SRP: $4.50 **GBTru: $20**

BELLRINGERS, THE - 3RD
Swingin' Bellringers

Mouse sitting on candy cane clapper.
Porc/Hndcr, 4.00", Dated

QX4415 SRP: $15.00 **GBTru: $85**

Betsey Clark

Child hugging deer.
Cameo, 3.37", Dated

QX5122 SRP: $8.50 **GBTru: $22**

Betsey Clark

Girl/fawn look at tree with star.
Handcrafted, 3.38", Dated
J Francis

QX4235 SRP: $9.00 **GBTru: $60**

BETSEY CLARK - 9TH
Christmas 1981

Girl bringing gifts to friends.
Glass Ball, 3.25", Dated

QX8022 SRP: $4.50 **GBTru: $26**

Candyville Express

Sugar frosted locomotive.
Handcrafted, 3.00"

QX4182 SRP: $7.50 **GBTru: $82**

Christmas Fantasy

Elf/ride on white goose.
Handcrafted, 3.75"

QX1554 SRP: $13.00 **GBTru: $82**

CROWN CLASSICS
Tree Photoholder

Christmas tree photoholder.
Acrylic, 3.87", Dated

QX5155 SRP: $5.50 **GBTru: $22**

CARROUSEL - 4TH
Skater's Carrousel

Family ice skating.
Handcrafted, 2.50", Dated

QX4275 SRP: $9.00 **GBTru: $80**

Christmas In The Forest

Forest animals/Christmas blossoms.
Glass Ball, 3.25", Dated

QX8135 SRP: $4.50 **GBTru: $125**

CROWN CLASSICS
Unicorn

Unicorn at rest.
Cameo, 3.37", Dated

QX5165 SRP: $8.50 **GBTru: $22**

Christmas 1981 - Schneeberg

Santa/tree collage design.
Satin Ball, 3.25", Dated

QX8095 SRP: $4.50 **GBTru: $20**

Christmas Magic

Gnome Santa skates with friends.
Satin Ball, 3.25", Dated

QX8102 SRP: $4.50 **GBTru: $25**

Daughter

Kitten napping near doll & gifts.
Satin Ball, 3.25", Dated

QX6075 SRP: $4.50 **GBTru: $24**

Christmas Dreams

Boy gazes at teddy (panorama).
Handcrafted, 3.25", Dated
D Lee

QX4375 SRP: $12.00 **GBTru: $180**

CROWN CLASSICS
Angel

Stained-glass look angel.
Acrylic, 3.75"

QX5075 SRP: $4.50 **GBTru: $24**

DISNEY
Disney

Mickey as Sorcerer's Apprentice.
Satin Ball, 3.25", Dated

QX8055 SRP: $4.50 **GBTru: $24**

Divine Miss Piggy, The

Miss Piggy as angel w/halo & wings.
Handcrafted, 4.00"
J Francis

QX4255 SRP: $12.00 **GBTru: $78**

Drummer Boy

Drummer boy.
Wood, 3.50"

QX1481 SRP: $2.50 **GBTru: $35**

Father

Reindeer in snowy forest.
Satin Ball, 3.25", Dated

QX6095 SRP: $4.50 **GBTru: $14**

First Christmas Together

Couple ice skating.
Glass Ball, 3.25", Dated

QX7062 SRP: $4.50 **GBTru: $24**

First Christmas Together

First Christmas Together.
Acrylic, 3.00", Dated

QX5055 SRP: $5.50 **GBTru: $18**

Friendly Fiddler, The

Rabbit musician.
Handcrafted, 3.25"
D Lee

QX4342 SRP: $8.00 **GBTru: $70**

Friendship

Holiday flowers and fruits/caption.
Satin Ball, 3.25", Dated

QX7042 SRP: $4.50 **GBTru: $12**

Friendship

Squirrel with songbook.
Acrylic, 3.25", Dated

QX5035 SRP: $5.50 **GBTru: $25**

FROSTED IMAGES
Angel

Frosted angel.
Handcrafted, 1.50"

QX5095 SRP: $4.00 **GBTru: $38**

FROSTED IMAGES
Mouse

Frosted mouse.
Handcrafted, 1.50"

QX5082 SRP: $4.00 **GBTru: $20**

FROSTED IMAGES
Snowman

Frosted snowman.
Handcrafted, 1.50"

QX5102 SRP: $4.00 **GBTru: $20**

FROSTY FRIENDS - 2ND
Frosty Friends

Child and pup snuggle in igloo.
Handcrafted, 2.00", Dated

QX4335 SRP: $8.00 **GBTru: $375**

Gift Of Love, The

Red roses & holly leaves.
Glass Ball, 3.25", Dated

QX7055 SRP: $4.50 **GBTru: $18**

Godchild

Angel with puppy.
Satin Ball, 3.25", Dated

QX6035 SRP: $4.50 **GBTru: $15**

Granddaughter

Rocking horse.
Satin Ball, 3.25", Dated

QX6055 SRP: $4.50 **GBTru: $20**

Grandfather

Printed message for grandfather.
Glass Ball, 3.25", Dated

QX7015 SRP: $4.50 **GBTru: $14**

Grandmother

Lace and poinsettia border message.
Satin Ball, 3.25", Dated

QX7022 SRP: $4.50 **GBTru: $14**

Grandparents

Holiday basket with fruit/candy/gifts.
Glass Ball, 3.25", Dated

QX7035 SRP: $4.50 **GBTru: $14**

Grandson

Santa & reindeer make toys.
Satin Ball, 3.25", Dated

QX6042 SRP: $4.50 **GBTru: $20**

HERE COMES SANTA - 3RD
Rooftop Deliveries

Santa in old style truck.
Handcrafted, 4.00", Dated

QX4382 SRP: $13.00 **GBTru: $275**

HOLIDAY CHIMES
Snowman Chimes

Mr. Snowman and family.
Chrome, 4.00"

QX4455 SRP: $5.50 **GBTru: $24**

HOLIDAY HIGHLIGHTS
Christmas Star

Star.
Acrylic, 3.50", Dated

QX5015 SRP: $5.50 **GBTru: $18**

HOLIDAY HIGHLIGHTS
Shepherd Scene

Shepherd and lambs watch star.
Acrylic, 4.00", Dated

QX5002 SRP: $5.50 **GBTru: $18**

Home

Victorian home at holidays.
Satin Ball, 3.25", Dated

QX7095 SRP: $4.50 **GBTru: $18**

Ice Fairy

Frosted white winged fairy.
Acrylic/Handcrafted, 4.13"
D Lee

QX4315 SRP: $6.50 **GBTru: $85**

Let Us Adore Him

Nativity scene.
Glass Ball, 3.25", Dated

QX8115 SRP: $4.50 **GBTru: $50**

LITTLE TRIMMERS
Puppy Love

Puppy.
Handcrafted, 1.12"

QX4062 SRP: $3.50 **GBTru: $35**

Ice Sculptor, The

Bear creates self-portrait.
Handcrafted, 3.10"
D Lee

QX4322 SRP: $8.00 **GBTru: $85**

LITTLE TRIMMERS
Clothespin Drummer Boy

Drummer boy.
Handcrafted, 3.00"

QX4082 SRP: $4.50 **GBTru: $45**

LITTLE TRIMMERS
Stocking Mouse, The

Mouse in knitted stocking.
Handcrafted, 2.25"

QX4122 SRP: $4.50 **GBTru: $75**

Joan Walsh Anglund

Children decorate/read story.
Satin Ball, 3.25", Dated
JW Anglund

QX8042 SRP: $4.50 **GBTru: $16**

LITTLE TRIMMERS
Jolly Snowman

Snowman.
Handcrafted, 2.25"

QX4075 SRP: $3.50 **GBTru: $42**

Love

Heart.
Acrylic, 3.50", Dated

QX5022 SRP: $5.50 **GBTru: $45**

Kermit The Frog

Kermit on sled.
Handcrafted, 3.38"
J Francis

QX4242 SRP: $9.00 **GBTru: $85**

LITTLE TRIMMERS
Perky Penguin

Penguin.
Handcrafted, 1.25"

QX4095 SRP: $3.50 **GBTru: $46**

Love And Joy

3 doves suspended from heart.
Porcelain, 3.75", Dated

QX4252 SRP: $9.00 **GBTru: $72**

Marty Links

Children with candy cane & puppy.
Satin Ball, 3.25", Dated

QX8082 SRP: $4.50 **GBTru: $15**

Mary Hamilton

Angels enjoy holiday activities.
Glass Ball, 3.25", Dated

QX8062 SRP: $4.50 **GBTru: $16**

Merry Christmas

"Merry Christmas" design.
Glass Ball, 3.25", Dated

QX8142 SRP: $4.50 **GBTru: $15**

Mother

Red roses.
Satin Ball, 3.25", Dated

QX6082 SRP: $4.50 **GBTru: $14**

Mother and Dad

Holly & poinsettia frame hearts.
Satin Ball, 3.25", Dated

QX7002 SRP: $4.50 **GBTru: $14**

Muppets

Kermit as Santa/M. Piggy awaits Santa.
Satin Ball, 3.25", Dated

QX8075 SRP: $4.50 **GBTru: $30**

**NORMAN ROCKWELL - 2ND
Carolers, The**

Musicians and carolers.
Cameo, 3.37", Dated

QCX5115 SRP: $8.50 **GBTru: $38**

Peanuts

Snoopy decks the halls.
Satin Ball, 3.25", Dated

QX8035 SRP: $4.50 **GBTru: $30**

Plush Christmas Teddy

Teddy in stocking cap & ribbon bow.
Plush, 4.00"

QX4042 SRP: $5.50 **GBTru: $15**

Plush Raccoon Tunes

Vested raccoon carrying song book.
Plush, 4.00"

QX4055 SRP: $5.50 **GBTru: $15**

**ROCKING HORSE - 1ST
Dappled**

Rocking horse.
Handcrafted, 2.00", Dated
L Sickman

QX4222 SRP: $9.00 **GBTru: $575**

Sailing Santa

Santa in hot air balloon.
Handcrafted, 5.00", Dated

QX4395 SRP: $13.00 **GBTru: $200**

Santa's Coming

Santa w/toys leaving North Pole.
Satin Ball, 3.25", Dated

QX8122 SRP: $4.50 **GBTru: $25**

Santa's Surprise

Santa uses red stars on tree.
Satin Ball, 3.25", Dated

QX8155 SRP: $4.50 **GBTru: $18**

Sewn Calico Kitty

Calico quilted cat.
Fabric, 3.00"

QX4035 SRP: $3.00 **GBTru: $15**

Sewn Cardinal Cutie

Quilted cardinal.
Fabric, 3.00"

QX4002 SRP: $3.00 **GBTru: $15**

Sewn Gingham Dog

Quilted gingham pup.
Fabric, 3.00"

QX4022 SRP: $3.00 **GBTru: $15**

Sewn Peppermint Mouse

Candy striped mouse.
Fabric, 3.00"

QX4015 SRP: $3.00 **GBTru: $18**

SNOOPY & FRIENDS - 3RD
Snoopy & Friends

Snoopy on sled (panorama).
Handcrafted, 3.25", Dated
J Francis

QX4362 SRP: $12.00 **GBTru: $95**

Son

Design of squares.
Satin Ball, 3.25", Dated

QX6062 SRP: $4.50 **GBTru: $24**

Space Santa

Santa in space suit & helmet.
Handcrafted, 3.00", Dated

QX4302 SRP: $6.50 **GBTru: $90**

St. Nicholas

Father Christmas with lantern.
Tin, 4.38", Dated
L Sickman

QX4462 SRP: $5.50 **GBTru: $58**

Star Swing

Girl in a star swing.
Brass/Hndcr, 3.63", Dated
L Sickman

QX4215 SRP: $5.50 **GBTru: $32**

Teacher

Stocking with apples.
Satin Ball, 3.25", Dated

QX8002 SRP: $4.50 **GBTru: $12**

1982

THIMBLE - 4TH
Thimble Angel
Little Trimmers
Angel carrying tree in thimble.
Handcrafted, 1.50"
QX4135 SRP: $4.50 **GBTru: $120**

Topsy-Turvy Tunes
Opossum hangs upside-down w/book.
Handcrafted, 3.00"
D Lee
QX4295 SRP: $7.50 **GBTru: $70**

Traditional (Black Santa)
Santa feeds forest animals.
Satin Ball, 3.25", Dated
QX8015 SRP: $4.50 **GBTru: $85**

Well-Stocked Stocking, A
Knitted stocking with toys.
Handcrafted, 4.50"
QX1547 SRP: $9.00 **GBTru: $62**

25th Christmas Together
Snow covered night scene.
Glass Ball, 3.25", Dated
QX2116 SRP: $4.50 **GBTru: $15**

50th Christmas Together
Gold & burgundy "50th Christmas...".
Glass Ball, 3.25", Dated
QX2123 SRP: $4.50 **GBTru: $15**

Baby's First Christmas
White rattle with baby scene.
Handcrafted, 3.00", Dated
E Seale
QX4553 SRP: $13.00 **GBTru: $30**

Baby's First Christmas
Teddy with block.
Acrylic, 3.50", Dated
E Seale
QX3023 SRP: $5.50 **GBTru: $24**

Baby's First Christmas (Boy)
Decorated for boy.
Satin Ball, 3.25", Dated
QX2163 SRP: $4.50 **GBTru: $15**

Baby's First Christmas (Girl)
Decorated for girl.
Satin Ball, 3.25", Dated
QX2073 SRP: $4.50 **GBTru: $15**

Baby's First Christmas - Photoholder
Stuffed stocking picture frame.
Acrylic, 4.25", Dated
QX3126 SRP: $6.50 **GBTru: $18**

Baroque Angel

Angel with banner.
Brass/Hndcr, 4.50"
D Lee

QX4566 SRP: $15.00 **GBTru: $162**

Brass Bell

Bell.
Brass, 2.40"
D Lee

QX4606 SRP: $12.00 **GBTru: $20**

CARROUSEL - 5TH
Snowman Carrousel

Skating Snowmen w/winter sports gear.
Handcrafted, 3.00", Dated
E Seale

QX4783 SRP: $10.00 **GBTru: $95**

BELLRINGERS, THE - 4TH
Angel Bellringer

Bell with angel in wreath.
Handcrafted, 2.75", Dated
D Lee

QX4556 SRP: $15.00 **GBTru: $85**

Brass Promotional Ornament

Christmas village scene.
Brass, 2.37"

None SRP: $3.50 **GBTru: $35**

Christmas Angel

Angel with candle.
Glass Ball, 3.25", Dated

QX2206 SRP: $4.50 **GBTru: $20**

Betsey Clark

Angel decorat'g Chrstmas tree.
Cameo, 3.37", Dated

QX3056 SRP: $8.50 **GBTru: $22**

Brass Santa And Reindeer

Santa with reindeer.
Brass/Hndcr, 2.25"
L Sickman

QX4676 SRP: $9.00 **GBTru: $42**

Christmas Memories

Decorated picture frame.
Acrylic, 4.13", Dated
L Sickman

QX3116 SRP: $6.50 **GBTru: $18**

BETSEY CLARK - 10TH
Joys Of Christmas

Children reading story.
Satin Ball, 3.25", Dated

QX2156 SRP: $4.50 **GBTru: $25**

Brass Santa's Sleigh

Santa in sleigh with toys.
Brass, 2.63"
E Seale

QX4786 SRP: $9.00 **GBTru: $25**

Cloisonné Angel

Angel in heart.
Cloisonné, 2.62"

QX1454 SRP: $12.00 **GBTru: $75**

CLOTHESPIN SOLDIER - 1ST
British

Soldier in red, white, blue.
Handcrafted, 3.28"
L Sickman

QX4583 SRP: $5.00 **GBTru: $125**

COLORS OF CHRISTMAS
Nativity

"Stained glass" portrait of Holy Family.
Acrylic, 4.00"

QX3083 SRP: $4.50 **GBTru: $34**

COLORS OF CHRISTMAS
Santa's Flight

"Stained glass" Santa in hot air balloon.
Handcrafted, 4.25", Dated

QX3086 SRP: $4.50 **GBTru: $35**

Cowboy Snowman

Snowman dressed as cowboy.
Handcrafted, 2.87"

QX4806 SRP: $8.00 **GBTru: $50**

Currier & Ives

Couple in horse-drawn sleigh.
Glass Ball, 3.25", Dated

QX2013 SRP: $4.50 **GBTru: $15**

Cycling Santa

Santa on velocipede.
Handcrafted, 4.37"

QX4355 SRP: $20.00 **GBTru: $145**

Daughter

Colorful Christmas candy assortment.
Satin Ball, 3.25", Dated

QX2046 SRP: $4.50 **GBTru: $22**

DESIGNER KEEPSAKES
Merry Christmas

"Merry Christmas" "Happy New Year".
Glass Ball, 3.25"

QX2256 SRP: $4.50 **GBTru: $16**

DESIGNER KEEPSAKES
Old Fashioned Christmas

Children decorating for Christmas.
Glass Ball, 3.25"

QX2276 SRP: $4.50 **GBTru: $36**

DESIGNER KEEPSAKES
Old World Angels

Angels holding candles.
Glass Ball, 3.25"

QX2263 SRP: $4.50 **GBTru: $20**

DESIGNER KEEPSAKES
Patterns Of Christmas

Oriental poinsettias.
Glass Ball, 3.25"

QX2266 SRP: $4.50 **GBTru: $18**

DESIGNER KEEPSAKES
Stained Glass

Holly and poinsettia design.
Glass Ball, 3.25"

QX2283 SRP: $4.50 **GBTru: $18**

DESIGNER KEEPSAKES

Twelve Days Of Christmas

Twelve Days Of Christmas.
Glass Ball, 3.25", Dated

QX2036 SRP: $4.50 **GBTru: $25**

Disney

Seven dwarfs.
Satin Ball, 3.50", Dated

QX2173 SRP: $4.50 **GBTru: $28**

Elfin Artist

Elf paints ribbon candy.
Handcrafted, 3.00"
L Sickman

QX4573 SRP: $9.00 **GBTru: $40**

Embroidered Tree

Embroidered tree.
Fabric, 4.50"

QX4946 SRP: $6.50 **GBTru: $28**

Father

Woodcut style decorated ball.
Satin Ball, 3.25", Dated
L Sickman

QX2056 SRP: $4.50 **GBTru: $14**

First Christmas Together

Couple ice skating.
Cameo, 3.37", Dated

QX3066 SRP: $8.50 **GBTru: $25**

First Christmas Together

Redbirds highlighting snowy scene.
Glass Ball, 3.25", Dated

QX2113 SRP: $4.50 **GBTru: $22**

First Christmas Together

Contemporary Christmas tree.
Acrylic, 4.25", Dated
E Seale

QX3026 SRP: $5.50 **GBTru: $20**

First Christmas Together: Locket

Heart locket with 2 photo inserts.
Brass, 2.63", Dated
E Seale

QX4563 SRP: $15.00 **GBTru: $24**

Friendship

Animals ice skating.
Satin Ball, 3.25", Dated

QX2086 SRP: $4.50 **GBTru: $20**

Friendship

Puppy w/cap hold'g kitten in stocking.
Acrylic, 3.25", Dated

QX3046 SRP: $5.50 **GBTru: $22**

FROSTY FRIENDS - 3RD
Frosty Friends

Eskimo on icicle.
Handcrafted, 4.10", Dated
E Seale

QX4523 SRP: $8.00 **GBTru: $250**

Godchild
Angel reaching for snowflake.
Glass Ball, 3.25", Dated
QX2226 SRP: $4.50 **GBTru: $18**

Granddaughter
Animals holding garland.
Satin Ball, 3.25", Dated
QX2243 SRP: $4.50 **GBTru: $22**

Grandfather
Deer leaping.
Satin Ball, 3.25", Dated
QX2076 SRP: $4.50 **GBTru: $14**

Grandmother
Ribbon, lace, and embroidery design.
Satin Ball, 3.25", Dated
QX2003 SRP: $4.50 **GBTru: $14**

Grandparents
Covered bridge & houses/snowy hill.
Glass Ball, 3.25", Dated
QX2146 SRP: $4.50 **GBTru: $14**

Grandson
Bunnies sled riding.
Satin Ball, 3.25", Dated
QX2246 SRP: $4.50 **GBTru: $22**

HERE COMES SANTA - 4TH
Jolly Trolley
Santa in trolley.
Handcrafted, 3.38", Dated
L Sickman
QX4643 SRP: $15.00 **GBTru: $125**

HOLIDAY CHIMES
Angel Chimes
Angels w/Poinsettia suspended from snowflake.
Chrome-pltd Brass, 4.50"
QX5026 SRP: $5.50 **GBTru: $425**

HOLIDAY CHIMES
Bell Chimes
Bells with snowflakes.
Chrome Plated Brass, 3.00
L Sickman
QX4943 SRP: $5.50 **GBTru: $22**

HOLIDAY CHIMES
Tree Chimes
Trees with bells and doves.
Stamped Brass, 4.50"
E Seale
QX4846 SRP: $5.50 **GBTru: $45**

HOLIDAY HIGHLIGHTS
Angel
Angel playing harp.
Acrylic, 3.50"
QX3096 SRP: $5.50 **GBTru: $22**

HOLIDAY HIGHLIGHTS
Christmas Magic
Rabbit looking at ornament.
Acrylic, 3.87"
QX3113 SRP: $5.50 **GBTru: $22**

Christmas Sleigh

Sleigh with toys.
Acrylic, 3.75", Dated

QX3093 SRP: $5.50 **GBTru: $65**

Children around tree.
Satin Ball, 3.25", Dated
JW Anglund

QX2193 SRP: $4.50 **GBTru: $16**

Christmas Kitten

Kitten with bell.
Handcrafted, 1.25"

QX4543 SRP: $4.00 **GBTru: $32**

HOLIDAY WILDLIFE - 1ST
Cardinalis

Cardinals on pine tree.
Wood, 4.00", Dated

QX3133 SRP: $7.00 **GBTru: $325**

Jogging Santa

Santa jogging.
Handcrafted, 2.87", Dated

QX4576 SRP: $8.00 **GBTru: $30**

LITTLE TRIMMERS
Cookie Mouse

Mouse sleeping on cookie.
Handcrafted, 2.10", Dated
L Sickman

QX4546 SRP: $4.50 **GBTru: $45**

ICE SCULPTURES
Arctic Penguin

Penguin.
Acrylic, 1.50"

QX3003 SRP: $4.00 **GBTru: $18**

Jolly Christmas Tree

Smiling Christmas tree.
Handcrafted, 2.87"

QX4653 SRP: $6.50 **GBTru: $75**

LITTLE TRIMMERS
Dove Love

Dove in heart.
Acrylic, 2.00"
L Sickman

QX4623 SRP: $4.50 **GBTru: $40**

ICE SCULPTURES
Snowy Seal

Smiling seal.
Acrylic, 1.62"

QX3006 SRP: $4.00 **GBTru: $18**

Kermit The Frog

Kermit skiing.
Handcrafted, 3.19"
D Lee

QX4956 SRP: $11.00 **GBTru: $70**

LITTLE TRIMMERS
Jingling Teddy

Teddy with bell.
Flocked, 2.13"
E Seale

QX4776 SRP: $4.00 **GBTru: $30**

LITTLE TRIMMERS
Merry Moose

Moose on ice skates.
Handcrafted, 1.75"

QX4155 SRP: $5.50 **GBTru: $50**

Mary Hamilton

Angels ringing bell.
Satin Ball, 3.25", Dated
M Hamilton

QX2176 SRP: $4.50 **GBTru: $18**

Mother & Dad

Holly leaves & greens w/red ribbon.
Glass Ball, 3.25", Dated

QX2223 SRP: $4.50 **GBTru: $14**

LITTLE TRIMMERS
Musical Angel

Angel with lyre.
Handcrafted, 2.00"
D Lee

QX4596 SRP: $5.50 **GBTru: $135**

Miss Piggy & Kermit

Kermit/garland & Miss Piggy w/gifts.
Satin Ball, 3.25", Dated

QX2183 SRP: $4.50 **GBTru: $35**

Muppets Party

Muppets partying.
Satin Ball, 3.25", Dated

QX2186 SRP: $4.50 **GBTru: $40**

Love

Wreath of flowers.
Satin Ball, 3.25", Dated

QX2096 SRP: $4.50 **GBTru: $15**

Moments Of Love

White stagecoach on snow.
Satin Ball, 3.25", Dated

QX2093 SRP: $4.50 **GBTru: $18**

MUSICAL GIFT
Baby's First Christmas

Baby w/ toys/display stand.
Classic shape, 4.50", Dated, ♪

Tune: Brahms Lullaby

QMB9007 SRP: $16.00 **GBTru: $75**

Love

Gold inscription with holly leaves.
Acrylic, 4.12", Dated

QX3043 SRP: $5.50 **GBTru: $25**

Mother

Poinsettia bouquet and garland.
Glass Ball, 3.25", Dated

QX2053 SRP: $4.50 **GBTru: $14**

MUSICAL GIFT
First Christmas Together

Sleigh ride/display stand.
Classic shape, 4.50", Dated, ♪

Tune: White Christmas

QMB9019 SRP: $16.00 **GBTru: $75**

MUSICAL GIFT
Love

Pine cones/display stand.
Classic shape, 4.50", Dated, ♪

Tune: What The World Needs Now

QMB9009 SRP: $16.00 **GBTru: $80**

Peanuts

Snoopy cycling with Woodstock.
Satin Ball, 3.25", Dated

QX2006 SRP: $4.50 **GBTru: $35**

ROCKING HORSE - 2ND
Black

Black rocking horse.
Handcrafted, 4.00", Dated
L Sickman

QX5023 SRP: $10.00 **GBTru: $350**

New Home

Night scene of snowy village.
Satin Ball, 3.25", Dated

QX2126 SRP: $4.50 **GBTru: $15**

Peeking Elf

Elf peeking over silver ball.
Handcrafted, 3.12"

QX4195 SRP: $6.50 **GBTru: $29**

Santa

Santa portraits.
Glass Ball, 3.25", Dated
T Blackshear

QX2216 SRP: $4.50 **GBTru: $18**

Norman Rockwell

3 scenes with young boy.
Satin Ball, 3.25", Dated

QX2023 SRP: $4.50 **GBTru: $20**

Pinecone Home

Mouse in pinecone home.
Handcrafted, 2.80"
D Lee

QX4613 SRP: $8.00 **GBTru: $160**

Santa Bell

Santa with boots that ring bell.
Porcelain, 3.62"

QX1487 SRP: $15.00 **GBTru: $55**

NORMAN ROCKWELL - 3RD
Filling The Stockings

Santa laughing/tiny stocking.
Cameo, 3.37", Dated

QX3053 SRP: $8.50 **GBTru: $25**

Raccoon Surprises

Raccoon with stocking.
Handcrafted, 3.00"
D Lee

QX4793 SRP: $9.00 **GBTru: $125**

Santa's Workshop

Santa in workshop painting dollhouse.
Handcrafted, 3.00"
D Lee

QX4503 SRP: $10.00 **GBTru: $58**

Season For Caring

Shepherd following star.
Satin Ball, 3.25", Dated

QX2213 SRP: $4.50 **GBTru: $20**

Spirit Of Christmas, The

Santa in biplane.
Handcrafted, 2.00", Dated
L Sickman

QX4526 SRP: $10.00 **GBTru: $105**

THIMBLE - 5TH
Thimble Mouse
Little Trimmers
White mouse soldier.
Handcrafted, 2.37"

QX4513 SRP: $5.00 **GBTru: $65**

Sister

Girl ice skating/girl petting bunny.
Glass Ball, 3.25", Dated

QX2083 SRP: $4.50 **GBTru: $25**

Teacher

Elves' shadows form "Christmas".
Glass Ball, 3.25", Dated

QX2143 SRP: $4.50 **GBTru: $12**

Three Kings

Three Kings following star.
Cameo, 3.38", Dated
T Blackshear

QX3073 SRP: $8.50 **GBTru: $20**

SNOOPY & FRIENDS - 4TH
Snoopy & Friends

Snoopy on sleigh (panorama).
Handcrafted, 3.25", Dated
E Seale

QX4803 SRP: $13.00 **GBTru: $75**

Teacher

Snowy schoolhouse photoholder.
Acrylic, 4.00", Dated
L Sickman

QX3123 SRP: $6.50 **GBTru: $12**

TIN LOCOMOTIVE - 1ST
Tin Locomotive

Red, blue, silver locomotive.
Tin, 3.63", Dated
L Sickman

QX4603 SRP: $13.00 **GBTru: $550**

Son

Marching band in red & blue.
Satin Ball, 3.25", Dated

QX2043 SRP: $4.50 **GBTru: $20**

Teacher - Apple

Apple shape w/red caption.
Acrylic, 3.50", Dated
E Seale

QX3016 SRP: $5.50 **GBTru: $10**

Tin Soldier

British tin soldier.
Tin, 4.88"
L Sickman

QX4836 SRP: $6.50 **GBTru: $45**

1983

1983

Modern "1983" design.
Glass Ball, 3.25", Dated

QX2209 SRP: $4.50 **GBTru: $16**

25th Christmas Together

Snowflakes on silver bell.
Glass Bell, 2.50", Dated

QX2247 SRP: $4.50 **GBTru: $16**

Angel Messenger

Angel with "1983" brass banner.
Handcrafted, 2.00", Dated
E Seale

QX4087 SRP: $6.50 **GBTru: $95**

Angels

Pastel angels.
Glass Ball, 3.25"

QX2197 SRP: $5.00 **GBTru: $20**

Annunciation, The

Angel speaking to Mary.
Glass Ball, 3.25"

QX2167 SRP: $4.50 **GBTru: $25**

Baby's First Christmas

Rocking horse.
Cameo, 3.25", Dated
L Sickman

QX3019 SRP: $7.50 **GBTru: $15**

Baby's First Christmas

Baby in folk art baby cradle.
Handcrafted, 3.20", Dated
D Lee

QX4027 SRP: $14.00 **GBTru: $35**

Baby's First Christmas

Book Photo Holder.
Acrylic, 3.87", Dated

QX3029 SRP: $7.00 **GBTru: $18**

Baby's First Christmas - Boy

Teddy bears at play.
Satin Ball, 3.25", Dated

QX2009 SRP: $4.50 **GBTru: $20**

Baby's First Christmas - Girl

Red dress & bonnet.
Satin Ball, 3.25", Dated

QX2007 SRP: $4.50 **GBTru: $20**

Baby's Second Christmas

Snowpeople/snowman/tree.
Satin Ball, 3.25", Dated

QX2267 SRP: $4.50 **GBTru: $25**

Baroque Angels

Two angels with white wings.
Handcrafted, 2.50"
D Lee

QX4229 SRP: $13.00 **GBTru: $85**

Betsey Clark

Angel on cloud fishing for star.
Handcrafted, 3.50"

QX4401 SRP: $9.00 **GBTru: $24**

CARROUSEL - 6TH & FINAL
Santa And Friends

Santa leading marching band.
Handcrafted, 3.25", Dated
L Sickman

QX4019 SRP: $11.00 **GBTru: $45**

Bell Wreath

Wreath with 7 bells.
Brass, 3.75"
L Sickman

QX4209 SRP: $6.50 **GBTru: $25**

BETSEY CLARK - 11TH
Christmas Happiness

Boys and girls on carousel.
Glass Ball, 3.25", Dated

QX2119 SRP: $4.50 **GBTru: $22**

Child's Third Christmas

Santa with toy bag.
Satin Ball, 3.25", Dated

QX2269 SRP: $4.50 **GBTru: $20**

BELLRINGERS, THE - 5TH
Teddy Bellringer

Teddy rings bell with star.
Porc/Hndcr, 2.87", Dated

QX4039 SRP: $15.00 **GBTru: $95**

Brass Santa

Front and back - Santa head.
Brass, 4.00"
E Seale

QX4239 SRP: $9.00 **GBTru: $18**

Christmas Joy

Muffin with dog and rabbit.
Satin Ball, 3.25", Dated

QX2169 SRP: $4.50 **GBTru: $22**

Betsey Clark

Child sleeping on moon.
Handcrafted, 3.00"
E Seale

QX4047 SRP: $6.50 **GBTru: $25**

Caroling Owl

Owl on ring with carol book.
Handcrafted, 2.25"
E Seale

QX4117 SRP: $4.50 **GBTru: $30**

Christmas Koala

Flocked koala w/tree sprig & berries.
Handcrafted, 2.25"
E Seale

QX4199 SRP: $4.00 **GBTru: $30**

Christmas Wonderland

Animals celebrate/peek-thru 2nd scene.
Glass Ball, 3.25", Dated

QX2219 SRP: $4.50 **GBTru: $105**

CLOTHESPIN SOLDIER - 2ND
Early American

Colonial soldier with drum.
Handcrafted, 2.50"
L Sickman

QX4029 SRP: $5.00 **GBTru: $45**

CROWN CLASSICS
Enameled Christmas Wreath

Patchwork wreath.
Enamel/Brass, 2.75", Dated

QX3119 SRP: $9.00 **GBTru: $12**

CROWN CLASSICS
Memories To Treasure

Santa photoholder.
Acrylic, 4.25", Dated

QX3037 SRP: $7.00 **GBTru: $18**

CROWN CLASSICS
Mother And Child

Mother and child.
Cameo, 3.75"

QX3027 SRP: $7.50 **GBTru: $28**

Currier & Ives

People skating on Central Park pond.
Glass Ball, 3.25", Dated

QX2159 SRP: $4.50 **GBTru: $16**

Daughter

Design of lace, ribbons, and pearls.
Glass Ball, 3.25", Dated

QX2037 SRP: $4.50 **GBTru: $35**

Diana, Porcelain Doll

Antique doll.
Porc/Fabric, 4.25"
D Lee

QX4237 SRP: $9.00 **GBTru: $22**

Disney

Mickey Mouse.
Glass Ball, 3.25", Dated

QX2129 SRP: $4.50 **GBTru: $45**

Embroidered Heart

Heart with flowers and greens.
Fabric, 4.75"

QX4217 SRP: $6.50 **GBTru: $18**

Embroidered Stocking

Lace trimmed, quilted filled stocking.
Fabric, 3.25"
L Sickman

QX4796 SRP: $6.50 **GBTru: $16**

First Christmas Together

Candy cane heart.
Glass Ball, 3.25", Dated
L Sickman

QX2089 SRP: $4.50 **GBTru: $20**

First Christmas Together

Winter woods.
Classic shape, 3.25", Dated

QX3107 SRP: $6.00 **GBTru: $28**

First Christmas Together

Couple in sleigh.
Cameo, 3.75", Dated

QX3017 SRP: $7.50 **GBTru: $18**

First Christmas Together

Bell with bow.
Acrylic, 4.25", Dated

QX3069 SRP: $6.00 **GBTru: $20**

First Christmas Together Brass Locket

Photo locket.
Brass, 2.75", Dated
E Seale

QX4329 SRP: $15.00 **GBTru: $30**

Friendship

Etched sentiment.
Acrylic, 5.00", Dated

QX3059 SRP: $6.00 **GBTru: $16**

Friendship

Eskimo child/polar bear.
Glass Ball, 3.25", Dated

QX2077 SRP: $4.50 **GBTru: $24**

FROSTY FRIENDS - 4TH
Frosty Friends

Eskimo with seal on ice.
Handcrafted, 1.75", Dated
E Seale

QX4007 SRP: $8.00 **GBTru: $275**

Godchild

Angel with red bird.
Glass Ball, 3.25", Dated

QX2017 SRP: $4.50 **GBTru: $14**

Grandchild's First Christmas

Baby in wicker carriage.
Handcrafted, 3.75", Dated

QX4309 SRP: $14.00 **GBTru: $30**

Grandchild's First Christmas

Christmas toys.
Classic shape, 3.25", Dated

QX3129 SRP: $6.00 **GBTru: $20**

Granddaughter

"Historical Collection" girls.
Glass Ball, 3.25", Dated

QX2027 SRP: $4.50 **GBTru: $20**

Grandmother

Farm snow scene.
Glass Ball, 3.25", Dated

QX2057 SRP: $4.50 **GBTru: $16**

Grandparents

Bell with wreath.
Ceramic, 3.00", Dated

QX4299 SRP: $6.50 **GBTru: $15**

Grandson

Puppy and kitten with ornament.
Satin Ball, 3.25", Dated

QX2019 SRP: $4.50 **GBTru: $20**

HALLMARK MUSICAL
Baby's First Christmas

Babies w/ candy canes/display stand.
Classic shape, 4.50", Dated, ♪

Tune: Schubert's Lullaby

QMB9039 SRP: $16.00 **GBTru: $76**

HALLMARK MUSICAL
Friendship

Muffin & friends/display stand.
Classic shape, 4.50", ♪

Tune: We Wish You A Merry Christmas

QMB9047 SRP: $16.00 **GBTru: $110**

HALLMARK MUSICAL
Nativity

Kings/nativity, display stand.
Classic shape, 4.50", ♪

Tune: Silent Night

QMB9049 SRP: $16.00 **GBTru: $135**

HALLMARK MUSICAL
Twelve Days of Christmas

Twelve Days of Christmas in bas-relief.
Handcrafted, 3.75", ♪

Tune: Twelve Days Of Christmas

QMB4159 SRP: $15.00 **GBTru: $90**

Here Comes Santa

Four Santa faces.
Glass Ball, 3.25", Dated

QX2177 SRP: $4.50 **GBTru: $26**

HERE COMES SANTA - 5TH
Santa Express

Santa on handcart with bear.
Handcrafted, 3.50", Dated
D Lee

QX4037 SRP: $13.00 **GBTru: $215**

Hitchhiking Santa

Summer Santa.
Handcrafted, 2.63"
E Seale

QX4247 SRP: $8.00 **GBTru: $30**

HOLIDAY HIGHLIGHTS
Christmas Stocking

Christmas stocking filled w/gifts.
Acrylic, 4.00", Dated

QX3039 SRP: $6.00 **GBTru: $35**

HOLIDAY HIGHLIGHTS
Star Of Peace

Four-pointed star.
Acrylic, 4.00"
E Seale

QX3047 SRP: $6.00 **GBTru: $15**

HOLIDAY HIGHLIGHTS
Time For Sharing

Girl with kitten.
Acrylic, 4.00", Dated

QX3077 SRP: $6.00 **GBTru: $25**

Holiday Puppy

Puppy with ribbon.
Handcrafted, 1.50"

QX4127 SRP: $3.50 **GBTru: $20**

Jack Frost

Jack Frost frosting window pane.
Handcrafted, 3.75"

QX4079 SRP: $9.00 **GBTru: $65**

Love

Winter woods/sleigh scene.
Glass Ball, 3.25", Dated

QX2079 SRP: $4.50 **GBTru: $15**

HOLIDAY SCULPTURE
Heart

Red heart.
Acrylic, 2.00"
L Sickman

QX3079 SRP: $4.00 **GBTru: $45**

Jolly Santa

Santa carrying full bag of toys.
Handcrafted, 2.00"

QX4259 SRP: $3.50 **GBTru: $30**

Love

Couple ice skating.
Acrylic, 4.00", Dated

QX3057 SRP: $6.00 **GBTru: $18**

HOLIDAY SCULPTURE
Santa

Santa face.
Acrylic, 2.00"

QX3087 SRP: $4.00 **GBTru: $28**

Love

Heart inside heart.
Porcelain, 3.13", Dated
L Sickman

QX4227 SRP: $13.00 **GBTru: $25**

Love Is A Song

Bell with Dickens characters.
Glass Bell, 2.50", Dated

QX2239 SRP: $4.50 **GBTru: $20**

HOLIDAY WILDLIFE - 2ND
Black-Capped Chickadee

Chickadee.
Wood, 3.00", Dated

QX3099 SRP: $7.00 **GBTru: $69**

Love

Needlework sampler.
Classic shape, 3.25", Dated

QX3109 SRP: $6.00 **GBTru: $35**

Madonna And Child

Madonna and Child.
Porcelain, 3.00"

QX4287 SRP: $12.00 **GBTru: $30**

Mailbox Kitten

Kitten in tin mailbox holding letters.
Handcrafted, 1.50", Dated

QX4157 SRP: $6.50 **GBTru: $55**

Mary Hamilton

Little girl praying with animals.
Glass Ball, 3.50", Dated

QX2137 SRP: $4.50 **GBTru: $30**

Miss Piggy

Miss Piggy skating.
Handcrafted, 4.50"

QX4057 SRP: $13.00 **GBTru: $180**

Mom And Dad

Bell with poinsettia and holly.
Ceramic, 3.00", Dated
S Pike

QX4297 SRP: $6.50 **GBTru: $16**

Mother

Heart trimmed in flowers.
Acrylic, 4.00", Dated

QX3067 SRP: $6.00 **GBTru: $18**

Mountain Climbing Santa

Santa mountain climbing.
Handcrafted, 2.43"
E Seale

QX4077 SRP: $6.50 **GBTru: $30**

Mouse In Bell

Mouse as clapper in bell.
Glass/Handcrafted, 4.00"

QX4197 SRP: $10.00 **GBTru: $50**

Mouse On Cheese

Mouse nibbling on cheese.
Handcrafted, 2.63"
L Sickman

QX4137 SRP: $6.50 **GBTru: $40**

Muppets, The

Miss Piggy, Kermit, and Fozzie.
Satin Ball, 3.25", Dated

QX2147 SRP: $4.50 **GBTru: $45**

New Home

Snow scene with carolers.
Satin Ball, 3.25", Dated

QX2107 SRP: $4.50 **GBTru: $26**

Norman Rockwell

Three family Christmas scenes.
Glass Ball, 3.25", Dated

QX2157 SRP: $4.50 **GBTru: $35**

NORMAN ROCKWELL - 4TH
Dress Rehearsal

Shepherd and angel.
Cameo, 3.00", Dated

QX3007 SRP: $7.50 **GBTru: $29**

Old Fashioned Christmas, An

Santa faces & children in olden dress.
Glass Ball, 3.25"

QX2179 SRP: $4.50 **GBTru: $16**

Peppermint Penguin

Penguin on peppermint unicycle.
Handcrafted, 2.75"

QX4089 SRP: $6.50 **GBTru: $40**

Santa's Many Faces

Santa scenes.
Classic shape, 3.25", Dated

QX3117 SRP: $6.00 **GBTru: $35**

Old-Fashioned Santa

Santa with brass bell.
Handcrafted, 5.12"
L Sickman

QX4099 SRP: $11.00 **GBTru: $65**

PORCELAIN BEAR - 1ST
Cinnamon

Bear with top.
Porcelain, 2.63"
P Dutkin

QX4289 SRP: $7.00 **GBTru: $70**

Santa's On His Way

Four Santa scenes/three-dimensional.
Handcrafted, 3.00"

QX4269 SRP: $10.00 **GBTru: $30**

Oriental Butterflies

Eight multi-colored butterflies.
Glass Ball, 3.25"

QX2187 SRP: $4.50 **GBTru: $18**

Rainbow Angel

Angel sliding down rainbow.
Handcrafted, 3.00"
D Lee

QX4167 SRP: $5.50 **GBTru: $115**

Scrimshaw Reindeer

Leaping reindeer.
Handcrafted, 3.25"
E Seale

QX4249 SRP: $8.00 **GBTru: $32**

Peanuts

Snoopy and Woodstock.
Satin Ball, 3.25", Dated

QX2127 SRP: $4.50 **GBTru: $29**

ROCKING HORSE - 3RD
Russet

Rocking horse.
Handcrafted, 4.00", Dated
L Sickman

QX4177 SRP: $10.00 **GBTru: $275**

Season's Greetings

"Seasons Greetings"/modern design.
Glass Ball, 3.25"

QX2199 SRP: $4.50 **GBTru: $18**

Shirt Tales

T-shirted walrus, penguin, bear.
Glass Ball, 3.50", Dated

QX2149 SRP: $4.50 **GBTru: $20**

Skiing Fox

Fox with green muffler skiing.
Handcrafted, 2.20"
D Lee

QX4207 SRP: $8.00 **GBTru: $25**

Teacher

Raccoon.
Acrylic, 3.75", Dated

QX3049 SRP: $6.00 **GBTru: $10**

Sister

Holiday treats/wreath.
Glass Ball, 3.25", Dated

QX2069 SRP: $4.50 **GBTru: $18**

Sneaker Mouse

Mouse sleeping in sneaker.
Handcrafted, 1.75"
E Seale

QX4009 SRP: $4.50 **GBTru: $30**

Teacher

Bell shaped "Special Teacher".
Glass Bell, 2.50", Dated

QX2249 SRP: $4.50 **GBTru: $8**

Skating Rabbit

Rabbit skating.
Handcrafted, 3.25"

QX4097 SRP: $8.00 **GBTru: $54**

SNOOPY & FRIENDS - 5TH & FINAL
Santa Snoopy

Snoopy Santa/bag of toys (panorama).
Handcrafted, 3.25", Dated
L Sickman

QX4169 SRP: $13.00 **GBTru: $70**

Tenth Christmas Together

French horn with doves bell.
Ceramic, 3.00", Dated

QX4307 SRP: $6.50 **GBTru: $15**

Ski Lift Santa

Santa on ski lift.
Hndcr/Brass, 3.87", Dated

QX4187 SRP: $8.00 **GBTru: $50**

Son

Snowman on horse/boy/house.
Satin Ball, 3.25", Dated

QX2029 SRP: $4.50 **GBTru: $24**

THIMBLE - 6TH
Thimble Elf
Little Trimmers
Elf enjoying thimble sundae.
Handcrafted, 2.00"

QX4017 SRP: $5.00 **GBTru: $34**

1984

TIN LOCOMOTIVE - 2ND
Tin Locomotive

Red and green engine.
Tin, 3.00", Dated
L Sickman

QX4049 SRP: $13.00 **GBTru: $275**

Tin Rocking Horse

Early American litho design horse.
Tin, 3.20"
L Sickman

QX4149 SRP: $6.50 **GBTru: $54**

Unicorn

Unicorn.
Porcelain, 4.00"

QX4267 SRP: $10.00 **GBTru: $60**

Wise Men, The

Three Wise Men with gifts.
Glass Ball, 3.25"

QX2207 SRP: $4.50 **GBTru: $35**

Alpine Elf

Elf playing Swiss horn.
Handcrafted, 3.50"
E Seale

QX4521 SRP: $6.00 **GBTru: $30**

Amanda

Doll in green dress.
Porc/Fabric, 4.75"

QX4321 SRP: $9.00 **GBTru: $28**

ART MASTERPIECE - 1ST
Artist: Giuliano Bugiardini:
Madonna & Children

Madonna and children.
Satin, 2.75"

QX3494 SRP: $6.50 **GBTru: $12**

Baby's First Christmas

Baby in sleigh.
Classic shape, 4.25", Dated, ♪

Tune: Babes In Toyland

QX9041 SRP: $16.00 **GBTru: $40**

Baby's First Christmas

Teddy bear on sleigh.
Handcrafted, 3.50", Dated

QX4381 SRP: $14.00 **GBTru: $30**

Baby's First Christmas

Round picture frame.
Fabric, 3.25", Dated

QX3001 SRP: $7.00 **GBTru: $16**

Baby's First Christmas

Teddy holding stocking.
Acrylic, 3.75", Dated

QX3401 SRP: $6.00 **GBTru: $24**

Baby's First Christmas - Boy

Locomotive with toys.
Satin Ball, 2.87", Dated

QX2404 SRP: $4.50 **GBTru: $20**

Bell Ringer Squirrel

Squirrel swings from bell acorn clapper.
Hndcr/Glass, 4.00"

QX4431 SRP: $10.00 **GBTru: $22**

Chickadee

Chickadee clip-on.
Porcelain, 3.25"
L Sickman

QX4514 SRP: $6.00 **GBTru: $38**

Baby's First Christmas - Girl

Baby girls with bunnies & birds.
Satin Ball, 2.87", Dated

QX2401 SRP: $4.50 **GBTru: $20**

BELLRINGERS, THE - 6TH & FINAL
Elfin Artist

Elf painting message on bell.
Porc/Hndcr, 3.50", Dated

QX4384 SRP: $15.00 **GBTru: $30**

Child's Third Christmas

Teddy bears decorating.
Satin Ball, 2.87", Dated

QX2611 SRP: $4.50 **GBTru: $15**

Baby's Second Christmas

Winnie-The-Pooh & friends.
Satin Ball, 2.87", Dated

QX2411 SRP: $4.50 **GBTru: $20**

BETSEY CLARK - 12TH
Days Are Merry

Children decorating home.
Glass Ball, 3.25", Dated

QX2494 SRP: $5.00 **GBTru: $25**

Christmas Memories Photoholder

Quilted photoholder.
Fabric, 3.00", Dated

QX3004 SRP: $6.50 **GBTru: $18**

Baby-Sitter

Mice kids & sitter at home.
Glass Ball, 3.00"

QX2531 SRP: $4.50 **GBTru: $12**

Betsey Clark Angel

Angel in pinafore playing mandolin.
Porcelain, 3.50"

QX4624 SRP: $9.00 **GBTru: $20**

Christmas Owl

Owl hanging stocking on moon.
Handcrafted/Acrylic, 3.75"

QX4441 SRP: $6.00 **GBTru: $28**

Christmas Prayer, A

Angels bless stars & release prayers.
Satin Ball, 2.87"

QX2461 SRP: $4.50 **GBTru: $20**

Classical Angel

Limited Edition of 24,700
Angel with display stand.
Porcelain, 5.00", Dated
D Lee

QX4591 SRP: $27.50 **GBTru: $95**

CLOTHESPIN SOLDIER - 3RD
Canadian Mountie

Soldier holding flag.
Handcrafted, 2.50"

QX4471 SRP: $5.00 **GBTru: $25**

Cuckoo Clock

Clock w/carved look/brass display.
Handcrafted, 3.25"
D Lee

QX4551 SRP: $10.00 **GBTru: $45**

Currier & Ives

Christmas Eve in the country.
Glass Ball, 2.87", Dated

QX2501 SRP: $4.50 **GBTru: $16**

Daughter

Poem with holly background.
Glass Ball, 3.00", Dated

QX2444 SRP: $4.50 **GBTru: $20**

Disney

Disney gang.
Glass Ball, 2.87", Dated

QX2504 SRP: $4.50 **GBTru: $30**

Father

Mandolin & horn in holly garland.
Acrylic, 3.25", Dated

QX2571 SRP: $6.00 **GBTru: $15**

First Christmas Together

Doves on holly branch.
Acrylic, 3.62", Dated

QX3421 SRP: $6.00 **GBTru: $20**

First Christmas Together

Reindeer prancing.
Classic shape, 4.00", Dated, ♪
D McGehee
Tune: Lara's Theme

QX9044 SRP: $16.00 **GBTru: $36**

First Christmas Together

Florentine finish photo locket.
Brass, 2.50", Dated
E Seale

QX4364 SRP: $15.00 **GBTru: $20**

First Christmas Together

Old fashioned couple/Waltz.
Cameo, 3.25", Dated
D McGehee

QX3404 SRP: $7.50 **GBTru: $10**

First Christmas Together

Partridges and holly design.
Glass Ball, 3.00", Dated

QX2451 SRP: $4.50 **GBTru: $18**

Flights Of Fantasy

Elves taking fantasy ride on birds.
Glass Ball, 2.87", Dated

QX2564 SRP: $4.50 **GBTru: $18**

Fortune Cookie Elf

Elf painting Christmas wish.
Handcrafted, 2.50"

QX4524 SRP: $4.50 **GBTru: $38**

Friendship

Carolers and musicians.
Glass Ball, 2.87", Dated

QX2481 SRP: $4.50 **GBTru: $12**

Frisbee Puppy

Puppy catching Frisbee.
Handcrafted, 2.75"

QX4444 SRP: $5.00 **GBTru: $54**

From Our Home to Yours

Sampler Christmas home scene.
Glass Ball, 2.87", Dated

QX2484 SRP: $4.50 **GBTru: $22**

FROSTY FRIENDS - 5TH
Frosty Friends

Eskimo ice fishing a gift.
Handcrafted, 2.50", Dated

QX4371 SRP: $8.00 **GBTru: $85**

Fun of Friendship, The

Child with deer.
Acrylic, 3.75", Dated

QX3431 SRP: $6.00 **GBTru: $40**

Gift Of Friendship, A

Muffin and her kitten.
Glass Ball, 3.00"

QX2604 SRP: $4.50 **GBTru: $18**

Gift Of Music

Elf wrapping present.
Handcrafted, 3.00", ♪
E Seale
Tune: Jingle Bells

QX4511 SRP: $15.00 **GBTru: $90**

Godchild

Elves painting berries.
Glass Ball, 3.00", Dated

QX2421 SRP: $4.50 **GBTru: $15**

Grandchild's First Christmas

Flocked lamb on wagon with toys.
Handcrafted, 3.38", Dated

QX4601 SRP: $11.00 **GBTru: $22**

QX2574	**Grandchild's First Christmas** Santa loading toys. Satin Ball, 2.87", Dated SRP: $4.50 **GBTru: $14**	QX2424	**Grandson** Bear family with train and tree. Glass Ball, 3.00", Dated SRP: $4.50 **GBTru: $20**	QX4451	**Holiday Friendship** Children greet/window (panorama). Handcrafted, 3.25" SRP: $13.00 **GBTru: $20**
QX2431	**Granddaughter** Sampler stitch saying. Glass Ball, 2.87", Dated SRP: $4.50 **GBTru: $22**	QX3444	**Gratitude** Ribbon and sleigh bells. Acrylic, 4.50" SRP: $6.00 **GBTru: $10**	QX4374	**Holiday Jester** Jester. Handcrafted, 5.25" L Sickman SRP: $11.00 **GBTru: $38**
QX2441	**Grandmother** Pastel flowers. Glass Ball, 2.87", Dated SRP: $4.50 **GBTru: $14**	QX4434	**Heartful Of Love** Puffed heart of roses. Bone China, 3.75", Dated SRP: $10.00 **GBTru: $25**	QX2534	**Holiday Starburst** Silver starburst. Glass Ball, 2.88", Dated SRP: $5.00 **GBTru: $15**
QX2561	**Grandparents** Snow scene. Glass Ball, 2.87", Dated SRP: $4.50 **GBTru: $14**	QX4324	**HERE COMES SANTA - 6TH** **Santa's Deliveries** Santa delivering trees in truck. Handcrafted, 3.25", Dated SRP: $13.00 **GBTru: $85**	QX3474	**HOLIDAY WILDLIFE - 3RD** **Ring-Necked Pheasant** Pheasants in snow. Wood, 3.00", Dated SRP: $7.25 **GBTru: $25**

Katybeth

Angel with slipped halo holding star.
Porcelain, 2.25"

QX4631 SRP: $9.00 **GBTru: $24**

Madonna And Child

Madonna/Infant/Dove of Peace.
Acrylic, 4.00"

QX3441 SRP: $6.00 **GBTru: $35**

Mother And Dad

French horn/holly/candle/song book.
Bone China, 3.00", Dated

QX2581 SRP: $6.50 **GBTru: $10**

Kit

Boy in green cap carrying candy cane.
Handcrafted, 2.75"

QX4534 SRP: $5.50 **GBTru: $22**

Marathon Santa

Santa with Olympic torch.
Handcrafted, 2.25", Dated

QX4564 SRP: $8.00 **GBTru: $30**

Muffin

"Muffin" with gift.
Handcrafted, 2.75"
D Lee

QX4421 SRP: $5.50 **GBTru: $25**

Love

Mimes.
Glass Ball, 2.87", Dated

QX2554 SRP: $4.50 **GBTru: $20**

Miracle Of Love, The

Heart with ribbon.
Acrylic, 4.00", Dated

QX3424 SRP: $6.00 **GBTru: $25**

Muppets, The

Miss Piggy & Kermit in wreaths.
Glass Ball, 2.87"

QX2514 SRP: $4.50 **GBTru: $30**

Love... The Spirit Of Christmas

Christmas fruit & flowers.
Glass Ball, 2.87", Dated

QX2474 SRP: $4.50 **GBTru: $18**

Mother

Etched saying w/fir branch garland.
Acrylic, 3.25", Dated

QX3434 SRP: $6.00 **GBTru: $14**

Musical Angel

Snagged angel with brass horn.
Handcrafted, 1.25"

QX4344 SRP: $5.50 **GBTru: $68**

Napping Mouse

Mouse sleeping in shell.
Handcrafted, 1.75"

QX4351 SRP: $5.50 **GBTru: $45**

NORMAN ROCKWELL - 5TH
Caught Napping

Kids nap/wing chair/Santa .
Cameo, 3.00", Dated

QX3411 SRP: $7.50 **GBTru: $15**

Peace On Earth

Angel with harp.
Cameo, 3.00"

QX3414 SRP: $7.50 **GBTru: $24**

Needlepoint Wreath

Needlepoint wreath.
Fabric, 3.50"

QX4594 SRP: $6.50 **GBTru: $12**

NOSTALGIC HOUSES & SHOPS - 1ST
Victorian Dollhouse

Decorated/furnished home.
Handcrafted, 3.25"

QX4481 SRP: $13.00 **GBTru: $225**

Peanuts

Snoopy/Woodstock/friends/snowman.
Satin Ball, 2.87", Dated

QX2521 SRP: $4.50 **GBTru: $35**

New Home

Country village Holiday snow scene.
Glass Ball, 2.88", Dated

QX2454 SRP: $4.50 **GBTru: $32**

Nostalgic Sled

Flexible flyer sled.
Handcrafted, 3.50"
L Sickman

QX4424 SRP: $6.00 **GBTru: $20**

PEANUTS
Snoopy And Woodstock

Snoopy & Woodstock skiing.
Handcrafted, 4.25"
E Seale

QX4391 SRP: $7.50 **GBTru: $88**

Norman Rockwell

3 panels from Dickens' Christmas Carol.
Glass Ball, 2.88", Dated
D McGehee

QX2511 SRP: $4.50 **GBTru: $16**

Old Fashioned Rocking Horse

Rocking horse.
Acrylic/Brass, 3.25"

QX3464 SRP: $7.50 **GBTru: $15**

Peppermint 1984

Candy cane numbers "1984".
Handcrafted, 2.75", Dated
D Lee

QX4561 SRP: $4.50 **GBTru: $50**

Polar Bear Drummer

Bear drumming.
Handcrafted, 2.25"
E Seale

QX4301 SRP: $4.50 **GBTru: $18**

PORCELAIN BEAR - 2ND
Cinnamon

Bear holding a jingle bell.
Porcelain, 2.50"

QX4541 SRP: $7.00 **GBTru: $20**

Raccoon's Christmas

Raccoon in treehouse.
Handcrafted, 2.75"
E Seale

QX4474 SRP: $9.00 **GBTru: $50**

Reindeer Racetrack

Racing reindeer.
Glass Ball, 3.00"

QX2544 SRP: $4.50 **GBTru: $18**

ROCKING HORSE - 4TH
Appaloosa

Rocking horse.
Handcrafted, 4.00", Dated
L Sickman

QX4354 SRP: $10.00 **GBTru: $68**

Roller Skating Rabbit

Bunny in shoe skate.
Handcrafted, 2.50"
E Seale

QX4571 SRP: $5.00 **GBTru: $20**

Santa

Santa riding on reindeer.
Fabric, 4.00"

QX4584 SRP: $7.50 **GBTru: $14**

Santa Mouse

Mouse dressed as Santa.
Handcrafted, 2.00"
B Siedler

QX4334 SRP: $4.50 **GBTru: $55**

Santa Star

Star dressed as Santa.
Handcrafted, 3.50"

QX4504 SRP: $5.50 **GBTru: $40**

Santa Sulky Driver

Santa with trotting horse.
Brass, 1.75"

QX4361 SRP: $9.00 **GBTru: $20**

Savior Is Born, A

Biblical quote with nativity scene.
Glass Ball, 2.87"

QX2541 SRP: $4.50 **GBTru: $18**

Shirt Tales

T-shirt friends throwing snowballs.
Satin Ball, 2.87"

QX2524 SRP: $4.50 **GBTru: $15**

Sister
Poinsettia bouquet on bell.
Bone China, 3.00", Dated
○ QX2594 SRP: $6.50 **GBTru: $12**

Son
Whimsical holiday letters.
Glass Ball, 3.00", Dated
○ QX2434 SRP: $4.50 **GBTru: $20**

Three Kittens In A Mitten
Kittens in knitted mitten.
Handcrafted, 3.50"
D Lee
○ QX4311 SRP: $8.00 **GBTru: $48**

Snowmobile Santa
Santa on snowmobile.
Handcrafted, 2.75"
○ QX4314 SRP: $6.50 **GBTru: $30**

Teacher
Apple delivery by elves.
Glass Ball, 3.00", Dated
○ QX2491 SRP: $4.50 **GBTru: $10**

TIN LOCOMOTIVE - 3RD
Tin Locomotive
Antique design train engine.
Tin, 2.50", Dated
○ QX4404 SRP: $14.00 **GBTru: $90**

Snowshoe Penguin
Penguin on snowshoes with gift.
Handcrafted, 3.00"
L Sickman
○ QX4531 SRP: $6.50 **GBTru: $35**

Ten Years Together
Winter scene on bell.
Bone China, 3.00", Dated
○ QX2584 SRP: $6.50 **GBTru: $12**

Twelve Days Of Christmas
French blue & white bas relief.
Handcrafted, 3.75", ♪
E Seale
Tune: Twelve Days Of Christmas
○ QX4159 SRP: $15.00 **GBTru: $98**

Snowy Seal
Flocked white seal.
Handcrafted, 1.50"
E Seale
○ QX4501 SRP: $4.00 **GBTru: $15**

THIMBLE - 7TH
Thimble Angel
Little Trimmers
Angel holding thimble of stars.
Handcrafted, 1.75"
○ QX4304 SRP: $5.00 **GBTru: $50**

TWELVE DAYS OF CHRISTMAS, THE - 1ST
Partiridge In A Pear Tree
Partridge in a pear tree.
Acrylic, 3.00", Dated
○ QX3484 SRP: $6.00 **GBTru: $270**

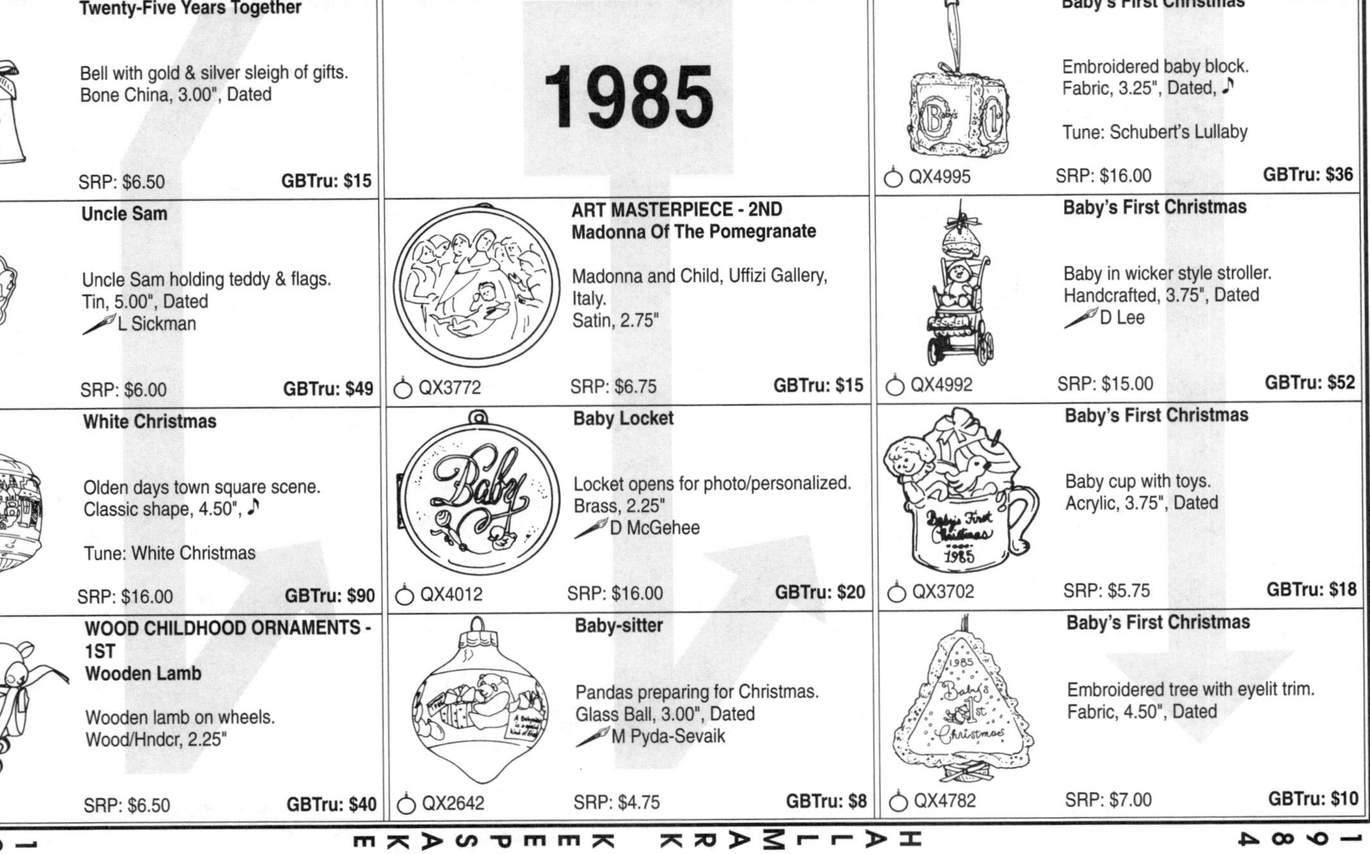

1985

Twenty-Five Years Together

Bell with gold & silver sleigh of gifts.
Bone China, 3.00", Dated

QX2591 SRP: $6.50 **GBTru: $15**

Uncle Sam

Uncle Sam holding teddy & flags.
Tin, 5.00", Dated
L Sickman

QX4491 SRP: $6.00 **GBTru: $49**

White Christmas

Olden days town square scene.
Classic shape, 4.50", ♪

Tune: White Christmas

QX9051 SRP: $16.00 **GBTru: $90**

WOOD CHILDHOOD ORNAMENTS - 1ST
Wooden Lamb

Wooden lamb on wheels.
Wood/Hndcr, 2.25"

QX4394 SRP: $6.50 **GBTru: $40**

ART MASTERPIECE - 2ND
Madonna Of The Pomegranate

Madonna and Child, Uffizi Gallery, Italy.
Satin, 2.75"

QX3772 SRP: $6.75 **GBTru: $15**

Baby Locket

Locket opens for photo/personalized.
Brass, 2.25"
D McGehee

QX4012 SRP: $16.00 **GBTru: $20**

Baby-sitter

Pandas preparing for Christmas.
Glass Ball, 3.00", Dated
M Pyda-Sevaik

QX2642 SRP: $4.75 **GBTru: $8**

Baby's First Christmas

Embroidered baby block.
Fabric, 3.25", Dated, ♪

Tune: Schubert's Lullaby

QX4995 SRP: $16.00 **GBTru: $36**

Baby's First Christmas

Baby in wicker style stroller.
Handcrafted, 3.75", Dated
D Lee

QX4992 SRP: $15.00 **GBTru: $52**

Baby's First Christmas

Baby cup with toys.
Acrylic, 3.75", Dated

QX3702 SRP: $5.75 **GBTru: $18**

Baby's First Christmas

Embroidered tree with eyelit trim.
Fabric, 4.50", Dated

QX4782 SRP: $7.00 **GBTru: $10**

Baby's First Christmas

Baby with toys.
Satin Ball, 2.88", Dated
L Votruba

QX2602 SRP: $5.00 **GBTru: $15**

Betsey Clark

Boy angel with lamb.
Porcelain, 2.50"
B Clark

QX5085 SRP: $8.50 **GBTru: $25**

Candy Apple Mouse

Mouse napping on candy apple.
Handcrafted, 3.75", Dated
L Sickman

QX4705 SRP: $6.50 **GBTru: $68**

Baby's Second Christmas

Teddy on stick horse.
Handcrafted, 3.50", Dated

QX4785 SRP: $6.00 **GBTru: $30**

BETSEY CLARK - 13TH & FINAL
Special Kind Of Feeling

Angel children polish stars.
Glass Ball, 3.25", Dated
S Pike

QX2632 SRP: $5.00 **GBTru: $25**

Child's Third Christmas

Flocked teddy in sneaker.
Handcrafted, 2.25", Dated
E Seale

QX4755 SRP: $6.00 **GBTru: $24**

Baker Elf

Elf icing cookie.
Handcrafted, 3.00", Dated
E Seale

QX4912 SRP: $5.75 **GBTru: $30**

Bottlecap Fun Bunnies

Mom & baby w/ bottlecap sled.
Handcrafted, 2.25"
B Siedler

QX4815 SRP: $7.75 **GBTru: $25**

Children In The Shoe

Old shoe house from rhyme.
Handcrafted, 3.25"
E Seale

QX4905 SRP: $9.50 **GBTru: $45**

Beary Smooth Ride

Teddy on tricycle.
Handcrafted, 1.75"
L Sickman

QX4805 SRP: $6.50 **GBTru: $18**

Candle Cameo

Traditional lit candle.
Cameo, 3.00", Dated
S Pike

QX3742 SRP: $6.75 **GBTru: $12**

Christmas Treats

Two candy canes as stained glass.
Glass, 3.25"

QX5075 SRP: $5.50 **GBTru: $15**

CLOTHESPIN SOLDIER - 4TH
Scottish Highlander

Soldier in plaid kilt and tam.
Handcrafted, 2.50"
L Sickman

QX4715 SRP: $5.50 **GBTru: $22**

COUNTRY CHRISTMAS
Sheep At Christmas

Old fashioned carved sheep.
Handcrafted, 3.25", Dated
L Sickman

QX5175 SRP: $8.25 **GBTru: $20**

Disney Christmas, A

Mickey as Santa filling stockings.
Glass Ball, 3.00", Dated

QX2712 SRP: $4.75 **GBTru: $30**

COUNTRY CHRISTMAS
Country Goose

Goose with wreath.
Wood, 3.00"
M Pyda-Sevaik

QX5185 SRP: $7.75 **GBTru: $10**

COUNTRY CHRISTMAS
Whirligig Santa

Santa as toy with movable arms.
Wood, 4.00"

QX5192 SRP: $12.50 **GBTru: $15**

Do Not Disturb Bear

Bear sleeping in log.
Handcrafted, 3.00"
E Seale

QX4812 SRP: $7.75 **GBTru: $20**

COUNTRY CHRISTMAS
Old Fashioned Doll

Doll in colonial dress.
Porcelain/Fabric, 5.50"

QX5195 SRP: $14.50 **GBTru: $32**

Dapper Penguin

Penguin in top hat and tails.
Handcrafted, 2.25"
E Seale

QX4772 SRP: $5.00 **GBTru: $25**

Doggy In A Stocking

Terrier and bone in yarn sock.
Handcrafted, 3.00"

QX4742 SRP: $5.50 **GBTru: $35**

COUNTRY CHRISTMAS
Rocking Horse Memories

Rocking horse.
Wood/Fabric, 3.25", Dated
L Votruba

QX5182 SRP: $10.00 **GBTru: $14**

Daughter

Rose and holly silk screened look.
Wood, 3.25", Dated

QX5032 SRP: $5.50 **GBTru: $14**

Engineering Mouse

Mouse in locomotive/wind-up key.
Handcrafted, 2.00"
B Siedler

QX4735 SRP: $5.50 **GBTru: $20**

Father

Old fashioned painted design sleigh.
Wood, 3.00", Dated
L Votruba

QX3762 SRP: $6.50 **GBTru: $10**

First Christmas Together

Woven heart.
Fabric/Wood, 2.50", Dated

QX5072 SRP: $8.00 **GBTru: $10**

Friendship

Early American village scene.
Satin, 3.00", Dated
M Pyda-Sevaik

QX3785 SRP: $6.75 **GBTru: $10**

First Christmas Together

Hearts border/photo locket.
Brass, 2.50", Dated
E Seale

QX4005 SRP: $16.75 **GBTru: $20**

First Christmas Together

Romantic silhouettes.
Glass Ball, 2.37", Dated

QX2612 SRP: $4.75 **GBTru: $16**

From Our House To Yours

Neighbors visit/embroidered house.
Fabric, 4.00", Dated
J Pattee

QX5202 SRP: $7.75 **GBTru: $10**

First Christmas Together

Two doves with banner.
Acrylic, 3.50", Dated

QX3705 SRP: $6.75 **GBTru: $18**

Fraggle Rock Holiday

The Gang and Sprocket.
Glass Ball, 3.00", Dated

QX2655 SRP: $4.75 **GBTru: $10**

FROSTY FRIENDS - 6TH
Frosty Friends

Eskimo and sled dog in kayak.
Handcrafted, 2.00", Dated
E Seale

QX4822 SRP: $8.50 **GBTru: $76**

First Christmas Together

Double heart clapper bell.
Porcelain, 2.00", Dated
L Sickman

QX4935 SRP: $13.00 **GBTru: $24**

Friendship

Red satin embroidered box.
Satin/Hndcr, 2.00", Dated
J Pattee

QX5062 SRP: $7.75 **GBTru: $10**

Godchild

Antique card design of children.
Satin, 2.75", Dated
D McGehee

QX3802 SRP: $6.75 **GBTru: $10**

Good Friends

Penguins playing in snow.
Glass Ball, 3.00", Dated

QX2652 SRP: $4.75 **GBTru: $25**

Grandchild's First Christmas

Santa and baby/elves and toys.
Satin Ball, 2.88", Dated
L Votruba

QX2605 SRP: $5.00 **GBTru: $14**

Grandchild's First Christmas

Knitted bootie full of toys.
Hndcr/Fabric, 3.25", Dated

QX4955 SRP: $11.00 **GBTru: $20**

Granddaughter

Stencil animal design.
Glass Ball, 2.87", Dated

QX2635 SRP: $4.75 **GBTru: $18**

Grandmother

Floral design.
Glass Ball, 3.00", Dated
J Pattee

QX2625 SRP: $4.75 **GBTru: $14**

Grandparents

White poinsettia on laquer-look.
Handcrafted, 2.75", Dated
S Pike

QX3805 SRP: $7.00 **GBTru: $8**

Grandson

Antique train.
Glass Ball, 2.88", Dated
L Votruba

QX2622 SRP: $4.75 **GBTru: $20**

Heart Full Of Love

Winter scene w/cardinals.
Satin, 3.00", Dated

QX3782 SRP: $6.75 **GBTru: $15**

Heavenly Trumpeter

Limited Edition of 24,700
Angel playing horn/displayer.
Porcelain, 5.00"
D Lee

QX4052 SRP: $27.50 **GBTru: $90**

HEIRLOOM CHRISTMAS
Charming Angel

Angel in lace dress.
Fabric, 3.25"
M Pyda-Sevaik

QX5125 SRP: $9.75 **GBTru: $18**

HEIRLOOM CHRISTMAS
Keepsake Basket

Crochet, satin, and lace sachet.
Fabric, 2.50"
S Pike

QX5145 SRP: $15.00 **GBTru: $15**

HEIRLOOM CHRISTMAS
Lacy Heart

Lacy heart with sachet.
Fabric, 3.00"

QX5112 SRP: $8.75 **GBTru: $18**

HEIRLOOM CHRISTMAS
Snowflake

Crochet with satin snowflake.
Fabric, 4.25"
J Pattee

QX5105 SRP: $6.50 **GBTru: $12**

HOLIDAY WILDLIFE - 4TH
California Partridge

Two partridges in a meadow.
Wood, 3.00", Dated

QX3765 SRP: $7.50 **GBTru: $20**

Kitty Mischief

Cat with ball of yarn.
Handcrafted, 2.00"
P Dutkin

QX4745 SRP: $5.00 **GBTru: $18**

HEIRLOOM CHRISTMAS
Victorian Lady

Doll head with lace and velvet.
Porc/Fabric, 3.75"

QX5132 SRP: $9.50 **GBTru: $15**

Hugga Bunch

Hugga Bunch kids celebrating.
Glass Ball, 2.37"

QX2715 SRP: $5.00 **GBTru: $10**

Lamb And Legwarmers

Lamb in knitted legwarmers.
Handcrafted, 3.00"

QX4802 SRP: $7.00 **GBTru: $15**

HERE COMES SANTA - 7TH
Santa's Fire Engine

Santa with fire engine.
Handcrafted, 3.00", Dated
L Sickman

QX4965 SRP: $14.00 **GBTru: $55**

Ice Skating Owl

Owl skating.
Handcrafted, 2.00"
B Siedler

QX4765 SRP: $5.00 **GBTru: $15**

Love At Christmas

Hearts with love caption.
Acrylic, 3.25"
D McGehee

QX3715 SRP: $5.75 **GBTru: $38**

Holiday Heart

Puffed heart on heart "LOVE".
Porcelain, 2.00"

QX4982 SRP: $8.00 **GBTru: $18**

Kit The Shepherd

Boy as shepherd in fabric headdress.
Handcrafted, 2.50"
B Siedler

QX4845 SRP: $5.75 **GBTru: $28**

Merry Mouse

Mouse with Santa cap.
Handcrafted, 2.50"
P Dutkin

QX4032 SRP: $4.50 **GBTru: $25**

Merry Shirt Tales

Shirt Tales participating/winter sports.
Glass Ball, 3.00", Dated

QX2672 SRP: $4.75 **GBTru: $18**

MINIATURE CRECHE - 1ST
Wood & Woven Straw

Holy Family Nativity.
Wood/Straw
E Seale

QX4825 SRP: $8.75 **GBTru: $20**

Mother

Raindrop shape w/caption.
Acrylic, 3.38", Dated
S Pike

QX3722 SRP: $6.75 **GBTru: $10**

Mother And Dad

Embossed paisley design bell.
Porcelain, 3.00", Dated
L Votruba

QX5092 SRP: $7.75 **GBTru: $14**

Mouse Wagon

Mouse in wagon brings gift of cheese.
Handcrafted, 2.00", Dated

QX4762 SRP: $5.75 **GBTru: $65**

Muffin The Angel

Girl dressed up as an angel.
Handcrafted, 2.50"
B Siedler

QX4835 SRP: $5.75 **GBTru: $25**

Nativity Scene

Angels/birds/bunnies at manger.
Glass Ball, 3.00", Dated

QX2645 SRP: $4.75 **GBTru: $25**

New Home

Variety of Victorian houses.
Glass Ball, 3.00", Dated
M Pyda-Sevaik

QX2695 SRP: $4.75 **GBTru: $22**

Niece

Teardrop shape with caption.
Acrylic, 3.75", Dated

QX5205 SRP: $5.75 **GBTru: $8**

Night Before Christmas

Flip page story w/stand (panorama).
Handcrafted, 3.25"
E Seale

QX4494 SRP: $13.00 **GBTru: $35**

Norman Rockwell

Santa in 3 scenes.
Glass Ball, 2.88", Dated
D McGehee

QX2662 SRP: $4.75 **GBTru: $18**

NORMAN ROCKWELL - 6TH
Jolly Postman

Postman with kids.
Cameo, 3.00", Dated
D McGehee

QX3745 SRP: $7.50 **GBTru: $15**

NOSTALGIC HOUSES & SHOPS - 2ND
Old Fashioned Toy Shop

Toy shop and owner's apartment.
Handcrafted, 2.50", Dated
D Lee

QX4975 SRP: $13.75 **GBTru: $100**

PEANUTS
Snoopy & Woodstock

Snoopy playing hockey.
Handcrafted, 1.75"
B Siedler

QX4915 SRP: $7.50 **GBTru: $52**

ROCKING HORSE - 5TH
Pinto

Pinto pony.
Handcrafted, 4.00", Dated
L Sickman

QX4932 SRP: $10.75 **GBTru: $50**

Old Fashioned Wreath

Etched brass wreath of toys.
Acrylic, 3.25", Dated

QX3735 SRP: $7.50 **GBTru: $18**

PORCELAIN BEAR - 3RD
Cinnamon

Bear with candy cane.
Porcelain, 2.25"
P Dutkin

QX4792 SRP: $7.50 **GBTru: $55**

SANTA CLAUS - THE MOVIE
Santa Claus

Santa with toy bags/photo.
Lacquer-look, "Elfmade" emblem, 3.50"

QX3005 SRP: $6.75 **GBTru: $5**

Peaceful Kingdom

Lion with lamb.
Acrylic, 3.00", Dated
S Pike

QX3732 SRP: $5.75 **GBTru: $22**

Porcelain Bird

Tufted titmouse clip-on.
Porcelain, 2.00"
L Sickman

QX4795 SRP: $6.50 **GBTru: $38**

SANTA CLAUS - THE MOVIE
Santa's Village

Snow covers Santa's village/photo.
Lacquer-look, "Elfmade" emblem, 2.25"

QX3002 SRP: $6.75 **GBTru: $7**

Peanuts

Snoopy/Woodstock & friends singing.
Glass Ball, 3.00", Dated

QX2665 SRP: $4.75 **GBTru: $25**

Rainbow Brite & Friends

Rainbow & sprites w/stars & flakes.
Glass Ball, 2.87", Dated

QX2682 SRP: $4.75 **GBTru: $20**

Santa Pipe

Meerschaum design pipe.
Handcrafted, 4.50"
P Dutkin

QX4942 SRP: $9.50 **GBTru: $25**

Santa's Ski Trip

Santa on ski lift gondola.
Handcrafted, 3.25", Dated
E Seale

QX4962 SRP: $12.00 **GBTru: $50**

Sewn Photoholder

Embroidered hearts and flowers.
Fabric, 3.25", Dated
S Pike

QX3795 SRP: $7.00 **GBTru: $24**

Sister

Heart and holly design on bell.
Porcelain, 2.75", Dated
J Pattee

QX5065 SRP: $7.25 **GBTru: $16**

Skateboard Raccoon

Flocked raccoon on skateboard.
Handcrafted, 2.50"
P Dutkin

QX4732 SRP: $6.50 **GBTru: $30**

Snow-Pitching Snowman

Snowman pitches snowball.
Handcrafted, 2.00"
D Lee

QX4702 SRP: $4.50 **GBTru: $15**

Soccer Beaver

Beaver playing soccer.
Handcrafted, 2.50"
P Dutkin

QX4775 SRP: $6.50 **GBTru: $15**

Son

Terrier with sign.
Handcrafted, 2.00", Dated
B Siedler

QX5025 SRP: $5.50 **GBTru: $40**

Special Friends

Doll w/teddy/caption.
Acrylic, 3.00", Dated
D Palmiter

QX3725 SRP: $5.75 **GBTru: $10**

Special Edition
Santa on sleigh w/deer, wishbone hanger.
Handcrafted, 4.75"
D Lee

QX4985 SRP: $22.50 **GBTru: $125**

Stardust Angel

Angel brushing stardust from star.
Handcrafted, 2.00"
D Lee

QX4752 SRP: $5.75 **GBTru: $32**

Sun And Fun Santa

Santa with inner tube.
Handcrafted, 2.75", Dated
B Siedler

QX4922 SRP: $7.75 **GBTru: $25**

Swinging Angel Bell

Angel riding swing inside bell.
Hndcr/Glass, 3.75"
B Siedler

QX4925 SRP: $11.00 **GBTru: $22**

Teacher

Owl sits on blackboard with lesson.
Handcrafted, 3.00", Dated

QX5052 SRP: $6.00 **GBTru: $16**

TWELVE DAYS OF CHRISTMAS, THE - 2ND
Two Turtle Doves

Two turtle doves.
Acrylic, 3.00", Dated
S Pike

QX3712 SRP: $6.50 **GBTru: $50**

WOOD CHILDHOOD ORNAMENTS - 2ND
Wooden Train

Train and log car with logs.
Wood, 3.50"
P Dutkin

QX4722 SRP: $7.00 **GBTru: $54**

THIMBLE - 8TH
Thimble Santa
Little Trimmers
Santa carrying tree.
Handcrafted, 2.13"
B Siedler

QX4725 SRP: $5.50 **GBTru: $32**

Twenty-Five Years Together

Wreath of hollies on plate with stand.
Porcelain, 3.25", Dated

QX5005 SRP: $8.00 **GBTru: $12**

1986

TIN LOCOMOTIVE - 4TH
Tin Locomotive

Old fashioned locomotive.
Tin, 3.50", Dated
L Sickman

QX4972 SRP: $14.75 **GBTru: $80**

WINDOWS OF THE WORLD - 1ST
Mexico - Feliz Navidad

Mexican boy with pinata.
Handcrafted, 3.00", Dated
D Lee

QX4902 SRP: $9.75 **GBTru: $85**

Acorn Inn

Squirrel in acorn.
Handcrafted, 2.00"
D Unruh

QX4243 SRP: $8.50 **GBTru: $22**

Trumpet Panda

Flocked panda playing trumpet.
Handcrafted, 2.00"
E Seale

QX4712 SRP: $4.50 **GBTru: $20**

With Appreciation

Caption with snowflakes.
Acrylic, 3.50", Dated

QX3752 SRP: $6.75 **GBTru: $8**

ART MASTERPIECE - 3RD & FINAL
Madonna And Child With The Infant St. John

Lorenzo DiCridi: Madonna and Child.
Satin, 3.25"
D McGehee

QX3506 SRP: $6.75 **GBTru: $10**

Baby Locket

Baby locket.
Brass, 2.25", Dated
D McGehee

QX4123 SRP: $16.00 **GBTru: $25**

Baby's First Christmas

Baby mobile.
Handcrafted, 3.50", Dated
L Sickman

QX4126 SRP: $9.00 **GBTru: $38**

Baby's First Christmas

Lamb with stocking.
Acrylic, 3.75", Dated
D Palmiter

QX3803 SRP: $6.00 **GBTru: $20**

Baby's First Christmas

Baby on rocking horse.
Satin Ball, 2.88", Dated
J Pattee

QX2713 SRP: $5.50 **GBTru: $20**

Baby's First Christmas Photoholder

Heart photoholder.
Fabric, 3.75", Dated
J Pattee

QX3792 SRP: $8.00 **GBTru: $22**

Baby's Second Christmas

Mouse with stocking.
Handcrafted, 1.75", Dated
B Siedler

QX4133 SRP: $6.50 **GBTru: $24**

Baby-Sitter

Baby toys.
Glass Ball, 3.00", Dated

QX2756 SRP: $4.75 **GBTru: $8**

BETSEY CLARK: HOME FOR CHRISTMAS - 1ST
Home For Christmas

Children decorating for Christmas.
Glass Ball, 2.88", Dated
S Pike

QX2776 SRP: $5.00 **GBTru: $24**

Bluebird

Bluebird clip-on.
Porcelain, 3.33"
L Sickman

QX4283 SRP: $7.25 **GBTru: $58**

Chatty Penguin

Penguin.
Plush, 3.63",
K Crow

QX4176 SRP: $5.75 **GBTru: $15**

Child's Third Christmas

Panda in Santa outfit.
Fabric, 2.33", Dated
L Votruba

QX4136 SRP: $6.50 **GBTru: $18**

Christmas Beauty

Laquer-look holly branches.
Handcrafted, 2.75"
J Pattee

QX3223 SRP: $6.00 **GBTru: $8**

CHRISTMAS MEDLEY
Christmas Guitar

Guitar.
Handcrafted, 3.00", Dated
D Unruh

QX5126 SRP: $7.00 **GBTru: $22**

CHRISTMAS MEDLEY
Joyful Carolers

Carolers.
Handcrafted, 3.25", Dated
L Sickman

QX5136 SRP: $9.75 **GBTru: $29**

COUNTRY TREASURES
Country Sleigh

Sleigh.
Handcrafted, 2.00", Dated
L Sickman

QX5113 SRP: $10.00 **GBTru: $24**

CHRISTMAS MEDLEY
Favorite Tin Drum

Drum.
Tin, 2.00"
L Sickman

QX5143 SRP: $8.50 **GBTru: $25**

CLOTHESPIN SOLDIER - 5TH
French Officer

French officer.
Handcrafted, 2.00"
L Sickman

QX4063 SRP: $5.50 **GBTru: $22**

COUNTRY TREASURES
Little Drummers

Drummers.
Handcrafted, 4.00"
K Crow

QX5116 SRP: $12.50 **GBTru: $20**

CHRISTMAS MEDLEY
Festive Treble Clef

Bell with treble clef.
Handcrafted, 3.88"
B Siedler

QX5133 SRP: $8.75 **GBTru: $15**

Coca-Cola Santa

Gold Crown Open House
Santa with Cola.
Glass Ball, 2.87"

QX02796 SRP: $4.75 **GBTru: $10**

COUNTRY TREASURES
Nutcracker Santa

Santa as nutcracker.
Handcrafted, 3.38"
D Unruh

QX5123 SRP: $10.00 **GBTru: $42**

CHRISTMAS MEDLEY
Holiday Horn

Horn.
Porcelain, 3.00"
D Unruh

QX5146 SRP: $8.00 **GBTru: $22**

Cookies For Santa

Cookies on plate.
Handcrafted, 2.75", Dated
D McGehee

QX4146 SRP: $4.50 **GBTru: $20**

COUNTRY TREASURES
Remembering Christmas

Plate: Quilt design w/stand.
Porcelain, 3.25", Dated

QX5106 SRP: $8.75 **GBTru: $25**

COUNTRY TREASURES
Welcome, Christmas

Angel in heart frame.
Handcrafted, 2.63", Dated
K Crow

QX5103 SRP: $8.25 **GBTru: $30**

Daughter

Girl in stocking.
Handcrafted, 3.50", Dated
E Seale

QX4306 SRP: $5.75 **GBTru: $35**

Father

French horn.
Wood, 3.25", Dated
L Votruba

QX4313 SRP: $6.50 **GBTru: $14**

Fifty Years Together

Holly design bell.
Porcelain, 3.45", Dated
S Pike

QX4006 SRP: $10.00 **GBTru: $12**

First Christmas Together

Heart locket.
Brass, 2.25", Dated

QX4003 SRP: $16.00 **GBTru: $18**

First Christmas Together

Two turtle doves in cage.
Handcrafted, 4.00", Dated
L Sickman

QX4096 SRP: $12.00 **GBTru: $15**

First Christmas Together

Two hearts in teardrop shape.
Acrylic, 3.45", Dated
D McGehee

QX3793 SRP: $7.00 **GBTru: $10**

First Christmas Together

Two cardinals in winter scene.
Glass Ball, 2.87", Dated

QX2703 SRP: $4.75 **GBTru: $15**

Friends Are Fun

Arctic pals in sleigh.
Glass Ball, 2.88", Dated
K Crow

QX2723 SRP: $4.75 **GBTru: $39**

Friendship Greeting

Pattern envelope.
Fabric, 2.75", Dated

QX4273 SRP: $8.00 **GBTru: $10**

Friendship's Gift

Mouse in Santa cap.
Acrylic, 3.00", Dated

QX3816 SRP: $6.00 **GBTru: $12**

From Our Home To Yours

Basket of fruit.
Acrylic, 3.25", Dated

QX3833 SRP: $6.00 **GBTru: $14**

FROSTY FRIENDS - 7TH
Frosty Friends

Eskimo with baby reindeer.
Handcrafted, 2.25", Dated
B Siedler

QX4053 SRP: $8.50 **GBTru: $70**

Glowing Christmas Tree

Decorated tree.
Acrylic, 3.25", Dated
J Pattee

QX4286 SRP: $7.00 **GBTru: $12**

Godchild

Bears holding sign.
Satin Ball, 2.87", Dated

QX2716 SRP: $4.75 **GBTru: $14**

Grandchild's First Christmas

Bear sleeping in basket.
Handcrafted, 2.25", Dated

QX4116 SRP: $10.00 **GBTru: $12**

Granddaughter

Children in holiday spirits.
Glass Ball, 2.88, Dated
J Lyle

QX2736 SRP: $4.75 **GBTru: $20**

Grandmother

Quilt resembling Christmas trees.
Satin Ball, 2.88", Dated
J Pattee

QX2743 SRP: $4.75 **GBTru: $14**

Grandparents

Two doves with heart bell.
Porcelain, 5.50", Dated
J Pattee

QX4323 SRP: $7.50 **GBTru: $15**

Grandson

Animals with banner.
Glass Ball, 3.00", Dated
L Votruba

QX2733 SRP: $4.75 **GBTru: $24**

Gratitude

Cardinal on holly branch.
Satin/Wood, 5.00", Dated
S Pike

QX4326 SRP: $6.00 **GBTru: $8**

Happy Christmas To Owl

Owl reads book to friend.
Handcrafted, 3.00"
D Unruh

QX4183 SRP: $6.00 **GBTru: $20**

Heathcliff

Heathcliff with angel.
Handcrafted, 3.25"
E Seale

QX4363 SRP: $7.50 **GBTru: $22**

Heavenly Dreamer

Angel sleeping on cloud.
Handcrafted, 1.38"
D Lee

QX4173 SRP: $5.75 **GBTru: $35**

Heirloom Snowflake

Crocheted edging on satin.
Fabric, 4.25"
J Pattee

QX5153 SRP: $6.75 **GBTru: $18**

HERE COMES SANTA - 8TH
Kringle's Kool Treats

Santa with ice cream cart.
Handcrafted, 4.00", Dated
B Siedler

QX4043 SRP: $14.00 **GBTru: $58**

Holiday Jingle Bell

Jingle bell w/reindeer bas relief.
Handcrafted, 2.75", Dated, ♪

Tune: Jingle Bells

QX4046 SRP: $16.00 **GBTru: $40**

HOLIDAY WILDLIFE - 5TH
Cedar Waxwing

Two birds on branch.
Wood, 2.50", Dated

QX3216 SRP: $7.50 **GBTru: $18**

Husband

Duck with wreath.
Cameo, 2.75", Dated
S Pike

QX3836 SRP: $8.00 **GBTru: $12**

Jolly Hiker

Hiking Santa.
Handcrafted, 2.00"
B Siedler

QX4832 SRP: $5.00 **GBTru: $28**

Jolly St. Nick

Special Edition
Nast art: Santa w/stock'g & toys.
Porcelain, 5.50"
D Unruh

QX4296 SRP: $22.50 **GBTru: $45**

Joy Of Friends

Family ice skating.
Satin, 2.75"
J Pattee

QX3823 SRP: $6.75 **GBTru: $10**

Katybeth

Angel with star.
Porcelain, 2.50"

QX4353 SRP: $7.00 **GBTru: $22**

Li'l Jingler

Raccoon hanging from jingle bells.
Handcrafted, 2.00"
E Seale

QX4193 SRP: $6.75 **GBTru: $30**

Loving Memories

Heart shadow box w/bell/gift/teddy.
Handcrafted, 5.25", Dated
E Seale

QX4093 SRP: $9.00 **GBTru: $22**

Magi, The

Three Kings.
Glass Ball, 3.00", Dated
S Pike

QX2726 SRP: $4.75 **GBTru: $15**

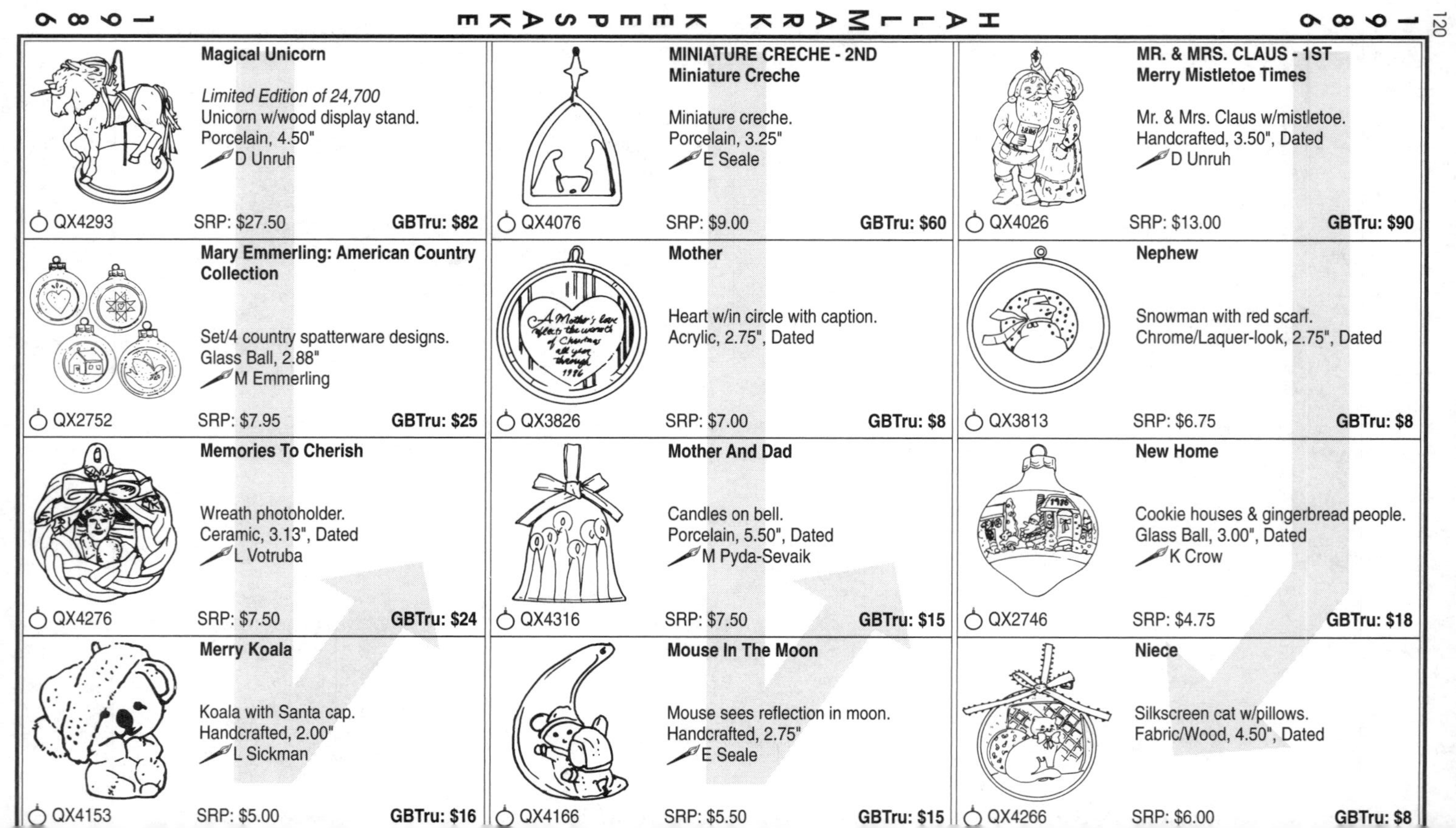

Magical Unicorn

Limited Edition of 24,700
Unicorn w/wood display stand.
Porcelain, 4.50"
D Unruh

QX4293 SRP: $27.50 **GBTru: $82**

Mary Emmerling: American Country Collection

Set/4 country spatterware designs.
Glass Ball, 2.88"
M Emmerling

QX2752 SRP: $7.95 **GBTru: $25**

Memories To Cherish

Wreath photoholder.
Ceramic, 3.13", Dated
L Votruba

QX4276 SRP: $7.50 **GBTru: $24**

Merry Koala

Koala with Santa cap.
Handcrafted, 2.00"
L Sickman

QX4153 SRP: $5.00 **GBTru: $16**

MINIATURE CRECHE - 2ND
Miniature Creche

Miniature creche.
Porcelain, 3.25"
E Seale

QX4076 SRP: $9.00 **GBTru: $60**

Mother

Heart w/in circle with caption.
Acrylic, 2.75", Dated

QX3826 SRP: $7.00 **GBTru: $8**

Mother And Dad

Candles on bell.
Porcelain, 5.50", Dated
M Pyda-Sevaik

QX4316 SRP: $7.50 **GBTru: $15**

Mouse In The Moon

Mouse sees reflection in moon.
Handcrafted, 2.75"
E Seale

QX4166 SRP: $5.50 **GBTru: $15**

MR. & MRS. CLAUS - 1ST
Merry Mistletoe Times

Mr. & Mrs. Claus w/mistletoe.
Handcrafted, 3.50", Dated
D Unruh

QX4026 SRP: $13.00 **GBTru: $90**

Nephew

Snowman with red scarf.
Chrome/Laquer-look, 2.75", Dated

QX3813 SRP: $6.75 **GBTru: $8**

New Home

Cookie houses & gingerbread people.
Glass Ball, 3.00", Dated
K Crow

QX2746 SRP: $4.75 **GBTru: $18**

Niece

Silkscreen cat w/pillows.
Fabric/Wood, 4.50", Dated

QX4266 SRP: $6.00 **GBTru: $8**

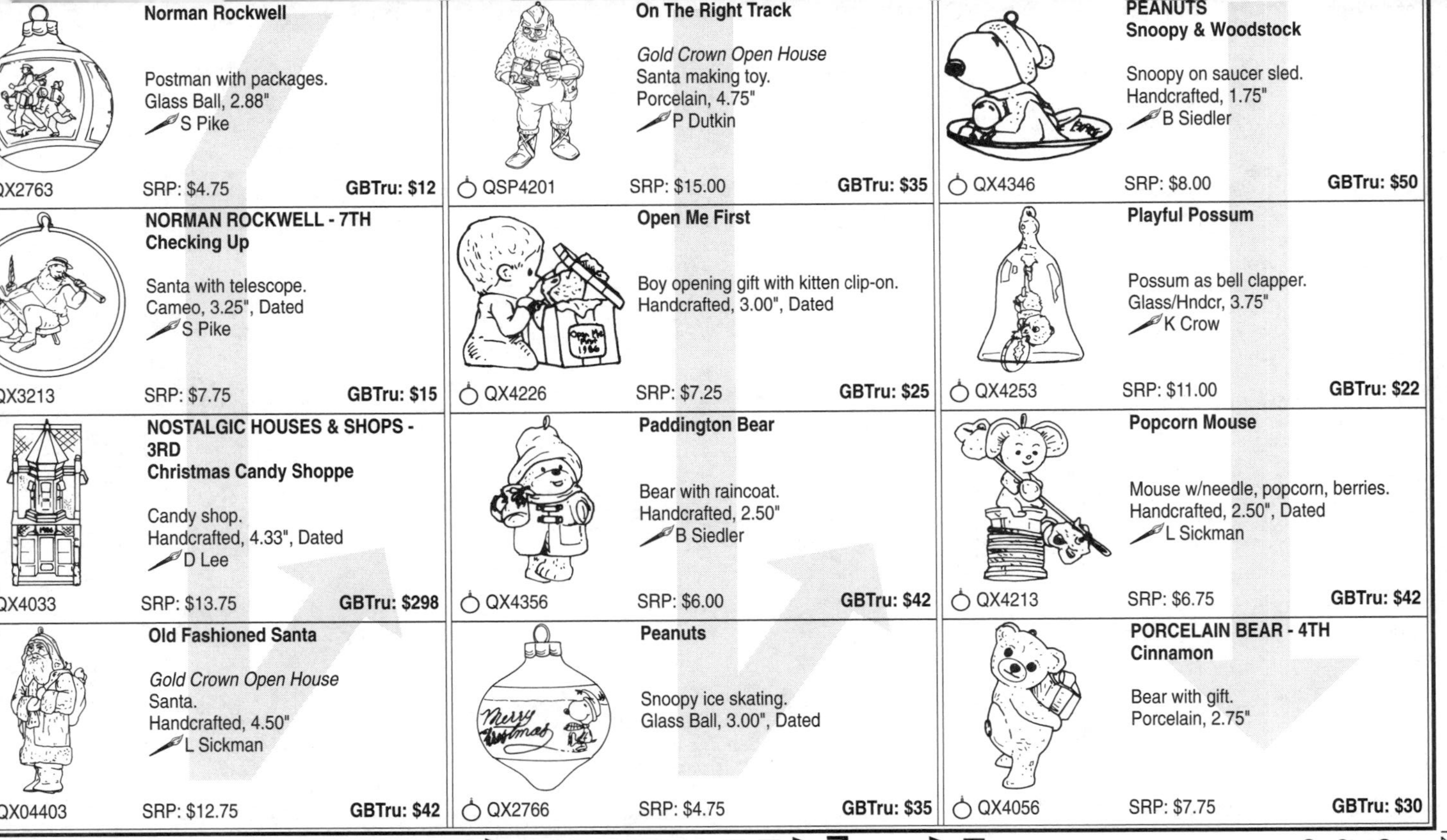

Norman Rockwell

Postman with packages.
Glass Ball, 2.88"
S Pike

QX2763 SRP: $4.75 **GBTru: $12**

NORMAN ROCKWELL - 7TH
Checking Up

Santa with telescope.
Cameo, 3.25", Dated
S Pike

QX3213 SRP: $7.75 **GBTru: $15**

NOSTALGIC HOUSES & SHOPS - 3RD
Christmas Candy Shoppe

Candy shop.
Handcrafted, 4.33", Dated
D Lee

QX4033 SRP: $13.75 **GBTru: $298**

Old Fashioned Santa

Gold Crown Open House
Santa.
Handcrafted, 4.50"
L Sickman

QX04403 SRP: $12.75 **GBTru: $42**

On The Right Track

Gold Crown Open House
Santa making toy.
Porcelain, 4.75"
P Dutkin

QSP4201 SRP: $15.00 **GBTru: $35**

Open Me First

Boy opening gift with kitten clip-on.
Handcrafted, 3.00", Dated

QX4226 SRP: $7.25 **GBTru: $25**

Paddington Bear

Bear with raincoat.
Handcrafted, 2.50"
B Siedler

QX4356 SRP: $6.00 **GBTru: $42**

Peanuts

Snoopy ice skating.
Glass Ball, 3.00", Dated

QX2766 SRP: $4.75 **GBTru: $35**

PEANUTS
Snoopy & Woodstock

Snoopy on saucer sled.
Handcrafted, 1.75"
B Siedler

QX4346 SRP: $8.00 **GBTru: $50**

Playful Possum

Possum as bell clapper.
Glass/Hndcr, 3.75"
K Crow

QX4253 SRP: $11.00 **GBTru: $22**

Popcorn Mouse

Mouse w/needle, popcorn, berries.
Handcrafted, 2.50", Dated
L Sickman

QX4213 SRP: $6.75 **GBTru: $42**

PORCELAIN BEAR - 4TH
Cinnamon

Bear with gift.
Porcelain, 2.75"

QX4056 SRP: $7.75 **GBTru: $30**

Puppy's Best Friend

Dog with elf.
Handcrafted, 2.25"
D Unruh

QX4203 SRP: $6.50 **GBTru: $22**

Santa And His Reindeer

Gold Crown Open House
Santa with reindeer.
Handcrafted, 2.00"

QX04406 SRP: $9.75 **GBTru: $28**

Shirt Tales Parade

Animal parade.
Glass Ball, 2.88"

QX2773 SRP: $4.75 **GBTru: $10**

Rah Rah Rabbit

Rabbit as cheerleader.
Handcrafted, 2.50", Dated
K Crow

QX4216 SRP: $7.00 **GBTru: $25**

Santa's Hot Tub

Santa with reindeer in tub.
Handcrafted, 3.00"
E Seale

QX4263 SRP: $12.00 **GBTru: $45**

Sister

Teddy on wreath/brass frame.
Satin, 2.75", Dated
L Votruba

QX3806 SRP: $6.75 **GBTru: $12**

REINDEER CHAMPS - 1ST
Dasher

Reindeer jogging.
Handcrafted, 2.88", Dated
B Siedler

QX4223 SRP: $7.50 **GBTru: $135**

Santa's Panda Pal

Gold Crown Open House
Flocked Panda.
Handcrafted, 2.25"

QX04413 SRP: $5.00 **GBTru: $10**

Ski Tripper

Girl holding skis.
Handcrafted, 2.13"
B Siedler

QX4206 SRP: $6.75 **GBTru: $15**

ROCKING HORSE - 6TH
Palomino

Rocking horse.
Handcrafted, 4.00", Dated
L Sickman

QX4016 SRP: $10.75 **GBTru: $50**

Season Of The Heart

Family on sleigh ride.
Glass Ball, 3.00"
J Pattee

QX2706 SRP: $4.75 **GBTru: $12**

Snow Buddies

Mouse with snow mouse.
Handcrafted, 2.25"
P Dutkin

QX4236 SRP: $8.00 **GBTru: $22**

Son

Boy in stocking.
Handcrafted, 4.00", Dated
E Seale

QX4303 SRP: $5.75 **GBTru: $30**

Sweetheart

Gazebo w/decorated tree, can personalize.
Handcrafted, 3.50", Dated
E Seale

QX4086 SRP: $11.00 **GBTru: $60**

Timeless Love

"LOVE" with caption.
Acrylic, 3.00", Dated
L Votruba

QX3796 SRP: $6.00 **GBTru: $20**

Special Delivery

Penguin w/gift of sardines.
Handcrafted, 2.00"
B Siedler

QX4156 SRP: $5.00 **GBTru: $20**

Teacher

Mouse with apple.
Glass Ball, 2.88", Dated

QX2753 SRP: $4.75 **GBTru: $8**

TIN LOCOMOTIVE - 5TH
Tin Locomotive

Locomotive.
Tin, 3.50", Dated
L Sickman

QX4036 SRP: $14.75 **GBTru: $70**

Star Brighteners

Angels with stars.
Acrylic, 2.75", Dated
L Votruba

QX3226 SRP: $6.00 **GBTru: $14**

Ten Years Together

Roses & holly on bell.
Porcelain, 3.00", Dated

QX4013 SRP: $7.50 **GBTru: $15**

Tipping The Scales

Santa on scale.
Handcrafted, 2.75", Dated
P Dutkin

QX4186 SRP: $6.75 **GBTru: $15**

Statue Of Liberty, The

Statue of Liberty.
Acrylic, 3.45", Dated
M Pyda-Sevaik

QX3843 SRP: $6.00 **GBTru: $19**

THIMBLE - 9TH
Thimble Partridge
Little Trimmers
Partridge in thimble.
Handcrafted, 1.62"

QX4066 SRP: $5.75 **GBTru: $22**

Touchdown Santa

Santa in football outfit.
Handcrafted, 3.00", Dated
P Dutkin

QX4233 SRP: $8.00 **GBTru: $35**

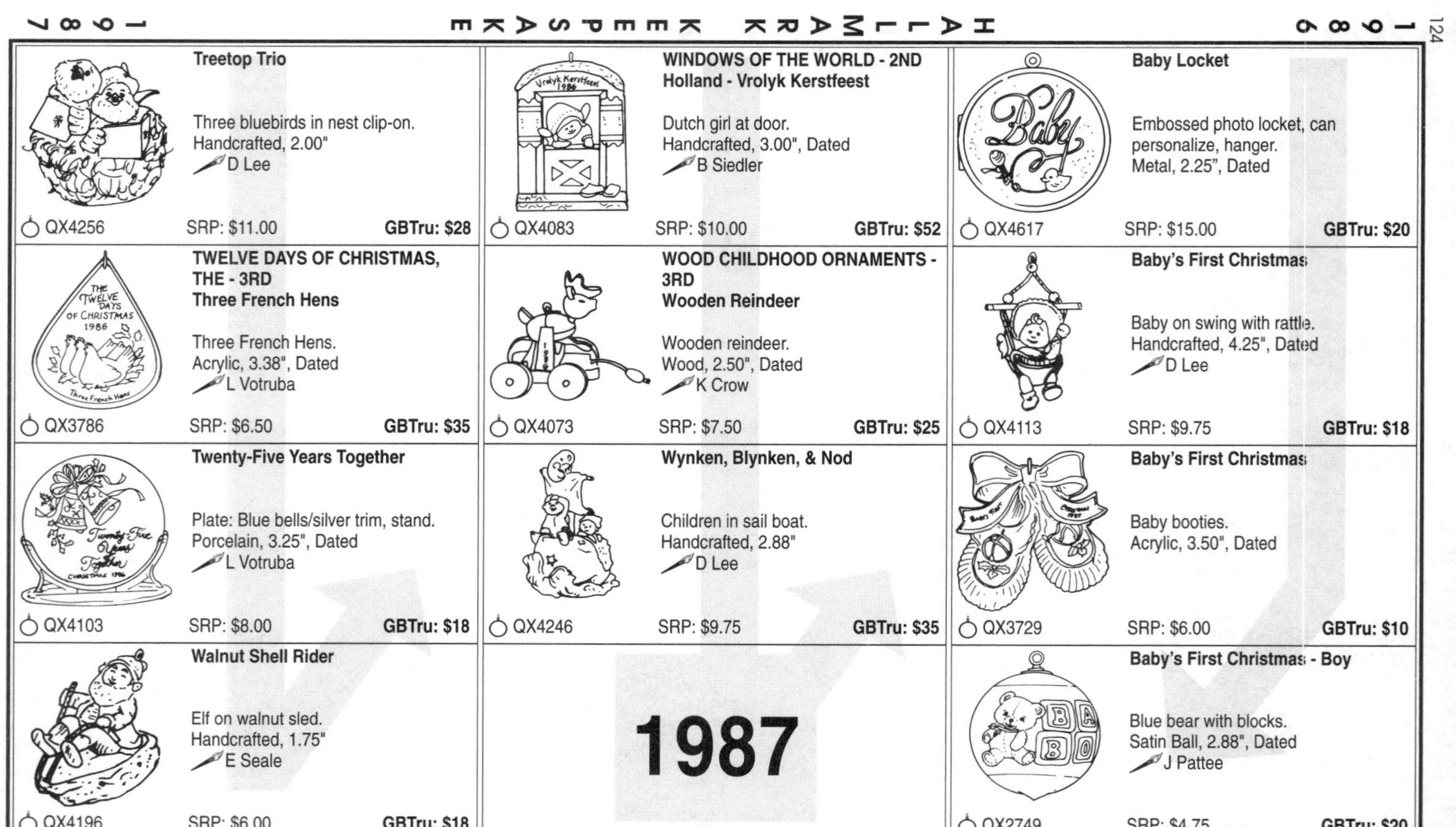

Treetop Trio

Three bluebirds in nest clip-on.
Handcrafted, 2.00"
D Lee

QX4256 SRP: $11.00 **GBTru: $28**

TWELVE DAYS OF CHRISTMAS, THE - 3RD
Three French Hens

Three French Hens.
Acrylic, 3.38", Dated
L Votruba

QX3786 SRP: $6.50 **GBTru: $35**

Twenty-Five Years Together

Plate: Blue bells/silver trim, stand.
Porcelain, 3.25", Dated
L Votruba

QX4103 SRP: $8.00 **GBTru: $18**

Walnut Shell Rider

Elf on walnut sled.
Handcrafted, 1.75"
E Seale

QX4196 SRP: $6.00 **GBTru: $18**

WINDOWS OF THE WORLD - 2ND
Holland - Vrolyk Kerstfeest

Dutch girl at door.
Handcrafted, 3.00", Dated
B Siedler

QX4083 SRP: $10.00 **GBTru: $52**

WOOD CHILDHOOD ORNAMENTS - 3RD
Wooden Reindeer

Wooden reindeer.
Wood, 2.50", Dated
K Crow

QX4073 SRP: $7.50 **GBTru: $25**

Wynken, Blynken, & Nod

Children in sail boat.
Handcrafted, 2.88"
D Lee

QX4246 SRP: $9.75 **GBTru: $35**

1987

Baby Locket

Embossed photo locket, can personalize, hanger.
Metal, 2.25", Dated

QX4617 SRP: $15.00 **GBTru: $20**

Baby's First Christmas

Baby on swing with rattle.
Handcrafted, 4.25", Dated
D Lee

QX4113 SRP: $9.75 **GBTru: $18**

Baby's First Christmas

Baby booties.
Acrylic, 3.50", Dated

QX3729 SRP: $6.00 **GBTru: $10**

Baby's First Christmas - Boy

Blue bear with blocks.
Satin Ball, 2.88", Dated
J Pattee

QX2749 SRP: $4.75 **GBTru: $20**

Baby's First Christmas - Girl

Girl dressed in pink w/blocks.
Satin Ball, 2.88", Dated
J Pattee

QX2747 SRP: $4.75 **GBTru: $18**

Baby's First Christmas Photoholder

Wreath photoholder for baby.
Fabric, 3.25", Dated

QX4619 SRP: $7.50 **GBTru: $20**

Baby's Second Christmas

Clown-in-the-box.
Handcrafted, 2.75", Dated
D Lee

QX4607 SRP: $5.75 **GBTru: $24**

Babysitter

Bunnies baking cookies.
Glass Ball, 3.00", Dated
S Pike

QX2797 SRP: $4.75 **GBTru: $12**

Beary Special

Bear with ornament.
Handcrafted, 2.50"
B Siedler

QX4557 SRP: $4.75 **GBTru: $20**

BETSEY CLARK: HOME FOR CHRISTMAS - 2ND
Home For Christmas

Children trim tree.
Glass Ball, 2.88", Dated
S Pike

QX2727 SRP: $5.00 **GBTru: $22**

Carousel Reindeer

Club: Keepsake of Membership
Charter yr caption/Reindeer carousel/ club logo.
Handcrafted, 3.75", Dated
L Sickman

QXC5817 SRP: $8.00 **GBTru: $45**

Child's Third Christmas

Child on reindeer.
Handcrafted, 3.00", Dated
K Crow

QX4599 SRP: $5.75 **GBTru: $20**

Chocolate Chipmunk

Chipmunk on chocolate chip cookie.
Handcrafted, 2.00"
E Seale

QX4567 SRP: $6.00 **GBTru: $38**

Christmas Cuddle

Kitten hugs mouse.
Handcrafted, 2.75"

QX4537 SRP: $5.75 **GBTru: $28**

Christmas Is Gentle

Limited Edition of 24,700
Lambs in basket, hand numbered.
Bone China, 3.00", Dated
E Seale

QX4449 SRP: $17.50 **GBTru: $40**

Christmas Keys

Piano.
Handcrafted, 2.00"
D Unruh

QX4739 SRP: $5.75 **GBTru: $24**

CHRISTMAS PIZZAZZ
Christmas Fun Puzzle

Puzzle with Santa, reindeer, mouse.
Handcrafted, 2.50"
D Lee

QX4679 SRP: $8.00 **GBTru: $22**

CHRISTMAS PIZZAZZ
Jolly Follies

Three top-hatted penguins.
Handcrafted, 2.00"
K Crow

QX4669 SRP: $8.50 **GBTru: $22**

CLOTHESPIN SOLDIER - 6TH & FINAL
Sailor

Clothespin sailor.
Handcrafted, 2.25"
L Sickman

QX4807 SRP: $5.50 **GBTru: $22**

CHRISTMAS PIZZAZZ
Doc Holiday

Cowboy Santa on reindeer.
Handcrafted, 4.00"
E Seale

QX4677 SRP: $8.00 **GBTru: $40**

CHRISTMAS PIZZAZZ
Mistletoad

Toad holds onto rope.
Handcrafted, 3.75"
K Crow

QX4687 SRP: $7.00 **GBTru: $28**

COLLECTOR'S PLATE - 1ST
Light Shines At Christmas

Children decorate tree, stand.
Porcelain, 3.25", Dated
L Votruba

QX4817 SRP: $8.00 **GBTru: $56**

CHRISTMAS PIZZAZZ
Happy Holidata

Mice on computer.
Handcrafted, 1.50"
B Siedler

QX4717 SRP: $6.50 **GBTru: $28**

CHRISTMAS PIZZAZZ
St. Louie Nick

Santa blowing horn.
Handcrafted, 3.50"
P Dutkin

QX4539 SRP: $7.75 **GBTru: $30**

Constitution, The

Honors 200th Anniversary Constitution.
Acrylic, 2.50", Dated
J Pattee

QX3777 SRP: $6.50 **GBTru: $18**

CHRISTMAS PIZZAZZ
Holiday Hourglass

Hourglass snowman in Santa cap.
Handcrafted, 3.00"
D Unruh

QX4707 SRP: $8.00 **GBTru: $24**

Christmas Time Mime

Limited Edition of 24,700
Mime Santa w/ teddy; bag w/stars; stand, poem.
Porcelain, 2.50"
D Unruh

QX4429 SRP: $27.50 **GBTru: $40**

CRAYOLA
Bright Christmas Dreams

Mice in Crayola box.
Handcrafted, 4.00", Dated
B Siedler

QX4737 SRP: $7.25 **GBTru: $98**

Currier & Ives: American Farm Scene

Wintry farm scene.
Glass Ball, 2.88"
J Lyle

QX2829 SRP: $4.75 **GBTru: $18**

Dad

Polar bear with ties.
Handcrafted, 3.00", Dated
B Siedler

QX4629 SRP: $6.00 **GBTru: $30**

Daughter

Reindeer pulling swan sleigh.
Handcrafted, 1.25", Dated
L Sickman

QX4637 SRP: $5.75 **GBTru: $24**

December Showers

Angel on cloud with umbrella.
Handcrafted, 2.50"
D Lee

QX4487 SRP: $5.50 **GBTru: $25**

Dr. Seuss: The Grinch's Christmas

Dr. Seuss with wreath.
Glass Ball, 2.87"

QX2783 SRP: $4.75 **GBTru: $79**

Favorite Santa

Special Edition
Santa w/ stocking, poem.
Porcelain, 5.50"
P Dutkin

QX4457 SRP: $22.50 **GBTru: $28**

Fifty Years Together

Poinsettia design bell.
Porcelain, 5.00", Dated
E Seale

QX4437 SRP: $8.00 **GBTru: $15**

First Christmas Together

Heart-shaped locket.
Brass, 2.25", Dated

QX4469 SRP: $15.00 **GBTru: $20**

First Christmas Together

Heart-shaped alpine cottage.
Handcrafted, 3.00", Dated

QX4467 SRP: $9.50 **GBTru: $10**

First Christmas Together

Two raccoons share shirt.
Handcrafted, 2.50", Dated

QX4459 SRP: $8.00 **GBTru: $25**

First Christmas Together

Two swans swimming.
Acrylic, 2.50", Dated

QX3719 SRP: $6.50 **GBTru: $12**

First Christmas Together

Two lovebirds with poinsettias.
Glass Ball, 2.88", Dated
J Lyle

QX2729 SRP: $4.75 **GBTru: $10**

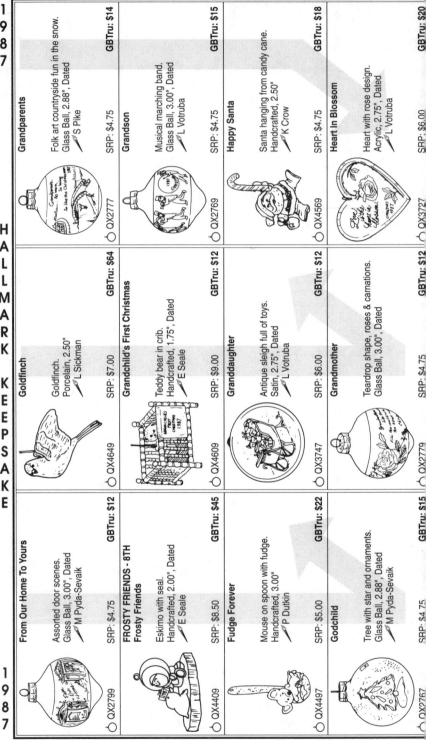

From Our Home To Yours

Assorted door scenes.
Glass Ball, 3.00", Dated
M Pyda-Sevaik

QX2799 SRP: $4.75 **GBTru: $12**

Goldfinch

Goldfinch.
Porcelain, 2.50"
L Sickman

QX4649 SRP: $7.00 **GBTru: $64**

Grandparents

Folk art countryside fun in the snow.
Glass Ball, 2.88", Dated
S Pike

QX2777 SRP: $4.75 **GBTru: $14**

FROSTY FRIENDS - 8TH
Frosty Friends

Eskimo with seal.
Handcrafted, 2.00", Dated
E Seale

QX4409 SRP: $8.50 **GBTru: $45**

Grandchild's First Christmas

Teddy bear in crib.
Handcrafted, 1.75", Dated
E Seale

QX4609 SRP: $9.00 **GBTru: $12**

Grandson

Musical marching band.
Glass Ball, 3.00", Dated
L Votruba

QX2769 SRP: $4.75 **GBTru: $15**

Fudge Forever

Mouse on spoon with fudge.
Handcrafted, 3.00"
P Dutkin

QX4497 SRP: $5.00 **GBTru: $22**

Granddaughter

Antique sleigh full of toys.
Satin, 2.75", Dated
L Votruba

QX3747 SRP: $6.00 **GBTru: $12**

Happy Santa

Santa hanging from candy cane.
Handcrafted, 2.50"
K Crow

QX4569 SRP: $4.75 **GBTru: $18**

Godchild

Tree with star and ornaments.
Glass Ball, 2.88", Dated
M Pyda-Sevaik

QX2767 SRP: $4.75 **GBTru: $15**

Grandmother

Teardrop shape, roses & carnations.
Glass Ball, 3.00", Dated

QX2779 SRP: $4.75 **GBTru: $12**

Heart In Blossom

Heart with rose design.
Acrylic, 2.75", Dated
L Votruba

QX3727 SRP: $6.00 **GBTru: $20**

Heavenly Harmony

Angel hanging from bell w/rope.
Handcrafted, 4.25", ♪
K Crow
Tune: Joy To The World

QX4659 SRP: $15.00 **GBTru: $28**

HOLIDAY WILDLIFE - 6TH
Snow Goose

Flying geese.
Wood, 2.50", Dated
L Votruba

QX3717 SRP: $7.50 **GBTru: $15**

Icy Treat

Penguin with popsicle.
Handcrafted, 2.25"
B Siedler

QX4509 SRP: $4.50 **GBTru: $15**

HERE COMES SANTA - 9TH
Santa's Woody

Santa in car.
Handcrafted, 2.00", Dated
K Crow

QX4847 SRP: $14.00 **GBTru: $72**

Hot Dogger

Santa on skis.
Handcrafted, 2.50"
D Unruh

QX4719 SRP: $6.50 **GBTru: $12**

Jack Frosting

Jack brushing glitter on leaf.
Handcrafted, 2.50"
E Seale

QX4499 SRP: $7.00 **GBTru: $55**

Holiday Greetings

Christmas tree w/"Season's
Greetings".
Foil, 2.75", Dated

QX3757 SRP: $6.00 **GBTru: $6**

Husband

Couple in ivory sleigh.
Cameo, 3.25", Dated
L Votruba

QX3739 SRP: $7.00 **GBTru: $10**

Jammie Pies

Little boy with caption.
Glass Ball, 2.87", Dated

QX2839 SRP: $4.75 **GBTru: $12**

HOLIDAY HEIRLOOM - 1ST
Holiday Heirloom
Limited Edition of 34,600: #2 & #3 are part of Club pcs.
Wreath w/ bell.
Crystal/Silver, 3.25", Dated
D Unruh

QX4857 SRP: $25.00 **GBTru: $36**

I Remember Santa

Santa with gifts.
Glass Ball, 2.88", Dated
J Lyle

QX2789 SRP: $4.75 **GBTru: $22**

Jogging Through The Snow

Jogging rabbit with radio.
Handcrafted, 3.00", Dated
P Dutkin

QX4577 SRP: $7.25 **GBTru: $18**

Joy Ride
Biking Santa with reindeer.
Handcrafted, 3.50", Dated
E Seale
QX4407 SRP: $11.50 **GBTru: $85**

Joyous Angels
Three angels beneath a star.
Handcrafted, 4.00"
E Seale
QX4657 SRP: $7.75 **GBTru: $24**

Let It Snow
Boy in winter clothes.
Handcrafted, 3.00"
QX4589 SRP: $6.50 **GBTru: $24**

Love Is Everywhere
Cardinals in wintry scene.
Glass Ball, 2.88", Dated
J Lyle
QX2787 SRP: $4.75 **GBTru: $22**

MINIATURE CRECHE - 3RD
Miniature Creche Brass
Miniature creche.
Brass, 3.50"
E Seale
QX4819 SRP: $9.00 **GBTru: $20**

Mother
"Mother is Another Word for Love".
Acrylic, 3.50", Dated
S Pike
QX3737 SRP: $6.50 **GBTru: $18**

Mother And Dad
Blue bell with Christmas tree.
Porcelain, 4.75", Dated
S Pike
QX4627 SRP: $7.00 **GBTru: $15**

MR. & MRS. CLAUS - 2ND
Home Cooking
Mr. & Mrs. Claus w/Cookies.
Handcrafted, 3.00", Dated
D Unruh
QX4837 SRP: $13.25 **GBTru: $45**

Nature's Decoration
Animals and birds.
Glass Ball, 2.88", Dated
L Votruba
QX2739 SRP: $4.75 **GBTru: $20**

New Home
Christmas home scene.
Mirrored Acrylic, 2.75", Dated
J Pattee
QX3767 SRP: $6.00 **GBTru: $22**

Niece
Frolicking lambs.
Glass Ball, 3.00", Dated
QX2759 SRP: $4.75 **GBTru: $8**

Night Before Christmas
Mouse sleeping in Santa's hat.
Handcrafted, 2.75"
K Crow
QX4517 SRP: $6.50 **GBTru: $28**

NORMAN ROCKWELL - 8TH
Christmas Dance, The

Girl dances w/dog, man plays bass.
Cameo, 3.25", Dated
D Palmiter

QX3707 SRP: $7.75 **GBTru: $12**

OLD-FASHIONED CHRISTMAS
Country Wreath

Country wreath.
Wood/Straw, 4.75"
M Pyda-Sevaik

QX4709 SRP: $5.75 **GBTru: $25**

OLD-FASHIONED CHRISTMAS
Nostalgic Rocker

Country style rocking horse.
Wood, 2.50"
L Sickman

QX4689 SRP: $6.50 **GBTru: $15**

Norman Rockwell's Christmas Scenes

A toast at Christmastime.
Glass Ball, 2.88", Dated
J Lyle

QX2827 SRP: $4.75 **GBTru: $10**

OLD-FASHIONED CHRISTMAS
Folk Art Santa

Folk Art Santa with tree.
Handcrafted, 4.00"
L Sickman

QX4749 SRP: $5.25 **GBTru: $34**

"Owliday" Wish

Owl on branch, eyechart.
Handcrafted, 2.00"
S Pike

QX4559 SRP: $6.50 **GBTru: $20**

North Pole Power & Light

Open House Promo
Elf changing bulb.
Handcrafted, 3.00", L
K Crow

627XPR9333 SRP: $2.95 **GBTru: $20**

OLD-FASHIONED CHRISTMAS
In A Nutshell

Open shell w/scenes, tree & fireplace.
Handcrafted, 1.50"
D Unruh

QX4697 SRP: $5.50 **GBTru: $22**

Paddington Bear

Bear chef.
Handcrafted, 3.00"
S Pike

QX4727 SRP: $5.50 **GBTru: $30**

NOSTALGIC HOUSES & SHOPS - 4TH
House On Main Street

Victorian house.
Handcrafted, 4.25", Dated
D Lee

QX4839 SRP: $14.00 **GBTru: $75**

OLD-FASHIONED CHRISTMAS
Little Whittler

Elf carving reindeer toy.
Handcrafted, 3.00"
P Dutkin

QX4699 SRP: $6.00 **GBTru: $28**

Peanuts

Snoopy/sled & Woodstock/skis.
Glass Ball, 2.87", Dated

QX2819 SRP: $4.75 **GBTru: $22**

PEANUTS **Snoopy & Woodstock** Snoopy & Woodstock with tree. Handcrafted, 2.50" B Siedler QX4729 SRP: $7.25 **GBTru: $44**	**Raccoon Biker** Raccoon on bicycle. Handcrafted, 3.00", Dated B Siedler QX4587 SRP: $7.00 **GBTru: $22**	**Santa At The Bat** Santa in baseball uniform w/bat. Handcrafted, 3.25", Dated B Siedler QX4579 SRP: $7.75 **GBTru: $18**
PORCELAIN BEAR - 5TH **Cinnamon** Bear with stocking. Porcelain, 2.12" QX4427 SRP: $7.75 **GBTru: $20**	**REINDEER CHAMPS - 2ND** **Dancer** Reindeer on ice skates. Handcrafted, 3.50", Dated B Siedler QX4809 SRP: $7.50 **GBTru: $42**	**Seasoned Greetings** Elf with pretzel. Handcrafted, 2.00" E Seale QX4549 SRP: $6.25 **GBTru: $18**
Pretty Kitty Cat hanging from rope in bell. Handcrafted, 3.50" K Crow QX4489 SRP: $11.00 **GBTru: $20**	**Reindoggy** Dog as reindeer. Handcrafted, 2.75" B Siedler QX4527 SRP: $5.75 **GBTru: $36**	**Sister** Heart design w/basket of poinsettias. Wood, 2.75", Dated L Sickman QX4747 SRP: $6.00 **GBTru: $12**
Promise Of Peace Dove with olive branch. Acrylic, 2.75" S Pike QX3749 SRP: $6.50 **GBTru: $15**	**ROCKING HORSE - 7TH** **White** White rocking horse. Handcrafted, 4.00", Dated L Sickman QX4829 SRP: $10.75 **GBTru: $55**	**Sleepy Santa** Santa sleeping in chair. Handcrafted, 2.75" K Crow QX4507 SRP: $6.25 **GBTru: $32**

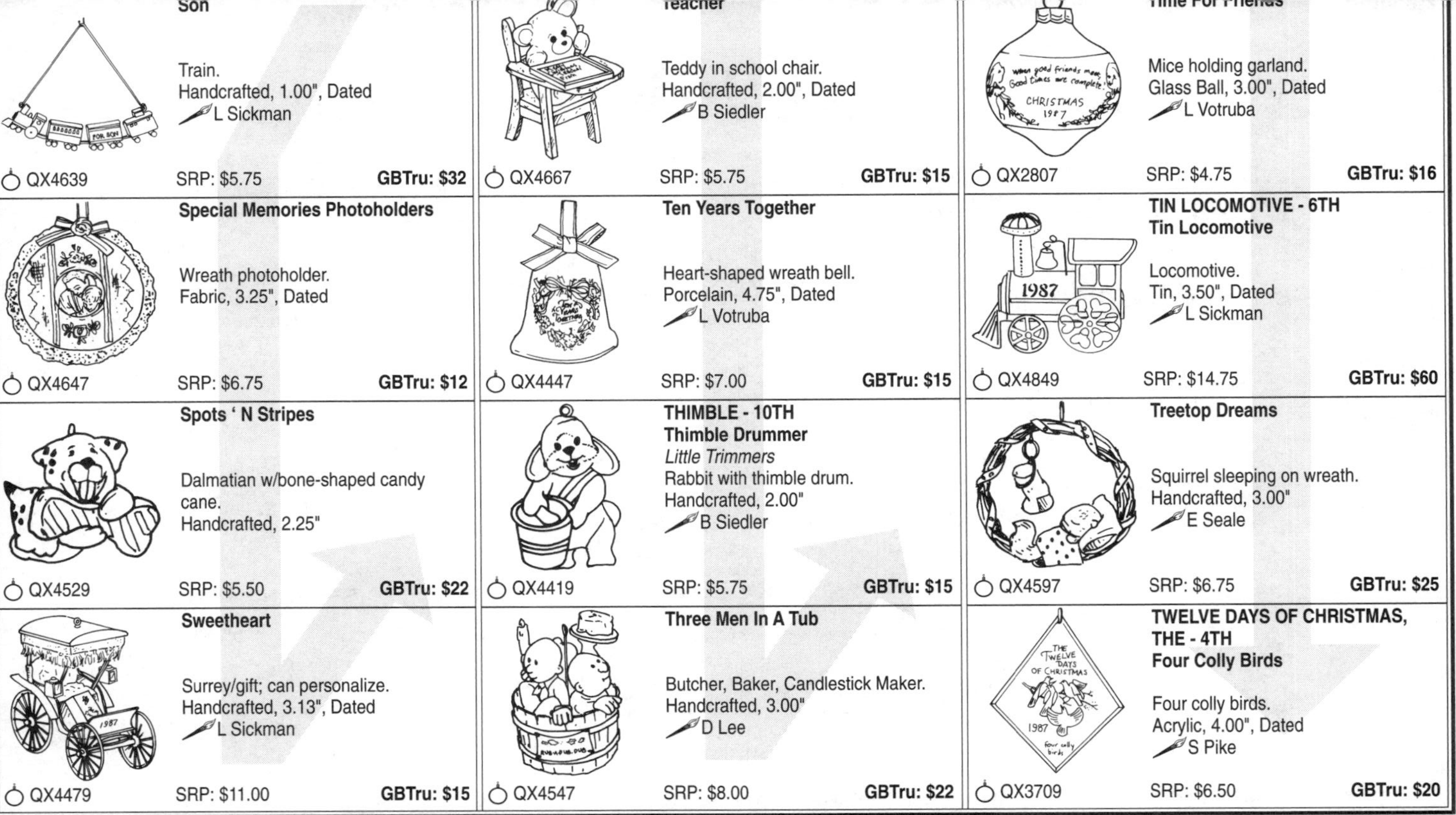

Son

Train.
Handcrafted, 1.00", Dated
L Sickman

QX4639 SRP: $5.75 **GBTru: $32**

Special Memories Photoholders

Wreath photoholder.
Fabric, 3.25", Dated

QX4647 SRP: $6.75 **GBTru: $12**

Spots ' N Stripes

Dalmatian w/bone-shaped candy cane.
Handcrafted, 2.25"

QX4529 SRP: $5.50 **GBTru: $22**

Sweetheart

Surrey/gift; can personalize.
Handcrafted, 3.13", Dated
L Sickman

QX4479 SRP: $11.00 **GBTru: $15**

Teacher

Teddy in school chair.
Handcrafted, 2.00", Dated
B Siedler

QX4667 SRP: $5.75 **GBTru: $15**

Ten Years Together

Heart-shaped wreath bell.
Porcelain, 4.75", Dated
L Votruba

QX4447 SRP: $7.00 **GBTru: $15**

THIMBLE - 10TH
Thimble Drummer
Little Trimmers
Rabbit with thimble drum.
Handcrafted, 2.00"
B Siedler

QX4419 SRP: $5.75 **GBTru: $15**

Three Men In A Tub

Butcher, Baker, Candlestick Maker.
Handcrafted, 3.00"
D Lee

QX4547 SRP: $8.00 **GBTru: $22**

Time For Friends

Mice holding garland.
Glass Ball, 3.00", Dated
L Votruba

QX2807 SRP: $4.75 **GBTru: $16**

TIN LOCOMOTIVE - 6TH
Tin Locomotive

Locomotive.
Tin, 3.50", Dated
L Sickman

QX4849 SRP: $14.75 **GBTru: $60**

Treetop Dreams

Squirrel sleeping on wreath.
Handcrafted, 3.00"
E Seale

QX4597 SRP: $6.75 **GBTru: $25**

TWELVE DAYS OF CHRISTMAS, THE - 4TH
Four Colly Birds

Four colly birds.
Acrylic, 4.00", Dated
S Pike

QX3709 SRP: $6.50 **GBTru: $20**

Twenty-Five Years Together

Plate: Cardinals on branch, stand.
Porcelain, 3.25", Dated

QX4439 SRP: $7.50 **GBTru: $15**

Warmth Of Friendship

Ornament-shape, gold foil caption.
Acrylic, 3.75", Dated

QX3759 SRP: $6.00 **GBTru: $10**

Wee Chimney Sweep

Mouse cleaning chimney.
Handcrafted, 3.00"
E Seale

QX4519 SRP: $6.25 **GBTru: $18**

WINDOWS OF THE WORLD - 3RD
Polynesia - Mele Kalikimaka

Polynesian child with ukulele.
Handcrafted, 3.00", Dated
D Lee

QX4827 SRP: $10.00 **GBTru: $20**

WOOD CHILDHOOD ORNAMENTS - 4TH
Wooden Horse

Wooden pull horse.
Wood, 2.25", Dated
B Siedler

QX4417 SRP: $7.50 **GBTru: $20**

Word Of Love

"LOVE" with red dangling heart.
Porcelain, 2.12", Dated

QX4477 SRP: $8.00 **GBTru: $18**

Wreath Of Memories

Club: Keepsake of Membership
Charter yr caption/repro HM designs/ club logo.
Handcrafted, 3.13", Dated
D Unruh

QXC5809 **GBTru: $40**

1988

Americana Drum

Drum.
Tin, 2.00", Dated
L Sickman

QX4881 SRP: $7.75 **GBTru: $25**

Angelic Minstrel

Club, Members Only, Limited Edition of 49,900
Angel with lyre/display stand.
Porcelain, 5.00"
D Lee

QX4084 SRP: $29.50 **GBTru: $40**

Arctic Tenor

Penguin in tuxedo with songbook.
Handcrafted, 1.75"
B Siedler

QX4721 SRP: $4.00 **GBTru: $15**

Baby Redbird

Baby cardinal (clip-on).
Handcrafted, 2.63"
R Chad

QX4101 SRP: $5.00 **GBTru: $12**

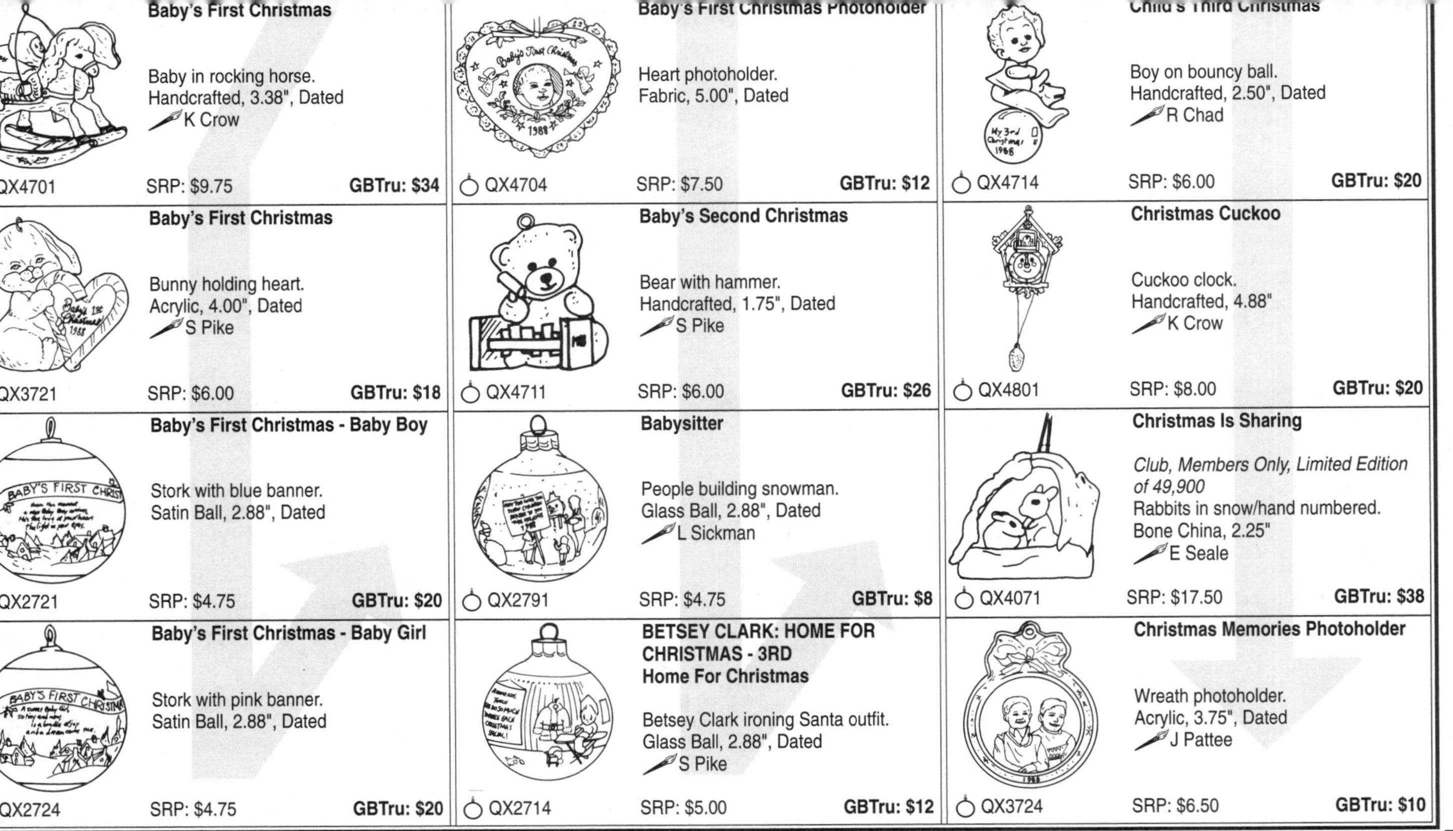

Baby's First Christmas

Baby in rocking horse.
Handcrafted, 3.38", Dated
K Crow

QX4701 SRP: $9.75 **GBTru: $34**

Baby's First Christmas Photoholder

Heart photoholder.
Fabric, 5.00", Dated

QX4704 SRP: $7.50 **GBTru: $12**

Child's Third Christmas

Boy on bouncy ball.
Handcrafted, 2.50", Dated
R Chad

QX4714 SRP: $6.00 **GBTru: $20**

Baby's First Christmas

Bunny holding heart.
Acrylic, 4.00", Dated
S Pike

QX3721 SRP: $6.00 **GBTru: $18**

Baby's Second Christmas

Bear with hammer.
Handcrafted, 1.75", Dated
S Pike

QX4711 SRP: $6.00 **GBTru: $26**

Christmas Cuckoo

Cuckoo clock.
Handcrafted, 4.88"
K Crow

QX4801 SRP: $8.00 **GBTru: $20**

Baby's First Christmas - Baby Boy

Stork with blue banner.
Satin Ball, 2.88", Dated

QX2721 SRP: $4.75 **GBTru: $20**

Babysitter

People building snowman.
Glass Ball, 2.88", Dated
L Sickman

QX2791 SRP: $4.75 **GBTru: $8**

Christmas Is Sharing

Club, Members Only, Limited Edition of 49,900
Rabbits in snow/hand numbered.
Bone China, 2.25"
E Seale

QX4071 SRP: $17.50 **GBTru: $38**

Baby's First Christmas - Baby Girl

Stork with pink banner.
Satin Ball, 2.88", Dated

QX2724 SRP: $4.75 **GBTru: $20**

BETSEY CLARK: HOME FOR CHRISTMAS - 3RD
Home For Christmas

Betsey Clark ironing Santa outfit.
Glass Ball, 2.88", Dated
S Pike

QX2714 SRP: $5.00 **GBTru: $12**

Christmas Memories Photoholder

Wreath photoholder.
Acrylic, 3.75", Dated
J Pattee

QX3724 SRP: $6.50 **GBTru: $10**

COLLECTOR'S PLATE - 2ND
Waiting For Santa

Kids on chair by fireplace, stand.
Porcelain, 3.25", Dated
L Votruba

QX4061 SRP: $8.00 **GBTru: $38**

Dad

Polar bear with socks.
Handcrafted, 2.75", Dated
B Siedler

QX4141 SRP: $7.00 **GBTru: $18**

Filled With Fudge

Mouse in cone with chocolate.
Handcrafted, 3.38"
E Seale

QX4191 SRP: $4.75 **GBTru: $28**

Cool Juggler

Snowman with snowballs.
Handcrafted, 4.75"
K Crow

QX4874 SRP: $6.50 **GBTru: $20**

Daughter

Gingerbread girl with tray.
Handcrafted, 3.63", Dated
J Pattee

QX4151 SRP: $5.75 **GBTru: $45**

First Christmas Together

Two bears in heart with gifts.
Handcrafted, 3.25", Dated
S Pike

QX4894 SRP: $9.00 **GBTru: $20**

CRAYOLA CRAYON
Teacher

Bunny w/crayon draws carrot.
Handcrafted, 2.25", Dated
S Pike

QX4171 SRP: $6.25 **GBTru: $16**

Feliz Navidad

Burro with hat and gift.
Handcrafted, 2.88"
D Unruh

QX4161 SRP: $6.75 **GBTru: $28**

First Christmas Together

"Our First Christmas Together".
Acrylic, 4.00", Dated
L Votruba

QX3731 SRP: $6.75 **GBTru: $20**

Cymbals Of Christmas

Angel on cloud with stars.
Handcrafted, 2.13"
D Lee

QX4111 SRP: $5.50 **GBTru: $24**

Fifty Years Together

"Fifty Years Together".
Acrylic, 3.13", Dated

QX3741 SRP: $6.75 **GBTru: $14**

First Christmas Together

Cardinals with evergreen.
Glass Ball, 2.88", Dated

QX2741 SRP: $4.75 **GBTru: $18**

Five Years Together

Five trees composed of hearts.
Glass Ball, 2.88", Dated
D McGehee

QX2744 SRP: $4.75 **GBTru: $16**

From Our Home To Yours

Snow people scenes.
Glass Ball, 2.88", Dated
J Pattee

QX2794 SRP: $4.75 **GBTru: $12**

FROSTY FRIENDS - 9TH
Frosty Friends

Eskimo wrapping pole with ribbon.
Handcrafted, 3.38", Dated
E Seale

QX4031 SRP: $8.75 **GBTru: $84**

Glowing Wreath

Ornament designs on wreath.
Brass, 3.50"
J Pattee

QX4921 SRP: $6.00 **GBTru: $10**

Go For The Gold

Santa in jogging suit with torch.
Handcrafted, 3.50", Dated
B Siedler

QX4174 SRP: $8.00 **GBTru: $18**

Godchild

Carolers.
Glass Ball, 2.88", Dated

QX2784 SRP: $4.75 **GBTru: $12**

Goin' Cross Country

Polar bear on skis.
Handcrafted, 3.25"
L Sickman

QX4764 SRP: $8.50 **GBTru: $20**

Gone Fishing

Santa with fishing pole.
Handcrafted, 2.50"
B Siedler

QX4794 SRP: $5.00 **GBTru: $15**

Granddaughter

Angel with star.
Glass Ball, 2.88", Dated
L Votruba

QX2774 SRP: $4.75 **GBTru: $18**

Grandmother

Tear drop shaped ball "Grandmother".
Glass Ball, 2.88", Dated

QX2764 SRP: $4.75 **GBTru: $14**

Grandparents

Tear drop shaped ball "Grandparents".
Glass Ball, 2.88", Dated
J Pattee

QX2771 SRP: $4.75 **GBTru: $16**

Grandson

Santa with snowflake.
Glass Ball, 2.88", Dated
L Votruba

QX2781 SRP: $4.75 **GBTru: $16**

Gratitude

Snowflake with tree.
Acrylic, 3.38", Dated
J Pattee

QX3754 SRP: $6.00 **GBTru: $10**

HERE COMES SANTA - 10TH
Kringle Koach

Santa in stagecoach.
Handcrafted, 3.25", Dated
K Crow

QX4001 SRP: $14.00 **GBTru: $30**

Hoe-Hoe-Hoe!

Santa with hoe.
Handcrafted, 2.38"
B Siedler

QX4221 SRP: $5.00 **GBTru: $10**

HOLIDAY HEIRLOOM - 2ND
Holiday Heirloom
Club, Members Only, Limited Edition of 34,600
Bell with angels.
Crystal/Sil Pltd, 3.50", Dated
D Unruh

QX4064 SRP: $25.00 **GBTru: $35**

Holiday Hero

Santa in football outfit.
Handcrafted, 2.63"
B Siedler

QX4231 SRP: $5.00 **GBTru: $20**

HOLIDAY WILDLIFE - 7TH & FINAL
Purple Finch

Finches on branch.
Wood, 2.50", Dated

QX3711 SRP: $7.75 **GBTru: $16**

Jingle Bell Clown

Clown with bell in reindeer sleigh.
Handcrafted, 3.00", Dated, ♪

Tune: Jingle Bells

QX4774 SRP: $15.00 **GBTru: $28**

Jolly Walrus

Walrus with wreath.
Handcrafted, 1.88"
A M Rogers

QX4731 SRP: $4.50 **GBTru: $20**

Kiss From Santa, A

Chocolate Santa with Hershey Kiss.
Handcrafted, 3.25"
D Unruh

QX4821 SRP: $4.50 **GBTru: $25**

Kiss The Claus

Santa chef.
Handcrafted, 2.75"
B Siedler

QX4861 SRP: $5.00 **GBTru: $15**

Kringle Moon

Quarter moon Santa.
Handcrafted, 3.13"
A M Rogers

QX4951 SRP: $5.50 **GBTru: $22**

Kringle Portrait

Santa face.
Handcrafted, 3.25"

QX4961 SRP: $7.50 **GBTru: $25**

Kringle Tree

Tree Santa.
Handcrafted, 3.38"

QX4954 SRP: $6.50 **GBTru: $45**

Love Grows

Blooming flowers.
Glass Ball, 2.88", Dated
L Votruba

QX2754 SRP: $4.75 **GBTru: $16**

Merry-Mint Unicorn

Unicorn on mint candy.
Porcelain, 3.75"
A M Rogers

QX4234 SRP: $8.50 **GBTru: $18**

Kringle's Toy Shop

Open House Promo
Elves make toys/children watch.
Handcrafted, 3.63"
E Seale

QLX7017 SRP: $24.50 **GBTru: $48**

Love Santa

Tennis player Santa.
Handcrafted, 2.50"
B Siedler

QX4864 SRP: $5.00 **GBTru: $12**

Midnight Snack

Mouse in doughnut.
Handcrafted, 2.50"
B Siedler

QX4104 SRP: $6.00 **GBTru: $18**

Little Jack Horner

Jack Horner with pie.
Handcrafted, 2.50"
B Siedler

QX4081 SRP: $8.00 **GBTru: $20**

MARY'S ANGELS - 1ST
Buttercup

Angel on cloud.
Handcrafted, 2.25"
R Chad

QX4074 SRP: $5.00 **GBTru: $25**

MINIATURE CRECHE - 4TH
Miniature Creche - Acrylic

Creche in star.
Acrylic, 2.75"
D Unruh

QX4034 SRP: $8.50 **GBTru: $15**

Love Fills The Heart

Heart with holly leaves.
Acrylic, 3.00"
L Votruba

QX3744 SRP: $6.00 **GBTru: $15**

MERRY MINIATURE
Seal Of Friendship
Club: Member Get Member
Seal balances ornament with Club logo.
Handcrafted, Dated
L Votruba

QXC5104 **GBTru: $55**

Mother

Heart design w/filigree ribbon.
Acrylic, 3.25", Dated

QX3751 SRP: $6.50 **GBTru: $15**

Mother And Dad

Candle with holly bell.
Porcelain, 3.00", Dated
J Lyle

QX4144 SRP: $8.00 **GBTru: $15**

MR. & MRS. CLAUS - 3RD
Shall We Dance

Mr. and Mrs. Claus dancing.
Handcrafted, 4.25", Dated
D Unruh

QX4011 SRP: $13.00 **GBTru: $45**

New Home

Santa with reindeer over house.
Acrylic, 2.50", Dated
L Votruba

QX3761 SRP: $6.00 **GBTru: $18**

Nick The Kick

Soccer player Santa.
Handcrafted, 2.25"
B Siedler

QX4224 SRP: $5.00 **GBTru: $15**

Noah's Ark

Pull toy replica of Noah's Ark.
Tin, 2.13"
L Sickman

QX4904 SRP: $8.50 **GBTru: $40**

NORMAN ROCKWELL - 9TH & FINAL
And To All A Good Night

Santa on chair.
Cameo, 3.25', Dated

QX3704 SRP: $7.75 **GBTru: $15**

Norman Rockwell: Christmas Scenes

Child saying a bedtime prayer.
Glass Ball, 2.88", Dated
J Lyle

QX2731 SRP: $4.75 **GBTru: $16**

NOSTALGIC HOUSES & SHOPS - 5TH
Hall Bro's Card Shop

Gift shop house.
Handcrafted, 4.25", Dated
D Lee

QX4014 SRP: $14.50 **GBTru: $40**

Old Fashioned Church

Old fashioned church.
Wood, 4.50"
L Sickman

QX4981 SRP: $4.00 **GBTru: $15**

Old Fashioned Schoolhouse

Old fashioned schoolhouse.
Wood, 3.00"
L Sickman

QX4971 SRP: $4.00 **GBTru: $18**

OREO Chocolate Sandwich Cookies

OREO cookie.
Handcrafted, 1.88"
D Unruh

QX4814 SRP: $4.00 **GBTru: $12**

Our Clubhouse

Club: Keepsake of Membership
Mouse in clubhouse/club logo.
Handcrafted, 2.50", Dated
B Siedler

QXC5804 **GBTru: $25**

Par For Santa

Golfer Santa.
Handcrafted, 2.63"
B Siedler

QX4791 SRP: $5.00 **GBTru: $10**

Peek-A-Boo Kitties

Kitten in basket.
Handcrafted, 5.00"
K Crow

QX4871 SRP: $7.50 **GBTru: $15**

REINDEER CHAMPS - 3RD
Prancer

Reindeer as basketball player.
Handcrafted, 3.50", Dated
B Siedler

QX4051 SRP: $7.50 **GBTru: $28**

Party Line

Two raccoons with Campbell cans.
Handcrafted, 1.75"
S Pike

QX4761 SRP: $8.75 **GBTru: $24**

Polar Bowler

Bowling Santa.
Handcrafted, 2.25"
B Siedler

QX4784 SRP: $5.00 **GBTru: $10**

ROCKING HORSE - 8TH
Dappled Gray

Rocking horse (grey with white).
Handcrafted, 4.00", Dated
L Sickman

QX4024 SRP: $10.75 **GBTru: $42**

Peanuts

Snoopy as Santa on sleigh.
Glass Ball, 2.88", Dated

QX2801 SRP: $4.75 **GBTru: $30**

PORCELAIN BEAR - 6TH
Cinnamon

Bear with heart.
Porcelain, 2.25"
S Pike

QX4044 SRP: $8.00 **GBTru: $20**

Sailing! Sailing!

Pull toy replica of sailboat.
Tin, 2.88"
L Sickman

QX4911 SRP: $8.50 **GBTru: $20**

PEANUTS
Snoopy & Woodstock

Snoopy and Woodstock in stocking.
Handcrafted, 2.38"
D Unruh

QX4741 SRP: $6.00 **GBTru: $30**

Purrfect Snuggle

Bear with kitten.
Handcrafted, 2.00"
A M Rogers

QX4744 SRP: $6.25 **GBTru: $16**

Santa Flamingo

Flamingo with Santa cap.
Handcrafted, 5.50"
M Pyda-Sevaik

QX4834 SRP: $4.75 **GBTru: $22**

Shiny Sleigh

Sleigh.
Brass, 1.38"
J Pattee

QX4924 SRP: $5.75 **GBTru: $10**

Sister

Girl with tree bell.
Porcelain, 3.00", Dated
L Votruba

QX4994 SRP: $8.00 **GBTru: $15**

Sleighful Of Dreams

Club: Keepsake of Membership
Sleigh with gift/club logo.
Handcrafted, 2.13", Dated
L Sickman

QXC5801 SRP: $8.00 **GBTru: $40**

Slipper Spaniel

Spaniel in slipper.
Handcrafted, 3.00"
K Crow

QX4724 SRP: $4.25 **GBTru: $15**

Soft Landing

Santa with pillow on rear.
Handcrafted, 3.00"
R Chad

QX4751 SRP: $7.00 **GBTru: $15**

Son

Gingerbread boy with tray.
Handcrafted, 3.63", Dated
J Pattee

QX4154 SRP: $5.75 **GBTru: $35**

Sparkling Tree

Tree with ornaments.
Brass, 3.38"
J Pattee

QX4931 SRP: $6.00 **GBTru: $12**

Spirit Of Christmas

Children holding hands.
Glass Ball, 2.88", Dated
J Lyle

QX2761 SRP: $4.75 **GBTru: $15**

Squeaky Clean

Mouse in bath tub.
Handcrafted, 2.38"
S Pike

QX4754 SRP: $6.75 **GBTru: $15**

Sweet Star

Squirrel on star cookie/clip-on.
Handcrafted, 1.75"
E Seale

QX4184 SRP: $5.00 **GBTru: $25**

Sweetheart

Swan sleigh.
Handcrafted, 3.38", Dated
D Unruh

QX4901 SRP: $9.75 **GBTru: $15**

Teeny Taster

Chipmunk on chocolate spoon.
Handcrafted, 4.38"
E Seale

QX4181 SRP: $4.75 **GBTru: $25**

Ten Years Together

Two deer on a hill.
Glass Ball, 2.88", Dated

QX2751 SRP: $4.75 **GBTru: $14**

THIMBLE - 11TH
Thimble Snowman
Little Trimmers
Snowman with thimble hat.
Handcrafted, 2.38"
B Siedler

QX4054 SRP: $5.75 **GBTru: $18**

TIN LOCOMOTIVE - 7TH
Tin Locomotive

Locomotive.
Tin, 3.00", Dated
L Sickman

QX4004 SRP: $14.75 **GBTru: $48**

Town Crier, The

Rabbit with bell in colonial outfit.
Handcrafted, 2.25"
E Seale

QX4734 SRP: $5.50 **GBTru: $20**

Travels With Santa

Mr. & Mrs. Claus in trailer.
Handcrafted, 2.00"
D Lee

QX4771 SRP: $10.00 **GBTru: $35**

TWELVE DAYS OF CHRISTMAS, THE - 5TH
Five Golden Rings

Five rings.
Acrylic, 3.00", Dated
S Pike

QX3714 SRP: $6.50 **GBTru: $15**

Twenty-Five Years Together

"25 Years Together".
Acrylic, 3.13", Dated
J Pattee

QX3734 SRP: $6.75 **GBTru: $14**

Twirls: Christmas Cardinal

Cardinal in tree.
Handcrafted, 2.88"
A M Rogers

QX4941 SRP: $4.75 **GBTru: $12**

Twirls: Loving Bear

Bear in wreath.
Handcrafted, 3.25"
A M Rogers

QX4934 SRP: $4.75 **GBTru: $18**

Twirls: Starry Angel

Angel in star.
Handcrafted, 2.88"
A M Rogers

QX4944 SRP: $4.75 **GBTru: $16**

Uncle Sam Nutcracker

Folk art Uncle Sam Nutcracker.
Handcrafted, 5.25", Dated
D Lee

QX4884 SRP: $7.00 **GBTru: $25**

Very Strawbeary

Bear with snowcone.
Handcrafted, 2.25"
P Dutkin

QX4091 SRP: $4.75 **GBTru: $15**

WINDOWS OF THE WORLD - 4TH
France - Joyeux Noel

Boy with dog on window.
Handcrafted, 3.50", Dated
D Lee

QX4021 SRP: $10.00 **GBTru: $24**

Year To Remember

"1988".
Ceramic, 3.75", Dated

QX4164 SRP: $7.00 **GBTru: $12**

BABY CELEBRATIONS
Baby's First Christmas 1989 - Boy
(See: QX2725)
Santa at cradle, spec box, ltd. dist
Gold Crown stores.
Satin Ball, 2.88", Dated

BBY1453 SRP: $4.75 **GBTru: $10**

Winter Fun

Three kids on toboggan.
Handcrafted, 2.00"
R Chad

QX4781 SRP: $8.50 **GBTru: $15**

1989

BABY CELEBRATIONS
Baby's First Christmas 1989 - Girl
(See: QX2722)
Santa at cradle, spec box, ltd. dist
Gold Crown stores.
Satin Ball, 2.88", Dated

BBY1553 SRP: $4.75 **GBTru: $10**

Wonderful Santacycle, The

Santa rides horse atop wheels.
Handcrafted, 4.25"
E Seale

QX4114 SRP: $22.50 **GBTru: $40**

BABY CELEBRATIONS
Baby's Christening 1989

Teddy bear, spec. box, ltd dist. Gold Crown stores.
Acrylic, 3.25", Dated

BBY1325 SRP: $7.00 **GBTru: $14**

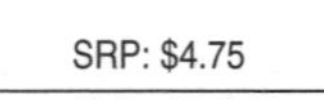

Baby Partridge

Baby partridge on tree.
Handcrafted, 2.75"
J Francis

QX4525 SRP: $6.75 **GBTru: $12**

WOOD CHILDHOOD ORNAMENTS - 5TH
Wooden Airplane

Wooden plane.
Wood, 1.63", Dated
P Dutkin

QX4041 SRP: $7.50 **GBTru: $20**

BABY CELEBRATIONS
Baby's First Birthday 1989

Clown Bear, spec. box, w/stand, ltd dist. Gold Crown stores.
Acrylic, 4.50", Dated

BBY1729 SRP: $5.50 **GBTru: $20**

Baby's First Christmas

Deer with stocking.
Acrylic, 3.44", Dated
J Francis

QX3815 SRP: $6.75 **GBTru: $12**

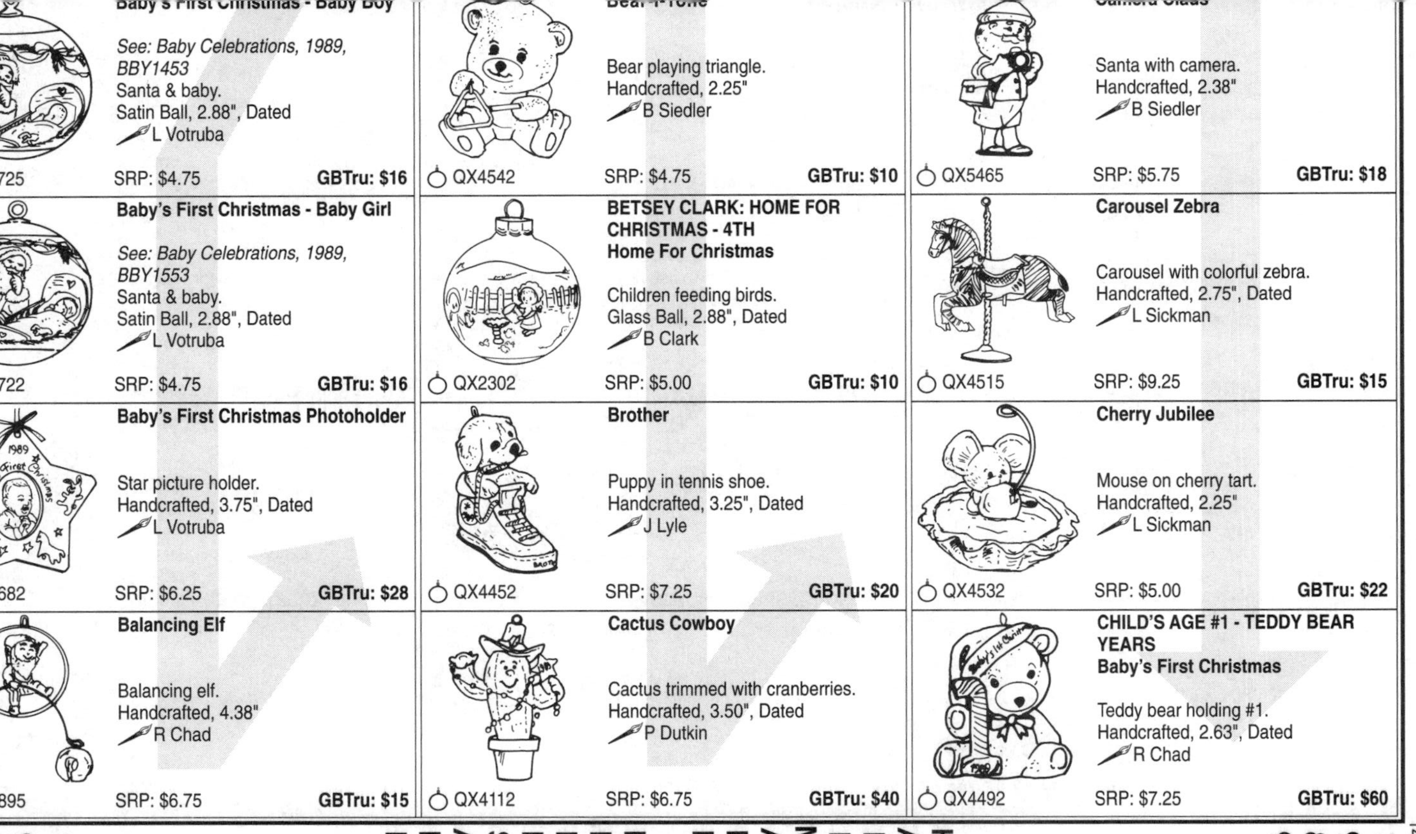

Baby's First Christmas - Baby Boy

See: Baby Celebrations, 1989, BBY1453
Santa & baby.
Satin Ball, 2.88", Dated
L Votruba

QX2725 SRP: $4.75 **GBTru: $16**

Baby's First Christmas - Baby Girl

See: Baby Celebrations, 1989, BBY1553
Santa & baby.
Satin Ball, 2.88", Dated
L Votruba

QX2722 SRP: $4.75 **GBTru: $16**

Baby's First Christmas Photoholder

Star picture holder.
Handcrafted, 3.75", Dated
L Votruba

QX4682 SRP: $6.25 **GBTru: $28**

Balancing Elf

Balancing elf.
Handcrafted, 4.38"
R Chad

QX4895 SRP: $6.75 **GBTru: $15**

Bear-I-Tone

Bear playing triangle.
Handcrafted, 2.25"
B Siedler

QX4542 SRP: $4.75 **GBTru: $10**

BETSEY CLARK: HOME FOR CHRISTMAS - 4TH
Home For Christmas

Children feeding birds.
Glass Ball, 2.88", Dated
B Clark

QX2302 SRP: $5.00 **GBTru: $10**

Brother

Puppy in tennis shoe.
Handcrafted, 3.25", Dated
J Lyle

QX4452 SRP: $7.25 **GBTru: $20**

Cactus Cowboy

Cactus trimmed with cranberries.
Handcrafted, 3.50", Dated
P Dutkin

QX4112 SRP: $6.75 **GBTru: $40**

Camera Claus

Santa with camera.
Handcrafted, 2.38"
B Siedler

QX5465 SRP: $5.75 **GBTru: $18**

Carousel Zebra

Carousel with colorful zebra.
Handcrafted, 2.75", Dated
L Sickman

QX4515 SRP: $9.25 **GBTru: $15**

Cherry Jubilee

Mouse on cherry tart.
Handcrafted, 2.25"
L Sickman

QX4532 SRP: $5.00 **GBTru: $22**

CHILD'S AGE #1 - TEDDY BEAR YEARS
Baby's First Christmas

Teddy bear holding #1.
Handcrafted, 2.63", Dated
R Chad

QX4492 SRP: $7.25 **GBTru: $60**

CHILD'S AGE #2 - TEDDY BEAR YEARS
Baby's Second Christmas

Teddy bear holding #2.
Handcrafted, 2.81", Dated
J Francis

QX4495 SRP: $6.75 **GBTru: $20**

CHILD'S AGE #3 - TEDDY BEAR YEARS
Child's Third Christmas

Teddy bear holding #3.
Handcrafted, 2.50", Dated
J Francis

QX4695 SRP: $6.75 **GBTru: $16**

CHILD'S AGE #4 - TEDDY BEAR YEARS
Child's Fourth Christmas

Teddy bear holding #4.
Handcrafted, 3.00", Dated
J Francis

QX5432 SRP: $6.75 **GBTru: $15**

CHILD'S AGE #5 - TEDDY BEAR YEARS
Child's Fifth Christmas

Teddy bear holding #5.
Handcrafted, 2.38", Dated
D Rhodus

QX5435 SRP: $6.75 **GBTru: $15**

CHRISTMAS CAROUSEL HORSE
Carousel Display Stand
Gold Crown Reach Program -
** w/any HM purchase*
Holds 4 horses/ribboned brass pole.
Hndcr/Brass, 4.50", Dated
J Lee

629XPR9723 SRP: $1.00* **GBTru: $10**

CHRISTMAS CAROUSEL HORSE - 1ST
Snow
Gold Crown Reach Program -
** w/any HM purchase*
White and gold prancing steed.
Hndcr/Brass, 3.19", Dated
J Lee

629XPR9719 SRP: $3.95* **GBTru: $30**

CHRISTMAS CAROUSEL HORSE - 2ND
Holly
Gold Crown Reach Program -
** w/any HM purchase*
Gray prancing steed.
Hndcr/Brass, 3.19", Dated
J Lee

629XPR9722 SRP: $3.95* **GBTru: $15**

CHRISTMAS CAROUSEL HORSE - 3RD
Star
Gold Crown Reach Program -
** w/any HM purchase*
Dark brown/white sock pranc'g steed.
Hndcr/Brass, 3.19", Dated
J Lee

629XPR9720 SRP: $3.95* **GBTru: $15**

CHRISTMAS CAROUSEL HORSE - 4TH
Ginger
Gold Crown Reach Program -
** w/any HM purchase*
Palomino prancing steed.
Hndcr/Brass, 3.19', Dated
J Lee

629XPR9721 SRP: $3.95* **GBTru: $15**

Christmas Is Peaceful

Club, Members Only,
Limited Edition of 49,900
Owls on branch/hand numbered.
Bone China, 2.50"
E Seale

QXC4512 SRP: $18.50 **GBTru: $35**

CHRISTMAS KITTY - 1ST
Christmas Kitty

Miss Kitty with basket of poinsettias.
Porcelain, 3.19"
A M Rogers

QX5445 SRP: $14.75 **GBTru: $25**

Claus Construction

Santa in shiny hard hat.
Handcrafted, 4.75"
E Seale

QX4885 SRP: $7.75 **GBTru: $18**

Collect A Dream

Club: Keepsake of Membership
Mouse naps in leaf hammock/club logo.
Handcrafted, 1.75", Dated
S Pike

QXC4285 SRP: $9.00 **GBTru: $38**

COLLECTOR'S PLATE - 3RD
Morning Of Wonder

Children with Christmas tree, stand.
Porcelain, 3.25", Dated
L Votruba

QX4612 SRP: $8.25 **GBTru: $15**

Cool Swing

Penguin on ice cube.
Hndcr/Acryl, 3.50"
K Crow

QX4875 SRP: $6.25 **GBTru: $36**

Country Cat

Cat in pull toy cart.
Handcrafted, 2.25"
M Pyda-Sevaik

QX4672 SRP: $6.25 **GBTru: $18**

Cranberry Bunny

Bunny with cranberries.
Handcrafted, 2.63"
A M Rogers

QX4262 SRP: $5.75 **GBTru: $14**

CRAYOLA CRAYON - 1ST
Bright Christmas Journey

Teddy on crayon raft.
Handcrafted, 3.00", Dated
L Sickman

QX4352 SRP: $8.75 **GBTru: $64**

Dad

Polar bear with shorts.
Handcrafted, 2.88", Dated

QX4412 SRP: $7.25 **GBTru: $12**

Daughter

Girl with hat box.
Handcrafted, 3.00", Dated
L Sickman

QX4432 SRP: $6.25 **GBTru: $9**

Deer Disguise

Children peeking out of deer costume.
Handcrafted, 1.75"
B Siedler

QX4265 SRP: $5.75 **GBTru: $18**

Feliz Navidad

Colorful pinata.
Handcrafted, 2.00"
M Pyda-Sevaik

QX4392 SRP: $6.75 **GBTru: $22**

Festive Angel

Angel.
Brass, 3.94"

QX4635 SRP: $6.75 **GBTru: $18**

Festive Year

Stained glass "1988".
Acrylic, 2.81", Dated
L Votruba

QX3842 SRP: $7.75 **GBTru: $14**

Fifty Years Together Photoholder

Fifty Years Together photoholder.
Porcelain, 3.75", Dated
A M Rogers

QX4862 SRP: $8.75 **GBTru: $10**

First Christmas Together

Bears sitting on log.
Glass Ball, 2.88", Dated

QX2732 SRP: $4.75 **GBTru: $12**

From Our Home To Yours

Mailbox with gifts.
Acrylic, 3.50", Dated

QX3845 SRP: $6.25 **GBTru: $10**

First Christmas, The

Nativity scene.
Cameo, 3.18"

QX5475 SRP: $7.75 **GBTru: $10**

Five Years Together

Swans in lake.
Glass Ball, 2.88", Dated

QX2735 SRP: $4.75 **GBTru: $10**

FROSTY FRIENDS - 10TH
Frosty Friends

Eskimo with sled on ice.
Hndcr/Acryl, 2.50", Dated
E Seale

QX4572 SRP: $9.25 **GBTru: $30**

First Christmas Together

Chipmunks on swing.
Handcrafted, 3.50", Dated
A M Rogers

QX4852 SRP: $9.75 **GBTru: $15**

Forty Years Together Photoholder

Forty Years Together photoholder.
Porcelain, 3.75", Dated
A M Rogers

QX5452 SRP: $8.75 **GBTru: $10**

Gentle Fawn

Deer with red bow.
Handcrafted, 2.94"
A M Rogers

QX5485 SRP: $7.75 **GBTru: $15**

First Christmas Together

Deer in snowy scene.
Acrylic, 2.44", Dated
D Rhodus

QX3832 SRP: $6.75 **GBTru: $15**

Friendship Time

Mice in teacup.
Handcrafted, 2.50", Dated

QX4132 SRP: $9.75 **GBTru: $25**

George Washington Bicentennial

Bicentennial George Washington.
Acrylic, 3.52", Dated

QX3862 SRP: $6.25 **GBTru: $12**

GIFT BRINGERS, THE - 1ST
St. Nicholas

Santa on horse bringing gifts.
Glass Ball, 3.00", Dated
L Votruba

QX2795 SRP: $5.00 **GBTru: $18**

Godchild

Angel holding star.
Acrylic, 2.75", Dated
J Francis

QX3112 SRP: $6.25 **GBTru: $7**

Goin' South

Traveler mouse takes Redbird Express.
Handcrafted, 2.00"
K Crow

QX4105 SRP: $4.25 **GBTru: $15**

Graceful Swan

Swan.
Brass, 2.25"

QX4642 SRP: $6.75 **GBTru: $18**

Granddaughter

Skating animals/Bunny etches year.
Glass Ball, 2.88", Dated

QX2782 SRP: $4.75 **GBTru: $12**

Granddaughter's First Christmas

Kitten in stocking.
Acrylic, 4.25", Dated
J Francis

QX3822 SRP: $6.75 **GBTru: $10**

Grandmother

Teardrop ball w/poinsettia garland.
Glass Ball, 2.88", Dated
J Lyle

QX2775 SRP: $4.75 **GBTru: $10**

Grandparents

Winter scene on peach glass ball.
Glass Ball, 2.88", Dated
J Lyle

QX2772 SRP: $4.75 **GBTru: $10**

Grandson

Santa climbs into chimney w/gifts.
Glass Ball, 2.88", Dated

QX2785 SRP: $4.75 **GBTru: $10**

Grandson's First Christmas

Puppy in stocking.
Acrylic, 4.25", Dated
J Francis

QX3825 SRP: $6.75 **GBTru: $12**

Gratitude

Holly tied w/ribbon, brass bezel.
Acrylic, 2.75", Dated
L Votruba

QX3852 SRP: $16.75 **GBTru: $10**

Gym Dandy

Santa in gym clothes.
Handcrafted, 2.50"
B Siedler

QX4185 SRP: $5.75 **GBTru: $10**

Hang In There

Mouse hanging from Santa hat.
Handcrafted, 3.00"
K Crow

QX4305 SRP: $5.25 **GBTru: $26**

HARK! IT'S HERALD - 1ST
Hark! It's Herald

Herald, the elf, plays chimes.
Handcrafted, 2.00", Dated
K Crow

QX4555 SRP: $6.75 **GBTru: $30**

HERE COMES SANTA - 11TH
Christmas Caboose

Santa in caboose.
Handcrafted, 3.25", Dated
K Crow

QX4585 SRP: $14.75 **GBTru: $45**

Here's The Pitch

Santa in baseball outfit.
Handcrafted, 2.50"
B Siedler

QX5455 SRP: $5.75 **GBTru: $18**

HOLIDAY HEIRLOOM - 3RD & FINAL
Holiday Heirloom
Club, Members Only, Limited Edition of 34,600
Bell with toys/display stand.
Lead Crystal, 2.50", Dated
D Unruh

QXC4605 SRP: $25.00 **GBTru: $35**

Hoppy Holidays

Bunny in shopping cart.
Handcrafted, 2.75", Dated
B Siedler

QX4692 SRP: $7.75 **GBTru: $15**

Horse Weathervane

Horse.
Handcrafted, 3.00"
L Sickman

QX4632 SRP: $5.75 **GBTru: $15**

Joyful Trio

Singing Angels hold banner.
Handcrafted, 2.25"
J Francis

QX4372 SRP: $9.75 **GBTru: $12**

Kristy Claus

Kristy Claus on skates.
Handcrafted, 3.00"
B Siedler

QX4245 SRP: $5.75 **GBTru: $12**

Language Of Love

Heart w/poinsettia, gold foil caption.
Acrylic, 3.00", Dated

QX3835 SRP: $6.25 **GBTru: $10**

Let's Play

Dog in doghouse.
Handcrafted, 2.75", Dated
K Crow

QX4882 SRP: $7.25 **GBTru: $25**

Mail Call

Raccoon delivering mail.
Handcrafted, 3.00"
E Seale

QX4522 SRP: $8.75 **GBTru: $15**

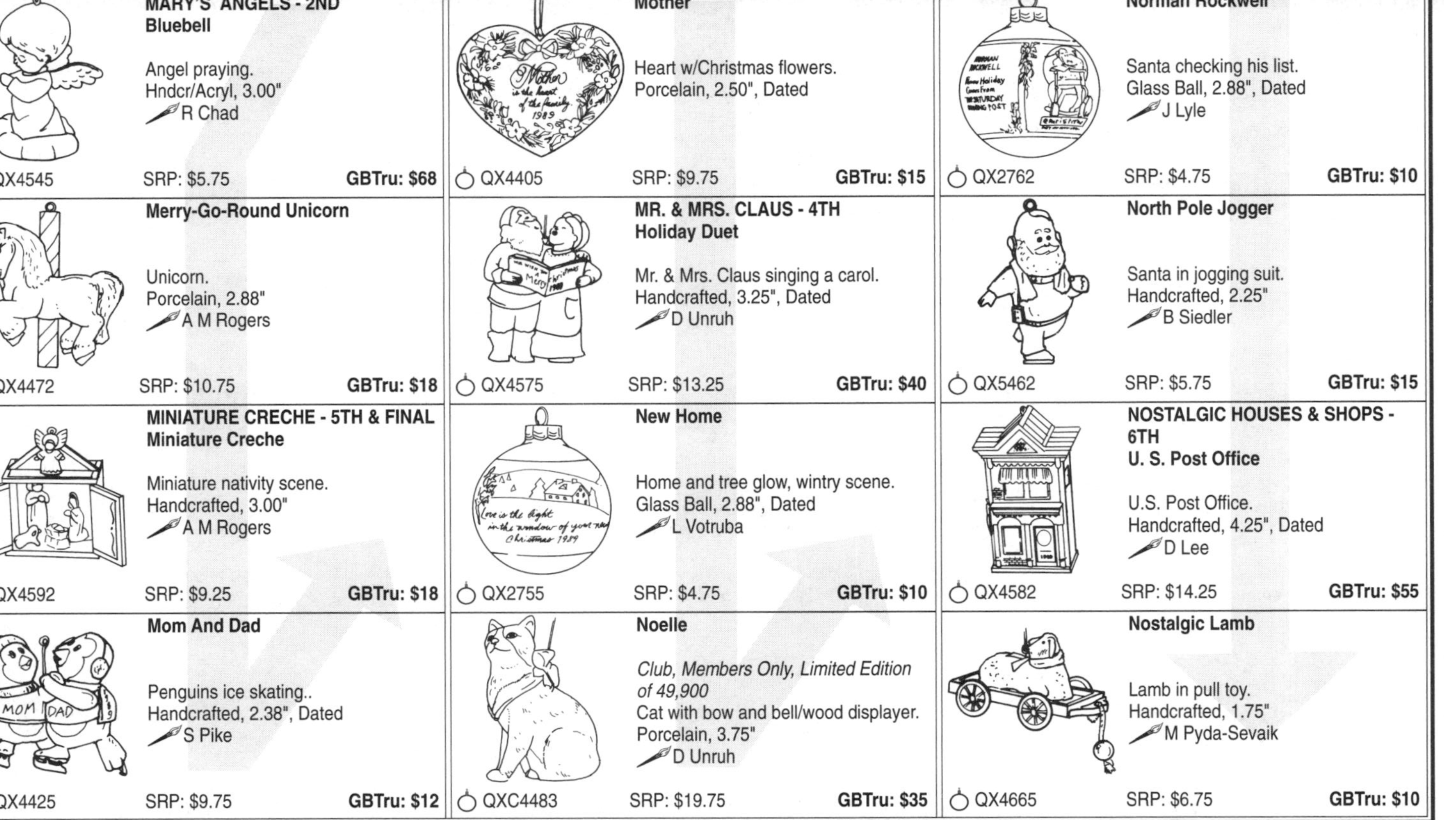

MARY'S ANGELS - 2ND
Bluebell

Angel praying.
Hndcr/Acryl, 3.00"
R Chad

QX4545 SRP: $5.75 **GBTru: $68**

Merry-Go-Round Unicorn

Unicorn.
Porcelain, 2.88"
A M Rogers

QX4472 SRP: $10.75 **GBTru: $18**

MINIATURE CRECHE - 5TH & FINAL
Miniature Creche

Miniature nativity scene.
Handcrafted, 3.00"
A M Rogers

QX4592 SRP: $9.25 **GBTru: $18**

Mom And Dad

Penguins ice skating..
Handcrafted, 2.38", Dated
S Pike

QX4425 SRP: $9.75 **GBTru: $12**

Mother

Heart w/Christmas flowers.
Porcelain, 2.50", Dated

QX4405 SRP: $9.75 **GBTru: $15**

MR. & MRS. CLAUS - 4TH
Holiday Duet

Mr. & Mrs. Claus singing a carol.
Handcrafted, 3.25", Dated
D Unruh

QX4575 SRP: $13.25 **GBTru: $40**

New Home

Home and tree glow, wintry scene.
Glass Ball, 2.88", Dated
L Votruba

QX2755 SRP: $4.75 **GBTru: $10**

Noelle

Club, Members Only, Limited Edition of 49,900
Cat with bow and bell/wood displayer.
Porcelain, 3.75"
D Unruh

QXC4483 SRP: $19.75 **GBTru: $35**

Norman Rockwell

Santa checking his list.
Glass Ball, 2.88", Dated
J Lyle

QX2762 SRP: $4.75 **GBTru: $10**

North Pole Jogger

Santa in jogging suit.
Handcrafted, 2.25"
B Siedler

QX5462 SRP: $5.75 **GBTru: $15**

NOSTALGIC HOUSES & SHOPS - 6TH
U. S. Post Office

U.S. Post Office.
Handcrafted, 4.25", Dated
D Lee

QX4582 SRP: $14.25 **GBTru: $55**

Nostalgic Lamb

Lamb in pull toy.
Handcrafted, 1.75"
M Pyda-Sevaik

QX4665 SRP: $6.75 **GBTru: $10**

NUTSHELL TRIO
Nutshell Dreams

Bedroom in nutshell.
Handcrafted, 1.50"
R Chad

QX4655 SRP: $5.75 **GBTru: $14**

On The Links

Santa in golf outfit.
Handcrafted, 2.50"
B Siedler

QX4192 SRP: $5.75 **GBTru: $15**

PEANUTS
Snoopy & Woodstock

Snoopy & Woodstock in top hats.
Handcrafted, 3.00"
D Rhodus

QX4332 SRP: $6.75 **GBTru: $28**

NUTSHELL TRIO
Nutshell Holiday

Fireplace in nutshell.
Handcrafted, 1.50"
A M Rogers

QX4652 SRP: $5.75 **GBTru: $18**

Ornament Express, The

Set/3, engine,coal car, caboose.
Handcrafted, 1.75"-2.25", Dated
L Sickman

QX5805 SRP: $22.00 **GBTru: $35**

Peanuts - A Charlie Brown Christmas

Peanuts gang by tree.
Glass Ball, 2.88", Dated

QX2765 SRP: $4.75 **GBTru: $45**

NUTSHELL TRIO
Nutshell Workshop

Workshop in nutshell.
Handcrafted, 1.50"
R Chad

QX4872 SRP: $5.75 **GBTru: $16**

Owliday Greetings

Owl with banner.
Handcrafted, 1.50"
S Pike

QX4365 SRP: $4.00 **GBTru: $15**

Peppermint Clown

Clown.
Handcrafted, 5.00"
P Dutkin

QX4505 SRP: $24.75 **GBTru: $28**

Old World Gnome

Gnome Santa.
Handcrafted, 3.25"

QX4345 SRP: $7.75 **GBTru: $18**

Paddington Bear

Paddington bear with drum.
Handcrafted, 4.25"
J Francis

QX4292 SRP: $5.75 **GBTru: $18**

Playful Angel

Angel on swing.
Handcrafted, 3.13"
D Lee

QX4535 SRP: $6.75 **GBTru: $18**

PORCELAIN BEAR - 7TH
Cinnamon

Bear with bag of candy.
Porcelain, 2.00"
S Pike

QX4615 SRP: $8.75 **GBTru: $16**

Rooster Weathervane

Rooster.
Handcrafted, 3.50"
L Sickman

QX4675 SRP: $5.75 **GBTru: $12**

Son

Boy with gift box.
Handcrafted, 3.00", Dated
L Sickman

QX4445 SRP: $6.25 **GBTru: $10**

REINDEER CHAMPS - 4TH
Vixen

Reindeer in tennis outfit.
Handcrafted, 3.25", Dated
B Siedler

QX4562 SRP: $7.75 **GBTru: $18**

Sea Santa

Santa in scuba gear.
Handcrafted, 2.50"
B Siedler

QX4152 SRP: $5.75 **GBTru: $15**

Sparkling Snowflake

Snowflake.
Brass, 3.38", Dated
J Lyle

QX5472 SRP: $7.75 **GBTru: $14**

ROCKING HORSE - 9TH
Bay

Rocking horse.
Handcrafted, 4.00", Dated
L Sickman

QX4622 SRP: $10.75 **GBTru: $35**

Sister

American folk art heart design.
Glass Ball, 2.88", Dated

QX2792 SRP: $4.75 **GBTru: $10**

Special Delivery

Seal in box.
Handcrafted, 2.00"
A M Rogers

QX4325 SRP: $5.25 **GBTru: $12**

Rodney Reindeer

Rodney Reindeer.
Handcrafted, 5.00", Dated
B Siedler

QX4072 SRP: $6.75 **GBTru: $16**

Snowplow Santa

Santa on skis.
Handcrafted, 2.31"
B Siedler

QX4205 SRP: $5.75 **GBTru: $15**

Spencer Sparrow, Esq.

Sparrow on cracker.
Handcrafted, 1.75"
S Pike

QX4312 SRP: $6.75 **GBTru: $15**

Stocking Kitten

Kitten in stocking.
Handcrafted, 2.75"
S Pike

QX4565 SRP: $6.75 **GBTru: $12**

Ten Years Together

Couple in horse-drawn sleigh.
Glass Ball, 2.88", Dated
J Lyle

QX2742 SRP: $4.75 **GBTru: $10**

TWELVE DAYS OF CHRISTMAS, THE - 6TH
Six Geese A-Laying

Heart with geese.
Acrylic, 3.00", Dated

QX3812 SRP: $6.75 **GBTru: $20**

Sweet Memories Pictureholder

Peppermint candy picture holder.
Handcrafted, 3.06", Dated

QX4385 SRP: $6.75 **GBTru: $10**

THIMBLE - 12TH & FINAL
Thimble Puppy
Little Trimmers
Puppy in thimble.
Handcrafted, 1.75"
A M Rogers

QX4552 SRP: $5.75 **GBTru: $12**

Twenty-Five Years Together Photoholder

"25 Years Together" picture frame.
Porcelain, 3.75", Dated
A M Rogers

QX4855 SRP: $8.75 **GBTru: $10**

Sweetheart

Bicycle built for two.
Handcrafted, 4.63", Dated
L Sickman

QX4865 SRP: $9.75 **GBTru: $22**

TIN LOCOMOTIVE - 8TH & FINAL
Tin Locomotive

Tin locomotive.
Tin, 3.19", Dated
L Sickman

QX4602 SRP: $14.75 **GBTru: $55**

Visit From Santa

Club: Keepsake of Membership
Santa w/bag & sled, can personalize.
Handcrafted, 4.00", Dated
K Crow

QXC5802 **GBTru: $35**

Teacher

Mouse with books.
Handcrafted, 2.25", Dated
B Siedler

QX4125 SRP: $5.75 **GBTru: $15**

TV Break

Santa in hammock.
Handcrafted, 3.00", Dated
D Lee

QX4092 SRP: $6.25 **GBTru: $14**

Wiggly Snowman

Snowman in top hat.
Handcrafted, 4.75"
D Rhodus

QX4892 SRP: $6.75 **GBTru: $18**

1990

WINDOWS OF THE WORLD - 5TH
Germany - Frohliche Weihnachten

Boy playing carols on concertina.
Handcrafted, 3.75", Dated
D Lee

QX4625 SRP: $10.75 **GBTru: $22**

WINTER SURPRISE - 1ST
Winter Surprise

Penguins decorate tree (peek-in egg).
Handcrafted, 3.25", Dated
J Francis

QX4272 SRP: $10.75 **GBTru: $20**

WOOD CHILDHOOD ORNAMENTS - 6TH & FINAL
Wooden Truck

Wooden truck with Christmas trees.
Wood, 2.00"

QX4595 SRP: $7.75 **GBTru: $14**

World Of Love

Children from all countries celebrate.
Glass Ball, 2.88", Dated

QX2745 SRP: $4.75 **GBTru: $12**

Across The Miles

Raccoon with poinsettia.
Acrylic, 3.50"
L Votruba

QX3173 SRP: $6.75 **GBTru: $12**

Angel Kitty

Kitty in angel costume with wand.
Handcrafted, 2.56", Dated
M Pyda-Sevaik

QX4746 SRP: $8.75 **GBTru: $24**

Armful Of Joy

Club: Members Only Ornament
Elf w/shopping bag w/club logo/ stack of gifts.
Handcrafted, 2.81", Dated
J Francis

QXC4453 SRP: $9.75 **GBTru: $30**

BABY CELEBRATIONS
Baby's Christening 1990

Lamb, spec box, Keepsake logo.
Porcelain, 2.25", Dated
J Lyle

BBY1326 SRP: $10.00 **GBTru: $15**

BABY CELEBRATIONS
Baby's First Christmas 1990

Bunny, spec box, Keepsake logo.
Porcelain, 2.13", Dated
A M Rogers

BBY1554 SRP: $10.00 **GBTru: $18**

BABY CELEBRATIONS
Baby's First Christmas 1990

Pony, spec box, Keepsake logo.
Porcelain, 2.63", Dated
J Lyle

BBY1454 SRP: $10.00 **GBTru: $18**

Baby Unicorn

Baby unicorn with gold ribbon.
Porcelain, 2.00"
A M Rogers

QX5486 SRP: $9.75 **GBTru: $14**

Baby's First Christmas

Baby in walker.
Handcrafted, 3.38", Dated
J Francis

QX4853 SRP: $9.75 **GBTru: $12**

Baby's First Christmas

Puppy in hot air balloon.
Acrylic, 4.25", Dated
A M Rogers

QX3036 SRP: $6.75 **GBTru: $9**

Baby's First Christmas - Baby Boy

Baby sleeping (boy).
Satin Ball, 2.88", Dated

QX2063 SRP: $4.75 **GBTru: $11**

Baby's First Christmas - Baby Girl

Baby sleeping (girl).
Satin Ball, 2.88", Dated

QX2066 SRP: $4.75 **GBTru: $15**

Baby's First Christmas Photoholder

Lace trimmed holly & flower wreath.
Fabric, 3.50", Dated

QX4843 SRP: $7.75 **GBTru: $12**

Bearback Rider

Penguin rides polar bear rocker.
Handcrafted, 3.25", Dated
K Crow

QX5483 SRP: $9.75 **GBTru: $20**

Beary Good Deal

Bear with Santa cards.
Handcrafted, 2.00"
B Siedler

QX4733 SRP: $6.75 **GBTru: $12**

BETSEY CLARK: HOME FOR CHRISTMAS - 5TH
Home For Christmas

Girls singing.
Glass Ball, 2.88", Dated
B Clark

QX2033 SRP: $5.00 **GBTru: $9**

Billboard Bunny

Bunny w/billboard & basket of eggs.
Handcrafted, 2.38"
J Lee

QX5196 SRP: $7.75 **GBTru: $12**

Born To Dance

Mouse in ballerina costume.
Handcrafted, 2.56"
S Pike

QX5043 SRP: $7.75 **GBTru: $18**

Brother

Dog sitting in baseball glove.
Handcrafted, 2.19", Dated
B Siedler

QX4493 SRP: $5.75 **GBTru: $10**

Child Care Giver

Teddy holding bunny.
Acrylic, 3.00", Dated

QX3166 SRP: $6.75 **GBTru: $10**

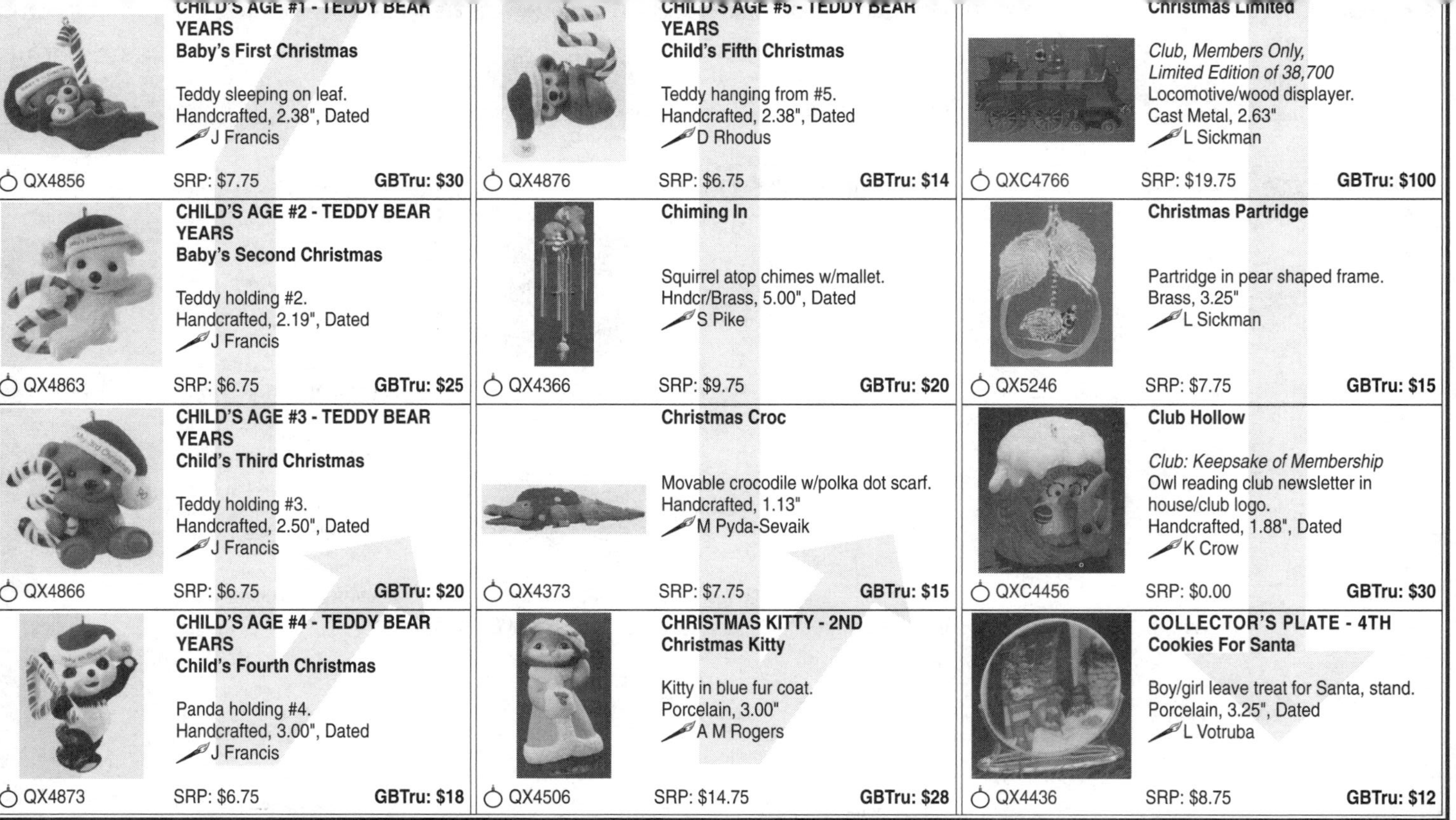

CHILD'S AGE #1 - TEDDY BEAR YEARS
Baby's First Christmas

Teddy sleeping on leaf.
Handcrafted, 2.38", Dated
J Francis

QX4856 SRP: $7.75 **GBTru: $30**

CHILD'S AGE #2 - TEDDY BEAR YEARS
Baby's Second Christmas

Teddy holding #2.
Handcrafted, 2.19", Dated
J Francis

QX4863 SRP: $6.75 **GBTru: $25**

CHILD'S AGE #3 - TEDDY BEAR YEARS
Child's Third Christmas

Teddy holding #3.
Handcrafted, 2.50", Dated
J Francis

QX4866 SRP: $6.75 **GBTru: $20**

CHILD'S AGE #4 - TEDDY BEAR YEARS
Child's Fourth Christmas

Panda holding #4.
Handcrafted, 3.00", Dated
J Francis

QX4873 SRP: $6.75 **GBTru: $18**

CHILD'S AGE #5 - TEDDY BEAR YEARS
Child's Fifth Christmas

Teddy hanging from #5.
Handcrafted, 2.38", Dated
D Rhodus

QX4876 SRP: $6.75 **GBTru: $14**

Chiming In

Squirrel atop chimes w/mallet.
Hndcr/Brass, 5.00", Dated
S Pike

QX4366 SRP: $9.75 **GBTru: $20**

Christmas Croc

Movable crocodile w/polka dot scarf.
Handcrafted, 1.13"
M Pyda-Sevaik

QX4373 SRP: $7.75 **GBTru: $15**

CHRISTMAS KITTY - 2ND
Christmas Kitty

Kitty in blue fur coat.
Porcelain, 3.00"
A M Rogers

QX4506 SRP: $14.75 **GBTru: $28**

Christmas Limited

Club, Members Only,
Limited Edition of 38,700
Locomotive/wood displayer.
Cast Metal, 2.63"
L Sickman

QXC4766 SRP: $19.75 **GBTru: $100**

Christmas Partridge

Partridge in pear shaped frame.
Brass, 3.25"
L Sickman

QX5246 SRP: $7.75 **GBTru: $15**

Club Hollow

Club: Keepsake of Membership
Owl reading club newsletter in house/club logo.
Handcrafted, 1.88", Dated
K Crow

QXC4456 SRP: $0.00 **GBTru: $30**

COLLECTOR'S PLATE - 4TH
Cookies For Santa

Boy/girl leave treat for Santa, stand.
Porcelain, 3.25", Dated
L Votruba

QX4436 SRP: $8.75 **GBTru: $12**

COMMEMORATIVE HEARTS
Fifty Years Together

"50 Years Together" heart.
Glass, 2.56", Dated
J Pattee

QX4906 SRP: $9.75 **GBTru: $12**

COMMEMORATIVE HEARTS
Forty Years Together

Heart "40 Years Together".
Glass, 2.56", Dated
J Pattee

QX4903 SRP: $9.75 **GBTru: $10**

COMMEMORATIVE HEARTS
Twenty-Five Years Together

Heart shaped with inscription.
Glass, 2.56", Dated
J Pattee

QX4896 SRP: $9.75 **GBTru: $12**

Copy Of Cheer

Mouse on copy machine.
Handcrafted, 2.06", Dated
B Siedler

QX4486 SRP: $7.75 **GBTru: $12**

Country Angel

Discontinued
Angel in green robe with gold trim.
Handcrafted

QX5046 SRP: $6.75 **GBTru: $100**

Coyote Carols

Coyotes carolling.
Handcrafted, 3.00"
J Lee

QX4993 SRP: $8.75 **GBTru: $18**

Cozy Goose

Goose wearing red vest.
Handcrafted, 3.13"
S Pike

QX4966 SRP: $5.75 **GBTru: $11**

CRAYOLA CRAYON - 2ND
Bright Moving Colors

Mouse in Crayola box sled.
Handcrafted, 2.25", Dated
K Crow

QX4586 SRP: $8.75 **GBTru: $44**

Dad

Lion in big red sweater.
Handcrafted, 2.50", Dated
J Lee

QX4533 SRP: $6.75 **GBTru: $12**

Dad-To-Be

Daddy rabbit.
Handcrafted, 3.00", Dated
B Siedler

QX4913 SRP: $5.75 **GBTru: $10**

Daughter

Snowgirl skating.
Handcrafted, 2.25", Dated
B Siedler

QX4496 SRP: $5.75 **GBTru: $10**

DICKENS CAROLER BELL - 1ST
Mr. Ashbourne
Special Edition
Victorian gentleman.
Porcelain, 4.25", Dated
R Chad

QX5056 SRP: $21.75 **GBTru: $25**

Donder's Diner

Diner with holiday decorations.
Handcrafted, 2.38", Dated
D Lee

QX4823 SRP: $13.75 **GBTru: $15**

Five Years Together

Reindeer prancing across snow.
Glass Ball, 2.88", Dated
L Votruba

QX2103 SRP: $4.75 **GBTru: $10**

Garfield

Garfield ice skating.
Chrome Ball, 2.78", Dated

QX2303 SRP: $4.75 **GBTru: $10**

Dove Of Peace

Club, Members Only,
Limited Edition of 25,400
Dove w/ brass banner/wood displayer.
Porcelain, 2.38"
L Sickman

QXC4476 SRP: $24.75 **GBTru: $40**

Friendship Kitten

Kitten with letter.
Handcrafted, 2.38", Dated
D Rhodus

QX4143 SRP: $6.75 **GBTru: $16**

Gentle Dreamers

Bunnies sleep'g/poinsettias (clip-on).
Handcrafted, 1.44"
J Francis

QX4756 SRP: $8.75 **GBTru: $25**

FABULOUS DECADE - 1ST
Fabulous Decade

Squirrel holding "1990".
Hndcr/Brass, 1.38", Dated
E Seale

QX4466 SRP: $7.75 **GBTru: $38**

From Our Home To Yours

Blue & red house with white fence.
Glass Ball, 2.88", Dated

QX2166 SRP: $4.75 **GBTru: $10**

GIFT BRINGERS, THE - 2ND
St. Lucia

St. Lucia and carolers.
Glass Ball, 2.88", Dated
L Votruba

QX2803 SRP: $5.00 **GBTru: $10**

Feliz Navidad

Mouse in red pepper stocking.
Handcrafted, 3.00", Dated

QX5173 SRP: $6.75 **GBTru: $20**

FROSTY FRIENDS - 11TH
Frosty Friends

Eskimo with seal on ice.
Hndcr/Acryl, 2.50", Dated
E Seale

QX4396 SRP: $9.75 **GBTru: $25**

Gingerbread Elf

Gingerbread elf with cookie tray.
Handcrafted, 3.69", Dated

QX5033 SRP: $5.75 **GBTru: $15**

Godchild

Bear with hat & scarf on sled.
Acrylic, 2.63", Dated
J Francis

QX3176 SRP: $6.75 **GBTru: $10**

Granddaughter's First Christmas

Mouse in hat box.
Acrylic, 3.56", Dated
J Francis

QX3106 SRP: $6.75 **GBTru: $10**

Grandson's First Christmas

Lamb in box.
Acrylic, 3.80", Dated
J Francis

QX3063 SRP: $6.75 **GBTru: $8**

Golf's My Bag

Reindeer in Santa's golf bag.
Handcrafted, 3.25"
J Lee

QX4963 SRP: $7.75 **GBTru: $20**

Grandmother

Mouse painting fence.
Glass Ball, 2.88", Dated
L Votruba

QX2236 SRP: $4.75 **GBTru: $10**

GREATEST STORY - 1ST
Greatest Story

Journey to Bethlehem/snowflake.
Brass/Prcln, 3.75", Dated
L Votruba

QX4656 SRP: $12.75 **GBTru: $15**

Goose Cart

Goose in green cart pull toy.
Handcrafted, 1.75"

QX5236 SRP: $7.75 **GBTru: $13**

Grandparents

Cones, greens, ribbons, candy decor.
Glass Ball, 2.88", Dated

QX2253 SRP: $4.75 **GBTru: $10**

Hang In There

Raccoon hanging on limb.
Handcrafted, 2.25"
E Seale

QX4713 SRP: $6.75 **GBTru: $15**

Granddaughter

Girl with geese.
Glass Ball, 2.88", Dated
J Lyle

QX2286 SRP: $4.75 **GBTru: $10**

Grandson

Bears decorating tree.
Glass Ball, 2.88", Dated
L Votruba

QX2293 SRP: $4.75 **GBTru: $10**

Happy Voices

Carolers by tree/shadow box.
Wood, 3.13"
L Votruba

QX4645 SRP: $6.75 **GBTru: $10**

Beaver with chain saw.
Handcrafted, 2.00", Dated
J Lee

QX4763 SRP: $9.75 **GBTru: $16**

Cardinals on holly branch.
Brass, 2.81", Dated
J Lyle

QX5243 SRP: $7.75 **GBTru: $12**

Dolphin poses in foil/ribbon wreath.
Handcrafted, 3.00"
A M Rogers

QX4683 SRP: $6.75 **GBTru: $22**

HARK! IT'S HERALD - 2ND
Hark! It's Herald

Elf with drum.
Handcrafted, 2.13", Dated
K Crow

QX4463 SRP: $6.75 **GBTru: $12**

Home For The Owlidays

Owl holds luggage.
Handcrafted, 2.25"

QX5183 SRP: $6.75 **GBTru: $11**

Joy Is In The Air

Santa soaring in parachute.
Handcrafted, 2.63", Dated
K Crow

QX5503 SRP: $7.75 **GBTru: $22**

HEART OF CHRISTMAS - 1ST
Heart Of Christmas

Three section Christmas scene.
Handcrafted, 2.00", Dated
E Seale

QX4726 SRP: $13.75 **GBTru: $70**

Hot Dogger

Hot dog on skis.
Handcrafted, 2.88", Dated
K Crow

QX4976 SRP: $7.75 **GBTru: $14**

King Klaus

Santa atop Empire State Building.
Handcrafted, 4.63"
E Seale

QX4106 SRP: $7.75 **GBTru: $12**

HERE COMES SANTA - 12TH
Festive Surrey

Santa in red and gray surrey.
Handcrafted, 3.13", Dated
L Sickman

QX4923 SRP: $14.75 **GBTru: $38**

Jesus Loves Me

Bunny with inscription.
Acrylic, 2.75"
J Pattee

QX3156 SRP: $6.75 **GBTru: $10**

Kitty's Best Pal

Santa with kitty in green stocking.
Handcrafted, 2.38", Dated
J Francis

QX4716 SRP: $6.75 **GBTru: $16**

Little Drummer Boy

Little boy/ragged clothes play'g drum.
Handcrafted, 2.38", Dated
D Unruh

QX5233 SRP: $7.75 **GBTru: $12**

Long Winter's Nap

Puppy sleeping in gift box.
Handcrafted, 1.38", Dated
A M Rogers

QX4703 SRP: $6.75 **GBTru: $15**

Lovable Dears

Child with pet fawn.
Handcrafted, 2.31"
D Unruh

QX5476 SRP: $8.75 **GBTru: $10**

MARY'S ANGELS - 3RD
Rosebud

Atop cloud, Angel holds candle.
Handcrafted, 3.13"
R Chad

Meow Mart

Cat in bag with ball of yarn.
Handcrafted, 1.25"
S Pike

QX4446 SRP: $7.75 **GBTru: $12**

MERRY OLDE SANTA - 1ST
Merry Olde Santa

Santa holding tiny tree.
Handcrafted, 4.75", Dated
E Seale

QX4736 SRP: $14.75 **GBTru: $65**

Mom And Dad

Mom and dad bears with cards.
Handcrafted, 2.50", Dated
R Chad

QX4593 SRP: $8.75 **GBTru: $15**

Mom-To-Be

Expectant bunny.
Handcrafted, 2.88", Dated
B Siedler

Mooy Christmas

Cow with red scarf.
Handcrafted, 2.06"

QX4933 SRP: $6.75 **GBTru: $20**

Mother

"Mother Is Love" filigree.
Ceramic, 2.88", Dated
L Votruba

QX4536 SRP: $8.75 **GBTru: $12**

Mouseboat

Mouse in nutshell boat.
Handcrafted, 3.00", Dated
E Seale

QX4753 SRP: $7.75 **GBTru: $12**

MR. & MRS. CLAUS - 5TH
Popcorn Party

Mr. & Mrs. Claus string popcorn.
Handcrafted, 3.00", Dated
D Unruh

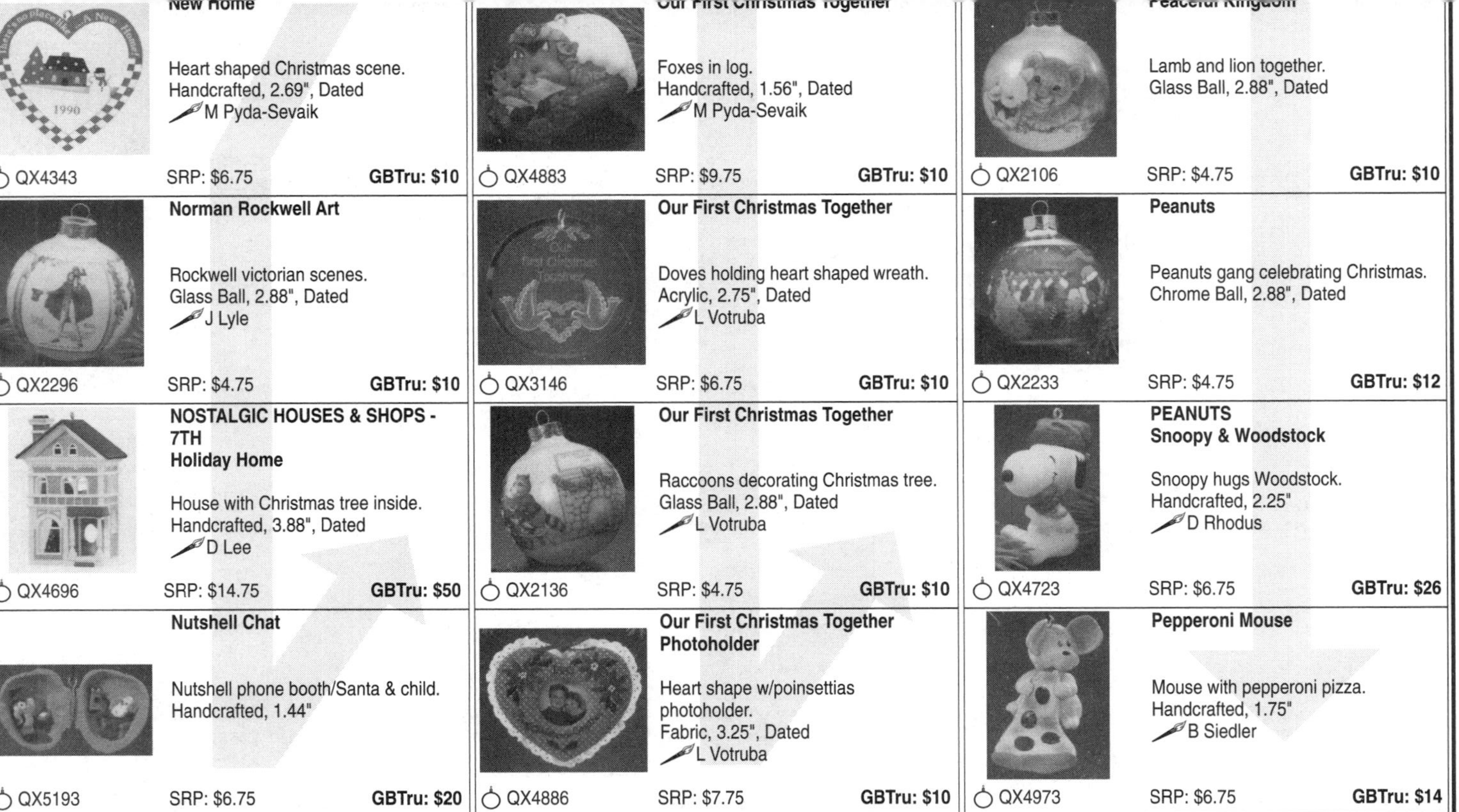

New Home

Heart shaped Christmas scene.
Handcrafted, 2.69", Dated
M Pyda-Sevaik

QX4343 SRP: $6.75 **GBTru: $10**

Norman Rockwell Art

Rockwell victorian scenes.
Glass Ball, 2.88", Dated
J Lyle

QX2296 SRP: $4.75 **GBTru: $10**

NOSTALGIC HOUSES & SHOPS - 7TH
Holiday Home

House with Christmas tree inside.
Handcrafted, 3.88", Dated
D Lee

QX4696 SRP: $14.75 **GBTru: $50**

Nutshell Chat

Nutshell phone booth/Santa & child.
Handcrafted, 1.44"

QX5193 SRP: $6.75 **GBTru: $20**

Our First Christmas Together

Foxes in log.
Handcrafted, 1.56", Dated
M Pyda-Sevaik

QX4883 SRP: $9.75 **GBTru: $10**

Our First Christmas Together

Doves holding heart shaped wreath.
Acrylic, 2.75", Dated
L Votruba

QX3146 SRP: $6.75 **GBTru: $10**

Our First Christmas Together

Raccoons decorating Christmas tree.
Glass Ball, 2.88", Dated
L Votruba

QX2136 SRP: $4.75 **GBTru: $10**

Our First Christmas Together
Photoholder

Heart shape w/poinsettias photoholder.
Fabric, 3.25", Dated
L Votruba

QX4886 SRP: $7.75 **GBTru: $10**

Peaceful Kingdom

Lamb and lion together.
Glass Ball, 2.88", Dated

QX2106 SRP: $4.75 **GBTru: $10**

Peanuts

Peanuts gang celebrating Christmas.
Chrome Ball, 2.88", Dated

QX2233 SRP: $4.75 **GBTru: $12**

PEANUTS
Snoopy & Woodstock

Snoopy hugs Woodstock.
Handcrafted, 2.25"
D Rhodus

QX4723 SRP: $6.75 **GBTru: $26**

Pepperoni Mouse

Mouse with pepperoni pizza.
Handcrafted, 1.75"
B Siedler

QX4973 SRP: $6.75 **GBTru: $14**

Perfect Catch

Santa catching baseball.
Handcrafted, 3.81", Dated
B Siedler

QX4693 SRP: $7.75 **GBTru: $12**

POLAR PENGUINS
Polar T.V.

Penguin watching TV.
Handcrafted, 1.63"
B Siedler

QX5166 SRP: $7.75 **GBTru: $15**

PORCELAIN BEARS - 8TH & FINAL
Cinnamon

Bear with decorated tree.
Porcelain, 1.56"

QX4426 SRP: $8.75 **GBTru: $16**

POLAR PENGUINS
Polar Jogger

Penguin in red sweatshirt.
Handcrafted, 1.63"
B Siedler

QX4666 SRP: $5.75 **GBTru: $15**

POLAR PENGUINS
Polar V.I.P.

Penguin with telephone and attache.
Handcrafted, 2.00"
B Siedler

QX4663 SRP: $5.75 **GBTru: $14**

REINDEER CHAMPS - 5TH
Comet

Reindeer soccer player.
Handcrafted, 3.19", Dated
B Siedler

QX4433 SRP: $7.75 **GBTru: $20**

POLAR PENGUINS
Polar Pair

Penguin with baby.
Handcrafted, 2.00"
B Siedler

QX4626 SRP: $5.75 **GBTru: $12**

POLAR PENGUINS
Polar Video

Penguin with video camera.
Handcrafted, 2.00"
B Siedler

QX4633 SRP: $5.75 **GBTru: $15**

ROCKING HORSE - 10TH
Appaloosa

Rocking horse.
Handcrafted, 4.00", Dated
L Sickman

QX4646 SRP: $10.75 **GBTru: $52**

POLAR PENGUINS
Polar Sport

Penguin in red sports car.
Handcrafted, 1.75"
B Siedler

QX5156 SRP: $7.75 **GBTru: $20**

Poolside Walrus

Walrus on reindeer float.
Handcrafted, 1.75"
J Lee

QX4986 SRP: $7.75 **GBTru: $15**

S. Claus Taxi

Santa in taxi cab.
Handcrafted, 2.00", Dated
P Dutkin

QX4686 SRP: $11.75 **GBTru: $20**

Santa w/comical nose & moustache.
Handcrafted, 2.50"
K Crow

QX4983 SRP: $6.75 **GBTru: $15**

Granny rabbit stitching.
Handcrafted, 2.50"
J Lee

QX5186 SRP: $7.75 **GBTru: $15**

Chipmunk teacher at blackboard.
Handcrafted, 2.38", Dated
E Seale

QX4483 SRP: $7.75 **GBTru: $8**

Sister

Red poinsettia decorations.
Glass Ball, 2.88", Dated

QX2273 SRP: $4.75 **GBTru: $10**

Stocking Pals

Koalas w/stocking, stringer orn..
Handcrafted, 3.25", Dated
E Seale

QX5493 SRP: $10.75 **GBTru: $16**

Ten Years Together

Winter scene with house & redbirds.
Glass Ball, 2.88", Dated
J Lyle

QX2153 SRP: $4.75 **GBTru: $10**

Son

Snowboy playing hockey.
Handcrafted, 1.88", Dated
B Siedler

QX4516 SRP: $5.75 **GBTru: $10**

Sugar Plum Fairy

Club, Members Only,
Limited Edition of 25,400
Fairy ballerina/wood displayer.
Porcelain, 5.50"
P Andrews

QXC4473 SRP: $27.75 **GBTru: $40**

Three Little Piggies

Three pigs in stocking.
Handcrafted, 2.63"
K Crow

QX4996 SRP: $7.75 **GBTru: $18**

Spoon Rider

Elves playing on spoon.
Handcrafted, 2.75"
P Andrews

QX5496 SRP: $9.75 **GBTru: $12**

Sweetheart

Wishing well.
Handcrafted, 3.13", Dated
D Rhodus

QX4893 SRP: $11.75 **GBTru: $18**

Time For Love

Cardinals on holly branch.
Glass Ball, 2.88", Dated
J Lyle

QX2133 SRP: $4.75 **GBTru: $12**

TWELVE DAYS OF CHRISTMAS, THE - 7TH
Seven Swans A-Swimming

Swan with holly/teardrop.
Acrylic, 3.38", Dated

QX3033 SRP: $6.75 **GBTru: $12**

Two Peas In A Pod

Two peas peek out of a pea pod.
Handcrafted, 3.75"
P Andrews

QX4926 SRP: $4.75 **GBTru: $30**

Welcome, Santa

Santa coming down chimney.
Handcrafted, 2.63"
K Crow

QX4773 SRP: $11.75 **GBTru: $18**

WINDOWS OF THE WORLD - 6TH & FINAL
Ireland - Nollaig Shona

Child at window look'g at leprechaun.
Handcrafted, 3.00", Dated
D Lee

QX4636 SRP: $10.75 **GBTru: $16**

WINTER SURPRISE - 2ND
Winter Surprise

Winter scene with penguin in eggshell.
Handcrafted, 3.25", Dated
J Francis

QX4443 SRP: $10.75 **GBTru: $12**

1991

Across The Miles

Brass framed oval w/ gold foil caption.
Acrylic, 2.63", Dated
J Lyle

QX3157 SRP: $6.75 **GBTru: $10**

All-Star

Turtle baseball player.
Handcrafted, 2.13", Dated
B Siedler

QX5329 SRP: $6.75 **GBTru: $14**

BABY CELEBRATIONS
Baby's Christening 1991

Lamb, spec box, Keepsake logo.
Porcelain, 2.25", Dated
J Lyle

BBY1317 SRP: $10.00 **GBTru: $10**

BABY CELEBRATIONS
Baby's First Christmas 1991

Bunny, spec box, Keepsake logo.
Porcelain, 2.13", Dated
A M Rogers

BBY1514 SRP: $10.00 **GBTru: $12**

BABY CELEBRATIONS
Baby's First Christmas 1991

Pony, spec box, Keepsake logo.
Porcelain, 2.63", Dated
J Lyle

BBY1416 SRP: $10.00 **GBTru: $15**

Baby's First Christmas

Teddy bear in bootie.
Silver Plated, 2.63", Dated
J Francis

QX5107 SRP: $7.75 **GBTru: $20**

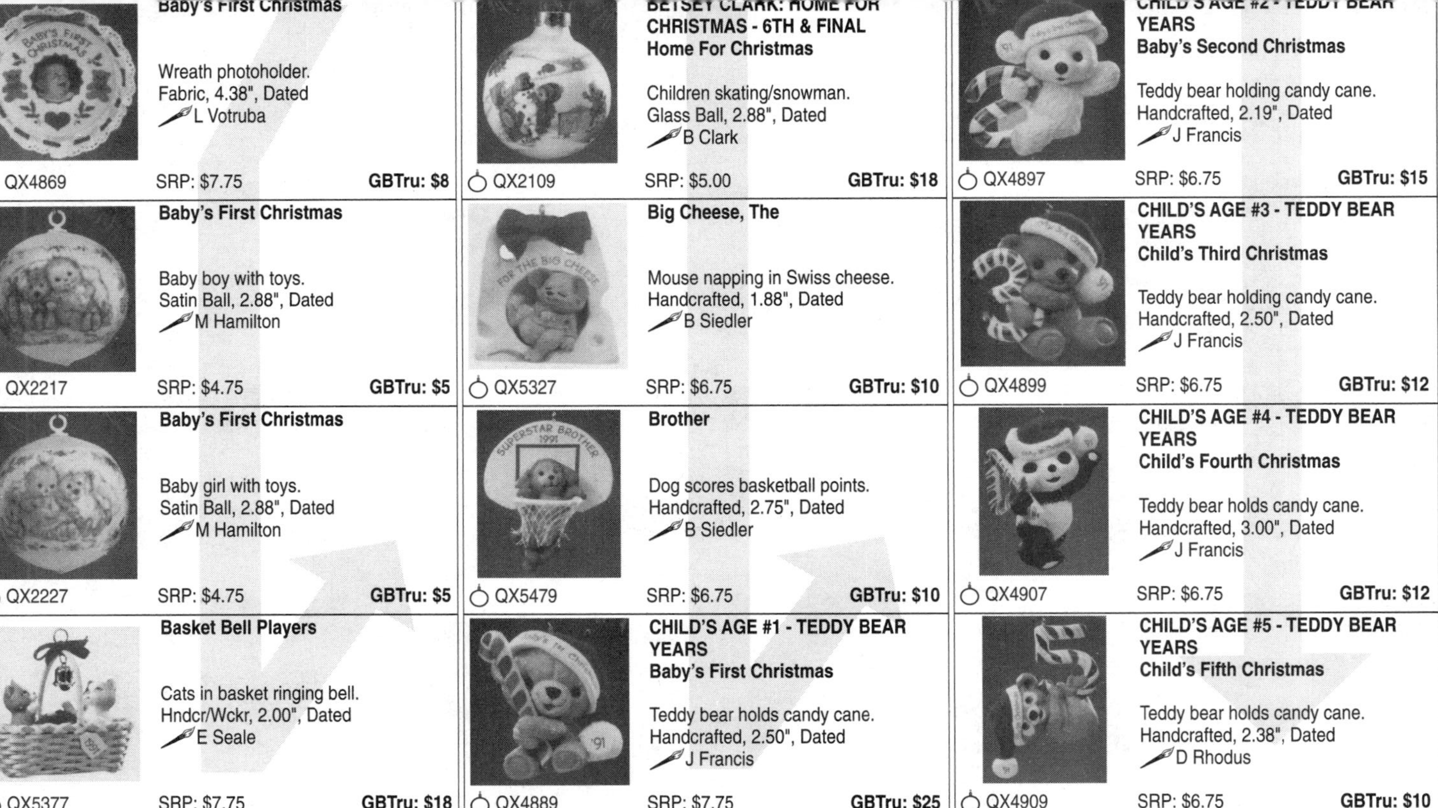

Baby's First Christmas

Wreath photoholder.
Fabric, 4.38", Dated
L Votruba

QX4869 SRP: $7.75 **GBTru: $8**

Baby's First Christmas

Baby boy with toys.
Satin Ball, 2.88", Dated
M Hamilton

QX2217 SRP: $4.75 **GBTru: $5**

Baby's First Christmas

Baby girl with toys.
Satin Ball, 2.88", Dated
M Hamilton

QX2227 SRP: $4.75 **GBTru: $5**

Basket Bell Players

Cats in basket ringing bell.
Hndcr/Wckr, 2.00", Dated
E Seale

QX5377 SRP: $7.75 **GBTru: $18**

BETSEY CLARK: HOME FOR CHRISTMAS - 6TH & FINAL
Home For Christmas

Children skating/snowman.
Glass Ball, 2.88", Dated
B Clark

QX2109 SRP: $5.00 **GBTru: $18**

Big Cheese, The

Mouse napping in Swiss cheese.
Handcrafted, 1.88", Dated
B Siedler

QX5327 SRP: $6.75 **GBTru: $10**

Brother

Dog scores basketball points.
Handcrafted, 2.75", Dated
B Siedler

QX5479 SRP: $6.75 **GBTru: $10**

CHILD'S AGE #1 - TEDDY BEAR YEARS
Baby's First Christmas

Teddy bear holds candy cane.
Handcrafted, 2.50", Dated
J Francis

QX4889 SRP: $7.75 **GBTru: $25**

CHILD'S AGE #2 - TEDDY BEAR YEARS
Baby's Second Christmas

Teddy bear holding candy cane.
Handcrafted, 2.19", Dated
J Francis

QX4897 SRP: $6.75 **GBTru: $15**

CHILD'S AGE #3 - TEDDY BEAR YEARS
Child's Third Christmas

Teddy bear holding candy cane.
Handcrafted, 2.50", Dated
J Francis

QX4899 SRP: $6.75 **GBTru: $12**

CHILD'S AGE #4 - TEDDY BEAR YEARS
Child's Fourth Christmas

Teddy bear holds candy cane.
Handcrafted, 3.00", Dated
J Francis

QX4907 SRP: $6.75 **GBTru: $12**

CHILD'S AGE #5 - TEDDY BEAR YEARS
Child's Fifth Christmas

Teddy bear holds candy cane.
Handcrafted, 2.38", Dated
D Rhodus

QX4909 SRP: $6.75 **GBTru: $10**

Child's Christmas, A

Baby on rug with blocks.
Handcrafted, 2.38", Dated
J Francis

QX4887 SRP: $9.75 **GBTru: $10**

Chilly Chap

Snowman ice cream cone.
Handcrafted, 3.75", Dated
D Lee

QX5339 SRP: $6.75 **GBTru: $15**

CHRISTMAS CAROL, A
Bob Cratchit

Father w/quill pen, Ledger book.
Porcelain, 3.94", Dated
D Unruh

QX4997 SRP: $13.75 **GBTru: $28**

CHRISTMAS CAROL, A
Ebenezer Scrooge

Scrooge.
Porcelain, 4.06", Dated
D Unruh

QX4989 SRP: $13.75 **GBTru: $40**

CHRISTMAS CAROL, A
Merry Carolers

Couple caroling.
Porcelain, 4.13", Dated
D Unruh

QX4799 SRP: $29.75 **GBTru: $85**

CHRISTMAS CAROL, A
Mrs. Cratchit

Mother/goose dinner.
Porcelain, 3.88", Dated
D Unruh

QX4999 SRP: $13.75 **GBTru: $28**

CHRISTMAS CAROL, A
Tiny Tim

Boy on stool/crutch.
Porcelain, 2.13", Dated
D Unruh

QX5037 SRP: $10.75 **GBTru: $28**

CHRISTMAS KITTY - 3RD & FINAL
Christmas Kitty

Kitten holding candy canes.
Handcrafted, 3.06"
A M Rogers

QX4377 SRP: $14.75 **GBTru: $22**

CLASSIC AMERICAN CARS - 1ST
1957 Corvette

Red Corvette convertible.
Handcrafted, 1.31", Dated
D Palmiter

QX4319 SRP: $12.75 **GBTru: $225**

CLAUS & CO. R.R. - 1ST
Locomotive
Gold Crown Reach Program -
**w/any HM purchase*
Locomotive.
Handcrafted, 1.63", Dated
D Palmiter

411XPR9730 SRP: $3.95* **GBTru: $25**

CLAUS & CO. R.R. - 2ND
Gift Car
Gold Crown Reach Program -
**w/any HM purchase*
Gift car.
Handcrafted, 1.56", Dated
D Palmiter

411XPR9731 SRP: $3.95* **GBTru: $10**

CLAUS & CO. R.R. - 3RD
Passenger Car
Gold Crown Reach Program -
**w/any HM purchase*
Passenger car.
Handcrafted, 1.75", Dated
D Palmiter

411XPR9732 SRP: $3.95* **GBTru: $10**

CLAUS & CO. R.R. - 4TH
Caboose
*Gold Crown Reach Program - *w/any HM purchase*
Caboose.
Handcrafted, 1.75", Dated
D Palmiter
411XPR9733 SRP: $3.95* **GBTru: $10**

CLAUS & CO. R.R. TRESTLE DISPLAYER
Trestle
*Gold Crown Reach Program - *w/any HM purchase*
Trestle.
Handcrafted, 7.00", Dated
D Palmiter
411XPR9734 SRP: $2.95* **GBTru: $8**

COLLECTOR'S PLATE - 5TH
Let It Snow!
Children build snowman, stand.
Porcelain, 3.25", Dated
L Votruba
QX4369 SRP: $8.75 **GBTru: $20**

COMMEMORATIVE GLASS HEARTS
Five Years Together
Faceted heart shape.
Glass, 2.56", Dated
QX4927 SRP: $7.75 **GBTru: $10**

COMMEMORATIVE GLASS HEARTS
Forty Years Together
Faceted heart shape.
Glass, 2.56", Dated
QX4939 SRP: $7.75 **GBTru: $10**

COMMEMORATIVE GLASS HEARTS
Ten Years Together
Faceted heart shape.
Glass, 2.56", Dated
QX4929 SRP: $7.75 **GBTru: $10**

COMMEMORATIVE PHOTOHOLDERS
Fifty Years Together Photoholder
Roses on wreath photoholder.
Hndcr/Brass, 3.25", Dated
L Votruba
QX4947 SRP: $8.75 **GBTru: $10**

COMMEMORATIVE PHOTOHOLDERS
Our First Christmas Together Photoholder
Doves on wreath photoholder.
Brass/Hndcr, 3.25", Dated
L Votruba
QX4917 SRP: $8.75 **GBTru: $10**

COMMEMORATIVE PHOTOHOLDERS
Twenty-Five Years Together Photoholder
Swans on wreath photoholder.
Hndcr/Chrome, 3.25", Dated
L Votruba
QX4937 SRP: $8.75 **GBTru: $8**

CRAYOLA CRAYON - 3RD
Bright Vibrant Carols
Bear playing crayon organ.
Handcrafted, 3.25", Dated
K Crow
QX4219 SRP: $9.75 **GBTru: $35**

Cuddly Lamb
Lamb with bow/flocked.
Handcrafted, 1.88"
A M Rogers
QX5199 SRP: $6.75 **GBTru: $10**

Dad
Polar bear dad as Mr. Fixit.
Handcrafted, 2.25", Dated
J Lee
QX5127 SRP: $7.75 **GBTru: $10**

Dad-To-Be

Kangaroo expectant father.
Handcrafted, 2.38", Dated
J Lee

QX4879 SRP: $5.75 **GBTru: $6**

Daughter

Mouse in pink slipper.
Handcrafted, 3.06", Dated
B Siedler

QX5477 SRP: $5.75 **GBTru: $6**

DICKENS CAROLER BELL - 2ND
Mrs. Beaumont
Special Edition
Old fashioned caroler.
Porcelain, 4.25", Dated
R Chad

QX5039 SRP: $21.75 **GBTru: $30**

Dinoclaus

Santa Claus dinosaur.
Handcrafted, 2.63", Dated
R Chad

QX5277 SRP: $7.75 **GBTru: $10**

Extra-Special Friends

Animal friends enjoy'g winter sports.
Glass Ball, 2.88", Dated

QX2279 SRP: $4.75 **GBTru: $8**

FABULOUS DECADE - 2ND
Fabulous Decade

Raccoon holding numbers "1991".
Hndcr/Brass, 1.75", Dated
E Seale

QX4119 SRP: $7.75 **GBTru: $30**

Feliz Navidad

Santa asleep under sombrero.
Handcrafted, 2.00", Dated
J Lee

QX5279 SRP: $6.75 **GBTru: $12**

Fiddlin' Around

Bear with fiddle.
Handcrafted, 2.88"
L Votruba

QX4387 SRP: $7.75 **GBTru: $12**

Five Years Together

Club: Spec. Gift:
Founding Charter Members
Quadra foil shape w/club logo.
Acrylic, 3.00", Dated

QXC3159 **GBTru: $40**

Folk Art Reindeer

Reindeer kneeling.
Wood/Brass, 2.31", Dated
L Votruba

QX5359 SRP: $8.75 **GBTru: $14**

Friends Are Fun

Bunnies on a see-saw.
Handcrafted, 2.94", Dated
K Crow

QX5289 SRP: $9.75 **GBTru: $18**

From Our Home To Yours

Bird fly'g card from bears to mice.
Glass Ball, 2.88", Dated
L Votruba

QX2287 SRP: $4.75 **GBTru: $5**

FROSTY FRIENDS - 12TH
Frosty Friends

Eskimo and penguin playing hockey.
Hndcr/Acryl, 1.88", Dated
S Pike

QX4327 SRP: $9.75 **GBTru: $30**

Gift Of Joy

"JOY" spelled in block forms.
Chrm/Brs/Cpr, 4.00", Dated
D McGehee

QX5319 SRP: $8.75 **GBTru: $15**

Grandmother

Teardrop/inscription.
Glass Ball, 2.88", Dated

QX2307 SRP: $4.75 **GBTru: $5**

Galloping Into Christmas

Club, Members Only,
Limited Edition of 28,400
Santa/horse pull toy /hand numbered.
Tin, 3.00"
L Sickman

QXC4779 SRP: $19.75 **GBTru: $98**

Godchild

Angel with trumpet.
Handcrafted, 2.06", Dated
R Bishop

QX5489 SRP: $6.75 **GBTru: $12**

Grandparents

Teardrop/inscription/country scene.
Glass Ball, 2.88", Dated
M Pyda-Sevaik

QX2309 SRP: $4.75 **GBTru: $5**

Garfield

Angel Garfield on star.
Handcrafted, 3.25", Dated
D Rhodus

QX5177 SRP: $7.75 **GBTru: $24**

Granddaughter

Bunnies/cross-stitch design/caption.
Glass Ball, 2.88", Dated
M Pyda-Sevaik

QX2299 SRP: $4.75 **GBTru: $5**

Grandson

Reindeer/cross-stitch/caption.
Glass Ball, 2.88", Dated
M Pyda-Sevaik

QX2297 SRP: $4.75 **GBTru: $5**

GIFT BRINGERS, THE - 3RD
Christkindl

Angel on deer delivers gifts.
Glass Ball, 2.88", Dated
L Votruba

QX2117 SRP: $5.00 **GBTru: $10**

Granddaughter's First Christmas

Pink bear holding "Granddaughter" letters.
Handcrafted, 4.25", Dated
R Chad

QX5119 SRP: $6.75 **GBTru: $8**

Grandson's First Christmas

Bear holding "Grandson" letters.
Handcrafted, 4.25", Dated
R Chad

QX5117 SRP: $6.75 **GBTru: $7**

GREATEST STORY - 2ND
Greatest Story

Shepherd scene within snowflake.
Porc/Brass, 3.75", Dated
L Votruba

QX4129 SRP: $12.75 **GBTru: $15**

HERE COMES SANTA - 13TH
Santa'a Antique Car

Santa in old fashioned car.
Handcrafted, 2.25", Dated
L Sickman

QX4349 SRP: $14.75 **GBTru: $40**

Jolly Wolly Santa

Two piece Santa container.
Tin, 3.25", Dated
L Sickman

QX5419 SRP: $7.75 **GBTru: $20**

HARK! IT'S HERALD - 3RD
Hark! It's Herald

Elf playing flute.
Handcrafted, 2.00", Dated
A M Rogers

QX4379 SRP: $6.75 **GBTru: $12**

Hidden Treasure & Li'l Keeper

Club: Keepsake of Membership
Unlock acorn lid, mini squirrel bonus gift/club logo.
Handcrafted, 2.13", Dated
K Crow

QXC4769 **GBTru: $32**

Jolly Wolly Snowman

Two piece snowman container.
Tin, 3.25", Dated
L Sickman

QX5427 SRP: $7.75 **GBTru: $18**

HEART OF CHRISTMAS - 2ND
Heart Of Christmas

3 winter scenes within heart locket.
Handcrafted, 2.00", Dated
E Seale

QX4357 SRP: $13.75 **GBTru: $28**

Hooked On Santa

Santa hooks himself fishing.
Handcrafted, 4.00"
J Lee

QX4109 SRP: $7.75 **GBTru: $15**

Jolly Wolly Soldier

Two piece soldier container.
Tin, 3.25", Dated
L Sickman

QX5429 SRP: $7.75 **GBTru: $18**

HEAVENLY ANGELS - 1ST
Heavenly Angels

Antique design angel.
Handcrafted, 3.06", Dated
J Lyle

QX4367 SRP: $7.75 **GBTru: $20**

Jesus Loves Me

Squirrel praying by bed.
Cameo, 2.75", Dated
D Rhodus

QX3147 SRP: $7.75 **GBTru: $10**

Joyous Memories Photoholder

Wreath photoholder (hand painted).
Handcrafted, 3.38", Dated
L Votruba

QX5369 SRP: $6.75 **GBTru: $12**

Mary Engelbreit

Santa leads a parade.
Glass Ball, 2.88", Dated
M Engelbreit

QX2237 SRP: $4.75 **GBTru: $25**

MARY'S ANGELS - 4TH
Iris

Angel sleeping on cloud.
Hndcr/Acryl, 2.00"
R Chad

QX4279 SRP: $6.75 **GBTru: $28**

MATCHBOX MEMORIES
Evergreen Inn

Vacation check-in.
Handcrafted, 1.44", Dated
E Seale

QX5389 SRP: $8.75 **GBTru: $12**

MATCHBOX MEMORIES
Holiday Cafe

Couple/holiday meal.
Handcrafted, 1.44", Dated
E Seale

QX5399 SRP: $8.75 **GBTru: $12**

MATCHBOX MEMORIES
Santa's Studio

Santa's workshop.
Handcrafted, 1.44", Dated
E Seale

QX5397 SRP: $8.75 **GBTru: $10**

MERRY OLDE SANTA - 2ND
Merry Olde Santa

Santa with gift bag & walking staff.
Handcrafted, 4.00", Dated
J Lee

QX4359 SRP: $14.75 **GBTru: $75**

Mom And Dad

Raccoons in stocking.
Handcrafted, 3.63", Dated

QX5467 SRP: $9.75 **GBTru: $10**

Mom-To-Be

Kangaroo expectant mother.
Handcrafted, 2.38", Dated
J Lee

QX4877 SRP: $5.75 **GBTru: $9**

Mother

Floral oval pendant w/caption.
Porcelain/Tin, 3.13", Dated

QX5457 SRP: $9.75 **GBTru: $25**

MR. & MRS. CLAUS - 6TH
Checking His List

Mr. & Mrs. Claus checking gift list.
Handcrafted, 3.00", Dated
D Unruh

QX4339 SRP: $13.75 **GBTru: $28**

New Home

Cardinal at birdhouse.
Handcrafted, 2.25", Dated
R Bishop

QX5449 SRP: $6.75 **GBTru: $18**

Noah's Ark

Wind-up Ark with rainbow.
Handcrafted, 3.00", Dated
K Crow

QX4867 SRP: $13.75 **GBTru: $30**

Norman Rockwell Art

Elves on Santa's lap with toys.
Glass Ball, 2.88", Dated
J Lyle

QX2259 SRP: $5.00 **GBTru: $10**

NOSTALGIA STYLE
Christmas Welcome

Fruit basket in ring shape.
Handcrafted, 3.38", Dated
L Sickman

QX5299 SRP: $9.75 **GBTru: $10**

NOSTALGIA STYLE
Partridge In A Pear Tree

Partridge in pear tree.
Handcrafted, 3.31", Dated
L Sickman

QX5297 SRP: $9.75 **GBTru: $12**

NOSTALGIA STYLE
Twirl-About Night Before Christmas

Santa on chimney.
Handcrafted, 3.25", Dated
L Sickman

QX5307 SRP: $9.75 **GBTru: $15**

NOSTALGIC HOUSES & SHOPS - 8TH
Fire Station

Fire station.
Handcrafted, 4.00", Dated
D Lee

QX4139 SRP: $14.75 **GBTru: $55**

Notes Of Cheer

Bear playing keyboard/flocked.
Handcrafted, 1.75", Dated
B Siedler

QX5357 SRP: $5.75 **GBTru: $12**

Nutshell Nativity

Shell opens to Nativity & 3 Kings.
Handcrafted, 1.44"
A M Rogers

QX5176 SRP: $6.75 **GBTru: $20**

Nutty Squirrel

Squirrel holding ribboned nut.
Handcrafted, 1.75"
S Pike

QX4833 SRP: $5.75 **GBTru: $10**

Old-Fashioned Sled

Bentwood runners on antique sled.
Handcrafted, 1.31", Dated
L Sickman

QX4317 SRP: $8.75 **GBTru: $15**

On A Roll

Mouse cutting ribbon from spool.
Handcrafted, 5.00", Dated
K Crow

QX5347 SRP: $6.75 **GBTru: $18**

Our First Christmas Together

Heart with doves.
Acrylic, 3.19", Dated
S Pike

QX3139 SRP: $6.75 **GBTru: $15**

Our First Christmas Together

Couple skating, teardrop shape.
Glass Ball, 2.88", Dated

QX2229 SRP: $4.75 **GBTru: $5**

PATRIOTIC
Flag Of Liberty

Armed Forces: Flag w/yellow ribbon.
Handcrafted, 3.50", Dated

QX5249 SRP: $6.75 **GBTru: $15**

Polar Circus Wagon

Polar bear in circus wagon.
Handcrafted, 2.88", Dated
L Sickman

QX4399 SRP: $13.75 **GBTru: $16**

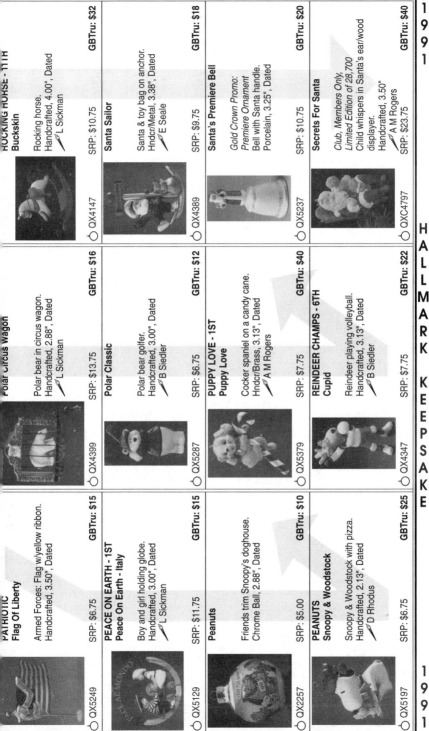

ROCKING HORSE - 11TH
Buckskin

Rocking horse.
Handcrafted, 4.00", Dated
L Sickman

QX4147 SRP: $10.75 **GBTru: $32**

PEACE ON EARTH - 1ST
Peace On Earth - Italy

Boy and girl holding globe.
Handcrafted, 3.00", Dated
L Sickman

QX5129 SRP: $11.75 **GBTru: $15**

Polar Classic

Polar bear golfer.
Handcrafted, 3.00", Dated
B Siedler

QX5287 SRP: $6.75 **GBTru: $12**

Santa Sailor

Santa & toy bag on anchor.
Hndcr/Metal, 3.38", Dated
E Seale

QX4389 SRP: $9.75 **GBTru: $18**

Peanuts

Friends trim Snoopy's doghouse.
Chrome Ball, 2.88", Dated

QX2257 SRP: $5.00 **GBTru: $10**

PUPPY LOVE - 1ST
Puppy Love

Cocker spaniel on a candy cane.
Hndcr/Brass, 3.13", Dated
A M Rogers

QX5379 SRP: $7.75 **GBTru: $40**

Santa's Premiere Bell

Gold Crown Promo:
Premiere Ornament
Bell with Santa handle.
Porcelain, 3.25", Dated

QX5237 SRP: $10.75 **GBTru: $20**

PEANUTS
Snoopy & Woodstock

Snoopy & Woodstock with pizza.
Handcrafted, 2.13", Dated
D Rhodus

QX5197 SRP: $6.75 **GBTru: $25**

REINDEER CHAMPS - 6TH
Cupid

Reindeer playing volleyball.
Handcrafted, 3.13", Dated
B Siedler

QX4347 SRP: $7.75 **GBTru: $22**

Secrets For Santa

Club, Members Only,
Limited Edition of 28,700
Child whispers in Santa's ear/wood displayer.
Handcrafted, 3.50"
A M Rogers

QXC4797 SRP: $23.75 **GBTru: $40**

Sister

Gingerbread angel w/cookie star.
Handcrafted, 3.75", Dated
J Lyle

QX5487 SRP: $6.75 **GBTru: $10**

Ski Lift Bunny

Bunny on ski lift.
Handcrafted, 2.75", Dated
J Lee

QX5447 SRP: $6.75 **GBTru: $10**

Snowy Owl

Owl on tree branch.
Handcrafted, 3.00"
L Sickman

QX5269 SRP: $7.75 **GBTru: $10**

Son

Mouse in red slipper.
Handcrafted, 3.19", Dated
B Siedler

QX5469 SRP: $5.75 **GBTru: $10**

Sweet Talk

Girl sharing candy cane with pony.
Handcrafted, 2.13"
D Unruh

QX5367 SRP: $8.75 **GBTru: $12**

Sweetheart

Heartshape/couple in sleigh.
Porcelain, 2.50", Dated

QX4957 SRP: $9.75 **GBTru: $18**

Teacher

Crayon design on ruled paper.
Glass Ball, 2.88", Dated
A M Rogers

QX2289 SRP: $4.75 **GBTru: $5**

TENDER TOUCHES
Fanfare Bear

Bear playing drum.
Handcrafted, 2.44", Dated
E Seale

QX5337 SRP: $8.75 **GBTru: $14**

TENDER TOUCHES
Glee Club Bears

Bears caroling.
Handcrafted, 2.00", Dated
E Seale

QX4969 SRP: $8.75 **GBTru: $10**

TENDER TOUCHES
Look Out Below

Mouse on sled.
Handcrafted, 1.75", Dated
E Seale

QX4959 SRP: $8.75 **GBTru: $10**

TENDER TOUCHES
Loving Stitches

Mrs. Chipmunk sewing.
Handcrafted, 2.25", Dated
E Seale

QX4987 SRP: $8.75 **GBTru: $25**

TENDER TOUCHES
Plum Delightful

Mrs. Raccoon w/dessert.
Handcrafted, 2.25", Dated
E Seale

QX4977 SRP: $8.75 **GBTru: $10**

TENDER TOUCHES
Snow Twins

Rabbit build'g snowbunny.
Handcrafted, 2.13", Dated
E Seale

QX4979 SRP: $8.75 **GBTru: $12**

TENDER TOUCHES
Yule Logger

Beaver with tree.
Handcrafted, 2.00", Dated
E Seale

QX4967 SRP: $8.75 **GBTru: $20**

Terrific Teacher

Owl stamping 'Terrific Teacher'.
Handcrafted, 2.25", Dated
L Sickman

QX5309 SRP: $6.75 **GBTru: $7**

Tramp And Laddie

Dog carrying cat in basket.
Handcrafted, 2.69"
J Francis

QX4397 SRP: $7.75 **GBTru: $12**

TWELVE DAYS OF CHRISTMAS, THE - 8TH
Eight Maids A-Milking

Maid milking cow.
Acrylic, 3.88", Dated

QX3089 SRP: $6.75 **GBTru: $10**

TWIRL-ABOUT
Our First Christmas Together

Heart with couple.
Handcrafted, 3.13", Dated
L Sickman

QX4919 SRP: $8.75 **GBTru: $12**

Under The Mistletoe

Rabbit sweethearts kissing.
Handcrafted, 2.38", Dated
S Pike

QX4949 SRP: $8.75 **GBTru: $18**

Up 'N' Down Journey

Santa and deer gallop with sleigh.
Handcrafted, 3.38", Dated
K Crow

QX5047 SRP: $9.75 **GBTru: $18**

WINNIE-THE-POOH
Christopher Robin

Young boy w/tree.
Handcrafted, 4.75"
B Siedler

QX5579 SRP: $9.75 **GBTru: $35**

WINNIE-THE-POOH
Kanga And Roo

Mother/baby kangaroo.
Handcrafted, 3.25"
B Siedler

QX5617 SRP: $9.75 **GBTru: $45**

WINNIE-THE-POOH
Piglet And Eeyore

Pig riding donkey.
Hndcr/Brass, 2.75"
B Siedler

QX5577 SRP: $9.75 **GBTru: $45**

WINNIE-THE-POOH
Rabbit

Rabbit holding a star.
Handcrafted, 3.00"
B Siedler

QX5607 SRP: $9.75 **GBTru: $35**

WINNIE-THE-POOH
Tigger

Tiger with present.
Handcrafted, 3.50"
B Siedler

QX5609 SRP: $9.75 **GBTru: $100**

WINNIE-THE-POOH
Winnie-The-Pooh

Pooh w/"Hunny" pot.
Handcrafted, 3.00"
B Siedler

QX5569 SRP: $9.75 **GBTru: $50**

WINTER SURPRISE - 3RD
Winter Surprise

Penguins singing carols/peek-in egg.
Handcrafted, 3.25", Dated
J Lyle

QX4277 SRP: $10.75 **GBTru: $15**

1992

Across The Miles

Winter country scene within a wreath.
Acrylic, 3.13", Dated
D Rhodus

QX3044 SRP: $6.75 **GBTru: $10**

Anniversary Year

Medallion style photohldr, can change year.
Brass/Chrome, 3.81", Dated
D Unruh

QX4851 SRP: $9.75 **GBTru: $8**

BABY ORNAMENTS
Baby's Christening 1992

Embroided Heart.
Fabric, 4.00", Dated

BBY1331 SRP: $8.50 **GBTru: $10**

BABY ORNAMENTS
Baby's First Christmas 1992

Plush Pink Bunny w/tag.
Plush, 3.00", Dated

BBY1557 SRP: $8.50 **GBTru: $10**

BABY ORNAMENTS
Baby's First Christmas 1992

Embroidered Blue Rock'g Horse.
Fabric, 4.00", Dated

BBY1456 SRP: $8.50 **GBTru: $10**

Baby's First Christmas

Baby sleeps in basket cradle.
Porcelain, 3.50", Dated
P Andrews

QX4581 SRP: $18.75 **GBTru: $30**

Baby's First Christmas - Baby Boy

Animals decorate for the holidays.
Satin Ball, 2.88", Dated
L Votruba

QX2191 SRP: $4.75 **GBTru: $10**

Baby's First Christmas - Baby Girl

Animals decorate for the holidays.
Satin Ball, 2.88", Dated
L Votruba

QX2204 SRP: $4.75 **GBTru: $10**

Baby's First Christmas Photoholder

Heart shap'd eyelet trim'd photoholder.
Fabric, 3.19", Dated
L Votruba

QX4641 SRP: $7.75 **GBTru: $8**

Bear Bell Champ

Bear lifts jingle bell barbells.
Hndcr/Brass, 2.19", Dated
E Seale

QX5071 SRP: $7.75 **GBTru: $10**

BETSEY'S COUNTRY CHRISTMAS - 1ST
Betsey's Country Christmas

Children dance to holiday songs.
Glass, 2.88", Dated
B Clark

QX2104 SRP: $5.00 **GBTru: $15**

Brother

Drummer boy plays toy drum.
Handcrafted, 4.13", Dated
K Crow

QX4684 SRP: $6.75 **GBTru: $10**

Cheerful Santa

African-American Santa waves hello.
Handcrafted, 3.13", Dated
D Unruh

QX5154 SRP: $9.75 **GBTru: $26**

CHILD'S AGE #1 - TEDDY BEAR YEARS
Baby's First Christmas

Teddy bear holds #1 candy cane.
Handcrafted, 2.13", Dated
J Francis

QX4644 SRP: $7.75 **GBTru: $20**

CHILD'S AGE #2 - TEDDY BEAR YEARS
Baby's Second Christmas

Baby bear holds #2 candy cane.
Handcrafted, 2.19", Dated
J Francis

QX4651 SRP: $6.75 **GBTru: $18**

CHILD'S AGE #3 - TEDDY BEAR YEARS
Child's Third Christmas

Baby teddy holds #3 candy cane.
Handcrafted, 2.50", Dated
J Francis

QX4654 SRP: $6.75 **GBTru: $12**

CHILD'S AGE #4 - TEDDY BEAR YEARS
Child's Fourth Christmas

Baby panda holds #4 candy cane.
Handcrafted, 3.00", Dated
J Francis

QX4661 SRP: $6.75 **GBTru: $12**

CHILD'S AGE #5 - TEDDY BEAR YEARS
Child's Fifth Christmas

Baby bear hangs from #5 candy cane.
Handcrafted, 2.38", Dated
D Rhodus

QX4664 SRP: $6.75 **GBTru: $12**

Child's Christmas, A

Teddy naps on lamb rocker/6 way personalize.
Handcrafted, 2.75", Dated
J Francis

QX4574 SRP: $9.75 **GBTru: $10**

CHRISTMAS SKY LINE
Sky Line Caboose

Train caboose car.
Metal, 2.00", Dated
L Sickman

QX5321 SRP: $9.75 **GBTru: $20**

CHRISTMAS SKY LINE
Sky Line Coal Car

Train coal car.
Metal, 1.88", Dated
L Sickman

QX5401 SRP: $9.75 **GBTru: $12**

CHRISTMAS SKY LINE
Sky Line Locomotive

Locomotive train car.
Metal, 1.75", Dated
L Sickman

QX5311 SRP: $9.75 **GBTru: $38**

CHRISTMAS SKY LINE
Sky Line Stock Car

Train stock car.
Metal, 1.88", Dated
L Sickman

QX5314 SRP: $9.75 **GBTru: $15**

Christmas Treasures

Club, Members Only,
Limited Edition of 15,500
Treasure chest w/ 3 mini toy ornaments/club logo.
Hndcr/Antq'd, 1.19-.94", Dated
R Chad

QXC5464 SRP: $22.00 **GBTru: $185**

CHRISTOPHER COLUMBUS 500TH ANNIVERSARY
Santa Maria

Santa Columbus sails on Santa Maria.
Handcrafted, 3.13", Dated
K Crow

QX5074 SRP: $12.75 **GBTru: $15**

CLASSIC AMERICAN CARS - 2ND
1966 Mustang

Mustang convertible automobile.
Handcrafted, 1.25", Dated
D Palmiter

QX4284 SRP: $12.75 **GBTru: $50**

COCA COLA SANTA
Please Pause Here
Haddon Sundblom Art
Santa takes Coke break/clip-on.
Handcrafted, 4.00", Dated
D Lee

QX5291 SRP: $14.75 **GBTru: $27**

COLLECTOR'S PLATE - 6TH & FINAL
Sweet Holiday Harmony

Pup & boy sing/girl plays piano, stand.
Porcelain, 3.25", Dated
L Votruba

QX4461 SRP: $8.75 **GBTru: $21**

CRAYOLA CRAYON - 4TH
Bright Blazing Colors

Dalmatian fireman/crayon fire truck.
Handcrafted, 2.13", Dated
K Crow

QX4264 SRP: $9.75 **GBTru: $25**

Dad

Dad rabbit naps in recliner.
Handcrafted, 2.31", Dated
B Siedler

QX4674 SRP: $7.75 **GBTru: $10**

Dad-To-Be

Proud dad rooster cock-a-doodles news.
Handcrafted, 2.38", Dated
J Lee

QX4611 SRP: $6.75 **GBTru: $8**

Daughter

Girl squirrel in airplane.
Handcrafted, 2.13", Dated
J Francis

QX5031 SRP: $6.75 **GBTru: $10**

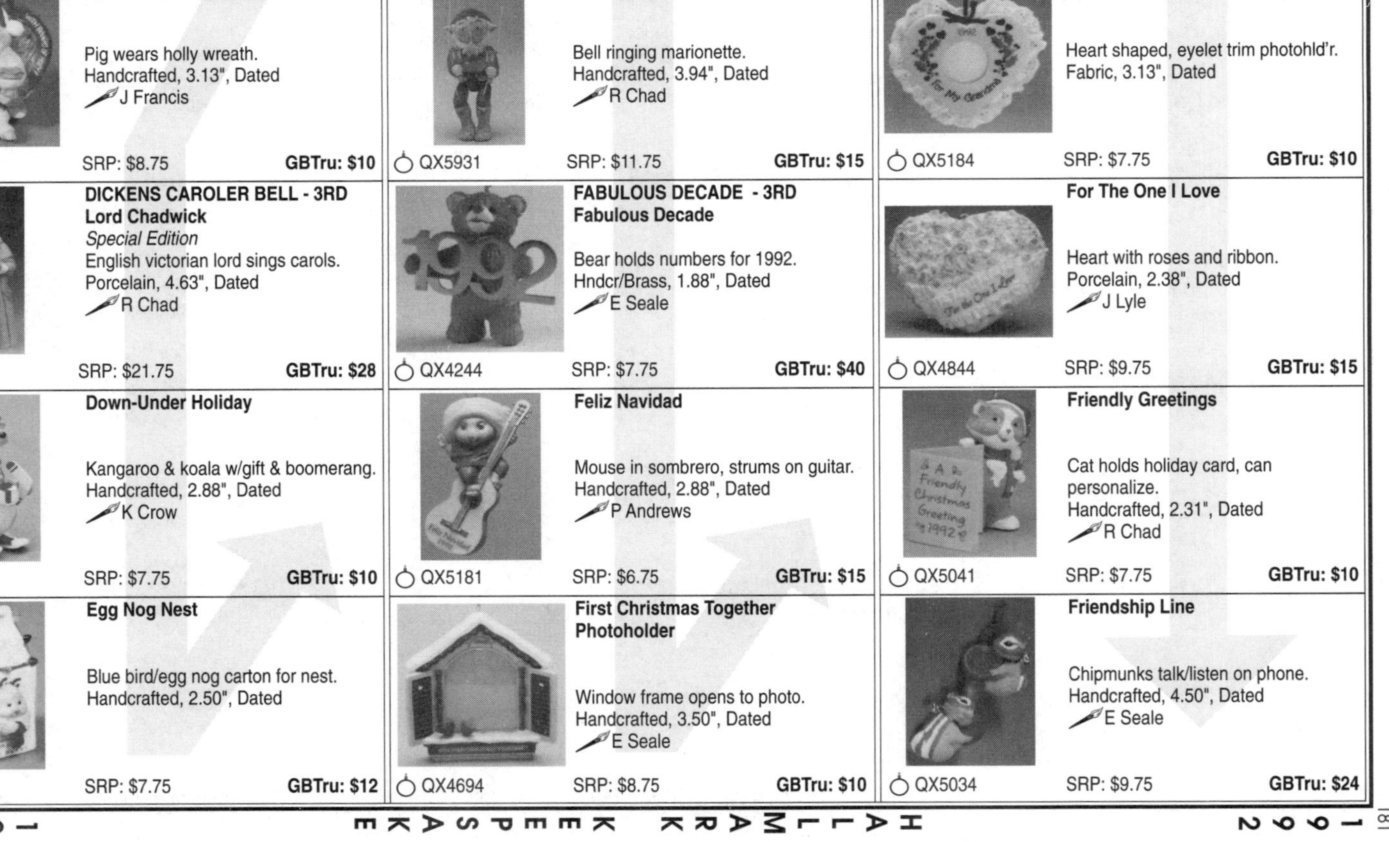

Deck The Hogs

Pig wears holly wreath.
Handcrafted, 3.13", Dated
J Francis

QX5204 | SRP: $8.75 | **GBTru: $10**

Bell ringing marionette.
Handcrafted, 3.94", Dated
R Chad

QX5931 | SRP: $11.75 | **GBTru: $15**

Heart shaped, eyelet trim photohld'r.
Fabric, 3.13", Dated

QX5184 | SRP: $7.75 | **GBTru: $10**

DICKENS CAROLER BELL - 3RD
Lord Chadwick
Special Edition
English victorian lord sings carols.
Porcelain, 4.63", Dated
R Chad

QX4554 | SRP: $21.75 | **GBTru: $28**

FABULOUS DECADE - 3RD
Fabulous Decade

Bear holds numbers for 1992.
Hndcr/Brass, 1.88", Dated
E Seale

QX4244 | SRP: $7.75 | **GBTru: $40**

For The One I Love

Heart with roses and ribbon.
Porcelain, 2.38", Dated
J Lyle

QX4844 | SRP: $9.75 | **GBTru: $15**

Down-Under Holiday

Kangaroo & koala w/gift & boomerang.
Handcrafted, 2.88", Dated
K Crow

QX5144 | SRP: $7.75 | **GBTru: $10**

Feliz Navidad

Mouse in sombrero, strums on guitar.
Handcrafted, 2.88", Dated
P Andrews

QX5181 | SRP: $6.75 | **GBTru: $15**

Friendly Greetings

Cat holds holiday card, can personalize.
Handcrafted, 2.31", Dated
R Chad

QX5041 | SRP: $7.75 | **GBTru: $10**

Egg Nog Nest

Blue bird/egg nog carton for nest.
Handcrafted, 2.50", Dated

QX5121 | SRP: $7.75 | **GBTru: $12**

First Christmas Together Photoholder

Window frame opens to photo.
Handcrafted, 3.50", Dated
E Seale

QX4694 | SRP: $8.75 | **GBTru: $10**

Friendship Line

Chipmunks talk/listen on phone.
Handcrafted, 4.50", Dated
E Seale

QX5034 | SRP: $9.75 | **GBTru: $24**

From Our Home To Yours Gingerbread snowman Christmas welcome. Glass Ball, 2.88", Dated L Votruba QX2131 SRP: $4.75 **GBTru: $10**	**Genius At Work** Elf builds toys. Handcrafted, 2.38", Dated K Crow QX5371 SRP: $10.75 **GBTru: $18**	**Gone Wishin'** Santa fishes for gifts in rowboat/ clip-on. Handcrafted, 1.69", Dated D Lee QX5171 SRP: $8.75 **GBTru: $12**
FROSTY FRIENDS - 13TH **Frosty Friends** Eskimo/ candy cane for whale friend. Hndcr/Acryl, 2.69", Dated J Lee QX4291 SRP: $9.75 **GBTru: $15**	**GIFT BRINGERS, THE - 4TH** **Kolyada** Russian elf maiden visits families. Glass Ball, 2.88", Dated L Votruba QX2124 SRP: $5.00 **GBTru: $10**	**Granddaughter** Girl mouse naps on apple core. Handcrafted, 1.75", Dated E Seale QX5604 SRP: $6.75 **GBTru: $10**
Fun On A Big Scale Hamster Santa & candy/ balance scale. Handcrafted, 3.19", Dated K Crow QX5134 SRP: $10.75 **GBTru: $15**	**Godchild** Adult and baby lamb rest together. Handcrafted, 1.63", Dated D Unruh QX5941 SRP: $6.75 **GBTru: $10**	**Granddaughter's First Christmas** Girl teddy with sack of toys. Handcrafted, 2.19", Dated B Siedler QX4634 SRP: $6.75 **GBTru: $10**
Garfield Garfield w/bedtime story bk/blanket. Handcrafted, 2.44", Dated D Palmiter QX5374 SRP: $7.75 **GBTru: $16**	**Golf's A Ball** Golf ball snowman. Handcrafted, 3.50", Dated L Schuler QX5984 SRP: $6.75 **GBTru: $18**	**Grandmother** Dolls, toys, & holly garlands. Glass Ball, 2.88", Dated QX2011 SRP: $4.75 **GBTru: $10**

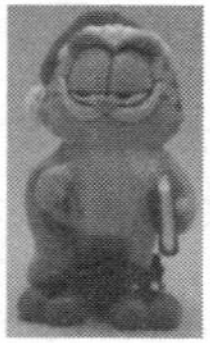

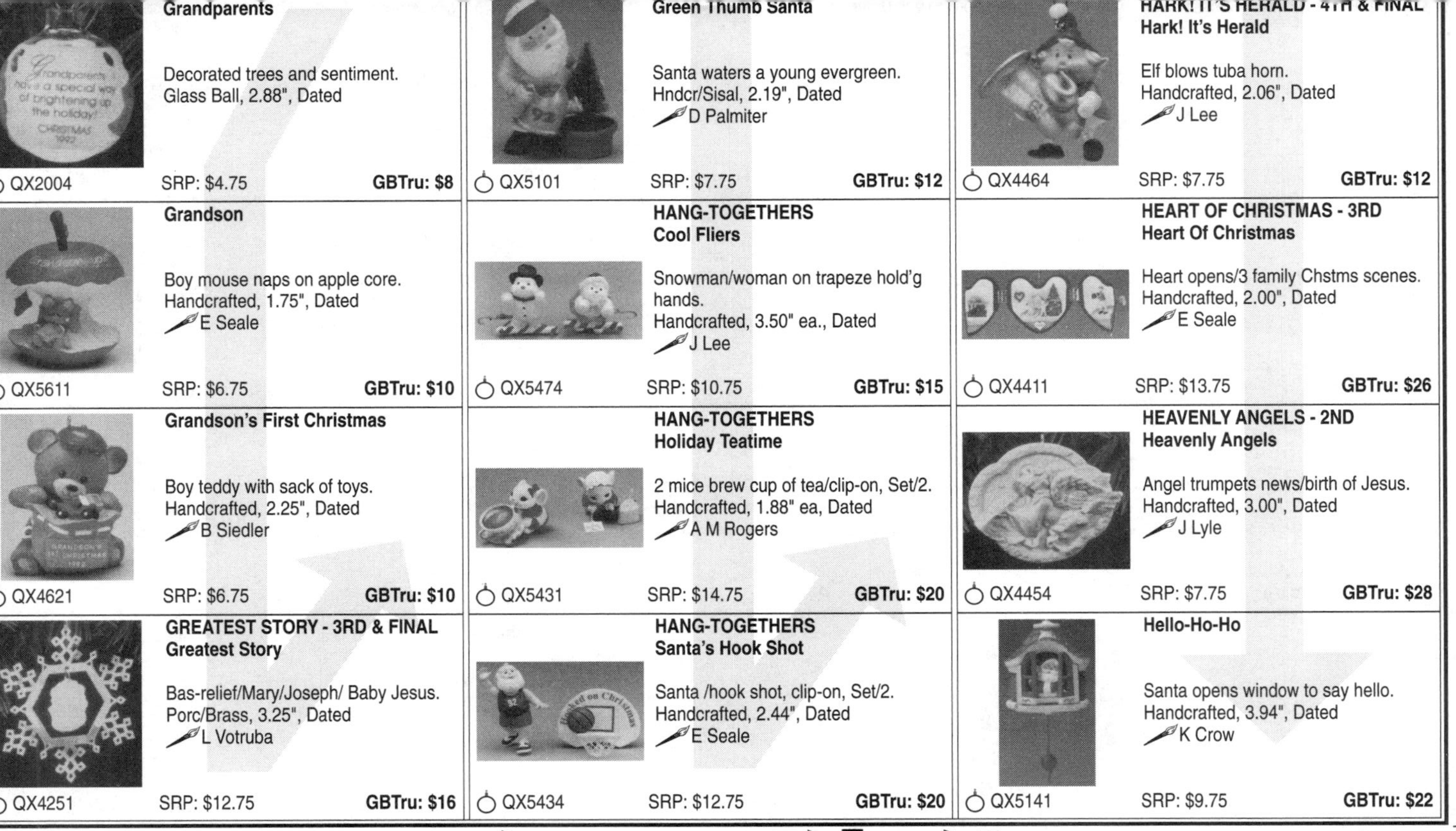

Grandparents

Decorated trees and sentiment.
Glass Ball, 2.88", Dated

QX2004 SRP: $4.75 **GBTru: $8**

Grandson

Boy mouse naps on apple core.
Handcrafted, 1.75", Dated
E Seale

QX5611 SRP: $6.75 **GBTru: $10**

Grandson's First Christmas

Boy teddy with sack of toys.
Handcrafted, 2.25", Dated
B Siedler

QX4621 SRP: $6.75 **GBTru: $10**

GREATEST STORY - 3RD & FINAL
Greatest Story

Bas-relief/Mary/Joseph/ Baby Jesus.
Porc/Brass, 3.25", Dated
L Votruba

QX4251 SRP: $12.75 **GBTru: $16**

Green Thumb Santa

Santa waters a young evergreen.
Hndcr/Sisal, 2.19", Dated
D Palmiter

QX5101 SRP: $7.75 **GBTru: $12**

HANG-TOGETHERS
Cool Fliers

Snowman/woman on trapeze hold'g hands.
Handcrafted, 3.50" ea., Dated
J Lee

QX5474 SRP: $10.75 **GBTru: $15**

HANG-TOGETHERS
Holiday Teatime

2 mice brew cup of tea/clip-on, Set/2.
Handcrafted, 1.88" ea, Dated
A M Rogers

QX5431 SRP: $14.75 **GBTru: $20**

HANG-TOGETHERS
Santa's Hook Shot

Santa /hook shot, clip-on, Set/2.
Handcrafted, 2.44", Dated
E Seale

QX5434 SRP: $12.75 **GBTru: $20**

HARK! IT'S HERALD - 4TH & FINAL
Hark! It's Herald

Elf blows tuba horn.
Handcrafted, 2.06", Dated
J Lee

QX4464 SRP: $7.75 **GBTru: $12**

HEART OF CHRISTMAS - 3RD
Heart Of Christmas

Heart opens/3 family Chstms scenes.
Handcrafted, 2.00", Dated
E Seale

QX4411 SRP: $13.75 **GBTru: $26**

HEAVENLY ANGELS - 2ND
Heavenly Angels

Angel trumpets news/birth of Jesus.
Handcrafted, 3.00", Dated
J Lyle

QX4454 SRP: $7.75 **GBTru: $28**

Hello-Ho-Ho

Santa opens window to say hello.
Handcrafted, 3.94", Dated
K Crow

QX5141 SRP: $9.75 **GBTru: $22**

HERE COMES SANTA - 14TH
Kringle Tours

Santa drives a tour bus.
Handcrafted, 2.63", Dated
L Sickman

QX4341 SRP: $14.75 **GBTru: $30**

Jesus Loves Me

Cameo of child.
Cameo/Brass, 2.88", Dated
P Andrews

QX3024 SRP: $7.75 **GBTru: $12**

MARY'S ANGELS - 5TH
Lily

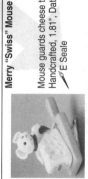

Sleepy angel rubs eyes.
Handcrafted, 2.44", Dated
R Chad

QX4274 SRP: $6.75 **GBTru: $50**

Holiday Memo

Chipmunk on stapler holds memo.
Handcrafted, 2.44", Dated
A M Rogers

QX5044 SRP: $7.75 **GBTru: $10**

KING OF ROCK AND ROLL
Elvis

Elvis in classic pose with guitar.
Brass Plated, 4.50", Dated
D Rhodus/J Lyle

QX5624 SRP: $14.75 **GBTru: $16**

Memories To Cherish

Filigree photoholder.
Porcelain, 3.63", Dated
P Andrews

QX5161 SRP: $10.75 **GBTru: $8**

Holiday Wishes

Two kittens on a wishbone.
Handcrafted, 2.44", Dated
S Pike

QX5131 SRP: $7.75 **GBTru: $15**

Love To Skate

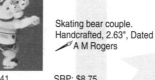

Skating bear couple.
Handcrafted, 2.63", Dated
A M Rogers

QX4841 SRP: $8.75 **GBTru: $15**

MERRY OLDE SANTA - 3RD
Merry Olde Santa

Old fashioned Santa puts horn in stocking.
Handcrafted, 4.13", Dated
D Unruh

QX4414 SRP: $14.75 **GBTru: $25**

Honest George

G. Washington denotes election year.
Handcrafted, 2.50", Dated
J Lee

QX5064 SRP: $7.75 **GBTru: $10**

Loving Shepherd

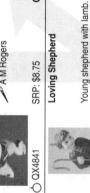

Young shepherd with lamb.
Hndcr/Brass, 2.81", Dated
P Andrews

QX5151 SRP: $7.75 **GBTru: $12**

Merry "Swiss" Mouse

Mouse guards cheese treat/clip-on.
Handcrafted, 1.81", Dated
E Seale

QX5114 SRP: $7.75 **GBTru: $12**

Mom

Mom rabbit naps in easy chair.
Handcrafted, 2.38", Dated
A M Rogers

QX5164 SRP: $7.75 **GBTru: $10**

MR. & MRS. CLAUS - 7TH
Gift Exchange

Mr. and Mrs. Claus exchange presents.
Handcrafted, 3.13", Dated
D Unruh

QX4294 SRP: $14.75 **GBTru: $20**

NORTH POLE NUTCRACKERS
Eric The Baker

Baker wear'g cap, apron, vest w/ cakes.
Wood/Fabric, 4.38", Dated
L Sickman

QX5244 SRP: $8.75 **GBTru: $15**

Mom And Dad

Mom/dad woodchuck string lites/stringer.
Handcrafted, 1.94", Dated
B Siedler

QX4671 SRP: $9.75 **GBTru: $20**

New Home

Mouse welcomes us to cupcake home.
Handcrafted, 2.50", Dated
S Pike

QX5191 SRP: $8.75 **GBTru: $15**

NORTH POLE NUTCRACKERS
Franz The Artist

Artist w/long brush & palette of colors.
Wood/Fabric, 4.63", Dated
L Sickman

QX5261 SRP: $8.75 **GBTru: $18**

Mom-To-Be

Mom hen nests on bow wrapped egg.
Handcrafted, 2.31", Dated
J Lee

QX4614 SRP: $6.75 **GBTru: $8**

Norman Rockwell Art

Musicians and caroler.
Glass Ball, 2.88", Dated
J Lyle

QX2224 SRP: $5.00 **GBTru: $12**

NORTH POLE NUTCRACKERS
Frieda The Animals' Friend

Nutcracker Frieda hold'g duck & egg.
Wood/Fabric, 4.38", Dated
L Sickman

QX5264 SRP: $8.75 **GBTru: $15**

Mother Goose

M. Goose reads story on goose swing.
Hndcr/Brass, 3.50", Dated
K Crow

QX4984 SRP: $13.75 **GBTru: $25**

North Pole Fire Fighter

Fireman Santa down pole w/toy bag.
Hndcr/Brass, 3.75", Dated
E Seale

QX5104 SRP: $9.75 **GBTru: $15**

NORTH POLE NUTCRACKERS
Ludwig The Musician

Musician/sheet music & french horn.
Wood/Fabric, 4.88", Dated
L Sickman

QX5281 SRP: $8.75 **GBTru: $15**

NORTH POLE NUTCRACKERS
Max The Tailor

Tailor/ needle w/yarn & toy animal.
Wood/Fabric, 4.38", Dated
L Sickman

QX5251 SRP: $8.75 **GBTru: $16**

NORTH POLE NUTCRACKERS
Otto The Carpenter

Carpenter w/mallet/house in progress.
Wood/Fabric, 4.38", Dated
L Sickman

QX5254 SRP: $8.75 **GBTru: $15**

NOSTALGIC HOUSES & SHOPS - 9TH
Five-And-Ten-Cent Store

Old five and dime variety store.
Handcrafted, 3.63", Dated
D Lee

QX4254 SRP: $14.75 **GBTru: $35**

O Christmas Tree

Gold Crown Exclusive
Ornament Premiere
Decorated tree forms handle of bell.
Porcelain, 3.25", Dated
L Votruba

QX5411 SRP: $10.75 **GBTru: $25**

Our First Christmas Together

Two mice in sugar bowl hold a heart.
Handcrafted, 2.88", Dated
J Lee

QX5061 SRP: $9.75 **GBTru: $12**

Our First Christmas Together

Hearts decorate a heart.
Acrylic, 3.00", Dated
L Votruba

QX3011 SRP: $6.75 **GBTru: $10**

OWLIVER - 1ST
Owliver

Owl reads story to his pal.
Handcrafted, 2.06", Dated
B Siedler

QX4544 SRP: $7.75 **GBTru: $14**

Partridge In A Pear Tree

Pear opens/partridge in boxer shorts.
Handcrafted, 4.13", Dated
B Siedler

QX5234 SRP: $8.75 **GBTru: $14**

PEACE ON EARTH - 2ND
Peace On Earth - Spain

Girl holds globe, boy with guitar.
Handcrafted, 3.00", Dated
L Sickman

QX5174 SRP: $11.75 **GBTru: $20**

Peanuts

Peanuts gang performs pageant.
Glass Ball, 2.88", Dated

QX2244 SRP: $5.00 **GBTru: $15**

PEANUTS
Snoopy & Woodstock

W'dst'ck hangs on skat'g Snoopy's hat.
Handcrafted, 2.75", Dated
A M Rogers

QX5954 SRP: $8.75 **GBTru: $22**

Polar Post

Bear mail carrier w/working compass.
Handcrafted, 2.88", Dated
E Seale

QX4914 SRP: $8.75 **GBTru: $14**

PUPPY LOVE - 2ND
Puppy Love

Schnauzer pup in basket w/plaid blanket.
Hndcr/Brass, 2.63", Dated
A M Rogers

QX4484 SRP: $7.75 **GBTru: $30**

Rodney Takes Flight

Club: Keepsake of Membership
Rodney in plane w/banner/club logo.
Handcrafted, 1.75", Dated
D Lee

QXC5081 **GBTru: $30**

SANTA AND HIS REINDEER - 4TH
Donder And Blitzen
Gold Crown Reach Program-
**w/any HM purchase.*
Donder & Blitzen, 4th position.
Hndcr/Brass, 3.31"
K Crow

495XPR9738 SRP: $4.95* **GBTru: $20**

Rapid Delivery

Elf paddles in flexible rubbery raft.
Handcrafted, 1.88", Dated
D Palmiter

QX5094 SRP: $8.75 **GBTru: $20**

SANTA AND HIS REINDEER - 1ST
Dasher And Dancer
Gold Crown Reach Program -
**w/any HM purchase.*
Dasher & Dancer, pack leaders.
Hndcr/Brass, 3.06"
K Crow

495XPR9735 SRP: $4.95* **GBTru: $15**

SANTA AND HIS REINDEER - 5TH
Santa Claus
Gold Crown Reach Program-
**w/any HM purchase.*
Santa in Sleigh, links w/reindeer.
Hndcr/Brass, 2.63", Dated
K Crow

495XPR9739 SRP: $4.95* **GBTru: $15**

REINDEER CHAMPS - 7TH
Donder

Reindeer baseball player.
Handcrafted, 3.06", Dated
B Siedler

QX5284 SRP: $8.75 **GBTru: $28**

SANTA AND HIS REINDEER - 2ND
Prancer And Vixen
Gold Crown Reach Program-
**w/any HM purchase.*
Prancer & Vixen, 2nd position.
Hndcr/Brass, 3.06"
K Crow

495XPR9736 SRP: $4.95* **GBTru: $12**

Santa's Club List

Club: Keepsake of Membership
Santa raccoon w/toy bag, candle, club list.
Handcrafted, 2.13", Dated
E Seale

QXC7291 SRP: $15.00 **GBTru: $26**

ROCKING HORSE - 12TH
Rocking Horse

Rocking horse.
Handcrafted, 4.00", Dated
L Sickman

QX4261 SRP: $10.75 **GBTru: $28**

SANTA AND HIS REINDEER - 3RD
Comet And Cupid
Gold Crown Reach Program-
**w/any HM purchase.*
Comet & Cupid, 3rd position.
Hndcr/Brass, 3.00"
K Crow

495XPR9737 SRP: $4.95* **GBTru: $12**

Santa's Roundup

Santa cowboy with lariat tree.
Handcrafted, 3.75", Dated
J Lee

QX5084 SRP: $8.75 **GBTru: $20**

Santa-Full!, A

See thru Santa has cookies in tummy.
Handcrafted, 3.00", Dated
J Francis

QX5991 SRP: $9.75 **GBTru: $30**

Sister

Little girl holds kitten in basket.
Handcrafted, 4.00", Dated
K Crow

QX4681 SRP: $6.75 **GBTru: $10**

Special Dog

Bone treats w/star trim'd dog house photohldr.
Handcrafted, 4.00", Dated
R Chad

QX5421 SRP: $7.75 **GBTru: $24**

Secret Pal

Raccoon special delivers a gift.
Handcrafted, 2.75", Dated
A M Rogers

QX5424 SRP: $7.75 **GBTru: $12**

Skiing 'Round

Furry friend on skis in snowball.
Hndcr/Brass, 3.63", Dated
J Lee

QX5214 SRP: $8.75 **GBTru: $18**

Stocked With Joy

Stocking filled with toys.
Pressed Tin, 4.75", Dated
L Sickman

QX5934 SRP: $7.75 **GBTru: $15**

SHOEBOX GREETINGS
Spirit Of Christmas Stress

Mrs. Lundquist frazzled by shopping.
Handcrafted, 3.50"
R Chad

QX5231 SRP: $8.75 **GBTru: $18**

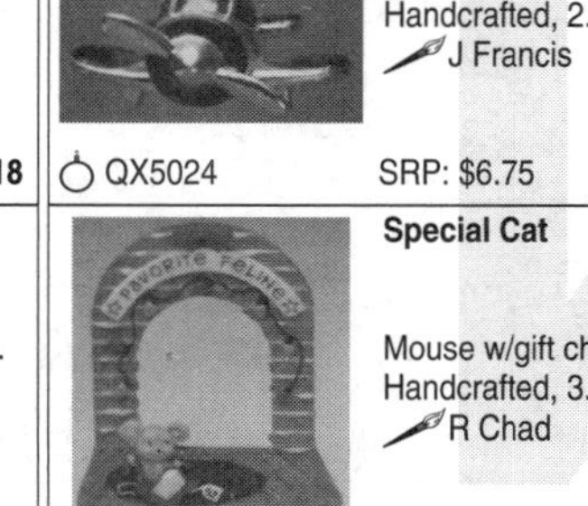

Son

Boy squirrel in airplane.
Handcrafted, 2.00", Dated
J Francis

QX5024 SRP: $6.75 **GBTru: $10**

Tasty Christmas

Twist tail and shark's mouth opens.
Handcrafted, 2.31", Dated
J Francis

QX5994 SRP: $9.75 **GBTru: $20**

Silver Star Train Set

Locomotive, Luggage & "Dome" cars.
Metal, 1.50" ea, Dated
L Sickman

QX5324 SRP: $28.00 **GBTru: $40**

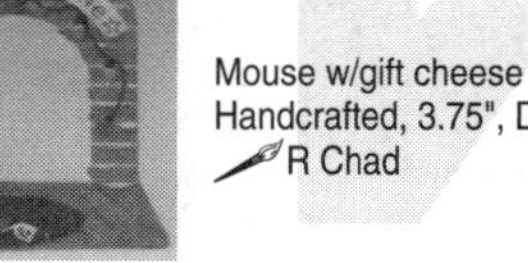

Special Cat

Mouse w/gift cheese on cat photohldr.
Handcrafted, 3.75", Dated
R Chad

QX5414 SRP: $7.75 **GBTru: $15**

Teacher

Children dressed for Christmas play.
Glass Ball, 2.88", Dated
M Englebreit

QX2264 SRP: $4.75 **GBTru: $10**

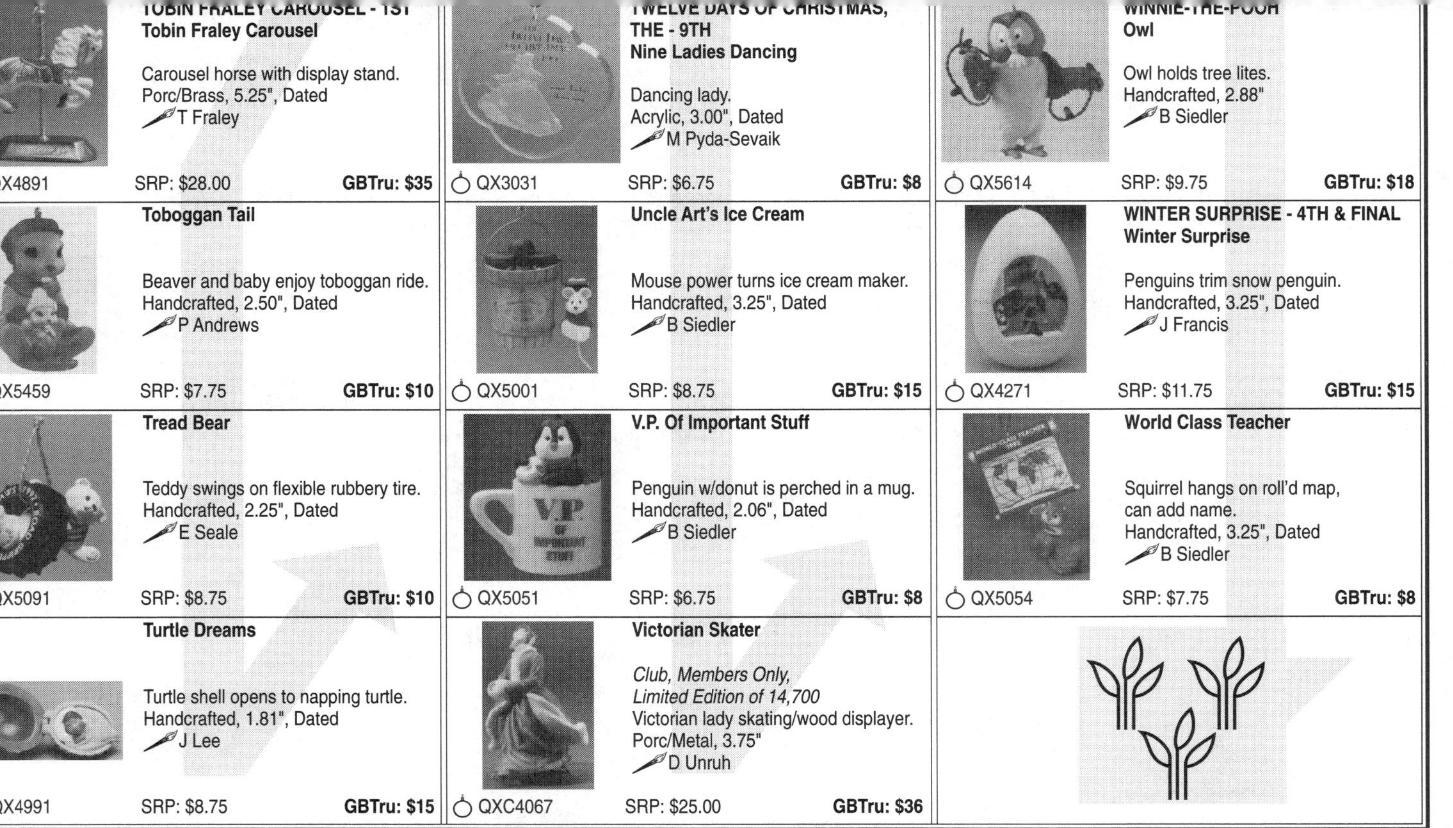

TOBIN FRALEY CAROUSEL - 1ST
Tobin Fraley Carousel

Carousel horse with display stand.
Porc/Brass, 5.25", Dated
T Fraley

QX4891 SRP: $28.00 **GBTru: $35**

TWELVE DAYS OF CHRISTMAS, THE - 9TH
Nine Ladies Dancing

Dancing lady.
Acrylic, 3.00", Dated
M Pyda-Sevaik

QX3031 SRP: $6.75 **GBTru: $8**

WINNIE-THE-POOH
Owl

Owl holds tree lites.
Handcrafted, 2.88"
B Siedler

QX5614 SRP: $9.75 **GBTru: $18**

Toboggan Tail

Beaver and baby enjoy toboggan ride.
Handcrafted, 2.50", Dated
P Andrews

QX5459 SRP: $7.75 **GBTru: $10**

Uncle Art's Ice Cream

Mouse power turns ice cream maker.
Handcrafted, 3.25", Dated
B Siedler

QX5001 SRP: $8.75 **GBTru: $15**

WINTER SURPRISE - 4TH & FINAL
Winter Surprise

Penguins trim snow penguin.
Handcrafted, 3.25", Dated
J Francis

QX4271 SRP: $11.75 **GBTru: $15**

Tread Bear

Teddy swings on flexible rubbery tire.
Handcrafted, 2.25", Dated
E Seale

QX5091 SRP: $8.75 **GBTru: $10**

V.P. Of Important Stuff

Penguin w/donut is perched in a mug.
Handcrafted, 2.06", Dated
B Siedler

QX5051 SRP: $6.75 **GBTru: $8**

World Class Teacher

Squirrel hangs on roll'd map,
can add name.
Handcrafted, 3.25", Dated
B Siedler

QX5054 SRP: $7.75 **GBTru: $8**

Turtle Dreams

Turtle shell opens to napping turtle.
Handcrafted, 1.81", Dated
J Lee

QX4991 SRP: $8.75 **GBTru: $15**

Victorian Skater

Club, Members Only,
Limited Edition of 14,700
Victorian lady skating/wood displayer.
Porc/Metal, 3.75"
D Unruh

QXC4067 SRP: $25.00 **GBTru: $36**

1993

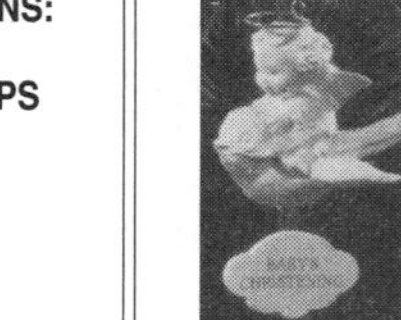

20TH ANNIVERSARY EDITION
Glowing Pewter Wreath

Filigree design pewter wreath.
Pewter, 3.69", Dated
D Unruh

QX5302 SRP: $18.75 **GBTru: $30**

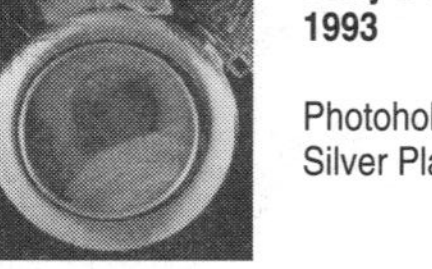

20TH ANNIVERSARY EDITIONS: COMPLEMENTS SERIES
FROSTY FRIENDS
Frosty Friends

Eskimo & penguin decorate igloo.
Handcrafted, 2.50", Dated
E Seale

QX5682 SRP: $20.00 **GBTru: $40**

20TH ANNIVERSARY EDITIONS: COMPLEMENTS SERIES
HERE COMES SANTA
Shopping With Santa

Santa/old fashioned delivery van.
Handcrafted, 3.50", Dated
L Sickman

QX5675 SRP: $24.00 **GBTru: $40**

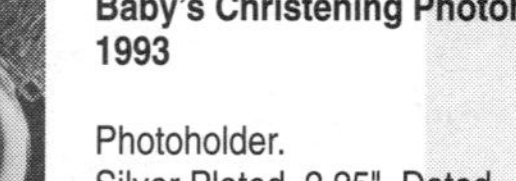

20TH ANNIVERSARY EDITIONS: COMPLEMENTS SERIES
NOSTALGIC HOUSES & SHOPS
Tannenbaum's Dept. Store
Store w/decorated tree/
shoppers/Santa.
Handcrafted, 4.94", Dated
D Lee

QX5612 SRP: $26.00 **GBTru: $50**

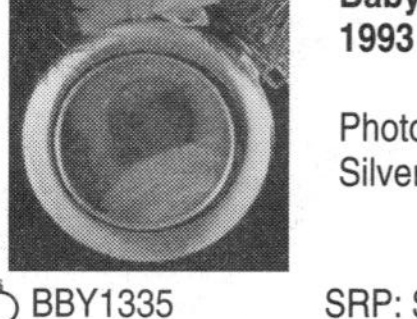

Across The Miles

Bear w/Memory book/far away friends.
Handcrafted, 1.69", Dated
J Francis

QX5912 SRP: $8.75 **GBTru: $12**

Anniversary Year Photoholder

Photoholder/personalize/# of years.
Brass/Chrome, 3.81", Dated
J Lyle

QX5972 SRP: $9.75 **GBTru: $8**

Apple For Teacher

Apple halves - slate/classroom w/mice.
Handcrafted, 2.38", Dated
E Seale

QX5902 SRP: $7.75 **GBTru: $10**

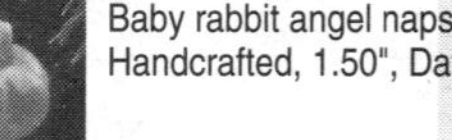

BABY ORNAMENTS
Baby's Christening 1993

Angel flies on bird.
Handcrafted, 3.06", Dated

BBY2917 SRP: $12.00 **GBTru: $15**

BABY ORNAMENTS
Baby's Christening Photoholder 1993

Photoholder.
Silver Plated, 2.25", Dated

BBY1335 SRP: $10.00 **GBTru: $12**

BABY ORNAMENTS
Baby's First Christmas 1993

Baby rabbit angel naps on cloud.
Handcrafted, 1.50", Dated

BBY2918 SRP: $12.00 **GBTru: $15**

BABY ORNAMENTS
Baby's First Christmas 1993

Baby cuddles on moon.
Handcrafted, 2.75", Dated

BBY2919 SRP: $14.00 **GBTru: $18**

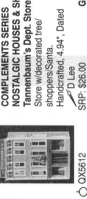

BABY ORNAMENTS
Baby's First Christmas Photoholder 1993

Photoholder.
Handcrafted, 2.75", Dated

BBY1470 SRP: $10.00 **GBTru: $12**

BABY ORNAMENTS
Granddaughter's First Christmas 1993

Cradle holds baby girl rabbit.
Handcrafted, 1.88", Dated

BBY2802 SRP: $14.00 **GBTru: $15**

BABY ORNAMENTS
Grandson's First Christmas 1993

Cradle holds baby boy rabbit.
Handcrafted, 1.88", Dated

BBY2801 SRP: $14.00 **GBTru: $15**

Baby's First Christmas

Silver baby rattle with red bow.
Silver Plated, 3.06", Dated
D Palmiter

QX5512 SRP: $18.75 **GBTru: $18**

Baby's First Christmas

Chipmunk in nutshell swing/rattle.
Handcrafted, 3.06", Dated
P Andrews

QX5515 SRP: $10.75 **GBTru: $15**

Baby's First Christmas - Baby Boy

Baby toys and animals circle ball orn.
Glass Ball, 2.88", Dated
L Votruba

QX2105 SRP: $4.75 **GBTru: $10**

Baby's First Christmas - Baby Girl

Baby toys and animals circle ball orn.
Glass Ball, 2.88", Dated
L Votruba

QX2092 SRP: $4.75 **GBTru: $10**

Baby's First Christmas Photoholder

Baby designs/photowreath with lace.
Hndcr/Lace, 4.75", Dated
A M Rogers

QX5522 SRP: $7.75 **GBTru: $10**

BEARINGERS OF VICTORIA CIRCLE, THE
Abernathy (Son)
*Gold Crown Reach Program - *w/any HM purchase.*
Son bear plays with boat pull toy.
Handcrafted

495XPR9747 SRP: $4.95* **GBTru: $6**

BEARINGERS OF VICTORIA CIRCLE, THE
Bernadette (Daughter)
*Gold Crown Reach Program - *w/any HM purchase.*
Daughter bear reads poem to teddy.
Handcrafted

495XPR9748 SRP: $4.95* **GBTru: $6**

BEARINGERS OF VICTORIA CIRCLE, THE
Fireplace Base
*Gold Crown Reach Program - *w/any HM purchase.*
Fireplace, clock/mantle, rug by hearth.
Handcrafted, Dated,

495XPR9749 SRP: $4.95* **GBTru: $6**

BEARINGERS OF VICTORIA CIRCLE, THE
Mama Bearinger
*Gold Crown Reach Program - *w/any HM purchase.*
Mom bear carries tray of Christmas treats.
Handcrafted

495XPR9745 SRP: $4.95* **GBTru: $8**

BEARINGERS OF VICTORIA CIRCLE, THE
Papa Bearinger
*Gold Crown Reach Program - *w/any HM purchase.*
Dad bear holds Christmas stockings.
Handcrafted
495XPR9746 SRP: $4.95* **GBTru: $6**

Beary Gifted
Hold'g frame, bear artist w/palette.
Handcrafted, 2.63", Dated
K Crow
QX5762 SRP: $7.75 **GBTru: $15**

BETSEY'S COUNTRY CHRISTMAS - 2ND
Betsey's Country Christmas
Winter scene w/Betsey & friends.
Glass Teardrop, 2.88", Dated
QX2062 SRP: $5.00 **GBTru: $10**

Big On Gardening
Elephant gardener w/trowel & flower.
Handcrafted, 2.50", Dated
L Votruba
QX5842 SRP: $9.75 **GBTru: $10**

Big Roller
Hamster races on exercise wheel.
Handcrafted, 3.06", Dated
B Siedler
QX5352 SRP: $8.75 **GBTru: $12**

Bird-Watcher
Bird birdwatcher spots Santa & sleigh.
Handcrafted, 2.44", Dated
J Lee
QX5252 SRP: $9.75 **GBTru: $12**

Bowling For ZZZ's
Mouse naps in bowling bag pocket.
Handcrafted, 1.81", Dated
J Francis
QX5565 SRP: $7.75 **GBTru: $10**

Brother
Pup in football helmet.
Handcrafted, 2.38", Dated
A M Rogers
QX5542 SRP: $6.75 **GBTru: $10**

Caring Nurse
Nurse bear checks baby's heartbeat.
Handcrafted, 1.25", Dated
J Francis
QX5785 SRP: $6.75 **GBTru: $10**

CHILD'S AGE #1 - TEDDY BEAR YEARS
Baby's First Christmas
#1 star cookie in teddy's stock'g.
Handcrafted, 2.19", Dated
K Crow
QX5525 SRP: $7.75 **GBTru: $14**

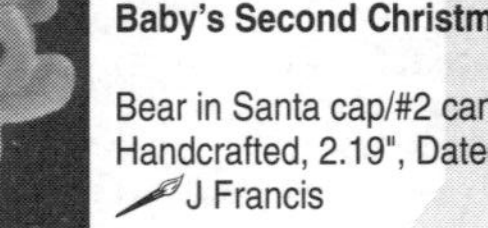

CHILD'S AGE #2 - TEDDY BEAR YEARS
Baby's Second Christmas
Bear in Santa cap/#2 candy cane.
Handcrafted, 2.19", Dated
J Francis
QX5992 SRP: $6.75 **GBTru: $14**

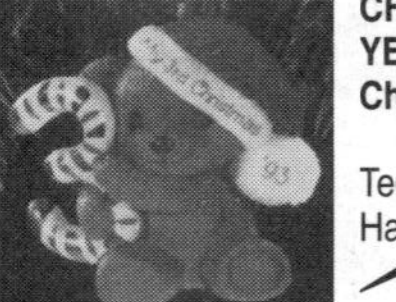

CHILD'S AGE #3 - TEDDY BEAR YEARS
Child's Third Christmas
Teddy bear/Santa cap/#3 candy cane.
Handcrafted, 2.50", Dated
J Francis
QX5995 SRP: $6.75 **GBTru: $12**

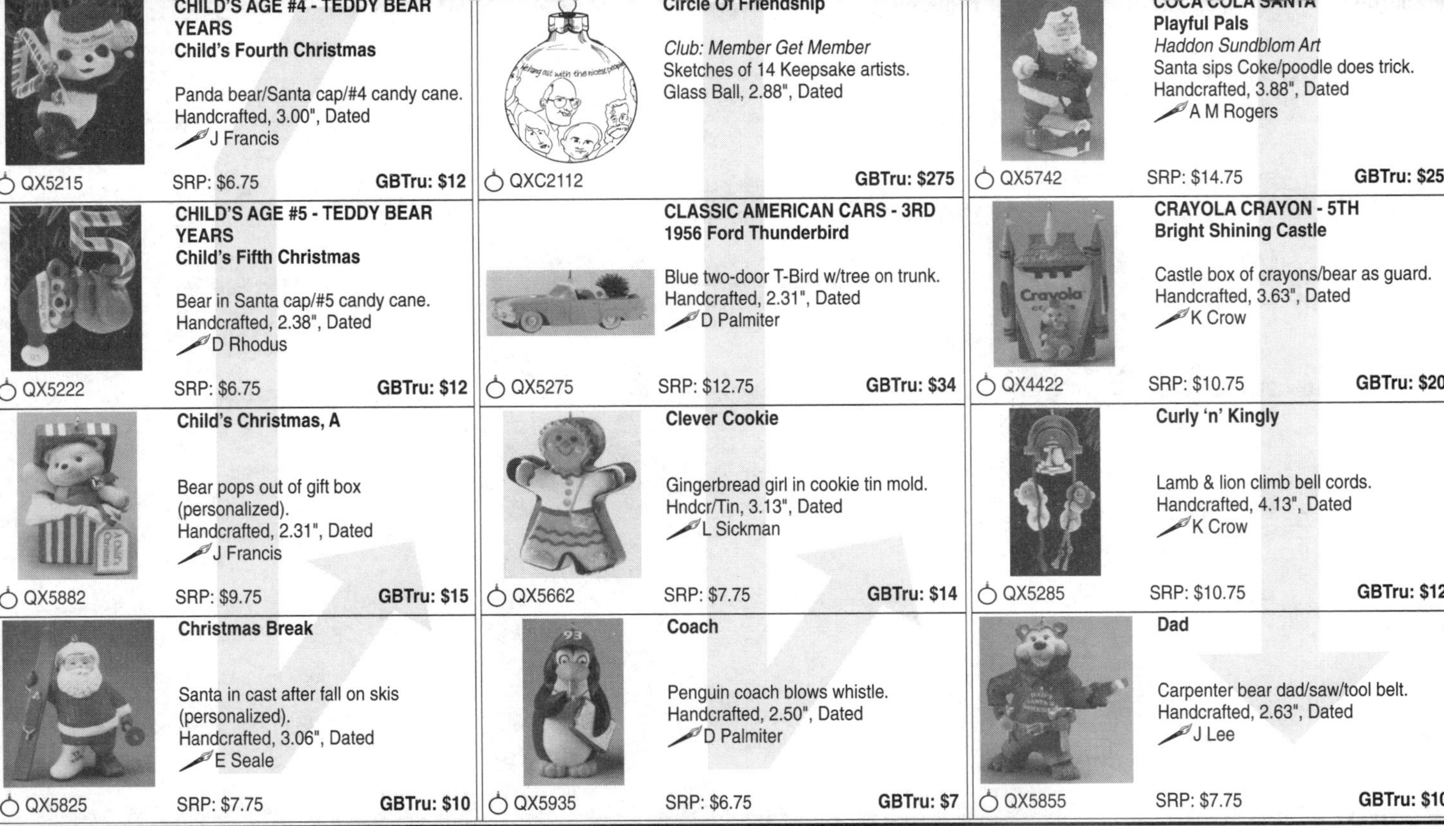

CHILD'S AGE #4 - TEDDY BEAR YEARS
Child's Fourth Christmas

Panda bear/Santa cap/#4 candy cane.
Handcrafted, 3.00", Dated
J Francis

QX5215 SRP: $6.75 **GBTru: $12**

CHILD'S AGE #5 - TEDDY BEAR YEARS
Child's Fifth Christmas

Bear in Santa cap/#5 candy cane.
Handcrafted, 2.38", Dated
D Rhodus

QX5222 SRP: $6.75 **GBTru: $12**

Child's Christmas, A

Bear pops out of gift box (personalized).
Handcrafted, 2.31", Dated
J Francis

QX5882 SRP: $9.75 **GBTru: $15**

Christmas Break

Santa in cast after fall on skis (personalized).
Handcrafted, 3.06", Dated
E Seale

QX5825 SRP: $7.75 **GBTru: $10**

Circle Of Friendship

Club: Member Get Member
Sketches of 14 Keepsake artists.
Glass Ball, 2.88", Dated

QXC2112 **GBTru: $275**

CLASSIC AMERICAN CARS - 3RD
1956 Ford Thunderbird

Blue two-door T-Bird w/tree on trunk.
Handcrafted, 2.31", Dated
D Palmiter

QX5275 SRP: $12.75 **GBTru: $34**

Clever Cookie

Gingerbread girl in cookie tin mold.
Hndcr/Tin, 3.13", Dated
L Sickman

QX5662 SRP: $7.75 **GBTru: $14**

Coach

Penguin coach blows whistle.
Handcrafted, 2.50", Dated
D Palmiter

QX5935 SRP: $6.75 **GBTru: $7**

COCA COLA SANTA
Playful Pals
Haddon Sundblom Art
Santa sips Coke/poodle does trick.
Handcrafted, 3.88", Dated
A M Rogers

QX5742 SRP: $14.75 **GBTru: $25**

CRAYOLA CRAYON - 5TH
Bright Shining Castle

Castle box of crayons/bear as guard.
Handcrafted, 3.63", Dated
K Crow

QX4422 SRP: $10.75 **GBTru: $20**

Curly 'n' Kingly

Lamb & lion climb bell cords.
Handcrafted, 4.13", Dated
K Crow

QX5285 SRP: $10.75 **GBTru: $12**

Dad

Carpenter bear dad/saw/tool belt.
Handcrafted, 2.63", Dated
J Lee

QX5855 SRP: $7.75 **GBTru: $10**

Dad-To-Bee

Future dad bee w/nosegay of flowers.
Handcrafted, 2.13", Dated
J Lee

QX5532 SRP: $6.75 **GBTru: $7**

Daughter

Flexible skat'g giraffe in green sweater.
Handcrafted, 4.44", Dated
L Votruba

QX5872 SRP: $6.75 **GBTru: $8**

DICKENS CAROLER BELL - 4TH & FINAL
Lady Daphne
Special Edition
Lady caroler/fur-trimmed coat & hat.
Porcelain, 4.25", Dated
R Chad

QX5505 SRP: $21.75 **GBTru: $20**

Dunkin' Roo

Kangaroo makes a dunk shot.
Handcrafted, 3.88", Dated
B Siedler

QX5575 SRP: $7.75 **GBTru: $10**

FABULOUS DECADE - 4TH
Fabulous Decade

Skunk holds up numbers for 1993.
Hndcr/Brass, 1.81", Dated
S Pike

QX4475 SRP: $7.75 **GBTru: $12**

Faithful Fire Fighter

Dalmatian fire dog ready to guard tree.
Handcrafted, 2.75", Dated
L Votruba

QX5782 SRP: $7.75 **GBTru: $15**

Feliz Navidad

Monk w/holiday greeting at Spanish church.
Hndcr/Brass, 2.94", Dated
D Lee

QX5365 SRP: $8.75 **GBTru: $12**

Fills The Bill

Pelican fisherman w/baited hook.
Handcrafted, 3.88", Dated
B Siedler

QX5572 SRP: $8.75 **GBTru: $10**

FROSTY FRIENDS - 14TH
Frosty Friends

Eskimo feeds dog at igloo doghouse.
Handcrafted, 2.19", Dated
J Lee

QX4142 SRP: $9.75 **GBTru: $15**

Gentle Tidings

Club, Members Only
Limited Edition of 17,500
Angel cuddles a lamb/wood displayer.
Porcelain, 4.56"
P Andrews

QXC5442 SRP: $25.00 **GBTru: $30**

GIFT BRINGERS, THE - 5TH & FINAL
Magi, The

Three Wise Men arrive with gifts.
Glass Ball, 2.88", Dated
L Votruba

QX2065 SRP: $5.00 **GBTru: $10**

Godchild

Child in pj's kneels in prayer w/teddy pal.
Handcrafted, 2.00", Dated
R Chad

QX5875 SRP: $8.75 **GBTru: $10**

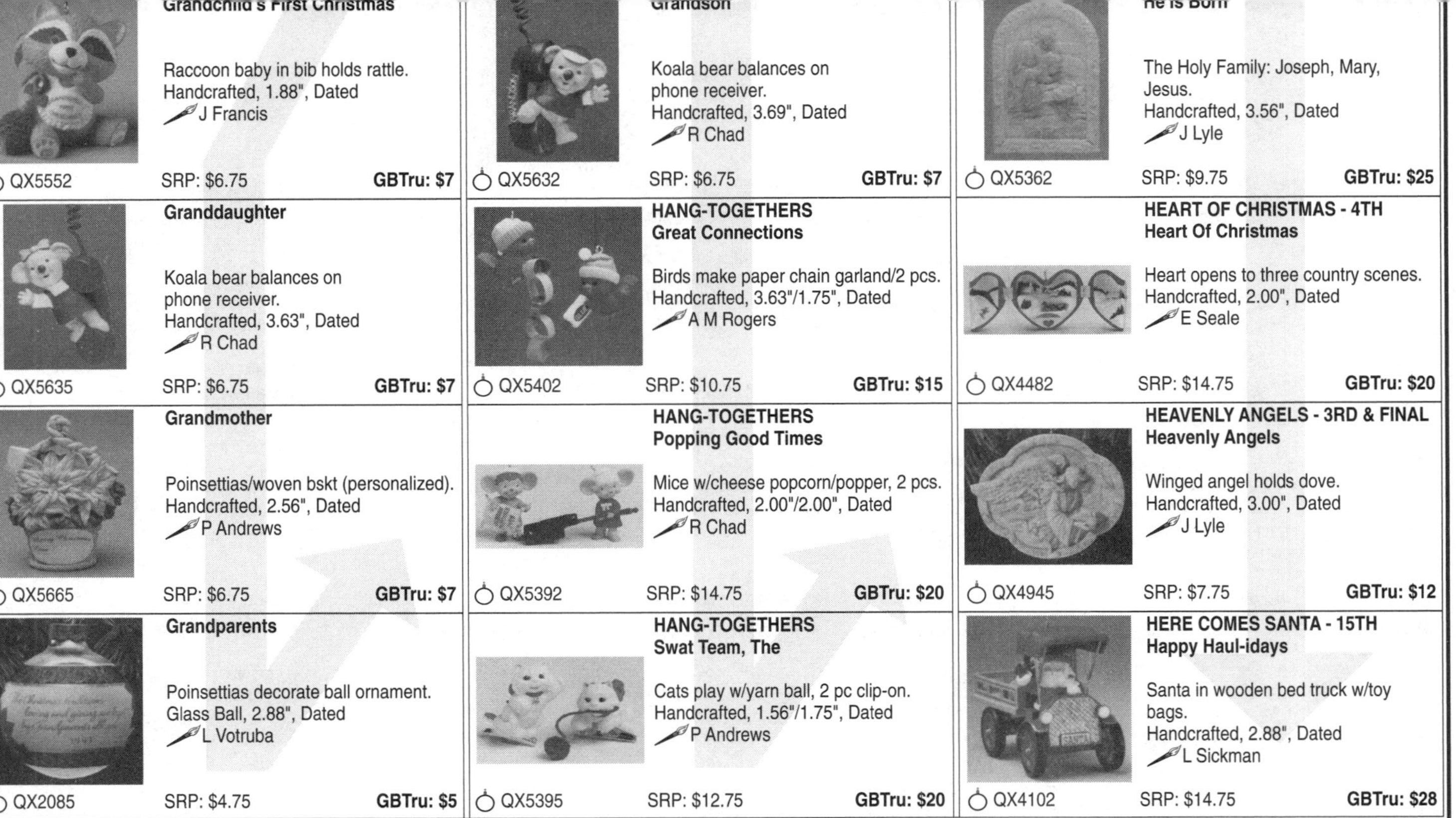

Grandchild's First Christmas

Raccoon baby in bib holds rattle.
Handcrafted, 1.88", Dated
J Francis

QX5552 SRP: $6.75 **GBTru: $7**

Grandson

Koala bear balances on phone receiver.
Handcrafted, 3.69", Dated
R Chad

QX5632 SRP: $6.75 **GBTru: $7**

He Is Born

The Holy Family: Joseph, Mary, Jesus.
Handcrafted, 3.56", Dated
J Lyle

QX5362 SRP: $9.75 **GBTru: $25**

Granddaughter

Koala bear balances on phone receiver.
Handcrafted, 3.63", Dated
R Chad

QX5635 SRP: $6.75 **GBTru: $7**

HANG-TOGETHERS
Great Connections

Birds make paper chain garland/2 pcs.
Handcrafted, 3.63"/1.75", Dated
A M Rogers

QX5402 SRP: $10.75 **GBTru: $15**

HEART OF CHRISTMAS - 4TH
Heart Of Christmas

Heart opens to three country scenes.
Handcrafted, 2.00", Dated
E Seale

QX4482 SRP: $14.75 **GBTru: $20**

Grandmother

Poinsettias/woven bskt (personalized).
Handcrafted, 2.56", Dated
P Andrews

QX5665 SRP: $6.75 **GBTru: $7**

HANG-TOGETHERS
Popping Good Times

Mice w/cheese popcorn/popper, 2 pcs.
Handcrafted, 2.00"/2.00", Dated
R Chad

QX5392 SRP: $14.75 **GBTru: $20**

HEAVENLY ANGELS - 3RD & FINAL
Heavenly Angels

Winged angel holds dove.
Handcrafted, 3.00", Dated
J Lyle

QX4945 SRP: $7.75 **GBTru: $12**

Grandparents

Poinsettias decorate ball ornament.
Glass Ball, 2.88", Dated
L Votruba

QX2085 SRP: $4.75 **GBTru: $5**

HANG-TOGETHERS
Swat Team, The

Cats play w/yarn ball, 2 pc clip-on.
Handcrafted, 1.56"/1.75", Dated
P Andrews

QX5395 SRP: $12.75 **GBTru: $20**

HERE COMES SANTA - 15TH
Happy Haul-idays

Santa in wooden bed truck w/toy bags.
Handcrafted, 2.88", Dated
L Sickman

QX4102 SRP: $14.75 **GBTru: $28**

HERSHEY
Warm And Special Friends

Mice/mugs/hot choc atop Hershey's Cocoa.
Hndcr/Metal, 3.31", Dated
L Sickman

QX5895 SRP: $10.75 **GBTru: $18**

HOLIDAY FLIERS
Tin Blimp

Santa steers airship to deliver toys.
Pressed Tin, 1.69", Dated
L Sickman

QX5625 SRP: $7.75 **GBTru: $16**

Icicle Bicycle

Snowman/bicycle of snowflakes & ice.
Handcrafted, 2.94", Dated
J Lee

QX5835 SRP: $9.75 **GBTru: $10**

High Top-Purr

Kitten in hi-top sneaker/real laces.
Handcrafted, 2.19", Dated
E Seale

QX5332 SRP: $8.75 **GBTru: $18**

HOLIDAY FLIERS
Tin Hot Air Balloon

Santa in balloon basket to deliver toys.
Pressed Tin, 2.63", Dated
L Sickman

QX5615 SRP: $7.75 **GBTru: $16**

It's In The Mail

Club: Keepsake of Membership
Mailmouse puts Courier in post box/ club logo.
Handcrafted, 2.63", Dated
E Seale

QXC5272 SRP: $0.00 **GBTru: $30**

HOLIDAY BARBIE - 1ST
Holiday BARBIE

BARBIE wears red gown.
Handcrafted, 3.50", Dated
P Andrews

QX5725 SRP: $14.75 **GBTru: $125**

Home For Christmas

Baseball star bunny/homeplate/ clip on.
Handcrafted, 1.75", Dated
B Siedler

QX5562 SRP: $7.75 **GBTru: $10**

Julianne And Teddy

Doll in dress w/lace trim w/teddy.
Hndcr/F'brc, 2.75", Dated
D Unruh

QX5295 SRP: $21.75 **GBTru: $35**

HOLIDAY FLIERS
Tin Airplane

Santa flies plane to deliver toys.
Pressed Tin, 1.31", Dated
L Sickman

QX5622 SRP: $7.75 **GBTru: $20**

Howling Good Time

Guitar play/sing'g Santa & howl'g dog.
Handcrafted, 3.00", Dated
A M Rogers

QX5255 SRP: $9.75 **GBTru: $18**

Little Drummer Boy

Boy playing drum.
Handcrafted, 2.75", Dated
D Palmiter

QX5372 SRP: $8.75 **GBTru: $12**

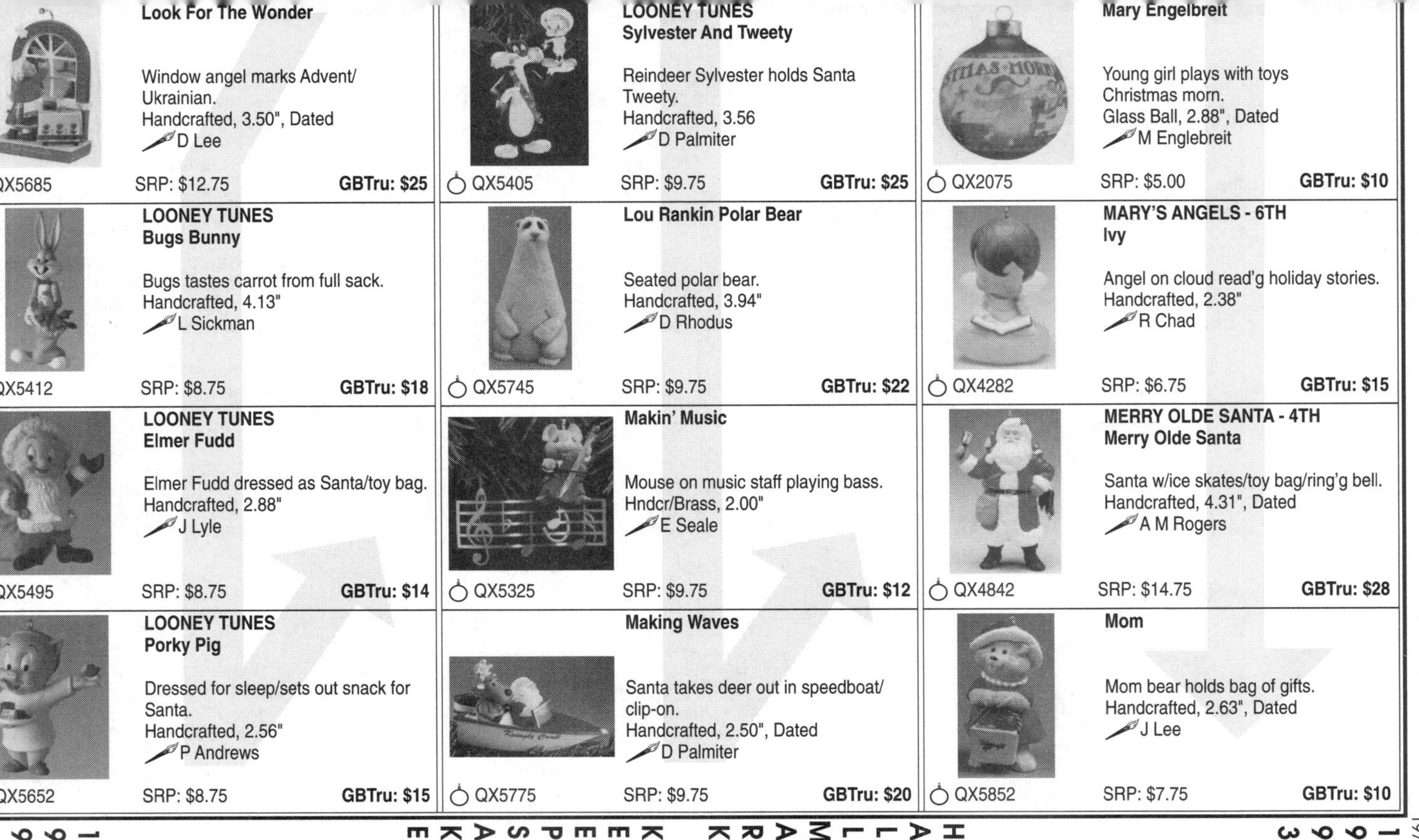

Look For The Wonder

Window angel marks Advent/ Ukrainian.
Handcrafted, 3.50", Dated
D Lee

QX5685 SRP: $12.75 **GBTru: $25**

LOONEY TUNES
Bugs Bunny

Bugs tastes carrot from full sack.
Handcrafted, 4.13"
L Sickman

QX5412 SRP: $8.75 **GBTru: $18**

LOONEY TUNES
Elmer Fudd

Elmer Fudd dressed as Santa/toy bag.
Handcrafted, 2.88"
J Lyle

QX5495 SRP: $8.75 **GBTru: $14**

LOONEY TUNES
Porky Pig

Dressed for sleep/sets out snack for Santa.
Handcrafted, 2.56"
P Andrews

QX5652 SRP: $8.75 **GBTru: $15**

LOONEY TUNES
Sylvester And Tweety

Reindeer Sylvester holds Santa Tweety.
Handcrafted, 3.56
D Palmiter

QX5405 SRP: $9.75 **GBTru: $25**

Lou Rankin Polar Bear

Seated polar bear.
Handcrafted, 3.94"
D Rhodus

QX5745 SRP: $9.75 **GBTru: $22**

Makin' Music

Mouse on music staff playing bass.
Hndcr/Brass, 2.00"
E Seale

QX5325 SRP: $9.75 **GBTru: $12**

Making Waves

Santa takes deer out in speedboat/ clip-on.
Handcrafted, 2.50", Dated
D Palmiter

QX5775 SRP: $9.75 **GBTru: $20**

Mary Engelbreit

Young girl plays with toys Christmas morn.
Glass Ball, 2.88", Dated
M Englebreit

QX2075 SRP: $5.00 **GBTru: $10**

MARY'S ANGELS - 6TH
Ivy

Angel on cloud read'g holiday stories.
Handcrafted, 2.38"
R Chad

QX4282 SRP: $6.75 **GBTru: $15**

MERRY OLDE SANTA - 4TH
Merry Olde Santa

Santa w/ice skates/toy bag/ring'g bell.
Handcrafted, 4.31", Dated
A M Rogers

QX4842 SRP: $14.75 **GBTru: $28**

Mom

Mom bear holds bag of gifts.
Handcrafted, 2.63", Dated
J Lee

QX5852 SRP: $7.75 **GBTru: $10**

Mom And Dad

Mom and Dad give each other matching moose slippers.
Handcrafted, 2.69", Dated
D Palmiter

QX5845 SRP: $9.75 **GBTru: $14**

Mom-To-Bee

Future mom bee carries pot of honey.
Handcrafted, 2.13", Dated
J Lee

QX5535 SRP: $6.75 **GBTru: $7**

MOTHER GOOSE - 1ST
Humpty-Dumpty

Book opens/Humpty-Dumpty bas-relief.
Handcrafted, 2.50", Dated
L Votruba/E Seale

QX5282 SRP: $13.75 **GBTru: $30**

MR. & MRS. CLAUS - 8TH
Fitting Moment, A

Mrs. Claus checks Santa's waistline.
Handcrafted, 3.13", Dated
J Francis

QX4202 SRP: $14.75 **GBTru: $28**

Nephew

Cowboy in western dress.
Handcrafted, 2.50", Dated
A M Rogers

QX5735 SRP: $6.75 **GBTru: $8**

New Home

Cottage tops new home key.
Enamel/Metal, 3.31", Dated
D Palmiter

QX5905 SRP: $7.75 **GBTru: $15**

Niece

Cowgirl in western dress.
Handcrafted, 2.50", Dated
A M Rogers

QX5732 SRP: $6.75 **GBTru: $8**

NOSTALGIC HOUSES & SHOPS - 10TH
Cozy Home

White victorian home with porches.
Handcrafted, 3.81", Dated
D Lee

QX4175 SRP: $14.75 **GBTru: $25**

On Her Toes

Ballerina in pink tutu & toe shoes.
Handcrafted, 3.94"
P Andrews

QX5265 SRP: $8.75 **GBTru: $12**

One-Elf Marching Band

Elf marches w/drum, cymbals & bell.
Handcrafted, 2.88", Dated
R Chad

QX5342 SRP: $12.75 **GBTru: $20**

Our Family Photoholder

House picture window w/Santa/roof.
Handcrafted, 4.56", Dated
D Unruh

QX5892 SRP: $7.75 **GBTru: $10**

Our First Christmas Together

Raccoon couple trim Christmas tree.
Handcrafted, 2.19", Dated
J Lee

QX5642 SRP: $9.75 **GBTru: $12**

Our First Christmas Together

Heart shaped wreath w/2 swans.
Acrylic, 3.13", Dated
P Andrews

QX3015 SRP: $6.75 **GBTru: $10**

PEACE ON EARTH - 3RD & FINAL
Peace On Earth - Poland

Boy/girl in native dress look at globe.
Handcrafted, 3.00", Dated
L Sickman

QX5242 SRP: $11.75 **GBTru: $20**

Peep Inside

Chickadee house opens to babies in nest.
Handcrafted, 2.44", Dated
D Lee

QX5322 SRP: $13.75 **GBTru: $18**

Our First Christmas Together

Cat couple snuggle on porch swing.
Handcrafted, 4.81", Dated
D Lee

QX5942 SRP: $10.75 **GBTru: $12**

Peanuts

Peanuts gang greets holiday in 5 languages.
Glass Ball, 2.88", Dated

QX2072 SRP: $5.00 **GBTru: $10**

People Friendly

Chipmunk trims computer(personalized).
Handcrafted, 2.31", Dated
E Seale

QX5932 SRP: $8.75 **GBTru: $10**

Our First Christmas Together Photoholder

Hearts & holly trim oval photoholder.
Handcrafted, 3.63", Dated
D Unruh

QX5952 SRP: $8.75 **GBTru: $8**

PEANUTS GANG, THE - 1ST
Charlie Brown

Charlie Brown w/snowman w/his face.
Handcrafted, 2.38", Dated
D Rhodus

QX5315 SRP: $9.75 **GBTru: $48**

Perfect Match

Mouse in container betw'n 2 tennis balls.
Handcrafted, 3.50", Dated
B Siedler

QX5772 SRP: $8.75 **GBTru: $12**

OWLIVER - 2ND
Owliver

Squirrel w/gift sees owl nap'g on limb.
Handcrafted, 2.38", Dated
B Siedler

QX5425 SRP: $7.75 **GBTru: $16**

Peek-A-Boo Tree

Forest animals pop in/out of tree.
Handcrafted, 4.19", Dated
K Crow

QX5245 SRP: $10.75 **GBTru: $15**

PERSONALIZED
Baby Block Photoholder

Teddy w/rattle sits atop baby block.
Handcrafted, 2.81"
J Francis

QP6035 SRP: $14.75 **GBTru: $14**

PERSONALIZED
Cool Snowman

Holiday greeting from snowman.
Glass Ball, 2.88"

QP6052 SRP: $8.75 **GBTru: $9.50**

PERSONALIZED
Here's Your Fortune

Chinese cookie with fortune.
Handcrafted, 1.81"
E Seale

QP6002 SRP: $10.75 **GBTru: $11.50**

PERSONALIZED
Playing Ball

Bear baseball player with bat.
Handcrafted, 3.69"
J Francis

QP6032 SRP: $12.75 **GBTru: $13.50**

PERSONALIZED
Festive Album Photoholder

Mouse hangs on ribbon marker (opens).
Handcrafted, 5.44"
L Votruba

QP6025 SRP: $12.75 **GBTru: $13.50**

PERSONALIZED
Mailbox Delivery

Raccoon hold'g Chsms card in mailbox.
Handcrafted, 1.88"
K Crow

QP6015 SRP: $14.75 **GBTru: $15.50**

PERSONALIZED
Reindeer In The Sky

Reindeer pull Santa sled/send greet'g.
Glass Ball, 2.88"

QP6055 SRP: $8.75 **GBTru: $9.50**

PERSONALIZED
Filled With Cookies

Squirrel checks choc chip cookies in acorn.
Handcrafted, 2.13"
A M Rogers

QP6042 SRP: $12.75 **GBTru: $13.50**

PERSONALIZED
On The Billboard

Elf paints message for Santa Sign Co.
Handcrafted, 2.13"
K Crow

QP6022 SRP: $12.75 **GBTru: $13.50**

PERSONALIZED
Santa Says

Santa/pull cord reveals messages.
Handcrafted, 2.94"
E Seale

QP6005 SRP: $14.75 **GBTru: $15.50**

PERSONALIZED
Goin Golfin'

Beaver golfer w/club sits atop golf ball.
Handcrafted, 2.81"
D Palmiter

QP6012 SRP: $12.75 **GBTru: $13.50**

PERSONALIZED
Peanuts

Peanuts friends w/holiday greeting.
Glass Ball, 2.88"

QP6045 SRP: $9.00 **GBTru: $10**

Pink Panther, The

Pink panther Santa/down chimney with toys.
Handcrafted, 3.00", Dated
D Palmiter

QX5755 SRP: $12.75 **GBTru: $15**

PUPPY LOVE - 3RD
Puppy Love

Golden retriever rides a toboggan.
Hndcr/Brass, 1.56", Dated
A M Rogers

QX5045 SRP: $7.75 **GBTru: $18**

REINDEER CHAMPS - 8TH & FINAL
Blitzen

Reindeer football player with full gear.
Handcrafted, 3.13", Dated
B Siedler

QX4331 SRP: $8.75 **GBTru: $14**

SHOEBOX GREETINGS
Maxine

Maxine in bunny slippers wears Santa beard.
Handcrafted, 3.44"
L Sickman

QX5385 SRP: $8.75 **GBTru: $12**

Putt-Putt Penguin

Penguin caddies Santa @ golf course.
Handcrafted, 3.00", Dated
J Lee

QX5795 SRP: $9.75 **GBTru: $12**

ROCKING HORSE - 13TH
Rocking Horse

Gray horse with flowing tail.
Handcrafted, 4.00", Dated
L Sickman

QX4162 SRP: $10.75 **GBTru: $22**

SHOWCASE - FOLK ART AMERICANA
Polar Bear Adventure

Polar bear carries elf & tree.
Handcrafted, 2.94", Dated
L Sickman

QK1055 SRP: $15.00 **GBTru: $70**

Quick As A Fox

Fox delivery service speed skates gift.
Handcrafted, 2.63", Dated
K Crow

QX5792 SRP: $8.75 **GBTru: $10**

Room For One More

Santa & reindeer scrunched in phone booth.
Handcrafted, 3.19", Dated
K Crow

QX5382 SRP: $8.75 **GBTru: $38**

SHOWCASE - FOLK ART AMERICANA
Angel In Flight

Wing'd angel w/spread arms/ bag of stars.
Handcrafted, 3.25", Dated
L Sickman

QK1052 SRP: $15.75 **GBTru: $50**

Ready For Fun

Gingerbread boy in cookie tin mold.
Hndcr/Tin, 3.13", Dated
J Lyle

QX5124 SRP: $7.75 **GBTru: $8**

Sharing Christmas

Club, Members Only
Limited Edition of 16,500
Bas-relief/seated b & g w/gift.
Handcrafted
J Lyle

QXC5435 SRP: $20.00 **GBTru: $25**

SHOWCASE - FOLK ART AMERICANA
Riding In The Woods

Forest elf rides a fox.
Handcrafted, 2.81", Dated
L Sickman

QK1065 SRP: $15.75 **GBTru: $65**

SHOWCASE - FOLK ART AMERICANA
Riding The Wind

Forest elf rides/back of snow goose.
Handcrafted, 2.06", Dated
L Sickman

QK1045 SRP: $15.75 **GBTru: $48**

SHOWCASE - HOLIDAY ENCHANTMENT
Journey To The Forest

Santa feeds deer in forest.
Porcelain, 4.50", Dated

QK1012 SRP: $13.75 **GBTru: $28**

SHOWCASE - OLD-WORLD SILVER
Silver Santa

European style engraved design.
Silver Plated, 3.31", Dated
D Unruh

QK1092 SRP: $24.75 **GBTru: $45**

SHOWCASE - FOLK ART AMERICANA
Santa Claus

Santa carrying toys.
Handcrafted, 4.63", Dated
L Sickman

QK1072 SRP: $16.75 **GBTru: $190**

SHOWCASE - HOLIDAY ENCHANTMENT
Magi, The

Wise Men on camels/
star of Bethlehem.
Porcelain, 3.75", Dated

QK1025 SRP: $13.75 **GBTru: $32**

SHOWCASE - OLD-WORLD SILVER
Silver Sleigh

European style engraved design.
Silver Plated, 3.13", Dated
D Palmiter

QK1082 SRP: $24.75 **GBTru: $32**

SHOWCASE - HOLIDAY ENCHANTMENT
Angelic Messengers

3 angels under Star of Bethlehem.
Porcelain, 4.38", Dated
L Votruba

QK1032 SRP: $13.75 **GBTru: $35**

SHOWCASE - HOLIDAY ENCHANTMENT
Visions Of Sugarplums

Child dreams of toys.
Porcelain, 3.50", Dated

QK1005 SRP: $13.75 **GBTru: $25**

SHOWCASE - OLD-WORLD SILVER
Silver Stars And Holly

European style engraved design.
Silver Plated, 3.06", Dated
D Palmiter

QK1085 SRP: $24.75 **GBTru: $32**

SHOWCASE - HOLIDAY ENCHANTMENT
Bringing Home The Tree

Boy/girl bring tree home thru forest.
Porcelain, 2.81", Dated
R Chad

QK1042 SRP: $13.75 **GBTru: $30**

SHOWCASE-OLD - WORLD SILVER
Silver Dove Of Peace

European style engraved design.
Silver Plated, 3.19", Dated
D Palmiter

QK1075 SRP: $24.75 **GBTru: $30**

SHOWCASE - PORTRAITS IN BISQUE
Christmas Feast

Mom lifts turkey platter above kids.
Porcelain, 3.50", Dated
S Pike

QK1152 SRP: $15.75 **GBTru: $28**

SHOWCASE - PORTRAITS IN BISQUE
Joy Of Sharing

Victorian girl & boy with gifts.
Porcelain, 3.25", Dated
J Lyle

QK1142 SRP: $15.75 **GBTru: $28**

SHOWCASE - PORTRAITS IN BISQUE
Mistletoe Kiss

Victorian couple w/sprig of mistletoe.
Porcelain, 3.63", Dated
S Pike

QK1145 SRP: $15.75 **GBTru: $28**

SHOWCASE - PORTRAITS IN BISQUE
Norman Rockwell - Filling The Stockings

Santa w/bag of toys holds baby sock.
Porcelain, 3.56", Dated
P Dutkin

QK1155 SRP: $15.75 **GBTru: $35**

SHOWCASE - PORTRAITS IN BISQUE
Norman Rockwell - Jolly Postman

Boys & dog walk with postman.
Porcelain, 3.25", Dated
P Dutkin

QK1162 SRP: $15.75 **GBTru: $28**

SIGNATURE COLLECTION - 1ST
Santa's Favorite Stop
Artist Tours
Santa w/list, toy bag at fireplace, 2 pc.
Handcrafted, Dated

QXC4125 SRP: $55.00 **GBTru: $425**

Silvery Noel

Silver child's block spells N-o-e-l.
Silver Plated, 2.00", Dated
J Lyle

QX5305 SRP: $12.75 **GBTru: $15**

Sister

Cheerleader kitten.
Handcrafted, 2.25", Dated
A M Rogers

QX5545 SRP: $6.75 **GBTru: $10**

Sister To Sister

Mice in open compact on powder puff.
Handcrafted, 2.31", Dated
E Seale

QX5885 SRP: $9.75 **GBTru: $45**

Smile! It's Christmas Photoholder

Exposed film roll is holder for 2 pics.
Handcrafted, 4.00", Dated
E Seale

QX5335 SRP: $9.75 **GBTru: $12**

Snow Bear Angel

Bear flaps arms & legs/snow angel.
Handcrafted, 2.75", Dated
J Lee

QX5355 SRP: $7.75 **GBTru: $10**

Snow Hideway

Fox sits at base of snowy wreath.
Handcrafted, 3.00", Dated
J Francis

QX5312 SRP: $9.75 **GBTru: $12**

Snowbird

Travel bird with camera & sunglasses.
Handcrafted, 2.63, Dated
J Lee

QX5765 SRP: $7.75 **GBTru: $10**

Son

Flexible skating giraffe in red sweater.
Handcrafted, 2.38", Dated
L Votruba

QX5865 SRP: $6.75 **GBTru: $7**

Special Cat Photoholder

Fish/bell decorate photoholder collar.
Hndcr/Brass, 4.13", Dated
L Votruba

QX5235 SRP: $7.75 **GBTru: $8**

Special Dog Photoholder

Bones/stars/hydrant on photoholder collar.
Handcrafted, 4.81", Dated
L Votruba

QX5962 SRP: $7.75 **GBTru: $8**

Star Of Wonder

Forest animals gaze at star of Bethlehem.
Handcrafted, 3.25", Dated
J Lyle

QX5982 SRP: $6.75 **GBTru: $20**

Star Teacher

Polar bear w/ photoholder (personalized).
Handcrafted, 2.94", Dated
P Andrews

QX5645 SRP: $5.75 **GBTru: $5**

Strange And Wonderful Love

Porcupine hugs cactus "tree".
Handcrafted, 2.81", Dated
L Sickman

QX5965 SRP: $8.75 **GBTru: $10**

SUPER HEROES
Superman

Superman readies for takeoff.
Handcrafted, 2.00"
R Chad

QX5752 SRP: $12.75 **GBTru: $32**

TENDER TOUCHES
You're Always Welcome
Premiere Event Ornament
Mrs. Bear w/welcome mat at door.
Handcrafted, 2.50", Dated
E Seale

QX5692 SRP: $9.75 **GBTru: $38**

That's Entertainment

Santa pulls bunny out of top hat.
Handcrafted, 2.94", Dated
B Siedler

QX5345 SRP: $8.75 **GBTru: $12**

To My Grandma Photoholder

Writing pad photoholder (personalized).
Handcrafted, 3.31", Dated
D Lee

QX5555 SRP: $7.75 **GBTru: $10**

TOBIN FRALEY CAROUSEL - 2ND
Tobin Fraley Carousel

Pranc'g white carousel horse & stand.
Handcrafted, 5.25", Dated
T Fraley

QX5502 SRP: $28.00 **GBTru: $30**

Top Banana

Monkey sits on bunch/ munching banana.
Handcrafted, 2.44", Dated
A M Rogers

QX5925 SRP: $7.75 **GBTru: $12**

Trimmed With Memories

Club: Keepsake of Membership - 20th Anniversary
Tree trimmed w/special series orns.
Handcrafted, 3.88", Dated
L Sickman

QXC5432 SRP: $12.00 **GBTru: $30**

Wake Up Call

Pup pulls cover from sleeping dad.
Handcrafted, 1.44", Dated
D Unruh

QX5262 SRP: $8.75 **GBTru: $12**

WINNIE-THE-POOH
Owl

Owl in hat, muffler & hot water bottle.
Handcrafted, 3.63"
B Siedler

QX5695 SRP: $9.75 **GBTru: $15**

TWELVE DAYS OF CHRISTMAS, THE - 10TH
Ten Lords A-Leaping

Clear heart-shaped/ gentleman leaping.
Acrylic, 3.00", Dated
R Chad

QX3012 SRP: $6.75 **GBTru: $12**

Water Bed Snooze

Polar bear naps on ice cube tray/clip-on.
Handcrafted, 1.75", Dated
J Lee

QX5375 SRP: $9.75 **GBTru: $15**

WINNIE-THE-POOH
Rabbit

Rabbit skates using fry pans on feet.
Handcrafted, 3.50"
B Siedler

QX5702 SRP: $9.75 **GBTru: $18**

TWIRL-ABOUT
Our First Christmas Together

Bride/groom dance/heart.
Brass/Slvr Pltd, 3.25", Dated
A M Rogers

QX5955 SRP: $18.75 **GBTru: $20**

WINNIE-THE-POOH
Eeyore

Eeyore holds tight to toboggan.
Handcrafted, 2.00"
B Siedler

QX5712 SRP: $9.75 **GBTru: $25**

WINNIE-THE-POOH
Tigger And Piglet

Wrap'd in Tigger's tail, Piglet skates w/pal.
Handcrafted, 3.75"
B Siedler

QX5705 SRP: $9.75 **GBTru: $36**

U.S. CHRISTMAS STAMPS - 1ST
U.S. Christmas Stamps
John Berkey design:1983.
Santa Claus, IN
1983 Christmas stamp with display stand.
Enamel/Copper, 2.31", Dated
L Sickman

QX5292 SRP: $10.75 **GBTru: $20**

WINNIE-THE-POOH
Kanga And Roo

Kanga & Roo ready to cross-country ski.
Handcrafted, 3.75"
B Siedler

QX5672 SRP: $9.75 **GBTru: $18**

WINNIE-THE-POOH
Winnie-The-Pooh

Pooh set to ski on barrel staves.
Handcrafted, 3.63"
B Siedler

QX5715 SRP: $9.75 **GBTru: $22**

1994

Across The Miles

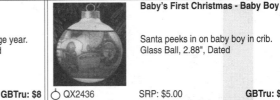

Raccoon with a note in a glass bottle.
Handcrafted, 2.56", Dated
P Andrews

QX5656 SRP: $8.95 **GBTru: $10**

All Pumped Up

Elf fills football with air.
Handcrafted, 2.44", Dated
D Rhodus

QX5923 SRP: $8.95 **GBTru: $15**

Angel Hare

Rabbit angel helps trim tree.
Hndcr/Brass, 3.38", Dated
L Sickman

QX5896 SRP: $8.95 **GBTru: $11**

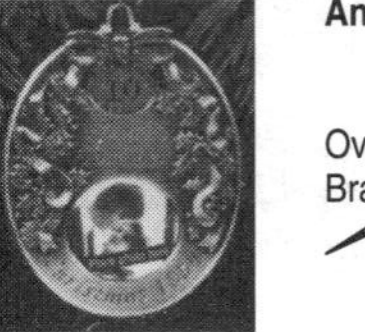

Anniversary Year

Oval photo frame/can change year.
Brass/Chrome, 3.81", Dated
R Bishop

QX5683 SRP: $10.95 **GBTru: $8**

Baby's First Christmas

Holly & bow decorate baby shoes.
Porc/Brass, 2.56", Dated
D Unruh

QX5633 SRP: $18.95 **GBTru: $20**

Baby's First Christmas

Baby block opens to teddy & personal message.
Handcrafted, 2.06", Dated
E Seale

QX5743 SRP: $12.95 **GBTru: $15**

Baby's First Christmas

Bear, rocking horse & stars: photoholder.
Handcrafted, 3.31", Dated
L Votruba

QX5636 SRP: $7.95 **GBTru: $8**

Baby's First Christmas - Baby Boy

Santa peeks in on baby boy in crib.
Glass Ball, 2.88", Dated

QX2436 SRP: $5.00 **GBTru: $8**

Baby's First Christmas - Baby Girl

Santa peeks in on baby girl in crib.
Glass Ball, 2.88", Dated

QX2433 SRP: $5.00 **GBTru: $8**

BARBIE -1ST
BARBIE Debut 1959
35th Anniversary Keepsake
Ornament Special Issues
1959 BARBIE in bathing suit.
Handcrafted, Dated

QX5006 SRP: $14.95 **GBTru: $40**

Barney

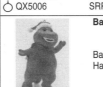

Barney Dinosaur on skates.
Handcrafted

QX5966 SRP: $9.95 **GBTru: $12**

BASEBALL HEROES - 1ST
Babe Ruth

Baseball star bats a homerun/ player card included.
Handcrafted, 3.38", Dated
D Rhodus

QX5323 SRP: $12.95 **GBTru: $50**

Beatles Gift Set, The

Beatles set/5 includes stage, drums.
Handcrafted, Dated
A M Rogers

QX5373 SRP: $48.00 **GBTru: $90**

BEATRIX POTTER
Tale Of Peter Rabbit, The

Peter Rabbit with mom and sisters.
Glass ball, 2.88", Dated

QX2443 SRP: $5.00 **GBTru: $10**

BETSEY'S COUNTRY CHRISTMAS - 3RD & FINAL
Betsey's Country Christmas

Children trim indoor tree.
Glass teardrop, 2.88", Dated

QX2403 SRP: $5.00 **GBTru: $10**

Big Shot

Mouse balances basketball.
Handcrafted, 2.88", Dated
B Siedler

QX5873 SRP: $7.95 **GBTru: $10**

Brother

Boy pup drives blue convertible.
Handcrafted, 2.50", Dated
S Pike

QX5516 SRP: $6.95 **GBTru: $10**

Busy Batter

Beaver carves his own bat.
Handcrafted, 2.63", Dated
B Siedler

QX5876 SRP: $7.95 **GBTru: $10**

Candy Caper

Mouse balances on candy jar.
Handcrafted, 2.69", Dated
P Andrews

QX5776 SRP: $8.95 **GBTru: $18**

Caring Doctor

Mouse checks gingerbread cookie.
Handcrafted, 2.56", Dated
A M Rogers

QX5823 SRP: $8.95 **GBTru: $10**

CAT NAPS - 1ST
Cat Naps

Cat naps in treat cookie jar.
Handcrafted, 2.88", Dated
D Rhodus

QX5313 SRP: $7.95 **GBTru: $30**

Champion Teacher

Worm pokes out of apple.
Handcrafted, 1.94", Dated
B Siedler

QX5836 SRP: $6.95 **GBTru: $10**

Cheers To You!

Bear rings in holiday cheer from stein.
Hndcr/Brass, 3.06"
K Crow

QX5796 SRP: $10.95 **GBTru: $15**

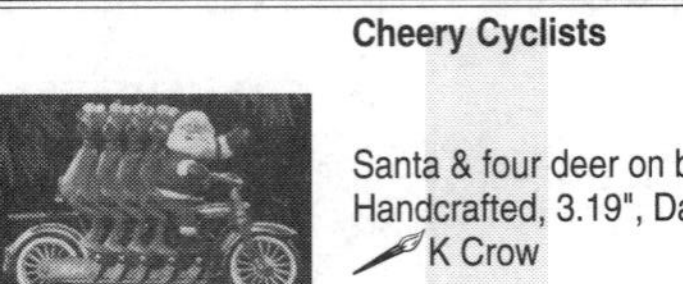

Cheery Cyclists

Santa & four deer on bike.
Handcrafted, 3.19", Dated
K Crow

QX5786 SRP: $12.95 **GBTru: $25**

Child Care Giver

Adult bear reads story to raccoon child.
Handcrafted, 2.13", Dated
L Votruba

QX5906 SRP: $7.95 **GBTru: $10**

CHILD'S AGE #1 - TEDDY BEAR YEARS
Baby's First Christmas

Star cookie in stocking held by teddy.
Handcrafted, 2.19", Dated

QX5713 SRP: $7.95 **GBTru: $15**

CHILD'S AGE #2 - TEDDY BEAR YEARS
Baby's Second Christmas

Bear holds Tree cookie in stocking.
Handcrafted, 2.38", Dated
K Crow

QX5716 SRP: $7.95 **GBTru: $15**

CHILD'S AGE #3 - TEDDY BEAR YEARS
Child's Third Christmas

Bear holds candy cane #3.
Handcrafted, 2.50", Dated
J Francis

QX5723 SRP: $6.95 **GBTru: $12**

CHILD'S AGE #4 - TEDDY BEAR YEARS
Child's Fourth Christmas

Panda bear holds candy cane #4.
Handcrafted, 3.00", Dated
J Francis

QX5726 SRP: $6.95 **GBTru: $12**

CHILD'S AGE #5 - TEDDY BEAR YEARS
Child's Fifth Christmas

Bear hangs from candy cane #5.
Handcrafted, 3.50", Dated
D Rhodus

QX5733 SRP: $6.95 **GBTru: $10**

CLASSIC AMERICAN CARS - 4TH
1957 Chevrolet Bel Air

Classic car filled w/presents and tree.
Handcrafted, 4.38", Dated
D Palmiter

QX5422 SRP: $12.95 **GBTru: $28**

Coach

Dog with whistle and equipment bag.
Handcrafted, 3.13", Dated
D Unruh

QX5933 SRP: $7.95 **GBTru: $10**

COCA COLA SANTA
Relaxing Moment
Haddon Sundblom Art
Seated Santa w/Coke kicks off boots.
Handcrafted, 2.56", Dated
J Francis

QX5356 SRP: $14.95 **GBTru: $25**

Cock-A-Doodle Christmas

Rooster crows from atop draft horse.
Handcrafted, 3.19", Dated
L Votruba

QX5396 SRP: $8.95 **GBTru: $10**

Colors Of Joy

Mouse fills brush with paint.
Handcrafted, 2.88", Dated
E Seale

QX5893 SRP: $7.95 **GBTru: $16**

CRAYOLA CRAYON - 6TH
Bright Playful Colors

Bear on crayon swing and playset.
Handcrafted, 3.38", Dated
K Crow

QX5273 SRP: $10.95 **GBTru: $18**

Extra-Special Delivery

Chipmunk delivers mail.
Handcrafted, 2.13", Dated
K Crow

QX5833 SRP: $7.95 **GBTru: $10**

FLINTSTONES, THE
Fred & Barney

Fred drives Barney in stone age car.
Handcrafted, 2.94", Dated
D Rhodus

QX5003 SRP: $14.95 **GBTru: $20**

Dad

Dad bear with loving cup trophy.
Handcrafted, 2.31", Dated
A M Rogers

QX5463 SRP: $7.95 **GBTru: $10**

FABULOUS DECADE - 5TH
Fabulous Decade

White rabbit carries brass "1994".
Handcrafted, 2.06", Dated
E Seale

QX5263 SRP: $7.95 **GBTru: $18**

Follow The Sun

Migrating bird in sleigh weathervane.
Handcrafted, 3.81", Dated
K Crow

QX5846 SRP: $8.95 **GBTru: $12**

Dad-To-Be

Lion brings home take-out snack.
Handcrafted, 2.56", Dated
S Pike

QX5473 SRP: $7.95 **GBTru: $8**

Feelin' Groovy

Santa giving the peace sign.
Handcrafted, 2.69", Dated

QX5953 SRP: $7.95 **GBTru: $20**

For My Grandma

Trimmed tree photoholder/
can personalize.
Handcrafted, 3.56", Dated
D Lee

QX5613 SRP: $6.95 **GBTru: $8**

Daughter

Pink dinosaur on rollerblades.
Handcrafted, 2.81", Dated
P Andrews

QX5623 SRP: $6.95 **GBTru: $7**

Feliz Navidad

Pup in sombrero pops out of pot.
Handcrafted, 2.81", Dated
A M Rogers

QX5793 SRP: $8.95 **GBTru: $20**

Friendly Push

Mice use ice skate for ride.
Handcrafted, 3.13", Dated
B Siedler

QX5686 SRP: $8.95 **GBTru: $10**

FROSTY FRIENDS - 15TH
Frosty Friends

Bear cub jumps thru wreath for fish treat.
Handcrafted, 2.56", Dated
E Seale

QX5293 SRP: $9.95 **GBTru: $18**

GARDEN ELVES
Daisy Days

Elf w/bouquet of Summer daisies.
Handcrafted, 2.88"
R Chad

QX5986 SRP: $9.95 **GBTru: $10**

GARDEN ELVES
Harvest Joy

Elf w/Autumn pumpkin.
Handcrafted, 2.81"
R Chad

QX5993 SRP: $9.95 **GBTru: $10**

GARDEN ELVES
Tulip Time

Elf w/flowerpot of Spring tulips.
Handcrafted, 2.31"
R Chad

QX5983 SRP: $9.95 **GBTru: $10**

GARDEN ELVES
Yuletide Cheer

Elf w Winter holly & tree.
Handcrafted, 2.81"
R Chad

QX5976 SRP: $9.95 **GBTru: $10**

Garfield

Cat carries teddy in stocking.
Handcrafted, 2.50", Dated

QX5753 SRP: $12.95 **GBTru: $18**

Gentle Nurse

Girl cares for pup with bandaged paw.
Handcrafted, 2.44", Dated
J Lyle

QX5973 SRP: $6.95 **GBTru: $12**

Godchild

Angel on a star swing.
Handcrafted, 3.50", Dated
A M Rogers

QX4453 SRP: $8.95 **GBTru: $15**

Godparent

Angel orchestra & loving sentiment.
Glass Ball, 2.88", Dated
M Hamilton

QX2423 SRP: $5.00 **GBTru: $8**

Grandchild's First Christmas

Mouse in pj's naps w/teddy: clip-on.
Handcrafted, 3.00", Dated
D Unruh

QX5676 SRP: $7.95 **GBTru: $12**

Granddaughter

Girl beaver w/double scoop ice cream cone.
Handcrafted, 2.25", Dated
S Pike

QX5523 SRP: $6.95 **GBTru: $10**

Grandmother

Gingerbread cookies in basket.
Hndcr/Fabric, 2.56", Dated
P Andrews

QX5673 SRP: $7.95 **GBTru: $10**

Grandpa

Grandpa hugs baby owl.
Handcrafted, 2.44", Dated
D Unruh

QX5616 SRP: $7.95 **GBTru: $12**

Grandparents

Cardinal & loving sentiment.
Glass Ball, 2.88", Dated

QX2426 SRP: $5.00 **GBTru: $5**

Grandson

Boy beaver with double scoop ice cream cone.
Handcrafted, 2.44", Dated
S Pike

QX5526 SRP: $6.95 **GBTru: $10**

HANG-TOGETHERS
Dear Santa Mouse

Mice write note to Santa, Set/2.
Handcrafted, 2.94"-2.19" , Dated
K Crow

QX5806 SRP: $14.95 **GBTru: $24**

HANG-TOGETHERS
Mistletoe Surprise

Chipmunk/holds mistletoe over sitting couple, Set/2.
Handcrafted, 1.50"/1.94", Dated
E Seale

QX5996 SRP: $12.95 **GBTru: $24**

HANG-TOGETHERS
Sweet Greeting

Kittens decorate X-Mas cookie, Set/2.
Handcrafted, 1.50"/1.75", Dated
D Palmiter

QX5803 SRP: $10.95 **GBTru: $18**

Happy Birthday, Jesus

Angel visits baby in manger: clip-on.
Handcrafted, 2.69", Dated
J Lyle

QX5423 SRP: $12.95 **GBTru: $18**

HEART OF CHRISTMAS - 5TH & FINAL
Heart Of Christmas

Mom cooking/family at dinner/tree.
Handcrafted, 4.50" open, Dated
E Seale

QX5266 SRP: $14.95 **GBTru: $20**

Hearts In Harmony

Kids join hands to form snowflake.
Porcelain, 3.00", Dated
P Andrews

QX4406 SRP: $10.95 **GBTru: $12**

Helpful Shepherd

Shepherd carries a lamb.
Hndcr/Brass, 2.69"
R Chad

QX5536 SRP: $8.95 **GBTru: $15**

HERE COMES SANTA - 16TH
Makin' Tractor Tracks

Santa drives tractor.
Handcrafted, 3.88", Dated
L Sickman

QX5296 SRP: $14.95 **GBTru: $50**

HERSHEY
Friendship Sundae

Mice add chocolate syrup to sundae.
Handcrafted, 3.25"
L Sickman

QX4766 SRP: $10.95 **GBTru: $22**

HOLIDAY BARBIE - 2ND
Holiday BARBIE

Holiday BARBIE in ball gown.
Handcrafted, Dated

QX5216 SRP: $14.95 **GBTru: $50**

In The Pink

Palm/drink/chair & shades for pink flamingo.
Handcrafted, 3.50", Dated
P Andrews

QX5763 SRP: $9.95 **GBTru: $16**

Joyous Song

Choir child sings a hymn.
Handcrafted, 3.56", Dated
P Andrews

QX4473 SRP: $8.95 **GBTru: $15**

Holiday Patrol

Dog patrolman stops traffic.
Handcrafted, 2.50", Dated
D Rhodus

QX5826 SRP: $8.95 **GBTru: $10**

It's A Strike

Chimp shows bowling style.
Handcrafted, 2.81", Dated
B Siedler

QX5856 SRP: $8.95 **GBTru: $10**

Jump-along Jackalope

Western outfit for rare jackalope.
Handcrafted, 3.44", Dated
J Francis

QX5756 SRP: $8.95 **GBTru: $15**

Holiday Pursuit

Club: Keepsake of Membership
Sherlock Holmes bear.
Handcrafted, Dated
J Francis

QXC4823 **GBTru: $25**

Jingle Bell Band

Mice play Jingle Bells.
Handcrafted, 4.00", Dated
K Crow

QX5783 SRP: $10.95 **GBTru: $22**

Keep On Mowin'

Santa mows grass.
Handcrafted, 3.13", Dated
B Siedler

QX5413 SRP: $8.95 **GBTru: $12**

Ice Show

Skating red bird on ice cube.
Handcrafted, 2.88", Dated
P Andrews

QX5946 SRP: $7.95 **GBTru: $12**

Jolly Holly Santa

Club, Members Only,
Limited Edition of 16,398
Victorian Santa.
Handcrafted, Dated
J Lyle

QXC4833 SRP: $22.00 **GBTru: $40**

Kickin' Roo

Kangeroo soccer player.
Handcrafted, 2.69", Dated
B Siedler

QX5916 SRP: $7.95 **GBTru: $12**

KIDDIE CAR CLASSICS - 1ST
Murray 'Champion'

Kiddie pedal car.
Cast Metal, 3.75", Dated
Don Palmiter

QX5426 SRP: $13.95 **GBTru: $75**

Kitty's Catamaran

Cat sails double-hulled boat.
Handcrafted, 4.56", Dated
E Seale

QX5416 SRP: $10.95 **GBTru: $12**

Kringle's Kayak

Santa uses kayak to deliver toys.
Handcrafted, 2.75", Dated
E Seale

QX5886 SRP: $7.95 **GBTru: $16**

LION KING, THE
Mufasa And Simba

Mufasa and Simba - father and son.
Handcrafted

QX5406 SRP: $14.95 **GBTru: $25**

LION KING, THE
Simba And Nala

Simba & Nala hang-togethers, Set/2.
Handcrafted

QX5303 SRP: $12.95 **GBTru: $26**

LION KING, THE
Timon And Pumbaa

Timon and Pumbaa.
Handcrafted

QX5366 SRP: $8.95 **GBTru: $18**

LOONEY TUNES
Daffy Duck

Daffy Duck as an angel.
Hndcr/Brass, 3.00"
D Palmiter

QX5415 SRP: $8.95 **GBTru: $18**

LOONEY TUNES
Road Runner & Wile E. Coyote

Coyote gives Road Runner a blast of a gift.
Handcrafted, 3.50"
R Chad

QX5602 SRP: $12.95 **GBTru: $24**

LOONEY TUNES
Speedy Gonzales

Speedy Gonzales on skis.
Handcrafted, 2.25"
D Palmiter

QX5343 SRP: $8.95 **GBTru: $15**

LOONEY TUNES
Tasmanian Devil

Tasmanian Devil wears light string.
Handcrafted, 2.63"
D Palmiter

QX5605 SRP: $8.95 **GBTru: $50**

LOONEY TUNES
Yosemite Sam

Yosemite Sam dances w/candy cane.
Handcrafted, 2.44"
D Palmiter

QX5346 SRP: $8.95 **GBTru: $14**

Lou Rankin Seal

Baby seal, clip-on.
Handcrafted, 3.31"
R Bishop

QX5456 SRP: $9.95 **GBTru: $20**

Lucinda And Teddy

Doll gives gift to teddy.
Hndcr/Brass/Fabric, 2.69", Dated
D Unruh

QX4813 SRP: $21.75 **GBTru: $24**

Magic Carpet Ride

Santa & toys fly on magic carpet.
Handcrafted, 3.13", Dated
E Seale

QX5883 SRP: $7.95 **GBTru: $20**

Majestic Deer

Club, Members Only,
Limited Edition of 27,180
White stag.
Porcelain/Pewter, Dated
D Unruh

QXC4836 SRP: $25.00 **GBTru: $35**

Making It Bright

Fresh paint for mailbox.
Handcrafted, 3.31", Dated
D Rhodus

QX5403 SRP: $8.95 **GBTru: $10**

Mary Engelbreit

Snowmen enjoy snowstorm.
Glass ball, 2.88", Dated
M Engelbreit

QX2416 SRP: $5.00 **GBTru: $10**

MARY'S ANGELS - 7TH
Jasmine

Angel dangles star from cloud.
Handcrafted, 2.88"
R Chad

QX5276 SRP: $6.95 **GBTru: $20**

Merry Fishmas

Mouse threads fishing line on hook.
Hndcr/Brass, 2.88", Dated
D Palmiter

QX5913 SRP: $8.95 **GBTru: $12**

MERRY MINIATURE
Happy Collecting
Club: Early Renewal
Pup in tote.
Handcrafted, Dated

QXC4803 **GBTru: $25**

MERRY OLDE SANTA - 5TH
Merry Olde Santa

Snowshoe Santa w/toy bag/tree/
wreath/lantern.
Handcrafted, 4.19", Dated
R Chad

QX5256 SRP: $14.95 **GBTru: $25**

Mom

Mom bear with loving cup trophy.
Handcrafted, 2.31", Dated
A M Rogers

QX5466 SRP: $7.95 **GBTru: $10**

Mom And Dad

Mom bunny helps dress Santa dad.
Handcrafted, 2.94", Dated
B Siedler

QX5666 SRP: $9.95 **GBTru: $12**

Mom-To-Be

Lioness snacks on ice cream.
Handcrafted, 2.50", Dated
S Pike

QX5506 SRP: $7.95 **GBTru: $10**

MOTHER GOOSE - 2ND
Hey Diddle, Diddle

Nursery rhyme book & poem.
Handcrafted, 2.50", Dated
E Seale

QX5213 SRP: $13.95 **GBTru: $34**

MR. & MRS. CLAUS - 9TH
Handwarming Present, A

Santa & Mrs. Claus w/pair of mittens.
Handcrafted, 3.25", Dated
D Unruh

QX5283 SRP: $14.95 **GBTru: $25**

Nephew

Santa's wagon pulled by deer.
Handcrafted, 2.50", Dated
J Francis

QX5546 SRP: $7.95 **GBTru: $8**

New Home

Squirrel waters flowers in acorn home.
Handcrafted, 2.31", Dated
P Andrews

QX5663 SRP: $8.95 **GBTru: $15**

Niece

Mrs. Claus' wagon pulled by deer.
Handcrafted, 2.38", Dated
J Francis

QX5543 SRP: $7.95 **GBTru: $8**

Norman Rockwell Art

Boy finds Santa suit in dad's dresser.
Handcrafted, 2.88", Dated
J Lyle

QX2413 SRP: $5.00 **GBTru: $7**

NOSTALGIC HOUSES & SHOPS - 11TH
Neighborhood Drugstore

Wooden Indian at entry of drugstore/ boot shop upstairs.
Handcrafted, 4.06", Dated
D Lee

QX5286 SRP: $14.95 **GBTru: $30**

On Cloud Nine

Club, Members Only
Angel in cloud.
Handcrafted, Dated
D Lee

QXC4853 SRP: $12.00 **GBTru: $25**

Open-And-Shut Holiday

Office file opens to a trim'd tree.
Handcrafted, 3.31", Dated
B Siedler

QX5696 SRP: $9.95 **GBTru: $10**

Our Christmas Together

Bird couple on holly nest/clip-on.
Handcrafted, 2.63", Dated
A M Rogers

QX4816 SRP: $9.95 **GBTru: $12**

Our Family

Poinsettia wreath photo frame.
Handcrafted, 3.63", Dated
P Andrews

QX5576 SRP: $7.95 **GBTru: $10**

Our First Christmas Together

Bear couple on sleighride.
Brass/Fabric, 3.25", Dated
P Andrews

QX5706 SRP: $18.95 **GBTru: $20**

Our First Christmas Together

Sweethearts kiss & exchange gifts.
Handcrafted, 2.38", Dated
R Bishop

QX5643 SRP: $9.95 **GBTru: $12**

OWLIVER - 3RD & FINAL
Owliver

Owl helps woodpeckers trim tree.
Handcrafted, 2.88", Dated
B Siedler

QX5226 SRP: $7.95 **GBTru: $14**

PERSONALIZED
Cookie Time

Chipmunk decorates tree cookie.
Handcrafted
L Votruba

QP6073 SRP: $12.95 **GBTru: $13.75**

Our First Christmas Together

Heart wreath w/ribbon & holly photo frame.
Handcrafted, 3.75", Dated
D Palmiter

QX5653 SRP: $8.95 **GBTru: $10**

PEANUTS GANG, THE - 2ND
Peanuts Gang, The

Lucy holds football for Charlie Brown.
Handcrafted, 2.44", Dated
R Bishop

QX5203 SRP: $9.95 **GBTru: $18**

PERSONALIZED
Etch-A-Sketch

Bear with child's toy.
Handcrafted
K Crow

QP6006 SRP: $12.95 **GBTru: $13.75**

Our First Christmas Together

Holly trims heart shows clasped hands.
Acrylic, 3.56", Dated
L Votruba

QX3186 SRP: $6.95 **GBTru: $8**

PERSONALIZED
Baby Block

Teddy w/rattle sits atop baby block.
Handcrafted
J Francis

QP6035 SRP: $14.95 **GBTru: $15.75**

PERSONALIZED
Festive Album Photoholder

Mouse hangs on ribbon marker (opens).
Handcrafted
L Votruba

QP6025 SRP: $12.95 **GBTru: $13.75**

Out Of This World Teacher

Raccoon sits atop world globe.
Handcrafted, 3.50", Dated
D Unruh

QX5766 SRP: $7.95 **GBTru: $10**

PERSONALIZED
Computer Cat 'n' Mouse

Cat on computer checks the mouse.
Handcrafted
E Seale

QP6046 SRP: $12.95 **GBTru: $13.75**

PERSONALIZED
From The Heart

Raccoon carves message on tree stump.
Handcrafted
D Rhodus

QP6036 SRP: $14.95 **GBTru: $15.75**

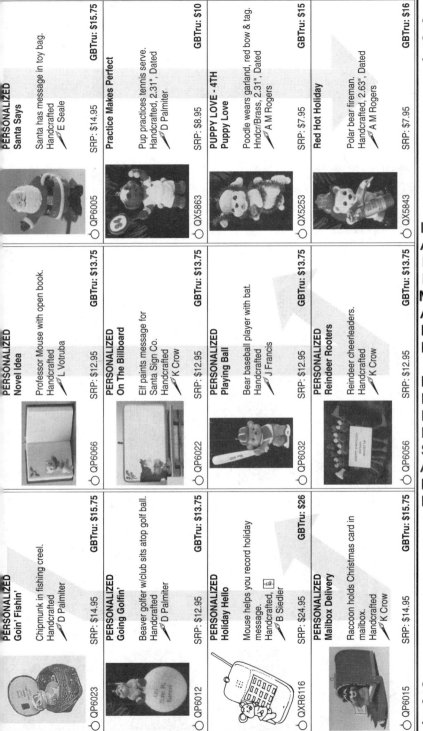

PERSONALIZED
Goin' Fishin'

Chipmunk in fishing creel.
Handcrafted
D Palmiter

QP6023 SRP: $14.95 **GBTru: $15.75**

PERSONALIZED
Novel Idea

Professor Mouse with open book.
Handcrafted
L Votruba

QP6066 SRP: $12.95 **GBTru: $13.75**

PERSONALIZED
Santa Says

Santa has message in toy bag.
Handcrafted
E Seale

QP6005 SRP: $14.95 **GBTru: $15.75**

PERSONALIZED
Going Golfin'

Beaver golfer w/club sits atop golf ball.
Handcrafted
D Palmiter

QP6012 SRP: $12.95 **GBTru: $13.75**

PERSONALIZED
On The Billboard

Elf paints message for
Santa Sign Co.
Handcrafted
K Crow

QP6022 SRP: $12.95 **GBTru: $13.75**

Practice Makes Perfect

Pup practices tennis serve.
Handcrafted, 2.31", Dated
D Palmiter

QX5863 SRP: $8.95 **GBTru: $10**

PERSONALIZED
Holiday Hello

Mouse helps you record holiday message.
Handcrafted,
B Siedler

QXR6116 SRP: $24.95 **GBTru: $26**

PERSONALIZED
Playing Ball

Bear baseball player with bat.
Handcrafted
J Francis

QP6032 SRP: $12.95 **GBTru: $13.75**

PUPPY LOVE - 4TH
Puppy Love

Poodle wears garland, red bow & tag.
Hndcr/Brass, 2.31", Dated
A M Rogers

QX5253 SRP: $7.95 **GBTru: $15**

PERSONALIZED
Mailbox Delivery

Raccoon holds Christmas card in mailbox.
Handcrafted
K Crow

QP6015 SRP: $14.95 **GBTru: $15.75**

PERSONALIZED
Reindeer Rooters

Reindeer cheerleaders.
Handcrafted
K Crow

QP6056 SRP: $12.95 **GBTru: $13.75**

Red Hot Holiday

Polar bear fireman.
Handcrafted, 2.63", Dated
A M Rogers

QX5843 SRP: $7.95 **GBTru: $16**

Reindeer Pro

Umbrella shelters deer on greens.
Handcrafted, 3.19", Dated
D Rhodus

QX5926 SRP: $7.95 **GBTru: $10**

ROCKING HORSE - 14TH
Rocking Horse

Rocking horse.
Handcrafted, 4.00", Dated
L Sickman

QX5016 SRP: $10.95 **GBTru: $24**

Santa's LEGO Sleigh

Santa & toys in LEGO sleigh.
Handcrafted, 2.25", Dated
K Crow

QX5453 SRP: $10.95 **GBTru: $25**

SARAH, PLAIN AND TALL - 1ST
Country Church, The
Gold Crown Reach Program -
**w/any HM purchase.*
Country church.
Handcrafted, Dated

795XPR9450 SRP: $7.95* **GBTru: $10**

SARAH, PLAIN AND TALL - 2ND
Mrs. Parkley's General Store
Gold Crown Reach Program -
**w/any HM purchase.*
General store.
Handcrafted, Dated

795XPR9451 SRP: $7.95* **GBTru: $12**

SARAH, PLAIN AND TALL - 3RD
Hays Train Station, The
Gold Crown Reach Program -
**w/any HM purchase.*
Train station.
Handcrafted, Dated

795XPR9452 SRP: $7.95* **GBTru: $12**

SARAH, PLAIN AND TALL - 4TH
Sarah's Prairie Home
Gold Crown Reach Program -
**w/any HM purchase.*
Prairie home.
Handcrafted, Dated

795XPR9453 SRP: $7.95* **GBTru: $12**

SARAH, PLAIN AND TALL - 5TH
Sarah's Maine Home
Gold Crown Reach Program -
**w/any HM purchase.*
Maine home.
Handcrafted, Dated

795XPR9454 SRP: $7.95* **GBTru: $15**

Secret Santa

Pup wears mask and antlers.
Handcrafted, 2.63", Dated
D Unruh

QX5736 SRP: $7.95 **GBTru: $14**

Sharp Flat, A

Performing mouse lives in violin.
Handcrafted, 3.75", Dated
K Crow

QX5773 SRP: $10.95 **GBTru: $15**

SHOEBOX GREETINGS
Feline Of Christmas, A

Cat swings from lights/stringer orn.
Handcrafted, 3.06", Dated
P Andrews

QX5816 SRP: $8.95 **GBTru: $25**

SHOWCASE - CHRISTMAS LIGHTS
Home For The Holidays

Home front facade welcomes
family & friends.
Porcelain, Dated,
D Palmiter

QK1123 SRP: $15.75 **GBTru: $20**

SHOWCASE - CHRISTMAS LIGHTS
Moonbeams

Crescent man in the moon with a star.
Porcelain, Dated,
P Andrews

QK1116 SRP: $15.75 **GBTru: $20**

SHOWCASE - FOLK ART
Going To Town

Elf rides pig, carrying baskets to town.
Handcrafted, Dated
L Sickman

QK1166 SRP: $15.75 **GBTru: $26**

SHOWCASE - HOLIDAY FAVORITES
Dapper Snowman

Snowman with hat/scarf/belt/
candy cane.
Crackle Glaze, Dated
L Votruba

QK1053 SRP: $13.75 **GBTru: $15**

SHOWCASE - CHRISTMAS LIGHTS
Mother And Child

Madonna & Child design.
Porcelain, Dated,
A M Rogers

QK1126 SRP: $15.75 **GBTru: $20**

SHOWCASE - FOLK ART
Racing Through The Snow

Snowshoed rooster is fast ride for elf.
Handcrafted, Dated
L Sickman

QK1173 SRP: $15.75 **GBTru: $42**

SHOWCASE - HOLIDAY FAVORITES
Graceful Fawn

Deer at rest with holly leaf collar.
Crackle Glaze, Dated
L Votruba

QK1033 SRP: $11.75 **GBTru: $15**

SHOWCASE - CHRISTMAS LIGHTS
Peaceful Village

Outdoor scene features church/village.
Porcelain, Dated,
R Chad

QK1106 SRP: $15.75 **GBTru: $20**

SHOWCASE - FOLK ART
Rarin' To Go

Woodsman elf/uses rabbit to
carry tree.
Handcrafted, Dated
L Sickman

QK1193 SRP: $15.75 **GBTru: $35**

SHOWCASE - HOLIDAY FAVORITES
Jolly Santa

Santa carries small Christmas tree.
Crackle Glaze, Dated
L Votruba

QK1046 SRP: $13.75 **GBTru: $18**

SHOWCASE - FOLK ART
Catching 40 Winks

Elf naps amid stack of gifts.
Handcrafted, Dated
L Sickman

QK1183 SRP: $16.75 **GBTru: $30**

SHOWCASE - FOLK ART
Roundup Time

Cowboy/package ladened cow
bring gifts.
Handcrafted, Dated
L Sickman

QK1176 SRP: $16.75 **GBTru: $22**

SHOWCASE - HOLIDAY FAVORITES
Joyful Lamb

Lamb at rest wears holly leaf collar.
Crackle Glaze, Dated
L Votruba

QK1036 SRP: $11.75 **GBTru: $15**

SHOWCASE - HOLIDAY FAVORITES
Peaceful Dove

Flying dove with outspread wings.
Crackle Glaze, Dated
L Votruba

QK1043 SRP: $11.75 **GBTru: $22**

SHOWCASE - OLD WORLD SILVER
Silver Bells

Each silver plated panel features bell design.
Silver Plated, Dated
D Unruh

QK1026 SRP: $24.75 **GBTru: $24**

SHOWCASE - OLD WORLD SILVER
Silver Bows

Openwork silver plated bows.
Silver Plated, Dated
D Palmiter

QK1023 SRP: $24.75 **GBTru: $24**

SHOWCASE - OLD WORLD SILVER
Silver Poinsettia

Silver plated poinsettia is central focus w/holly trim.
Silver Plated, Dated
D Unruh

QK1006 SRP: $24.75 **GBTru: $28**

SHOWCASE - OLD WORLD SILVER
Silver Snowflakes

Silver plated snowflake design.
Silver Plated, Dated
D Unruh

QK1016 SRP: $24.75 **GBTru: $24**

SIGNATURE COLLECTION - 2ND
Mrs. Claus' Cupboard
Artist Tours
Hallmark orns/decorate cupboard.
Handcrafted

QXC4843 SRP: $55.00 **GBTru: $130**

Sister

Girl pup drives pink convertible.
Handcrafted, 2.13", Dated
S Pike

QX5513 SRP: $6.95 **GBTru: $10**

Sister-To-Sister

Squirrels share gift inside acorn.
Handcrafted, 3.25", Dated
D Rhodus

QX5533 SRP: $9.95 **GBTru: $20**

Son

Green dinosaur on skateboard.
Handcrafted, 3.19", Dated
P Andrews

QX5626 SRP: $6.95 **GBTru: $7**

Special Cat

Fish bowl photo frame.
Acrylic, 3.50", Dated
D Rhodus

QX5606 SRP: $7.95 **GBTru: $8**

Special Dog

Rolled newspaper photo frame.
Handcrafted, 3.50", Dated
D Rhodus

QX5603 SRP: $7.95 **GBTru: $10**

Stamp Of Approval

Elves w/office stamp of approval.
Handcrafted, 2.06", Dated
L Sickman

QX5703 SRP: $7.95 **GBTru: $10**

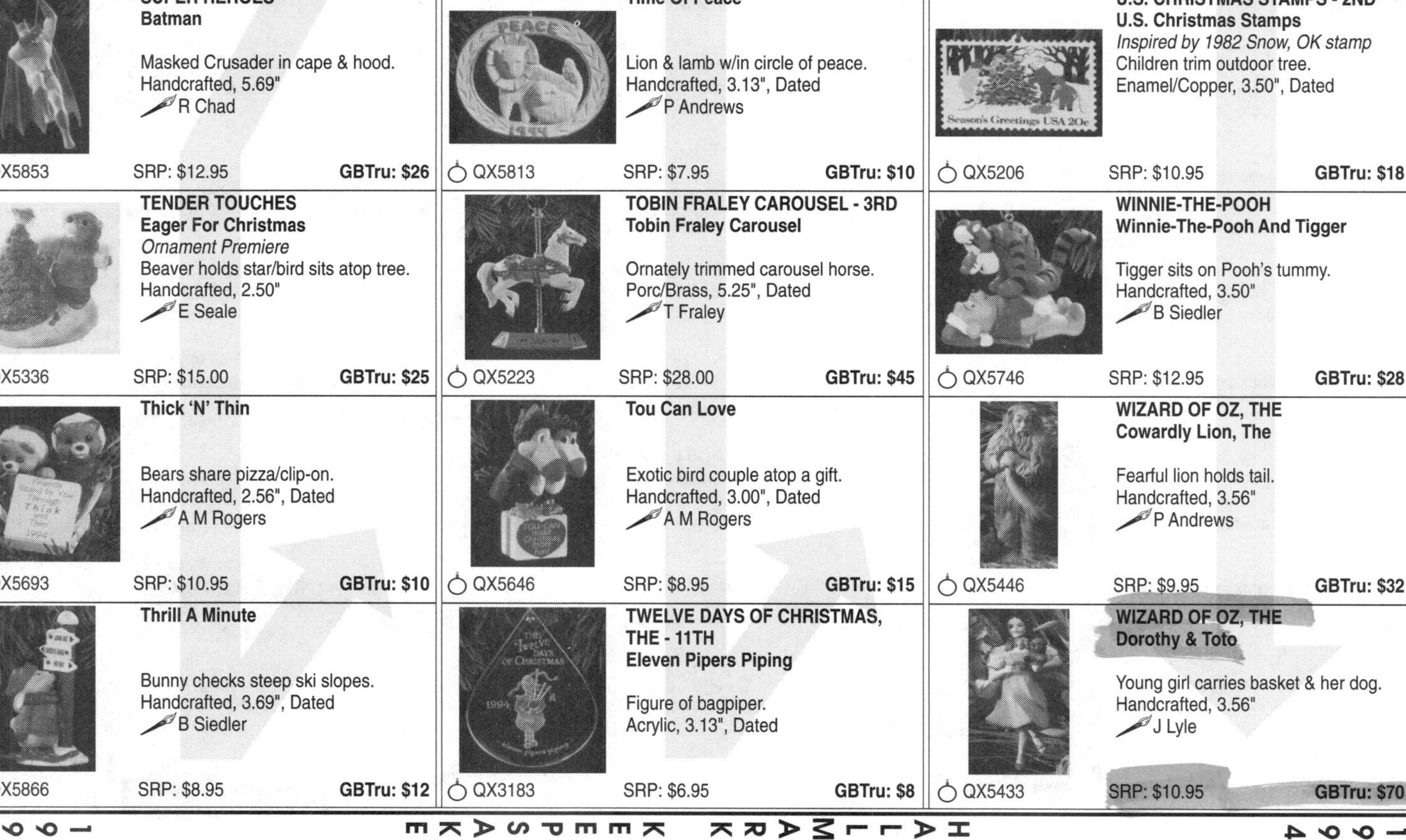

SUPER HEROES
Batman

Masked Crusader in cape & hood.
Handcrafted, 5.69"
R Chad

QX5853 SRP: $12.95 **GBTru: $26**

Time Of Peace

Lion & lamb w/in circle of peace.
Handcrafted, 3.13", Dated
P Andrews

QX5813 SRP: $7.95 **GBTru: $10**

U.S. CHRISTMAS STAMPS - 2ND
U.S. Christmas Stamps
Inspired by 1982 Snow, OK stamp
Children trim outdoor tree.
Enamel/Copper, 3.50", Dated

QX5206 SRP: $10.95 **GBTru: $18**

TENDER TOUCHES
Eager For Christmas
Ornament Premiere
Beaver holds star/bird sits atop tree.
Handcrafted, 2.50"
E Seale

QX5336 SRP: $15.00 **GBTru: $25**

TOBIN FRALEY CAROUSEL - 3RD
Tobin Fraley Carousel

Ornately trimmed carousel horse.
Porc/Brass, 5.25", Dated
T Fraley

QX5223 SRP: $28.00 **GBTru: $45**

WINNIE-THE-POOH
Winnie-The-Pooh And Tigger

Tigger sits on Pooh's tummy.
Handcrafted, 3.50"
B Siedler

QX5746 SRP: $12.95 **GBTru: $28**

Thick 'N' Thin

Bears share pizza/clip-on.
Handcrafted, 2.56", Dated
A M Rogers

QX5693 SRP: $10.95 **GBTru: $10**

Tou Can Love

Exotic bird couple atop a gift.
Handcrafted, 3.00", Dated
A M Rogers

QX5646 SRP: $8.95 **GBTru: $15**

WIZARD OF OZ, THE
Cowardly Lion, The

Fearful lion holds tail.
Handcrafted, 3.56"
P Andrews

QX5446 SRP: $9.95 **GBTru: $32**

Thrill A Minute

Bunny checks steep ski slopes.
Handcrafted, 3.69", Dated
B Siedler

QX5866 SRP: $8.95 **GBTru: $12**

TWELVE DAYS OF CHRISTMAS, THE - 11TH
Eleven Pipers Piping

Figure of bagpiper.
Acrylic, 3.13", Dated

QX3183 SRP: $6.95 **GBTru: $8**

WIZARD OF OZ, THE
Dorothy & Toto

Young girl carries basket & her dog.
Handcrafted, 3.56"
J Lyle

QX5433 SRP: $10.95 **GBTru: $70**

WIZARD OF OZ, THE
Scarecrow, The

Scarecrow dances down road to Oz.
Handcrafted, 3.88"
D Unruh

QX5436 SRP: $9.95 **GBTru: $32**

WIZARD OF OZ, THE
Tin Man, The

Silver Tin Man points to road to Oz.
Handcrafted, 3.81"
D Unruh

QX5443 SRP: $9.95 **GBTru: $35**

YULETIDE CENTRAL - 1ST
Yuletide Central

Train engine car.
Pressed Tin, 3.75", Dated
L Sickman

QX5316 SRP: $18.95 **GBTru: $50**

1995

Acorn 500

Squirrel wear'g acorn hat in race car.
Handcrafted, Dated
B Siedler

QX5929 SRP: $10.95 **GBTru: $12**

Across The Miles

Santa mouse looks at compass/
clip on.
Handcrafted, Dated
J Francis

QX5847 SRP: $8.95 **GBTru: $10**

Air Express

Flying squirrel delivers
Christmas cards.
Handcrafted, Dated
E Seale

QX5977 SRP: $7.95 **GBTru: $10**

ALL-AMERICAN TRUCKS - 1ST
1956 Ford Truck

Red pickup carries holiday tree.
Handcrafted, Dated
D Palmiter

QX5527 SRP: $13.95 **GBTru: $40**

Anniversary Year

Heart shap'd photoholder w/birds,
flowers, bow.
Handcrafted, Dated
D Unruh

QX5819 SRP: $8.95 **GBTru: $9**

Baby's First Christmas

Baby naps in baby cup/
tag to engrave.
Hndcr/Silver, Dated
P Andrews

QX5547 SRP: $18.95 **GBTru: $44**

Baby's First Christmas

Stork makes a baby delivery.
Handcrafted, Dated
P Andrews

QX5557 SRP: $9.95 **GBTru: $15**

Baby's First Christmas

Baby blocks photoholder.
Handcrafted, Dated
L Votruba

QX5549 SRP: $7.95 **GBTru: $9**

Baby's First Christmas (Boy)

Baby boys.
Glass Ball, 2.88", Dated

QX2319 SRP: $5.00 **GBTru: $8**

Baby's First Christmas (Girl)

Baby girls.
Glass Ball, 2.88", Dated

QX2317 SRP: $5.00 **GBTru: $8**

BARBIE - 2ND
Solo In The Spotlight

Barbie at microphone in black gown.
Handcrafted, Dated
P Andrews

QXI5049 SRP: $14.95 **GBTru: $25**

BARBIE SERIES COMPLEMENT
BARBIE Brunette Debut - 1959
Club Edition
Brunette Barbie in black & white swimsuit.
Handcrafted, Dated
P Andrews

QXC5397 SRP: $14.95 **GBTru: $50**

Barrel-Back Rider

Cowboy teddy bear rides barrel horse.
Handcrafted, Dated
J Francis

QX5189 SRP: $9.95 **GBTru: $15**

BASEBALL HEROES - 2ND
Lou Gehrig

Baseball star at bat/medallion/ player card incl.
Handcrafted, Dated
D Rhodus

QX5029 SRP: $12.95 **GBTru: $15**

Beverly And Teddy

Doll and teddy share book.
Handcrafted, Dated
D Unruh

QX5259 SRP: $21.75 **GBTru: $24**

Bingo Bear

Bear holds Bingo card.
Handcrafted, Dated
L Votruba

QX5919 SRP: $7.95 **GBTru: $10**

Bobbin' Along

Beaver fishes from duck's back.
Handcrafted, Dated
K Crow

QX5879 SRP: $8.95 **GBTru: $15**

Brother

Snowboy on skis.
Handcrafted, Dated
J Lyle

QX5679 SRP: $6.95 **GBTru: $8**

CAT NAPS - 2ND
Cat Naps

Cat naps on mitten/clip on.
Handcrafted, Dated
D Rhodus

QX5097 SRP: $7.95 **GBTru: $12**

Catch The Spirit

Squirrel has hot dog/fries while sitting in glove.
Handcrafted, Dated
B Siedler

QX5899 SRP: $7.95 **GBTru: $18**

CELEBRATION OF ANGELS - 1ST
Celebration Of Angels, A

Winged angel carries sheaf of food.
Handcrafted, Dated
P Andrews

QX5077 SRP: $12.95 **GBTru: $18**

CHARLIE BROWN CHRISTMAS, A
Base with WOODSTOCK and Tree
Gold Crown Reach Program -
**w/any HM purchase*
Woodstock sits on tree on snowy base.
Handcrafted
A M Rogers

395QRP4227 SRP: $3.95* **GBTru: $18**

CHARLIE BROWN CHRISTMAS, A
Charlie Brown
Gold Crown Reach Program -
**w/any HM purchase*
Charlie Brown rings bell.
Handcrafted
B Siedler

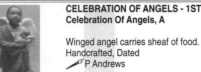

395QRP4207 SRP: $3.95* **GBTru: $25**

CHARLIE BROWN CHRISTMAS, A
Linus
Gold Crown Reach Program -
**w/any HM purchase*
Linus wears sweater, scarf & top hat.
Handcrafted
A M Rogers

395QRP4217 SRP: $3.95* **GBTru: $18**

CHARLIE BROWN CHRISTMAS, A
Lucy
Gold Crown Reach Program -
**w/any HM purchase*
Lucy holds candy cane.
Handcrafted
B Siedler

395QRP4209 SRP: $3.95* **GBTru: $10**

CHARLIE BROWN CHRISTMAS, A
SNOOPY
Gold Crown Reach Program -
**w/any HM purchase*
Top hat, sweater & scarf on Snoopy.
Handcrafted
A M Rogers

395QRP4219 SRP: $3.95* **GBTru: $24**

CHILD'S AGE #1 - TEDDY BEAR YEARS
Baby's First Christmas

Teddy holds stocking w/#1 star cookie.
Handcrafted, Dated
K Crow

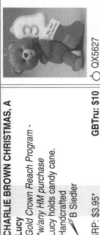

QX5559 SRP: $7.95 **GBTru: $15**

CHILD'S AGE #2 - TEDDY BEAR YEARS
Baby's Second Christmas

Teddy holds stocking with tree cookie.
Handcrafted, Dated
K Crow

QX5567 SRP: $7.95 **GBTru: $12**

CHILD'S AGE #3 - TEDDY BEAR YEARS
Child's Third Christmas

Teddy holds stocking with bell cookie.
Handcrafted, Dated
K Crow

QX5627 SRP: $7.95 **GBTru: $10**

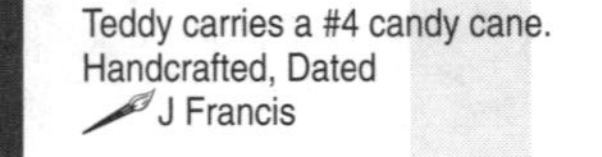

CHILD'S AGE #4 - TEDDY BEAR YEARS
Child's Fourth Christmas

Teddy carries a #4 candy cane.
Handcrafted, Dated
J Francis

QX5629 SRP: $6.95 **GBTru: $10**

CHILD'S AGE #5 - TEDDY BEAR YEARS
Child's Fifth Christmas

Teddy hangs from a #5 candy cane.
Handcrafted, Dated
D Rhodus

QX5637 SRP: $6.95 **GBTru: $10**

Christmas Fever

Bunny nurse holds thermometer.
Handcrafted, Dated
N Aube

QX5967 SRP: $7.95 **GBTru: $10**

Decorated Christmas tree with gifts.
Handcrafted
J Francis

QX5997 SRP: $10.95 **GBTru: $11**

Christmas Patrol

Black and white police car.
Handcrafted, Dated
P Andrews

QX5959 SRP: $7.95 **GBTru: $15**

CHRISTMAS VISITORS - 1ST
St. Nicholas

Bearded figure in long robe/staff.
Hndcr/Brass, Dated
A M Rogers

QX5087 SRP: $14.95 **GBTru: $25**

CLASSIC AMERICAN CAR SERIES COMPLEMENT
1958 Ford Edsel Citation Convertible
Club Edition
Red car w/tree & gifts in back seat.
Handcrafted, Dated
D Palmiter

QXC4167 SRP: $12.95 **GBTru: $68**

1969 Chevrolet Camaro

2-Door sports model w/racing stripes.
Handcrafted, Dated
D Palmiter

QX5239 SRP: $12.95 **GBTru: $15**

COCA COLA SANTA
Refreshing Gift
Haddon Sundblom Art
Santa holds popular Coke bottles.
Handcrafted, Dated
D Unruh

QX4067 SRP: $14.95 **GBTru: $22**

Collecting Memories

Club: Keepsake of Membership
Beaver puts special orns on display.
Handcrafted, Dated
B Siedler

QXC4117 **GBTru: $15**

CRAYOLA
Colorful World

Chipmunk colors card.
Handcrafted, Dated
K Crow

QX5519 SRP: $10.95 **GBTru: $20**

Bright 'n' Sunny Teepee

Brave bear Indian at teepee entry.
Handcrafted, Dated
P Andrews

QX5247 SRP: $10.95 **GBTru: $20**

Dad

Dad beaver carries home a tree.
Hndcr/Brush, Dated
B Siedler

QX5649 SRP: $7.95 **GBTru: $8**

Dad-To-Be

Boy bear reads parenting book.
Handcrafted, Dated
D Rhodus

QX5667 SRP: $7.95 **GBTru: $9**

Daughter

Girl panda bear holds pencil.
Handcrafted, Dated
D Palmiter

QX5677 SRP: $6.95 **GBTru: $8**

Dream On

Santa naps as child reads very long list.
Handcrafted, Dated
J Francis

QX6007 SRP: $10.95 **GBTru: $16**

Dudley The Dragon

Dragon in Santa hat holds toy bag.
Handcrafted
S Pike

QX6209 SRP: $10.95 **GBTru: $15**

FABULOUS DECADE - 6TH
Fabulous Decade

Otter lounges on year numerals.
Hndcr/Brass, Dated
E Seale

QX5147 SRP: $7.95 **GBTru: $14**

Faithful Fan

Beaver waves pennant while sitting on helmet.
Handcrafted, Dated
B Siedler

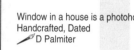

QX5897 SRP: $8.95 **GBTru: $12**

Feliz Navidad

Mouse sits on a chilli pepper.
Handcrafted, Dated
D Rhodus

QX5869 SRP: $7.95 **GBTru: $12**

Fishing For Fun

Club: Keepsake of Membership
Santa & reindeer ice fish for gifts & candy cane.
Handcrafted, Dated
E Seale

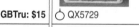

QX5207 **GBTru: $15**

FLINTSTONES, THE
Betty And Wilma

Ladies push turtle-powered shopping cart.
Handcrafted, Dated
D Rhodus

QX5417 SRP: $14.95 **GBTru: $15**

FOOTBALL LEGENDS - 1ST
Joe Montana - San Francisco

Football star throws pass/ player card included.
Handcrafted
D Rhodus

QXI5759 SRP: $14.95 **GBTru: $25**

FOOTBALL LEGENDS - COMPLEMENTARY SPECIAL ISSUE
Joe Montana - KC Chiefs
Number produced restricted
Football star played 2 seasons for KC Chiefs.
Handcrafted
D Rhodus

QXI6207 SRP: $14.95 **GBTru: $75**

For My Grandma

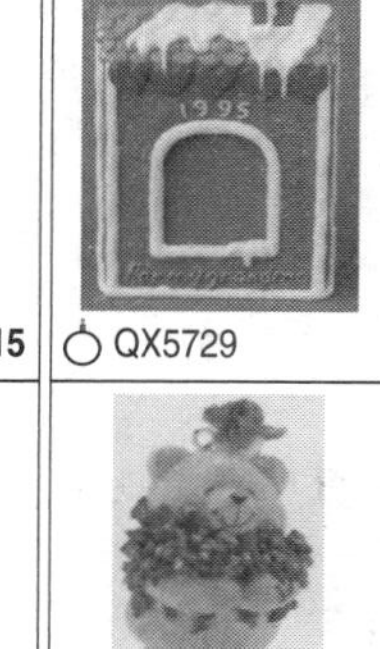

Window in a house is a photoholder.
Handcrafted, Dated
D Palmiter

QX5729 SRP: $6.95 **GBTru: $8**

Forever Friends Bear

Bird sits atop bear wrapped in garland.
Handcrafted
A Brownsward

QX5258 SRP: $8.95 **GBTru: $15**

Friendly Boost

Penguin helps friend put star on ice tree.
Handcrafted, Dated
D Palmiter

QX5827 SRP: $8.95 **GBTru: $15**

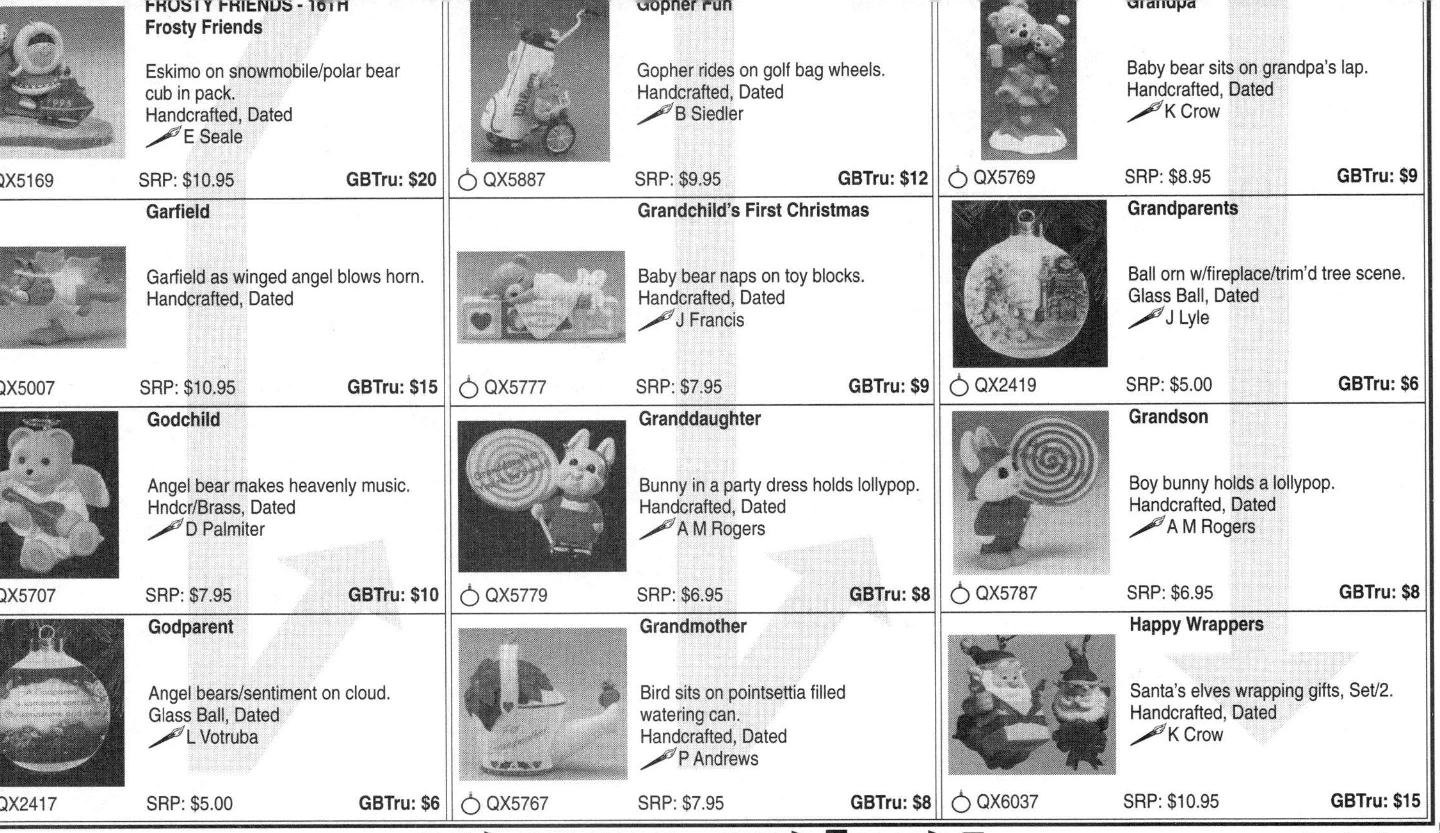

FROSTY FRIENDS - 16TH
Frosty Friends

Eskimo on snowmobile/polar bear cub in pack.
Handcrafted, Dated
E Seale

QX5169 SRP: $10.95 **GBTru: $20**

Gopher Fun

Gopher rides on golf bag wheels.
Handcrafted, Dated
B Siedler

QX5887 SRP: $9.95 **GBTru: $12**

Grandpa

Baby bear sits on grandpa's lap.
Handcrafted, Dated
K Crow

QX5769 SRP: $8.95 **GBTru: $9**

Garfield

Garfield as winged angel blows horn.
Handcrafted, Dated

QX5007 SRP: $10.95 **GBTru: $15**

Grandchild's First Christmas

Baby bear naps on toy blocks.
Handcrafted, Dated
J Francis

QX5777 SRP: $7.95 **GBTru: $9**

Grandparents

Ball orn w/fireplace/trim'd tree scene.
Glass Ball, Dated
J Lyle

QX2419 SRP: $5.00 **GBTru: $6**

Godchild

Angel bear makes heavenly music.
Hndcr/Brass, Dated
D Palmiter

QX5707 SRP: $7.95 **GBTru: $10**

Granddaughter

Bunny in a party dress holds lollypop.
Handcrafted, Dated
A M Rogers

QX5779 SRP: $6.95 **GBTru: $8**

Grandson

Boy bunny holds a lollypop.
Handcrafted, Dated
A M Rogers

QX5787 SRP: $6.95 **GBTru: $8**

Godparent

Angel bears/sentiment on cloud.
Glass Ball, Dated
L Votruba

QX2417 SRP: $5.00 **GBTru: $6**

Grandmother

Bird sits on pointsettia filled watering can.
Handcrafted, Dated
P Andrews

QX5767 SRP: $7.95 **GBTru: $8**

Happy Wrappers

Santa's elves wrapping gifts, Set/2.
Handcrafted, Dated
K Crow

QX6037 SRP: $10.95 **GBTru: $15**

Heaven's Gift

Holy Family, Set/2.
Handcrafted, Dated
P Andrews

QX6057 SRP: $20.00 **GBTru: $22**

HERE COMES SANTA - 17TH
Santa's Roadster

Santa drives old fashioned car.
Hndcr/Sisal, Dated
L Sickman

QX5179 SRP: $14.95 **GBTru: $25**

HERSHEY
Delivering Kisses

Mice deliver Hershey Kisses in wheelbarrow.
Handcrafted, Dated
L Sickman

QX4107 SRP: $10.95 **GBTru: $16**

Hockey Pup

Pup in ice skate holds stick & puck.
Handcrafted, Dated
K Crow

QX5917 SRP: $9.95 **GBTru: $10**

HOLIDAY BARBIE - 3RD
Holiday Barbie

Barbie in a green and white ball gown.
Handcrafted, Dated
P Andrews

QXI5057 SRP: $14.95 **GBTru: $34**

HOOP STARS - 1ST
Shaquille O'Neal

Basketball star holds basket rim/ player card included.
Handcrafted

QXI5517 SRP: $14.95 **GBTru: $25**

Important Memo

Mouse naps in top tray of desk memo box.
Handcrafted, Dated
L Sickman

QX5947 SRP: $8.95 **GBTru: $10**

In A Heartbeat

Mouse couple kiss atop mantle clock.
Handcrafted, Dated
P Andrews

QX5817 SRP: $8.95 **GBTru: $15**

In Time With Christmas

Mouse plays violin atop metronome.
Handcrafted, Dated
K Crow

QX6049 SRP: $12.95 **GBTru: $20**

Joy To The World

Member of church choir.
Handcrafted, Dated
P Andrews

QX5867 SRP: $8.95 **GBTru: $15**

KIDDIE CAR CLASSICS - 2ND
Murray Fire Truck

Toy fire truck pedal car with ladders.
Cast Metal, Dated
D Palmiter

QX5027 SRP: $13.95 **GBTru: $28**

LEGO Fireplace With Santa

Santa fills stockings on fireplace.
Handcrafted, Dated
K Crow

QX4769 SRP: $10.95 **GBTru: $20**

LION KING, THE
Simba, Pumbaa And Timon

Young adult Simba and friends.
Handcrafted
K Crow

QX6159 SRP: $12.95 **GBTru: $24**

Magic School Bus, The

Teacher/students about to embark on adventure.
Handcrafted, Dated
D Rhodus

QX5849 SRP: $10.95 **GBTru: $15**

MERRY OLDE SANTA - 6TH
Merry Olde Santa

Wear'g coat & cap, Santa w/toy bag.
Hndcr/Brass, Dated
P Andrews

QX5139 SRP: $14.95 **GBTru: $22**

LOONEY TUNES
Bugs Bunny

Bugs Bunny gets set to throw snowballs.
Handcrafted
R Chad

QX5019 SRP: $8.95 **GBTru: $18**

Mary Engelbreit

Rosy-cheeked stylized Santa.
Glass Ball, Dated
M Englebreit

QX2409 SRP: $5.00 **GBTru: $12**

Merry RV

Mr. & Mrs. Claus in camper vehicle.
Handcrafted, Dated
D Palmiter

QX6027 SRP: $12.95 **GBTru: $25**

LOONEY TUNES
Sylvester And Tweety

Sylvester reaches for Tweety on swing, Set/2.
Handcrafted
R Chad

QX5017 SRP: $13.95 **GBTru: $25**

MARY'S ANGELS - 8TH
Camellia

Bluebird perches on angel's hand.
Handcrafted
R Chad

QX5149 SRP: $6.95 **GBTru: $15**

Mom

Mom beaver strings popcorn garland.
Handcrafted, Dated
B Siedler

QX5647 SRP: $7.95 **GBTru: $9**

Lou Rankin Bear

Seated bear.
Handcrafted
B Siedler

QX4069 SRP: $9.95 **GBTru: $18**

MERRY MINIATURE
Wicked Stepsisters
Club: Gift for Gift Membership
Wicked stepsisters.
Handcrafted

S Pike

QXC4159 **GBTru: $38**

Mom And Dad

Snow couple snuggle.
Hndcr/Flitter, Dated
A M Rogers

QX5657 SRP: $9.95 **GBTru: $11**

Mom-To-Be

Pregnant bear w/toy & child bearing book.
Handcrafted, Dated
D Rhodus

QX5659 SRP: $7.95 **GBTru: $8**

MOTHER GOOSE - 3RD
Jack And Jill

Book opens to verse, scene & 3-D figures.
Handcrafted, Dated
E Seale/L Votruba

QX5099 SRP: $13.95 **GBTru: $20**

MR. & MRS. CLAUS - 10TH & FINAL
Christmas Eve Kiss

Mrs Claus gives Santa goodbye kiss.
Handcrafted, Dated
D Unruh

QX5157 SRP: $14.95 **GBTru: $25**

New Home

House brushes off welcome mat.
Handcrafted, Dated
P Andrews

QX5839 SRP: $8.95 **GBTru: $10**

NFL

Specialty Ball Orn Coordinates with Keepsake NFL Collection
Produced: 10 team 1995, 4 teams 1996
Team logo displayed.
Sample ornament is KC Chiefs.

PNA2035 **Carolina Panthers**
SRP: $5.95 **GBTru: $12**

BRS2035 **Chicago Bears**
SRP: $5.95 **GBTru: $20**

COW2035 **Dallas Cowboys**
SRP: $5.95 **GBTru: $25**

CHF2035 **Kansas City Chiefs**
SRP: $5.95 **GBTru: $20**

RDR2035 **Los Angeles Raiders**
SRP: $5.95 **GBTru: $20**

VIK2035 **Minnesota Vikings**
SRP: $5.95 **GBTru: $12**

NEP2035 **New England Patriots**
SRP: $5.95 **GBTru: $12**

EAG2035 **Philadelphia Eagles**
In '96, Team has a new Logo.
SRP: $5.95 **GBTru: $12**

FOR2035 **San Francisco 49's**
In '96, Team has a new logo.
SRP: $5.95 **GBTru: $20**

RSK2035 **Washington Redskins**
SRP: $5.95 **GBTru: $12**

NFL
Carolina Panthers Helmet

Fan cheers favorite team.
Handcrafted
B Siedler

QSR6227 SRP: $9.95 **GBTru: $20**

NFL
Chicago Bears Helmet

Fan cheers favorite team.
Handcrafted
B Siedler

QSR6237 SRP: $9.95 **GBTru: $35**

NFL
Dallas Cowboys Helmet

Fan cheers favorite team.
Handcrafted
B Siedler

QSR6217 SRP: $9.95 **GBTru: $60**

NFL
Kansas City Chiefs Helmet

Fan cheers favorite team.
Handcrafted
B Siedler

QSR6257 SRP: $9.95 **GBTru: $35**

NFL
Los Angeles Raiders Helmet

Fan cheers favorite team.
Handcrafted
B Siedler

QSR6249 SRP: $9.95 **GBTru: $110**

NFL
Minnesota Vikings Helmet

Fan cheers favorite team.
Handcrafted
B Siedler

QSR6267 SRP: $9.95 **GBTru: $20**

NFL
New England Patriots Helmet

Fan cheers favorite team.
Handcrafted
B Siedler

QSR6229 SRP: $9.95 **GBTru: $20**

NFL
Philadelphia Eagles Helmet

Fan cheers favorite team.
Handcrafted
B Siedler

QSR6259 SRP: $9.95 **GBTru: $20**

NFL
San Francisco 49's Helmet

Fan cheers favorite team.
Handcrafted
B Siedler

QSR6239 SRP: $9.95 **GBTru: $35**

NFL
Washington Redskins Helmet

Fan cheers favorite team.
Handcrafted
B Siedler

QSR6247 SRP: $9.95 **GBTru: $20**

NORMAN ROCKWELL
Santa's Visitors

N. Rockwell scene of kids with Santa.
Glass Ball, Dated

QX2407 SRP: $5.00 **GBTru: $7**

North Pole 911

Firemouseman gets ready to ring alarm.
Handcrafted, Dated
E Seale

QX5957 SRP: $10.95 **GBTru: $18**

NOSTALGIC HOUSES & SHOPS - 12TH
Town Church

White church with cross atop steeple.
Handcrafted, Dated
D Palmiter

QX5159 SRP: $14.95 **GBTru: $24**

NOSTALGIC HOUSES & SHOPS ACCESSORIES
Tree, Lampost & Auto

Set/3: tree, lampost, car.
Handcrafted
J Lyle

QX5089 SRP: $8.95 **GBTru: $25**

Number One Teacher

Mouse pupil writes in notebook.
Handcrafted, Dated
E Seale

QX5949 SRP: $7.95 **GBTru: $10**

Olympic Spirit Centennial Games Atlanta 1996, The

Medallion with Olympic flame.
Acrylic, Dated

QX3169 SRP: $7.95 **GBTru: $9**

On The Ice

Mouse skates with ice cube blades.
Handcrafted, Dated
K Crow

QX6047 SRP: $7.95 **GBTru: $10**

Our First Christmas Together

Mouse couple sits on heart & holds key.
Handcrafted, Dated
B Siedler

QX5799 SRP: $8.95 **GBTru: $10**

Packed With Memories

Photoholder school bag.
Handcrafted, Dated
E Seale

QX5639 SRP: $7.95 **GBTru: $8**

Our Christmas Together

Bunny couple decorate home with garland.
Handcrafted, Dated
J Lyle

QX5809 SRP: $6.95 **GBTru: $8**

Our First Christmas Together

Lights trim car/gifts on roof/photohld'r.
Handcrafted, Dated
E Seale

QX5807 SRP: $8.95 **GBTru: $10**

PEANUTS GANG, THE - 3RD
Peanuts Gang, The

Linus sits on a sled.
Handcrafted, Dated
B Siedler

QX5059 SRP: $9.95 **GBTru: $20**

Our Family

Treasure chest photoholder.
Handcrafted, Dated
R Chad

QX5709 SRP: $7.95 **GBTru: $8**

Our First Christmas Together

Heart shape.
Acrylic, Dated
J Lyle

QX3177 SRP: $6.95 **GBTru: $8**

Perfect Balance

Seal balances soccer ball on nose.
Handcrafted, Dated
B Siedler

QX5927 SRP: $7.95 **GBTru: $9**

Our First Christmas Together

Bear couple gaze at trim'd tree & snowy even'g.
Hndcr/Flitter, Dated
J Lyle

QX5797 SRP: $16.95 **GBTru: $26**

Our Little Blessings

Country boy & girl sit on painted settle.
Handcrafted, Dated
K Crow

QX5209 SRP: $12.95 **GBTru: $14**

PERSONALIZED
Baby Bear

Bear baby wears bib/holds candy cane.
Handcrafted
P Andrews

QP6157 SRP: $12.95 **GBTru: $13.75**

PERSONALIZED
Champ, The

Chipmunk holds loving cup.
Handcrafted
L Votruba

QP6127 SRP: $12.95 **GBTru: $13.75**

PERSONALIZED
Key Note

Mouse holds house key/ring.
Handcrafted
E Seale

QP6149 SRP: $12.95 **GBTru: $13.75**

PEZ Santa

Santa tops PEZ pack.
Handcrafted, Dated
J Francis

QX5267 SRP: $7.95 **GBTru: $9**

POCAHONTAS
Captain John Smith And Meeko

English explorer with raccoon.
Handcrafted
K Crow

QXI6169 SRP: $12.95 **GBTru: $15**

POCAHONTAS
Percy, Flit And Meeko

Bulldog, raccoon and butterfly.
Handcrafted
K Crow

QXI6179 SRP: $9.95 **GBTru: $16**

POCAHONTAS
Pocahontas

Native American maiden in canoe.
Handcrafted
K Crow

QXI6177 SRP: $12.95 **GBTru: $20**

POCAHONTAS
Pocahontas And Captain John Smith

English explorer w/Native American maiden.
Handcrafted
K Crow

QXI6197 SRP: $14.95 **GBTru: $18**

Polar Coaster

Penguin sleds down bear's back.
Handcrafted, Dated
K Crow

QX6117 SRP: $8.95 **GBTru: $15**

Popeye

Popeye holds up can of spinach.
Handcrafted
R Chad

QX5257 SRP: $10.95 **GBTru: $20**

PUPPY LOVE - 5TH
Puppy Love

Rottweiller pup with ribbon.
Hndcr/Brass, Dated
A M Rogers

QX5137 SRP: $7.95 **GBTru: $18**

Rejoice!

Angel gazes upon Holy Family.
Handcrafted, Dated
J Lyle

QX5987 SRP: $10.95 **GBTru: $15**

ROCKING HORSE - 15TH
Rocking Horse

Child's rocking horse.
Handcrafted, 4.00", Dated
L Sickman

QX5167 SRP: $10.95 **GBTru: $20**

ROCKING HORSE SERIES - 15TH ANNIVERSARY EDITION
Pewter Rocking Horse

Child's rocking horse.
Pewter, Dated
L Sickman

QX6167 SRP: $20.00 **GBTru: $30**

Roller Whiz

Turtle rollerblades.
Handcrafted, Dated
E Seale

QX5937 SRP: $7.95 **GBTru: $10**

Santa In Paris

Santa wraps garland around Eiffel Tower.
Handcrafted, Dated
L Sickman

QX5877 SRP: $8.95 **GBTru: $14**

Santa's Serenade

Owl plays harmonica / Santa plays guitar.
Handcrafted, Dated
K Crow

QX6017 SRP: $8.95 **GBTru: $12**

SHOEBOX GREETINGS
Cows Of Bali

Cow in a grass skirt carries a gift.
Handcrafted, Dated
P Andrews

QX5999 SRP: $8.95 **GBTru: $12**

SHOEBOX GREETINGS
Muletide Greetings

Mule leans on gate posts.
Handcrafted, Dated
R Chad

QX6009 SRP: $7.95 **GBTru: $14**

SHOWCASE - ALL IS BRIGHT
Angel Of Light

Angel is gilded as if gold leaf.
Handcrafted, Dated
P Andrews

QK1159 SRP: $11.95 **GBTru: $18**

SHOWCASE - ALL IS BRIGHT
Gentle Lullaby

Mother & child, gilded as if gold leaf.
Handcrafted, Dated
P Andrews

QK1157 SRP: $11.95 **GBTru: $18**

SHOWCASE - ANGEL BELLS
Carole

Winged angel.
Porcelain, Dated
L Votruba

QK1147 SRP: $12.95 **GBTru: $25**

SHOWCASE - ANGEL BELLS
Joy

Winged angel with slipped halo.
Porcelain, Dated
L Votruba

QK1137 SRP: $12.95 **GBTru: $25**

SHOWCASE - ANGEL BELLS
Noelle

Winged angel.
Porcelain, Dated
L Votruba

QK1139 SRP: $12.95 **GBTru: $25**

SHOWCASE - FOLK ART AMERICANA
Fetching The Firewood

Elf and husky tote wood with sleigh.
Handcrafted, Dated
L Sickman

QK1057 SRP: $15.95 **GBTru: $32**

SHOWCASE - FOLK ART AMERICANA
Fishing Party

Fisherman elf with walrus.
Handcrafted, Dated
L Sickman

QK1039 SRP: $15.95 **GBTru: $24**

SHOWCASE - HOLIDAY ENCHANTMENT
Away In The Manger

Painting of Baby Jesus in manger.
Porc/Gold, Dated

QK1097 SRP: $13.95 **GBTru: $24**

SHOWCASE - INVITATION TO TEA
Victorian Home Teapot

Teapot in shape of a house.
Handcrafted, Dated
P Andrews

QK1119 SRP: $15.95 **GBTru: $24**

SHOWCASE - FOLK ART AMERICANA
Guiding Santa

Angel guides Santa riding yak.
Handcrafted, Dated
L Sickman

QK1037 SRP: $18.95 **GBTru: $40**

SHOWCASE - HOLIDAY ENCHANTMENT
Following The Star

Painting of Three Wise Men story.
Porc/Gold, Dated
L Votruba

QK1099 SRP: $13.95 **GBTru: $24**

SHOWCASE - NATURE'S SKETCHBOOK
Backyard Orchard - Marjolein Bastin Art

Basket of fruit, 2 sided raised design.
Handcrafted, Dated
J Francis

QK1069 SRP: $18.95 **GBTru: $28**

SHOWCAS E - FOLK ART AMERICANA
Learning To Skate

Penguin & elf skate wearing pillow pads.
Handcrafted, Dated
L Sickman

QK1047 SRP: $14.95 **GBTru: $22**

SHOWCASE - INVITATION TO TEA
Cozy Cottage Teapot

Thatched roof country cottage.
Handcrafted, Dated
P Andrews

QK1127 SRP: $15.95 **GBTru: $20**

SHOWCASE - NATURE'S SKETCHBOOK
Christmas Cardinal - Marjolein Bastin Art
Cardinal sits on branch, 2 sided raised design.
Handcrafted, Dated
J Lyle

QK1077 SRP: $18.95 **GBTru: $45**

SHOWCASE - FOLK ART AMERICANA COMPLEMENT
Home From The Woods
Club Edition
Woodsman rides deer/brings home tree.
Handcrafted, Dated
L Sickman

QXC1059 SRP: $15.95 **GBTru: $40**

SHOWCASE - INVITATION TO TEA
European Castle Teapot

Turreted stone-look castle.
Handcrafted, Dated
P Andrews

QK1129 SRP: $15.95 **GBTru: $20**

SHOWCASE - NATURE'S SKETCHBOOK
Raising A Family - Marjolein Bastin Art
Mom bird feeds nest of babies, 2 sided raised design.
Handcrafted, Dated
J Lyle

QK1067 SRP: $18.95 **GBTru: $26**

SHOWCASE - NATURE'S SKETCHBOOK
Violets And Butterflies - Marjolein Bastin Art

Butterflies among field flowers.
Handcrafted, Dated
J Lyle

QK1079 SRP: $16.95 **GBTru: $26**

SHOWCASE - SYMBOLS OF CHRISTMAS
Jolly Santa

Santa with toy bag.
Handcrafted, Dated
P Andrews

QK1087 SRP: $15.95 **GBTru: $18**

SHOWCASE - SYMBOLS OF CHRISTMAS
Sweet Song

Christmas caroler.
Handcrafted, Dated
P Andrews

QK1089 SRP: $15.95 **GBTru: $18**

SIGNATURE COLLECTION - 3RD
Christmas Eve Bake-Off
Artist Tours
Mrs. Claus bakes cookies with help from elves.
Handcrafted, Dated
14 studio artists

QXC4049 SRP: $60.00 **GBTru: $130**

Sister

Snowgirl on skis.
Handcrafted, Dated
J Lyle

QX5687 SRP: $6.95 **GBTru: $9**

Sister To Sister

Girl mice in spice cabinet drawers.
Handcrafted, Dated
L Votruba

QX5689 SRP: $8.95 **GBTru: $12**

Ski Hound

Hound dog in sweater and hat is downhill skier.
Handcrafted, Dated
D Rhodus

QX5909 SRP: $8.95 **GBTru: $12**

Son

Boy panda bear holds pencil.
Handcrafted, Dated
D Palmiter

QX5669 SRP: $6.95 **GBTru: $7**

Special Cat

Cat in Santa suit photoholder.
Handcrafted, Dated
R Chad

QX5717 SRP: $7.95 **GBTru: $8**

Special Dog

Dog in Santa suit photoholder.
Handcrafted, Dated
R Chad

QX5719 SRP: $7.95 **GBTru: $8**

STAR TREK
Captain James T. Kirk

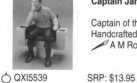

Captain of the Enterprise.
Handcrafted, Dated
A M Rogers

QXI5539 SRP: $13.95 **GBTru: $20**

STAR TREK
Captain Jean-Luc Picard

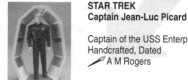

Captain of the USS Enterprise.
Handcrafted, Dated
A M Rogers

QXI5737 SRP: $13.95 **GBTru: $25**

STAR TREK
Ships of STAR TREK, The

Mini copies of Magic ornaments of Star Trek ships.
Handcrafted, Dated

QXI4109 | SRP: $19.95 | **GBTru: $25**

SUPER HEROES
Batmobile

Batman and Robin in the bat car.
Handcrafted
D Palmiter

QX5739 | SRP: $14.95 | **GBTru: $20**

Surfin' Santa

Santa delivers toys on a surf board.
Handcrafted, Dated
K Crow

QX6019 | SRP: $9.95 | **GBTru: $14**

Takin' A Hike

Mouse rope climbs hiking boot.
Handcrafted, Dated
J Francis

QX6029 | SRP: $7.95 | **GBTru: $8**

TENDER TOUCHES
Wish List
Premiere Ornament
Mouse writes list for Santa.
Handcrafted, Dated
E Seale

QX5859 | SRP: $15.00 | **GBTru: $18**

Tennis, Anyone?

Mouse decorates racquet with balls & holly.
Handcrafted, Dated
N Aube

QX5907 | SRP: $7.95 | **GBTru: $8**

THOMAS THE TANK ENGINE & FRIENDS
Thomas The Tank Engine - No. 1

Blue engine w/character face on front.
Handcrafted, Dated
D Rhodus

QX5857 | SRP: $9.95 | **GBTru: $15**

Three Wishes

Angel on cloud w/Love, Joy, and Peace stars.
Handcrafted, Dated
P Andrews

QX5979 | SRP: $7.95 | **GBTru: $12**

TOBIN FRALEY CAROUSEL - 4TH & FINAL
Tobin Fraley Carousel

Carousel horse on gold post displayer.
Porcelain, Dated
T Fraley

QX5069 | SRP: $28.00 | **GBTru: $35**

TURN-OF-THE-CENTURY PARADE - 1ST
Fireman, The
Showcase Collection
Horse drawn fire engine toy with bell.
Metal/Brass, Dated
K Crow

QK1027 | SRP: $16.95 | **GBTru: $30**

TWELVE DAYS OF CHRISTMAS, THE - 12TH & FINAL
Twelve Drummers Drumming

Parade drummer.
Acrylic, Dated

QX3009 | SRP: $6.95 | **GBTru: $10**

Two For Tea

Mice brew tea in a teapot.
Handcrafted, Dated
J Lyle

QX5829 | SRP: $9.95 | **GBTru: $18**

U.S. CHRISTMAS STAMPS - 3RD & FINAL
U.S. Christmas Stamps

Reproduction of Chrsms tree stamp w/displayer.
Enamel/Copper, Dated

QX5067 SRP: $10.95 **GBTru: $15**

Wheel Of Fortune - 20th Anniversary Edition

Mice cling to letters above prize wheel.
Handcrafted, Dated
L Sickman

QX6187 SRP: $12.95 **GBTru: $18**

YULETIDE CENTRAL - 2ND
Yuletide Central

Railroad car carries candy.
Pressed Tin, Dated
L Sickman

QX5079 SRP: $18.95 **GBTru: $20**

Vera The Mouse - Marjolein Bastin Art

Mouse trims tree/plate w/displayer.
Porcelain, Dated

QX5537 SRP: $8.95 **GBTru: $10**

WINNIE-THE-POOH
Winnie-The-Pooh And Tigger

Pooh stands on Tigger's shoulders to hang a star.
Handcrafted, Dated
B Siedler

QX5009 SRP: $12.95 **GBTru: $25**

1996

Waiting Up For Santa

Teddy bear in nightshirt and cap.
Handcrafted, Dated
D Palmiter

QX6106 SRP: $8.95 **GBTru: $12**

Winning Play, The

Mouse studies basketball game plan.
Handcrafted, Dated
B Siedler

QX5889 SRP: $7.95 **GBTru: $10**

101 Dalmatians

Promo: Gold Crown Holiday Open House, 101 points
Disc: 2 pups .

QXI6544 SRP: $12.95 **GBTru: $20**

Water Sports

Santa steers boat & Mrs Claus skis/Set/ 2.
Handcrafted, Dated
B Siedler

QX6039 SRP: $14.95 **GBTru: $24**

WIZARD OF OZ, THE
Glinda, Witch Of The North

Good witch in pink ball gown with star sceptor.
Handcrafted
J Lyle

QX5749 SRP: $13.95 **GBTru: $28**

Airmail For Santa

Club: Member Gets Member
Cardinal carries letter to Mr. & Mrs. Claus.
Handcrafted, Dated
A M Rogers

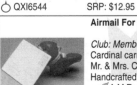

QXC4194 **GBTru: $15**

ALL GOD'S CHILDREN - 1ST
Christy - All God's Children

Girl paints a star.
Handcrafted, Dated
M Holcombe

QX5564 SRP: $12.95 **GBTru: $20**

AT THE BALLPARK - 1ST
Nolan Ryan

Star pitcher w/most no hitters; player card included.
Handcrafted, Dated
D Rhodus

QXI5711 SRP: $14.95 **GBTru: $30**

Baby's First Christmas - Beatrix Potter Art

Mom rabbit in rocker holds napping baby.
Porcelain, Dated
L Votruba

QX5744 SRP: $18.95 **GBTru: $25**

ALL-AMERICAN TRUCKS - 2ND
1955 Chevrolet Cameo

Pick-up truck carries tree in rear flatbed.
Handcrafted, Dated
P Andrews

QX5241 SRP: $13.95 **GBTru: $22**

Baby's First Christmas

Bessie Pease Gutman Art of baby: plate/displayer.
Fine Porcelain, Dated

QX5751 SRP: $10.95 **GBTru: $15**

BARBIE - 1ST
1988 Happy Holidays BARBIE
Complements Holiday BARBIE Series/ Club Edition
BARBIE wears red ball gown.
Handcrafted, Dated
P Andrews

QXC4181 SRP: $14.95 **GBTru: $50**

Antlers Aweigh!

Reindeer drives ski jet.
Handcrafted, Dated
R Chad

QX5901 SRP: $9.95 **GBTru: $15**

Baby's First Christmas

Teddy and rattle in baby shoe with jingle bell.
Handcrafted, Dated
P Andrews

QX5754 SRP: $9.95 **GBTru: $15**

BARBIE - 3RD
Enchanted Evening BARBIE

Doll in pink gown and fur stole.
Handcrafted, Dated
P Andrews

QXI6541 SRP: $14.95 **GBTru: $22**

Apple for Teacher

Chipmunk student gives apple to teacher.
Handcrafted, Dated
N Aube

QX6121 SRP: $7.95 **GBTru: $10**

Baby's First Christmas

Diaper pin opener displays photoholder.
Handcrafted, Dated
E Seale

QX5761 SRP: $7.95 **GBTru: $15**

BASEBALL HEROES - 3RD
Satchel Paige

Medallion of baseball player/player card included.
Handcrafted, Dated
D Rhodus

QX5304 SRP: $12.95 **GBTru: $15**

Bounce Pass

Bear dribbles basketball.
Handcrafted, Dated
B Siedler

QX6031 SRP: $7.95 **GBTru: $12**

Bowl 'em Over

Mouse w/very large bowling ball.
Handcrafted, Dated
B Siedler

QX6014 SRP: $7.95 **GBTru: $10**

CAT NAPS - 3RD
Cat Naps

Siamese cat naps in basket.
Handcrafted, Dated
D Rhodus

QX5641 SRP: $7.95 **GBTru: $15**

CELEBRATION OF ANGELS - 2ND
Celebration Of Angels, A

Winged angel.
Handcrafted, Dated
P Andrews

QX5634 SRP: $12.95 **GBTru: $18**

Child Care Giver

Baby bunny with bear care giver.
Handcrafted, Dated
B Siedler

QX6071 SRP: $8.95 **GBTru: $10**

CHILD'S AGE #1 - TEDDY BEAR YEARS
Baby's First Christmas

Teddy holds stocking with tree cookie.
Handcrafted, Dated
K Crow

QX5764 SRP: $7.95 **GBTru: $15**

CHILD'S AGE #2 - TEDDY BEAR YEARS
Baby's Second Christmas

Bear holds #2 tree cookie in stocking.
Handcrafted, Dated
K Crow

QX5771 SRP: $7.95 **GBTru: $16**

CHILD'S AGE #3 - TEDDY BEAR YEARS
Child's Third Christmas

Bear holds #3 bell cookie in stocking.
Handcrafted, Dated
K Crow

QX5774 SRP: $7.95 **GBTru: $15**

CHILD'S AGE #4 - TEDDY BEAR YEARS
Child's Fourth Christmas

Bear holds #4 drum cookie in stocking.
Handcrafted, Dated
K Crow

QX5781 SRP: $7.95 **GBTru: $15**

CHILD'S AGE #5 - TEDDY BEAR YEARS
Child's Fifth Christmas

Bears hangs onto #5 candy cane.
Handcrafted, Dated
D Rhodus

QX5784 SRP: $6.95 **GBTru: $15**

Christmas Joy

Holy Family.
Handcrafted, Dated
D Unruh

QX6241 SRP: $14.95 **GBTru: $18**

Christmas Snowman - Marjolein Bastin Art

Snowman with wreath & straw broom.
Handcrafted, Dated
D Unruh

QX6214 SRP: $9.95 **GBTru: $14**

CHRISTMAS VISITORS - 2ND
Christkindl

Winged angel carries tree & basket of toys.
Handcrafted, Dated
L Votruba

QX5631 SRP: $14.95 **GBTru: $18**

Come All Ye Faithful

Church opens to view of Holy Family.
Handcrafted, Dated
K Crow

QX6244 SRP: $12.95 **GBTru: $20**

DOLLS OF THE WORLD - 1ST
Native American BARBIE

Barbie wears Native American outfit.
Handcrafted, Dated
P Andrews

QX5561 SRP: $14.95 **GBTru: $20**

CLASSIC AMERICAN CARS - 6TH
1959 Cadillac De Ville

Cadillac convertible.
Handcrafted, Dated
D Palmiter

QX5384 SRP: $12.95 **GBTru: $18**

CRAYOLA CRAYON - 8TH
Bright Flying Colors

Mouse flys on crayon plane.
Handcrafted, Dated
K Crow

QX5391 SRP: $10.95 **GBTru: $20**

Evergreen Santa

Roly poly design Santa carries tree and star.
Handcrafted, Dated
J Lyle

QX5714 SRP: $22.00 **GBTru: $30**

Close-Knit Friends

Kittens in a basket.
Handcrafted, Dated
K Bricker

QX5874 SRP: $9.95 **GBTru: $12**

Dad

Dad bear with video camera.
Handcrafted, Dated
B Siedler

QX5831 SRP: $7.95 **GBTru: $10**

FABULOUS DECADE - 7TH
Fabulous Decade

Raccoon greets new year & holds up brass date .
Hndcr/Brass, Dated
E Seale

QX5661 SRP: $7.95 **GBTru: $14**

Coca Cola Santa
Welcome Guest
Haddon Sundblom Art
Santa holds bottle of Coke.
Handcrafted, Dated
D Unruh

QX5394 SRP: $14.95 **GBTru: $18**

Daughter

Girl bear with Jack-In-The-Box.
Handcrafted, Dated
P Andrews

QX6077 SRP: $8.95 **GBTru: $10**

Fan-tastic Season

Food vendor sell sports ornament.
Handcrafted, Dated
R Chad

QX5924 SRP: $9.95 **GBTru: $12**

Feliz Navidad

Animals sit on a serape on a beanpot.
Handcrafted, Dated
L Sickman

QX6304 SRP: $9.95 **GBTru: $15**

FOOTBALL LEGENDS - 2ND
Troy Aikman

Dallas Cowboy quarterback, player card included.
Handcrafted
D Rhodus

QXI5021 SRP: $14.95 **GBTru: $25**

FROSTY FRIENDS - 17TH
Frosty Friends

Child & penguin play ice pool.
Handcrafted, Dated
E Seale

QX5681 SRP: $10.95 **GBTru: $18**

"Get Hooked On Collecting" Starter Set: Book & Orn

Gold Crown Premiere & Holiday Event w/any HM Purchase
Mini orn of Santa Bear in Stock'g & book: HM collecting ornaments.

none SRP: $7.99 **GBTru: $10**

Glad Tidings

Winged angel.
Handcrafted, Dated
J Lyle

QX6231 SRP: $14.95 **GBTru: $18**

Goal Line Glory

Hockey player & goalie, Set/ 2.
Handcrafted, Dated
E Seale

QX6001 SRP: $12.95 **GBTru: $15**

Godchild

Mouse child says evening prayers.
Handcrafted, Dated
A M Rogers

QX5841 SRP: $8.95 **GBTru: $10**

Granddaughter

Cat takes ride on sled.
Handcrafted, Dated
A M Rogers

QX5697 SRP: $7.95 **GBTru: $9**

Grandma

Grandchild presents card to grandma.
Handcrafted, Dated
L Votruba

QX5844 SRP: $8.95 **GBTru: $10**

Grandpa

Grandchild & grandpa take tobbaggon ride.
Handcrafted, Dated
L Votruba

QX5851 SRP: $8.95 **GBTru: $10**

Grandson

Dog takes ride on sled.
Handcrafted, Dated
A M Rogers

QX5699 SRP: $7.95 **GBTru: $9**

Happy Holi-doze

Baseball player bear dozes in recliner.
Handcrafted, Dated
D Rhodus

QX5904 SRP: $9.95 **GBTru: $12**

Hearts Full Of Love

Sweethearts with heart bubble.
Handcrafted, Dated
D Rhodus

QX5814 SRP: $9.95 **GBTru: $12**

Hillside Express

Animals with toy bag tobaggon down the slope.
Handcrafted, Dated
N Aube

QX6134 SRP: $12.95 **GBTru: $16**

HUNCHBACK OF NOTRE DAME
Esmeralda And Djali

Gypsy girl dances, pet goat prances.
Handcrafted
K Crow

QXI6351 SRP: $14.95 **GBTru: $20**

HERE COMES SANTA - 18TH
Santa's 4X4

Santa drives to deliver tree and toys.
Handcrafted, Dated
E Seale

QX5684 SRP: $14.95 **GBTru: $22**

HOLIDAY BARBIE - 4TH
Holiday BARBIE

Doll wears fur-trimmed coat with muff, hat, over gold gown.
Handcrafted, Dated
P Andrews

QXI5371 SRP: $14.95 **GBTru: $20**

HUNCHBACK OF NOTRE DAME
Laverne, Victor and Hugo

3 Gargoyles from cathedral.
Handcrafted
K Crow

QXI6354 SRP: $12.95 **GBTru: $16**

HERSHEY
Time For A Treat

Mice on sled with chocolate candy bar.
Handcrafted, Dated
L Sickman

QX5464 SRP: $11.95 **GBTru: $15**

Holiday Haul

Reindeer brings tree home on tractor.
Handcrafted, Dated
L Sickman

QX6201 SRP: $14.95 **GBTru: $24**

HUNCHBACK OF NOTRE DAME
Quasimodo

Bell ringer of cathedral swings on bell rope.
Handcrafted
K Crow

QXI6341 SRP: $9.95 **GBTru: $14**

High Style

Woman styles hair into Christmas tree.
Handcrafted, Dated
R Chad

QX6064 SRP: $8.95 **GBTru: $14**

HOOP STARS - 2ND
Larry Bird

Star basketball player; player card included.
Handcrafted

QXI5014 SRP: $14.95 **GBTru: $22**

Hurrying Downstairs

Bear fireman slides down firepole.
Handcrafted, Dated
J Francis

QX6074 SRP: $8.95 **GBTru: $16**

I Dig Golf

Gopher digs up golf green.
Handcrafted, Dated
D Rhodus

QX5891 SRP: $10.95 **GBTru: $14**

It's A Wonderful Life

Anniversary Edition - 50 years
Final scene: A bell rings as Angel Clarence earns his wings.
Handcrafted, Dated,
K Crow

QXI6531 SRP: $14.95 **GBTru: $20**

Jackpot Jingle

Mouse plays slot machine to win.
Handcrafted, Dated
B Siedler

QX5911 SRP: $9.95 **GBTru: $12**

Jolly Wolly Ark

Roly poly Ark with Noah & animals.
Handcrafted, Dated
K Crow

QX6221 SRP: $12.95 **GBTru: $16**

KIDDIE CAR CLASSICS - 3RD
Murray Airplane

Open cockpit propeller airplane.
Cast Metal, Dated
D Palmiter

QX5364 SRP: $13.95 **GBTru: $18**

KIDDIE CAR CLASSICS SERIES COMPLEMENT
1937 Steelcraft Auburn By Murray
Club Edition
Copy of 1935 Auburn pedal car.
Die-Cast Metal, Dated
D Palmiter

QXC4174 SRP: $15.95 **GBTru: $55**

Kindly Shepherd

Shepherd holding crook carries lamb on shoulder.
Handcrafted, Dated
P Andrews

QX6274 SRP: $12.95 **GBTru: $14**

LANGUAGE OF FLOWERS - 1ST
Pansy
Showcase Collection
Winged angel holds pansy flowerholder.
Silver Plated, Dated
S Tague

QK1171 SRP: $15.95 **GBTru: $50**

Lighting The Way

Winged angel carries light.
Handcrafted, Dated
R Chad

QX6124 SRP: $12.95 **GBTru: $16**

LIONEL TRAIN - 1ST
700E Hudson Steam Locomotive

Train engine.
Die-Cast Metal, Dated

QX5531 SRP: $18.95 **GBTru: $55**

Little Song And Dance, A

Mouse play & dance on horn.
Handcrafted, Dated
K Crow

QX6211 SRP: $9.95 **GBTru: $12**

LOONEY TUNES
Foghorn Leghorn And Henery Hawk

Large rooster & small hawk hold ball ornament.
Handcrafted
R Chad

QX5444 SRP: $13.95 **GBTru: $15**

LOONEY TUNES
Marvin The Martian

Out of this world cartoon character from mars.
Handcrafted
R Chad

QX5451 SRP: $10.95 **GBTru: $15**

MADAME ALEXANDER - 1ST
Cinderella - 1995

Cinderella doll in ball gown.
Handcrafted
J Francis

QX6311 SRP: $14.95 **GBTru: $25**

Madonna And Child

Portrait in an embossed frame.
Stamped Tin, Dated
J de Ribera/L Sickman

QX6324 SRP: $12.95 **GBTru: $13**

Making His Rounds

African American Santa w/candle & toy sack.
Handcrafted, Dated
J Francis

QX6271 SRP: $14.95 **GBTru: $16**

MARY'S ANGELS - 9TH
Violet

Winged angel with lamb.
Handcrafted
M Hamilton/R Chad

QX5664 SRP: $6.95 **GBTru: $14**

Matchless Memories

Mouse plays matchbox piano.
Handcrafted, Dated
K Crow

QX6061 SRP: $9.95 **GBTru: $15**

Merry Carpoolers

Santa & reindeer ride together in ski gondola.
Handcrafted, Dated
K Crow

QX5884 SRP: $14.95 **GBTru: $20**

MERRY MINIATURE
Bashful Mistletoe
Ornament Premiere
Boy & girl by archway where mistletoe is fastened, Set/3.
Handcrafted, Dated
N Aube

QFM8054 SRP: $12.95 **GBTru: $20**

MERRY OLDE SANTA - 7TH
Merry Olde Santa

Santa in red, white & blue carries toys and flag.
Handcrafted, Dated
K Crow

QX5654 SRP: $14.95 **GBTru: $22**

Mom

Penguin sits atop holiday bag with gift.
Handcrafted, Dated
J Lyle

QX5824 SRP: $7.95 **GBTru: $10**

Mom And Dad

Bear couple hugging.
Handcrafted, Dated
D Rhodus

QX5821 SRP: $9.95 **GBTru: $12**

Mom-To-Be

Kangeroo mom with bottle & rattle.
Handcrafted, Dated
D Unruh

QX5791 SRP: $7.95 **GBTru: $8**

MOTHER GOOSE - 4TH
Mary Had A Little Lamb

Book opens to verse and to Mary with a lamb.
Handcrafted, Dated
E Seale/L Votruba

QX5644 SRP: $13.95 **GBTru: $16**

New Home

Chipmunk at mail box home.
Handcrafted, Dated
E Seale

QX5881 SRP: $8.95 **GBTru: $10**

NFL
Specialty Ball Ornaments Coordinate with Keepsake NFL Collection
See 1995 listings p. 224.
Produced: 14 teams 1996.
Team logo displayed.
Ball Orn

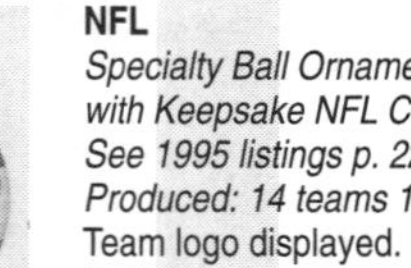

Item #	Name	SRP	GBTru
BIL2035	**Buffalo Bills**	$5.95	**$10**
PKR2035	**Green Bay Packers**	$5.95	**$10**
PIT2035	**Pittsburgh Steelers**	$5.95	**$10**
RAM2035	**St. Louis Rams**	$5.95	**$10**

NFL
Number 1 Fan - 30 NFL Teams
Mouse fan wears #1 oversize glove.
Sample displays KC Chiefs logo.
Handcrafted
D Unruh

Item #	Name	SRP	GBTru
QSR6484	**Arizona Cardinals**	$9.95	**$10**
QSR6364	**Atlanta Falcons**	$9.95	**$10**
QSR6391	**Browns**	$9.95	**$10**
QSR6371	**Buffalo Bills**	$9.95	**$10**
QSR6374	**Carolina Panthers**	$9.95	**$10**
QSR6381	**Chicago Bears**	$9.95	**$10**
QSR6384	**Cincinnati Bengals**	$9.95	**$10**
QSR6394	**Dallas Cowboys**	$9.95	**$10**
QSR6411	**Denver Broncos**	$9.95	**$15**
QSR6414	**Detroit Lions**	$9.95	**$10**
QSR6421	**Green Bay Packers**	$9.95	**$65**
QSR6431	**Indianapolis Colts**	$9.95	**$10**
QSR6434	**Jacksonville Jaguars**	$9.95	**$10**
QSR6361	**Kansas City Chiefs**	$9.95	**$15**
QSR6451	**Miami Dolphins**	$9.95	**$10**
QSR6454	**Minnesota Vikings**	$9.95	**$10**
QSR6461	**New England Patriots**	$9.95	**$10**
QSR6464	**New Orleans Saints**	$9.95	**$10**
QSR6471	**New York Giants**	$9.95	**$10**
QSR6474	**New York Jets**	$9.95	**$10**
QSR6441	**Oakland Raiders**	$9.95	**$10**
QSR6424	**Oilers**	$9.95	**$10**
QSR6481	**Philadelphia Eagles**	$9.95	**$10**
QSR6491	**Pittsburgh Steelers**	$9.95	**$10**
QSR6494	**San Diego Chargers**	$9.95	**$10**
QSR6501	**San Francisco 49ers**	$9.95	**$10**
QSR6504	**Seattle Seahawks**	$9.95	**$10**

St. Louis Rams
QSR6444 SRP: $9.95 **GBTru: $10**

Tampa Bay Buccaneers
QSR6511 SRP: $9.95 **GBTru: $10**

Washington Redskins
QSR6514 SRP: $9.95 **GBTru: $10**

Olive Oyl and Swee'Pea

Popeye's sweetheart holds baby Swee' Pea.
Handcrafted
R Chad

QX5481 SRP: $10.95 **GBTru: $14**

OLYMPIC SPIRIT
Parade Of Nations
Design: Champion Product, Inc.
Plate w/Nations flags; torch design on Global map; displayer.
Porcelain, Dated

QXE5741 SRP: $10.95 **GBTru: $12**

NORMAN ROCKWELL
Growth of a Leader

Ceramic plaque for Boy Scouts Of America.
Ceramic, Dated

QX5541 SRP: $9.95 **GBTru: $10**

OLYMPIC SPIRIT
Invitation To The Games

Trading card plaques honor 1896 & 1996 games, displayers, Set/2.
Ceramic, Dated
D McGehee

QXE5511 SRP: $14.95 **GBTru: $16**

On My Way Photoholder

School bus photo frame.
Handcrafted, Dated
S Tague

QX5861 SRP: $7.95 **GBTru: $10**

NORMAN ROCKWELL
Little Spooners

Boy & girl sit on bench watching sun set.
Handcrafted, Dated
D Unruh

QX5504 SRP: $12.95 **GBTru: $13**

OLYMPIC SPIRIT
IZZY- The Mascot

Olympic games mascot.
Handcrafted, Dated
D Palmiter

QXE5724 SRP: $9.95 **GBTru: $12**

Our Christmas Together

Couple on swing in gazebo.
Handcrafted, Dated
D Palmiter

QX5794 SRP: $18.95 **GBTru: $22**

NOSTALGIC HOUSES & SHOPS - 13TH
Victorian Painted Lady

Two story victorian home.
Handcrafted, Dated
D Palmiter

QX5671 SRP: $14.95 **GBTru: $20**

OLYMPIC SPIRIT
Olympic Triumph

Discus athlete.
Handcrafted, Dated
E Seale

QXE5731 SRP: $10.95 **GBTru: $12**

Our Christmas Together Photoholder

Couple in car at drive in movie.
Handcrafted, Dated
K Crow

QX5804 SRP: $8.95 **GBTru: $10**

Our First Christmas Together

Acrylic heart with 2 doves.
Acrylic, Dated
L Votruba

QX3051 SRP: $6.95 **GBTru: $8**

PEANUTS GANG, THE - 4TH & FINAL
PEANUTS Gang, The

Lucy writes wishlist to Santa.
Handcrafted, Dated
J Francis

QX5381 SRP: $9.95 **GBTru: $14**

Prayer For Peace

Girl holds prayer book & candle.
Handcrafted, Dated
J Lyle

QX6261 SRP: $7.95 **GBTru: $9**

Our First Christmas Together

Mouse couple on crescent cheese moon.
Dated
D Palmiter

QX5811 SRP: $9.95 **GBTru: $12**

Peppermint Surprise

Mouse hugs peppermint candy.
Handcrafted, Dated
S Pike

QX6234 SRP: $7.95 **GBTru: $10**

Precious Child

Madonna and Child.
Handcrafted, Dated
L Votruba

QX6251 SRP: $8.95 **GBTru: $9**

Our First Christmas Together
Collector Plate

Old fashioned portrait of boy and girl: displayer.
Porcelain, Dated

QX5801 SRP: $10.95 **GBTru: $11**

PEZ Snowman

Candy box becomes top-hattted snowman.
Handcrafted, Dated

QX6534 SRP: $7.95 **GBTru: $12**

Pup-Tenting

Pup naps in tent decorated with Christmas lights.
Handcrafted, Dated
D Palmiter

QX6011 SRP: $7.95 **GBTru: $10**

PEANUTS
Tree For SNOOPY, A
Complements '96 PEANUTS: A Tree For Woodstock QXM4767
Snoopy pulls sled carrying a tree.
Handcrafted, Dated
B Siedler

QX5507 SRP: $8.95 **GBTru: $12**

Polar Cycle

Polar bear gives penguin ride in bicycle basket.
Handcrafted, Dated
D Unruh

QX6034 SRP: $12.95 **GBTru: $14**

PUPPY LOVE - 6TH
Puppy Love

Pup sits up and holds stocking with bone.
Hndcr/Brass, Dated
A M Rogers

QX5651 SRP: $7.95 **GBTru: $15**

Regal Cardinal

Cardinal.
Handcrafted, Dated
J Francis

QX6204 SRP: $9.95 **GBTru: $12**

Santa

Club: Keepsake of Membership
Santa with bag of candy canes.
Handcrafted, Dated
B Siedler

QXC4164 **GBTru: $** **GBTru: $15**

SHOWCASE - COOKIE JAR FRIENDS
Clyde

Cookie jar dog dressed in hat and coat carries stocking of biscuits.
Porcelain, Dated
N Aube

QK1161 SRP: $15.95 **GBTru: $18**

Rocking Horse

Artist Tours
Honors Retirement of Rocking Horse Series.
24K Gold Plated

event SRP: $12.95 **GBTru: $30**

Sew Sweet

Bee embroiders a tree square.
Handcrafted, Dated
N Aube

QX5921 SRP: $8.95 **GBTru: $12**

SHOWCASE - FOLK ART AMERICANA
Caroling Angel

Winged angel with praying hands, eyes closed.
Stamped Copper, Dated
L Sickman

QK1134 SRP: $16.95 **GBTru: $20**

ROCKING HORSE - 16TH & FINAL
Rocking Horse

Decorated rocking horse.
Handcrafted, Dated
L Sickman

QX5674 SRP: $10.95 **GBTru: $16**

SHOEBOX GREETINGS - 10TH ANNIVERSARY
Maxine

Maxine & her pup send greetings.
Handcrafted, Dated
J Wagner/S Pike

QX6224 SRP: $9.95 **GBTru: $20**

SHOWCASE - FOLK ART AMERICANA
Mrs. Claus

Mrs. Claus carries lantern and teddy bear.
Copper, Dated
L Sickman

QK1204 SRP: $18.95 **GBTru: $22**

Rudolph The Red-Nosed Reindeer

Club: Keepsake of Membership
Red nose reindeer with jingle bell collar.
Handcrafted, Dated,
B Siedler

QXC7341 **GBTru: $** **GBTru: $20**

SHOWCASE - COOKIE JAR FRIENDS
Carmen

Cookie jar cat in hat and coat carries a mouse.
Porcelain, Dated
A M Rogers

QK1164 SRP: $15.95 **GBTru: $18**

SHOWCASE-FOLK ART AMERICANA
Santa's Gifts

Santa carries Christmas toys.
Copper/Brass, Dated
L Sickman

QK1124 SRP: $18.95 **GBTru: $24**

SHOWCASE - MAGI BELLS
Balthasar (Frankincense)

One of the Three Kings carries gift.
Porcelain
L Votruba

QK1174 SRP: $13.95 **GBTru: $15**

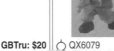

SHOWCASE - NATURE'S SKETCHBOOK
Christmas Bunny - Marjolein Bastin Art
Bunny sits by snow covered watering can.
Handcrafted, Dated
J Francis

QK1104 SRP: $18.95 **GBTru: $25**

SIGNATURE COLLECTION - 4TH AND FINAL
Santa's Toy Shop
Artist Tours
2 Ornaments and display: toy shop with elves & toys.
Handcrafted, Dated

QXC4201 SRP: $60.00 **GBTru: $125**

SHOWCASE - MAGI BELLS
Caspar (Myrrh)

One of the Three Kings carries gifts.
Porcelain
L Votruba

QK1184 SRP: $13.95 **GBTru: $15**

SHOWCASE - NATURE'S SKETCHBOOK
Holly Basket, The - Marjolein Bastin Art

Holly branches in basket.
Handcrafted, Dated
J Lyle

QK1094 SRP: $18.95 **GBTru: $22**

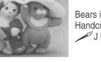

SIGNATURE COLLECTION: COMPLEMENTS TOY SHOP
Toy Shop Santa
Artist Tours
Companion Santa for Toy Shop.
Handcrafted
D Unruh

event SRP: $14.95 **GBTru: $35**

SHOWCASE - MAGI BELLS
Melchior (Gold)

One of the Three Kings carries gift.
Porcelain
L Votruba

QK1181 SRP: $13.95 **GBTru: $15**

SHOWCASE-SACRED MASTERWORKS
Madonna And Child: Art of Raphael

Mary & Infant Jesus.
Handcrafted, Dated
L Sickman

QK1144 SRP: $15.95 **GBTru: $20**

Sister To Sister

Bears in dress up clothes carry gift.
Handcrafted, Dated
J Lyle

QX5834 SRP: $9.95 **GBTru: $12**

SHOWCASE - NATURE'S SKETCHBOOK
Birds' Christmas Tree, The - Marjolein Bastin Art
Birds gather at tree decorated with seeds and bird food.
Handcrafted, Dated
D Unruh

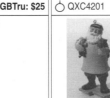

QK1114 SRP: $18.95 **GBTru: $22**

SHOWCASE-SACRED MASTERWORKS
Praying Madonna: Art of Sassoferrato

Mary, Mother of Christ.
Handcrafted, Dated
L Sickman

QK1154 SRP: $15.95 **GBTru: $20**

Son

Boy bear with hobby horse.
Handcrafted, Dated
D Palmiter

QX6079 SRP: $8.95 **GBTru: $10**

Special Dog Photoholder

Dog biscuit wreath photo frame.
Handcrafted, Dated
S Tague

QX5864 SRP: $7.95 **GBTru: $10**

STAR TREK
STAR TREK: 30 Years
Voice of Captain James T. Kirk
USS Enterprise spaceship & Galileo shuttlecraft: Set/2 w/displayer.
Die-Cast Metal, Dated,
L Norton/D Rhodus

QXI7534 SRP: $45.00 **GBTru: $78**

Tamika - Penda Kids

Child & pup with holiday treats.
Handcrafted, Dated
C Johnson/K Bricker

QX6301 SRP: $7.95 **GBTru: $8**

Star of the Show

Bunny ballerina.
Handcrafted, Dated
N Aube

QX6004 SRP: $8.95 **GBTru: $15**

STAR TREK
U.S.S. Voyager

Spacecraft.
Handcrafted, Dated,
L Norton

QXI7544 SRP: $24.00 **GBTru: $30**

Tender Lovin' Care

Doctor mouse checks heartbeat and temperature.
Handcrafted, Dated
E Seale

QX6114 SRP: $7.95 **GBTru: $10**

STAR TREK
Commander William T. Riker

Star Trek - Next Generation.
Handcrafted, Dated
A M Rogers

QXI5551 SRP: $14.95 **GBTru: $20**

SUPER HEROES
Spider-Man

Hero fights evil/ web lines for display.
Handcrafted
R Chad

QX5757 SRP: $12.95 **GBTru: $20**

TENDER TOUCHES
Welcome Sign
Ornament Premiere
Bear hangs Christmas wreath on window.
Handcrafted, Dated
E Seale

QX6331 SRP: $15.00 **GBTru: $16**

STAR TREK
Mr. Spock

Mr. Spock from the Enterprise.
Handcrafted, Dated
A M Rogers

QXI5544 SRP: $14.95 **GBTru: $22**

SUPER HEROES
Wonder Woman

Cartoon character fights evil.
Handcrafted
A M Rogers

QX5941 SRP: $12.95 **GBTru: $16**

Thank You, Santa Photoholder

Treats left for Santa picture holder.
Handcrafted, Dated
K Bricker

QX5854 SRP: $7.95 **GBTru: $10**

This Big!

Santa fisherman shows size of fish that got away.
Handcrafted, Dated
E Seale

QX5914 SRP: $9.95 **GBTru: $12**

Welcome Him

Farm animals gaze at Baby Jesus in manger.
Handcrafted, Dated
S Tague

QX6264 SRP: $8.95 **GBTru: $15**

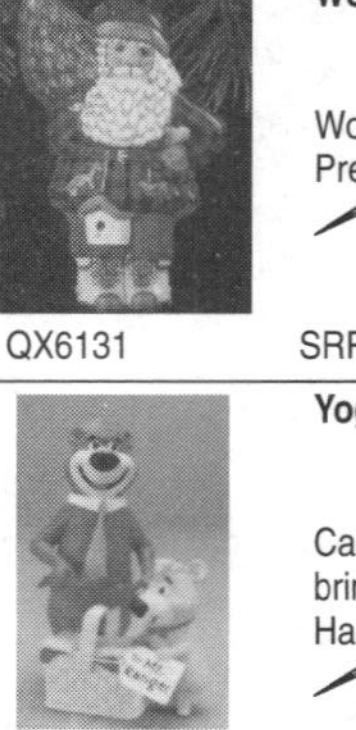

Woodland Santa

Woodsman Santa with tree & toys.
Pressed Tin
L Sickman

QX6131 SRP: $12.95 **GBTru: $15**

THOMAS THE TANK ENGINE & FRIENDS
Percy The Small Engine - No. 6.

Small Engine from favorite children's story.
Handcrafted
D Rhodus

QX6314 SRP: $9.95 **GBTru: $14**

WINNIE-THE-POOH
Winnie-The-Pooh And Piglet

Pooh Bear & Piglet walk arm in arm.
Handcrafted, Dated
B Siedler

QX5454 SRP: $12.95 **GBTru: $22**

Yogi Bear and Boo Boo

Cartoon bears in Jellystone Park bring basket to ranger.
Handcrafted
A M Rogers

QX5521 SRP: $12.95 **GBTru: $15**

Tonka Mighty Dump Truck

Big wheeled earth mover truck.
Die-Cast Metal, Dated

QX6321 SRP: $13.95 **GBTru: $20**

WIZARD OF OZ COLLECTION: COMPLEMENT
Wizard Of Oz, The
CLUB EDITION
Omaha state fair balloon carries "wizard" aloft.
Handcrafted
A M Rogers

QXC4161 SRP: $12.95 **GBTru: $60**

YULETIDE CENTRAL - 3RD
Yuletide Central

Mail railroad car.
Pressed Tin, Dated
L Sickman

QX5011 SRP: $18.95 **GBTru: $24**

TURN-OF-THE-CENTURY PARADE - 2ND
Uncle Sam
Showcase Collection
Uncle Sam on old fashioned tricycle carries flag & bell.
Die-Cast Metal with brass bell, Dated
K Crow

QK1084 SRP: $16.95 **GBTru: $25**

WIZARD OF OZ, THE
Witch Of The West

Wicked Witch from Book/Movie.
Handcrafted
J Lyle

QX5554 SRP: $13.95 **GBTru: $18**

Yuletide Cheer

Pup cheerleader.
Handcrafted, Dated
L Votruba

QX6054 SRP: $7.95 **GBTru: $10**

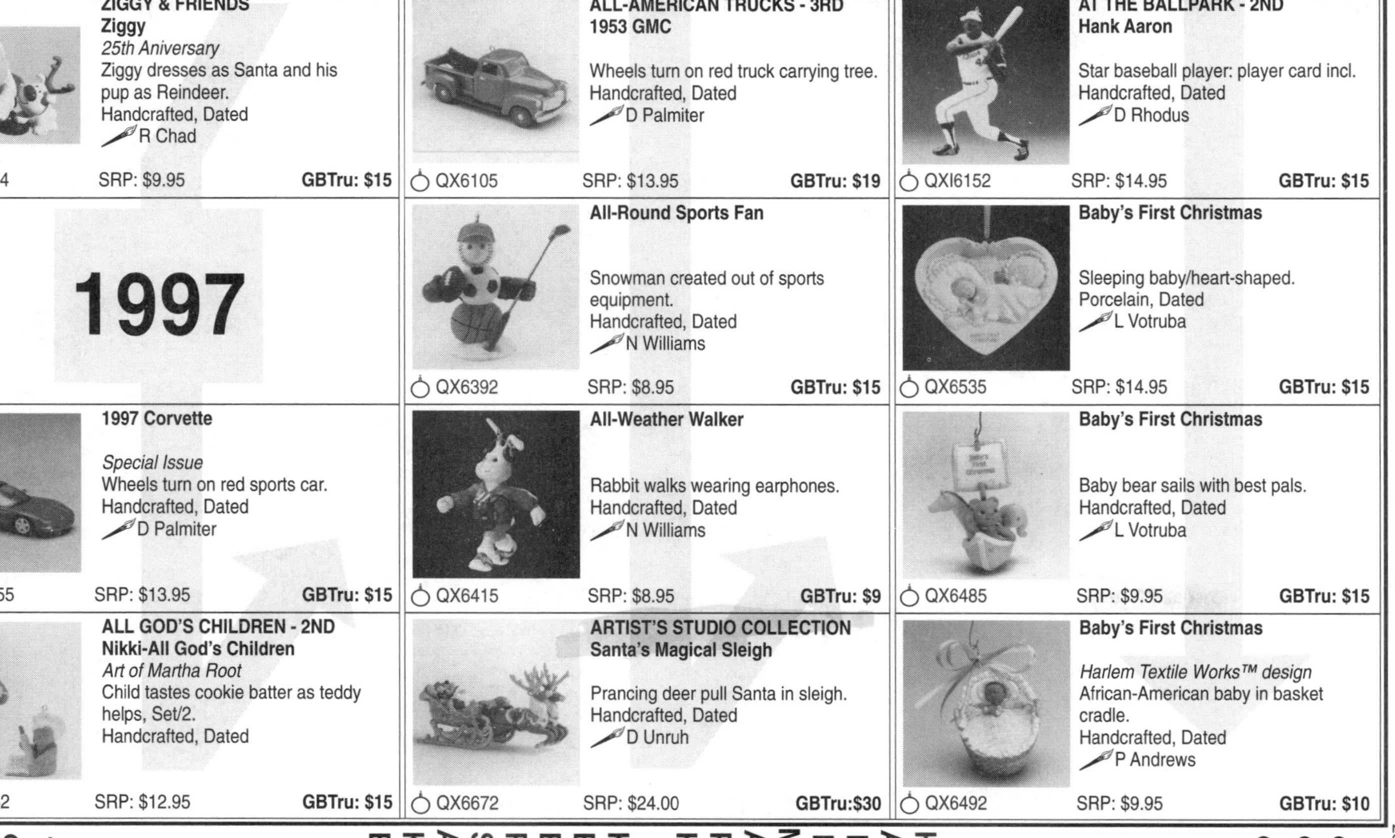

ZIGGY & FRIENDS
Ziggy
25th Anniversary
Ziggy dresses as Santa and his pup as Reindeer.
Handcrafted, Dated
R Chad
QX6524 SRP: $9.95 **GBTru: $15**

1997

1997 Corvette

Special Issue
Wheels turn on red sports car.
Handcrafted, Dated
D Palmiter
QXI6455 SRP: $13.95 **GBTru: $15**

ALL GOD'S CHILDREN - 2ND
Nikki-All God's Children
Art of Martha Root
Child tastes cookie batter as teddy helps, Set/2.
Handcrafted, Dated
QX6142 SRP: $12.95 **GBTru: $15**

ALL-AMERICAN TRUCKS - 3RD
1953 GMC

Wheels turn on red truck carrying tree.
Handcrafted, Dated
D Palmiter
QX6105 SRP: $13.95 **GBTru: $19**

All-Round Sports Fan

Snowman created out of sports equipment.
Handcrafted, Dated
N Williams
QX6392 SRP: $8.95 **GBTru: $15**

All-Weather Walker

Rabbit walks wearing earphones.
Handcrafted, Dated
N Williams
QX6415 SRP: $8.95 **GBTru: $9**

ARTIST'S STUDIO COLLECTION
Santa's Magical Sleigh

Prancing deer pull Santa in sleigh.
Handcrafted, Dated
D Unruh
QX6672 SRP: $24.00 **GBTru:$30**

AT THE BALLPARK - 2ND
Hank Aaron

Star baseball player: player card incl.
Handcrafted, Dated
D Rhodus
QXI6152 SRP: $14.95 **GBTru: $15**

Baby's First Christmas

Sleeping baby/heart-shaped.
Porcelain, Dated
L Votruba
QX6535 SRP: $14.95 **GBTru: $15**

Baby's First Christmas

Baby bear sails with best pals.
Handcrafted, Dated
L Votruba
QX6485 SRP: $9.95 **GBTru: $15**

Baby's First Christmas

Harlem Textile Works™ design
African-American baby in basket cradle.
Handcrafted, Dated
P Andrews
QX6492 SRP: $9.95 **GBTru: $10**

Baby's First Christmas

Baby rattle photoholder.
Handcrafted, Dated

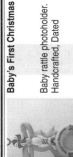

QX6482 SRP: $7.95 **GBTru: $10**

BARBIE - 2ND
1989 Happy Holiday BARBIE
Club Edition Compliments Holiday BARBIE Series
BARBIE wears white ball gown.
Handcrafted, Dated
P Andrews

QXC5162 SRP: $15.95 **GBTru: $45**

BARBIE - 4TH
Wedding Day 1959-1962
Special Issue
BARBIE as a bride.
Handcrafted, Dated
P Andrews

QXI6812 SRP: $15.95 **GBTru: $22**

BARBIE ORNAMENT SERIES COMPLEMENT
BARBIE And KEN Wedding Day
Special Issue
BARBIE & KEN as Bride and Groom.
Hndcr/Fabric, Dated
P Andrews/D Palmiter

QXI6815 SRP: $35.00 **GBTru: $40**

BASEBALL HEROES - 4TH & FINAL
Jackie Robinson
50th Anniversary 1947 - 1997
Sliding into home plate safe.
Handcrafted, Dated
D Rhodus

QX6202 SRP: $12.95 **GBTru: $14**

Biking Buddies

Pup rides in boy's tricycle basket.
Handcrafted, Dated
D Palmiter

QX6682 SRP: $12.95 **GBTru: $13**

Book Of The Year

Mouse sits with open photoholder.
Handcrafted, Dated
K Bricker

QX6645 SRP: $7.95 **GBTru: $8**

Breezin' Along

Ice skating mouse uses leaf as sail.
Handcrafted, Dated
E Seale

QX6722 SRP: $8.95 **GBTru: $9**

Bucket Brigade

Panda bear fireman tosses water from pail.
Handcrafted, Dated
J Francis

QX6382 SRP: $8.95 **GBTru: $9**

CAT NAPS - 4TH
Cat Naps

Ginger cat naps in overnight case.
Handcrafted, Dated
K Bricker

QX6205 SRP: $8.95 **GBTru: $10**

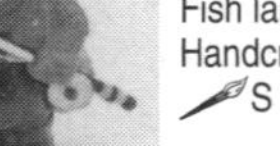

Catch Of The Day

Fish lands atop bear's nose.
Handcrafted, Dated
S Tague

QX6712 SRP: $9.95 **GBTru: $10**

CELEBRATION OF ANGELS, A - 3RD
Celebration Of Angels, A

Winged Angel.
Handcrafted, Dated
P Andrews

QX6175 SRP: $13.95 **GBTru: $14**

CHILD'S AGE #1 - TEDDY BEAR YEARS
Baby's First Christmas

Baby bear holds star cookie.
Handcrafted, Dated
K Crow

QX6495 SRP: $7.95 **GBTru: $15**

CHILD'S AGE #2 - TEDDY BEAR YEARS
Baby's Second Christmas

Baby bear with tree cookie.
Handcrafted, Dated
K Crow

QX6502 SRP: $7.95 **GBTru: $12**

CHILD'S AGE #3 - TEDDY BEAR YEARS
Child's Third Christmas

Baby bear holds bell cookie.
Handcrafted, Dated
K Crow

QX6505 SRP: $7.95 **GBTru: $10**

CHILD'S AGE #4 - TEDDY BEAR YEARS
Child's Fourth Christmas

Baby Panda bear holds drum cookie.
Handcrafted, Dated
K Crow

QX6512 SRP: $7.95 **GBTru: $8**

CHILD'S AGE #5 - TEDDY BEAR YEARS
Child's Fifth Christmas

Baby bear holds gift box cookie.
Handcrafted
K Crow

QX6515 SRP: $7.95 **GBTru: $8**

Christmas Checkup

Mouse Doc checks snowman's temperature.
Handcrafted, Dated
B Siedler

QX6385 SRP: $7.95 **GBTru: $8**

CHRISTMAS VISITORS - 3RD AND FINAL
Kolyada

Woman carries basket of food.
Handcrafted, Dated
L Votruba

QX6172 SRP: $14.95 **GBTru: $15**

CINDERELLA - 1ST
Cinderella

Cinderella arrives at the palace for ball.
Handcrafted, Dated

QXD4045 SRP: $14.95 **GBTru: $20**

CLASSIC AMERICAN CARS - 7TH
1969 Hurst Oldsmobile 442

Two-door white Olds with spoiler.
Handcrafted, Dated
D Palmiter

QX6102 SRP: $13.95 **GBTru: $20**

Classic Cross

Ornate scroll design Cross.
Metal, Dated
L Votruba

QX6805 SRP: $13.95 **GBTru: $14**

CLAUSES ON VACATION, THE - 1ST
Clauses On Vacation, The

Mr and Mrs Claus have gone fishing.
Handcrafted, Dated
B Siedler

QX6112 SRP: $14.95 **GBTru: $20**

Clever Camper

Beaver toasts marshmallow using pen knife.
Handcrafted, Dated
R Chad

QX6445 SRP: $7.95 **GBTru: $8**

COCA-COLA SANTA
Taking A Break

Santa sips a coke while rest'g on a rocker.
Handcrafted, Dated
D Unruh

QX6305 SRP: $14.95 **GBTru: $20**

CRAYOLA CRAYON - 8TH
Bright Rocking Colors

Bears rocks on a CRAYOLA box crayon horse.
Handcrafted, Dated
S Tague

QX6235 SRP: $12.95 **GBTru: $18**

Cycling Santa

Santa delivers toys on racer.
Handcrafted, Dated
N Williams

QX6425 SRP: $14.95 **GBTru: $18**

Dad

Dad mouse foamed up on shaving mug.
Handcrafted, Dated
B Siedler

QX6532 SRP: $8.95 **GBTru: $9**

Daughter

Stocking with picture of angel.
Pressed Tin, Dated
K Bricker

QX6612 SRP: $7.95 **GBTru: $10**

DISNEY - 101 DALMATIANS
Two - Tone

Half white, half spotted pup with candy cane.
Handcrafted

QXD4015 SRP: $9.95 **GBTru: $15**

DISNEY - ALADDIN & THE KING OF THIEVES
Jasmine & Aladdin

Jasmine & Aladdin on magic flying carpet.
Handcrafted, Dated

QXD4062 SRP: $14.95 **GBTru: $20**

DISNEY - CINDERELLA
Gus & Jaq

Mice help decorate ball gown.
Handcrafted, Dated

QXD4052 SRP: $12.95 **GBTru: $20**

DISNEY: HERCULES COLLECTION, THE
Hercules
Special Issue - Greek Mythology
Hero with drawn bow and arrow.
Handcrafted

QXI4005 SRP: $12.95 **GBTru: $16**

DISNEY: HERCULES COLLECTION, THE
Megara And Pegasus
Special Issue - Greek Mythology
Maiden rides on winged horse.
Handcrafted

QXI4012 SRP: $16.95 **GBTru: $18**

DISNEY - HUNCHBACK OF NOTRE DAME
Phoebus & Esmeralda

Phoebus lifts Esmeralda and they kiss.
Handcrafted

QXD6344 SRP: $14.95 **GBTru: $16**

DISNEY - LION KING, THE
Timon & Pumbaa

Timon rides behind wreath on Pumbaa's back.
Handcrafted, Dated

QXD4065 SRP: $12.95 **GBTru: $13**

DISNEY - LITTLE MERMAID COLLECTION, THE
Ariel
Special Issue
Mermaid with undersea friends.
Handcrafted

QXI4072 SRP: $12.95 **GBTru: $13**

DISNEY - MICKEY & CO.
New Pair Of Skates

Mickey learns to skate w/tied-on pillow/Minnie helps.
Handcrafted, Dated

QXD4032 SRP: $13.95 **GBTru: $20**

Downhill Run

Santa & reindeer race in ski sled.
Handcrafted, Dated
K Crow

QX6705 SRP: $9.95 **GBTru: $15**

DISNEY - MICKEY & CO.
Goofy's Ski Adventure

Goofy falls and catches Mickey & Donald in snowball.
Handcrafted, Dated

QXD4042 SRP: $12.95 **GBTru: $14**

DISNEY - SNOW WHITE & THE SEVEN DWARFS
Snow White
Anniversary Edition, 60 Years
Snow White opens box and Dopey pops out, Set/2.
Handcrafted, Dated

QXD4055 SRP: $16.95 **GBTru: $25**

Elegance On Ice

Girl figure skater.
Handcrafted, Dated
J Lyle

QX6432 SRP: $9.95 **GBTru: $10**

DISNEY - MICKEY & CO.
Mickey's Long Shot

Golfer Mickey can't find ball that's behind him.
Handcrafted, Dated

QXD6412 SRP: $10.95 **GBTru: $16**

DISNEY - WINNIE-THE-POOH
Waitin' On Santa

Pooh and pal Piglet nap on chair/ Santa's snack.
Handcrafted

QXD6365 SRP: $12.95 **GBTru: $20**

Expressly For Teacher

Teddy rides paper plane.
Handcrafted, Dated
S Tague

QX6375 SRP: $7.95 **GBTru: $8**

DISNEY - MICKEY & CO.
Mickey's Snow Angel

Mickey makes Angel in snow.
Handcrafted, Dated

QXD4035 SRP: $9.95 **GBTru: $15**

DOLLS OF THE WORLD - 2ND
Chinese BARBIE

BARBIE in traditional Chinese dress.
Handcrafted, Dated
A M Rogers

QX6162 SRP: $14.95 **GBTru: $16**

FABULOUS DECADE - 8TH
Fabulous Decade

Hedgehog holds brass year numerals.
Hndcr/Brass, Dated
E Seale

QX6232 SRP: $7.95 **GBTru: $12**

Feliz Navidad

Mouse adds lights to sombrero.
Handcrafted, Dated
E Seale

QX6665 SRP: $8.95 **GBTru: $12**

Friendship Blend

Mice share a tea break.
Handcrafted, Dated
E Seale

QX6655 SRP: $9.95 **GBTru: $12**

Granddaughter

Girl dressed as angel w/newspaper wings & slipped halo.
Handcrafted, Dated
S Tague

QX6622 SRP: $7.95 **GBTru: $8**

FOLK ART AMERICANA COLLECTION
Santa's Merry Path
Showcase Collection
Santa carries bags of toys.
Handcrafted, Dated
L Sickman

QX6785 SRP: $16.95 **GBTru: $25**

FROSTY FRIENDS - 18TH
Frosty Friends

Child and husky pup sail in ice boat.
Handcrafted, Dated
E Seale

QX6255 SRP: $10.95 **GBTru: $18**

Grandma

Grandma bear hugs grandchild.
Handcrafted, Dated
S Pike

QX6625 SRP: $8.95 **GBTru: $9**

FOLK ART AMERICANA COLLECTION
Leading The Way
Showcase Collection
Jingle bells on Moose.
Handcrafted, Dated
L Sickman

QX6782 SRP: $16.95 **GBTru: $25**

God's Gift Of Love

The Holy Family.
Porcelain, Dated
J Lyle

QX6792 SRP: $16.95 **GBTru: $17**

Grandson

Boy dressed as angel w/newspaper wings & slipped halo.
Handcrafted, Dated
S Tague

QX6615 SRP: $7.95 **GBTru: $8**

FOOTBALL LEGENDS - 3RD
Joe Namath

Football star: player card included.
Handcrafted
D Rhodus

QXI6182 SRP: $14.95 **GBTru: $18**

Godchild

Praying squirrel.
Handcrafted, Dated
K Bricker

QX6662 SRP: $7.95 **GBTru: $8**

HALLMARK ARCHIVES - 1ST
Donald's Surprising Gift
DISNEY includes Collector's Card
Donald gets caught up wrapping gift.
Handcrafted, Dated

QXD4025 SRP: $12.95 **GBTru: $18**

HALLMARK ARCHIVES COLLECTION
Angel Friend
Historical Collection, from Victorian design of 1880
Winged angel with nest of birds.
Porcelain, Dated
J Francis
QX6762 SRP: $14.95 **GBTru: $20**

HERSHEY'S
Sweet Discovery
Mouse puts straw in chocolate milk carton for sweet treat.
Handcrafted, Dated
L Sickman
QX6325 SRP: $11.95 **GBTru: $12**

Howdy Doody
Anniversary Edition, 50 years "It's Howdy Doody Time!"
Marionette pops out of TV set.
Handcrafted, Dated
T Larsen
QX6272 SRP: $12.95 **GBTru: $15**

HALLMARK ARCHIVES COLLECTION
Heavenly Song
Art by HM artist Bob Haas, Masterworks Collection
Winged Angel.
Acrylic, Dated
L Votruba
QX6795 SRP: $12.95 **GBTru: $14**

HOCKEY GREATS - 1ST
Wayne Gretzky
Ice hockey star player: trading card incl.
Handcrafted, Dated
D Unruh
QXI6275 SRP: $15.95 **GBTru: $22**

Jingle Bell Jester
Squirrel shakes acorn jingle bell.
Handcrafted, Dated
S Pike
QX6695 SRP: $9.95 **GBTru: $10**

HALLMARK ARCHIVES COLLECTION
Santa's Polar Friend
Historical Collection, from Victorian design of 1880
Santa with Polar Bear.
Handcrafted, Dated
R Chad
QX6755 SRP: $16.95 **GBTru: $22**

HOLIDAY BARBIE - 5TH
Holiday BARBIE
Special Issue
BARBIE wears holiday ball gown.
Handcrafted, Dated
P Andrews
QXI6212 SRP: $15.95 **GBTru: $16**

Juggling Stars
Winged angel juggles stars.
Handcrafted, Dated
S Tague
QX6595 SRP: $9.95 **GBTru: $10**

HERE COMES SANTA - 19TH
Claus-Mobile, The
Santa in a soap box racer delivers toys.
Handcrafted, Dated
S Tague
QX6262 SRP: $14.95 **GBTru: $15**

HOOP STARS - 3RD
Magic Johnson
Basketball star: player card included.
Handcrafted
QXI6832 SRP: $14.95 **GBTru: $18**

KIDDIE CAR CLASSICS - 4TH
Murray Dump Truck
Replica of pedal dump truck.
Cast Metal, Dated
D Palmiter
QX6195 SRP: $13.95 **GBTru: $20**

KIDDIE CAR CLASSICS SERIES COMPLEMENT
1937 Steelcraft Airflow By Murray
Club Edition
Copy of 1937 Steelcraft Airflow pedal car.
Die-cast Metal, Dated
D Palmiter
QXC5185 SRP: $15.95 **GBTru: $40**

LANGUAGE OF FLOWERS, THE - 2ND
Snowdrop Angel
Showcase Collection
Angel carries basket of snowdrops.
Hndcr/Slvr Pltd, Dated
S Tague
QX1095 SRP: $15.95 **GBTru: $16**

LEGEND OF THREE KINGS COLLECTION
King Noor - First King
Collector's Card enclosed
African King.
Handcrafted, Dated
P Andrews
QX6552 SRP: $12.95 **GBTru: $14**

Lion And Lamb
Lion cradles lamb in paws.
Handcrafted, Dated
N Williams
QX6602 SRP: $7.95 **GBTru: $8**

LIONEL TRAIN - 2ND
1950 Santa Fe F3 Diesel Locomotive
Wheels turn on locomotive car.
Die-Cast Metal, Dated
QX6145 SRP: $18.95 **GBTru: $30**

Lone Ranger, The
Lunchbox opens/closes, shows Texas ranger.
Pressed Tin, Dated
Steve Goslin Design
QX6265 SRP: $12.95 **GBTru: $30**

LOONEY TUNES
Michigan J. Frog
Cartoon and TV star Frog in top hat.
Handcrafted
R Chad
QX6332 SRP: $9.95 **GBTru: $12**

Love To Sew
Angel spells LOVE with pins.
Handcrafted, Dated
S Tague
QX6435 SRP: $7.95 **GBTru: $8**

MADAME ALEXANDER - 2ND
Little Red Riding Hood - 1991
Fairy tale child takes basket to grandmother.
Handcrafted, Dated
J Francis
QX6155 SRP: $14.95 **GBTru: $20**

Madonna del Rosario
Art of Bartolomé Esteban Murillo
Madonna and Child.
Handcrafted, Dated
L Sickman
QX6545 SRP: $12.95 **GBTru: $13**

MAJESTIC WILDERNESS - 1ST
Snowshoe Rabbits In Winter
Art of Mark Newman
Rabbits in snowy burrow.
Handcrafted, Dated
QX5694 SRP: $12.95 **GBTru: $25**

MARILYN MONROE - 1ST
Marilyn Monroe
Marilyn in a trademark form-fitting gown.
Handcrafted, Dated
P Andrews
QX5704 SRP: $14.95 **GBTru: $18**

MARY'S ANGELS - 10TH
Daisy - Mary's Angels
Mary Hamilton design
Angels waters daisies growing on cloud.
Handcrafted
R Chad
QX6242 SRP: $7.95 **GBTru: $12**

MICKEY'S HOLIDAY PARADE - 1ST
Bandleader Mickey
DISNEY: Mickey & Co.
Mickey bangs big bass drum.
Handcrafted, Dated
QXD4022 SRP: $13.95 **GBTru: $16**

Mr. Potato Head
Child's toy that featured changable parts.
Handcrafted, Dated
B Siedler
QX6335 SRP: $10.95 **GBTru: $16**

Meadow Snowman
Snowman w/tree branch arms has hat/scarf & broom.
Pressed Tin, Dated
L Sickman
QX6715 SRP: $12.95 **GBTru: $13**

Mom
Mom mouse on teapot has a cuppa.
Handcrafted, Dated
B Siedler
QX6525 SRP: $8.95 **GBTru: $9**

Mrs. Claus' Story
1997 Studio Edition offered at Artists On Tour Events to Club Members.
Companion to Trimming Santa's Tree.
Santa's wife reads story to elves trimming tree.
Handcrafted, Dated
J Eschrich/K Kline
QXC5175 SRP: $14.95 **GBTru: $15**

MERRY MINIATURES
Snowbear Season
Ornament Premiere
Bears add accessories to snowbearman, Set/3.
Handcrafted, Dated
J Eschrich
QFM8602 SRP: $12.95 **GBTru: $13**

Mom And Dad
Mom sits on stack of gifts dad carries.
Handcrafted, Dated
B Siedler
QX6522 SRP: $9.95 **GBTru: $10**

Nativity Tree
Angel, Holy Family, 3 Kings & lambs, become tree shape.
Handcrafted, Dated
D Unruh
QX6575 SRP: $14.95 **GBTru: $18**

MERRY OLDE SANTA - 8TH
Merry Olde Santa
Cardinals perch on old fashioned Santa.
Handcrafted, Dated
J Lyle
QX6225 SRP: $14.95 **GBTru: $18**

MOTHER GOOSE - 5TH AND FINAL
Little Boy Blue
Book opens/sleeping farm boy in bas-relief.
Handcrafted, Dated
E Seale
QX6215 SRP: $13.95 **GBTru: $15**

NATURE'S SKETCHBOOK
Garden Bouquet
Showcase Collection: Art of Marjolein Bastin
Garden flowers.
Handcrafted, Dated
J Lyle
QX6752 SRP: $14.95 **GBTru: $16**

NATURE'S SKETCHBOOK
Honored Guests
Showcase Collection: Art of Marjolein Bastin
Nuthatches and Chickadees at feeder.
Handcrafted, Dated
J Francis

○ QX6745 SRP: $14.95 **GBTru: $15**

NBA COLLECTION

NBA top team plaque: logo on front/ facts on back/displayer incl..
Ceramic, Dated
Sample ornament is Chicago Bulls.

○ QSR1222	**Charlotte Hornets**	SRP: $9.95	**GBTru: $10**
○ QSR1232	**Chicago Bulls**	SRP: $9.95	**GBTru: $10**
○ QSR1242	**Detroit Pistons**	SRP: $9.95	**GBTru: $10**
○ QSR1245	**Houston Rockets**	SRP: $9.95	**GBTru: $10**
○ QSR1252	**Indiana Pacers**	SRP: $9.95	**GBTru: $10**
○ QSR1262	**Los Angeles Lakers**	SRP: $9.95	**GBTru: $10**
○ QSR1272	**New York Knickerbockers**	SRP: $9.95	**GBTru: $10**
○ QSR1282	**Orlando Magic**	SRP: $9.95	**GBTru: $10**
○ QSR1292	**Phoenix Suns**	SRP: $9.95	**GBTru: $10**
○ QSR1295	**Seattle Supersonics**	SRP: $9.95	**GBTru: $10**

New Home

Christmas stocking is home for mice.
Handcrafted, Dated
S Pike

○ QX6652 SRP: $8.95 **GBTru: $10**

NFL COLLECTION
Team logo on football blimp piloted by Santa. Sample ornament is Green Bay Packers.
Handcrafted, Dated
B Siedler

○ QSR5505	**Arizona Cardinals**	SRP: $9.95	**GBTru: $10**
○ QSR5305	**Atlanta Falcons**	SRP: $9.95	**GBTru: $10**
○ QSR5352	**Baltimore Ravens**	SRP: $9.95	**GBTru: $10**
○ QSR5312	**Buffalo Bills**	SRP: $9.95	**GBTru: $10**
○ QSR5315	**Carolina Panthers**	SRP: $9.95	**GBTru: $10**
○ QSR5322	**Chicago Bears**	SRP: $9.95	**GBTru: $10**
○ QSR5325	**Cincinnati Bengals**	SRP: $9.95	**GBTru: $10**
○ QSR5355	**Dallas Cowboys**	SRP: $9.95	**GBTru: $10**
○ QSR5362	**Denver Broncos**	SRP: $9.95	**GBTru: $10**
○ QSR5365	**Detroit Lions**	SRP: $9.95	**GBTru: $10**
○ QSR5372	**Green Bay Packers**	SRP: $9.95	**GBTru: $15**
○ QSR5375	**Houston Oilers**	SRP: $9.95	**GBTru: $10**
○ QSR5411	**Indianapolis Colts**	SRP: $9.95	**GBTru: $10**
○ QSR5415	**Jacksonville Jaguars**	SRP: $9.95	**GBTru: $10**
○ QSR5302	**Kansas City Chiefs**	SRP: $9.95	**GBTru: $10**
○ QSR5472	**Miami Dolphins**	SRP: $9.95	**GBTru: $10**
○ QSR5475	**Minnesota Vikings**	SRP: $9.95	**GBTru: $10**
○ QSR5482	**New England Patriots**	SRP: $9.95	**GBTru: $10**
○ QSR5485	**New Orleans Saints**	SRP: $9.95	**GBTru: $10**
○ QRS5492	**New York Giants**	SRP: $9.95	**GBTru: $10**
○ QRS5495	**New York Jets**	SRP: $9.95	**GBTru: $10**
○ QSR5422	**Oakland Raiders**	SRP: $9.95	**GBTru: $10**
○ QSR5502	**Philadelphia Eagles**	SRP: $9.95	**GBTru: $10**
○ QSR5512	**Pittsburgh Steelers**	SRP: $9.95	**GBTru: $15**
○ QSR5515	**San Diego Chargers**	SRP: $9.95	**GBTru: $10**
○ QSR5522	**San Francisco 49ers**	SRP: $9.95	**GBTru: $15**
○ QSR5525	**Seattle Seahawks**	SRP: $9.95	**GBTru: $10**
○ QSR5425	**St. Louis Rams**	SRP: $9.95	**GBTru: $10**
○ QSR5532	**Tampa Bay Buccaneers**	SRP: $9.95	**GBTru: $10**
○ QSR5535	**Washington Redskins**	SRP: $9.95	**GBTru: $10**

NIGHT BEFORE CHRISTMAS, THE - 175TH ANNIVERSARY MOORE'S POEM
Away To The Window
Club: Keepsake of Membership
Father looks out the window, watched by mouse.
Handcrafted, Dated
N Williams
QXC5135 **GBTru: $15**

NIGHT BEFORE CHRISTMAS, THE - 175TH ANNIVERSARY MOORE'S POEM
Happy Christmas To All
Club: Keepsake of Membership
Santa & sleigh fly over home watched by mouse.
Handcrafted, Dated
N Williams
QXC5132 **GBTru: $25**

NORMAN ROCKWELL ART
Marbles Champion
Inspired by The Saturday Evening Post cover 9/2/39
Girl takes on marbles game challenge.
Handcrafted
D Unruh
QX6342 SRP: $10.95 **GBTru: $11**

NOSTALGIC HOUSES AND SHOPS - 14TH
Cafe
Food and beverages are served at Cafe.
Handcrafted, Dated
D Palmiter
QX6245 SRP: $16.95 **GBTru: $20**

Our Christmas Together
Couple ride in old fashioned sleigh.
Pewter, Dated
QX6475 SRP: $16.95 **GBTru: $17**

Our First Christmas Together
Doves perch on double heart photoholder.
Handcrafted, Dated
S Pike
QX6472 SRP: $8.95 **GBTru: $9**

Our First Christmas Together
Chipmunks in acorn home.
Handcrafted, Dated
E Seale
QX6465 SRP: $10.95 **GBTru: $11**

Our First Christmas Together
Heart shape with caption.
Acrylic, Dated
QX3182 SRP: $7.95 **GBTru: $8**

Playful Shepherd
Boy rides rocking "horse" lamb.
Handcrafted, Dated
S Tague
QX6592 SRP: $9.95 **GBTru: $10**

Porcelain Hinged Box
Snowman box opens at waist.
Porcelain, Dated
L Votruba
QX6772 SRP: $14.95 **GBTru: $25**

Praise Him
Angel watches over Holy Family creche scene.
Handcrafted, Dated
L Sickman
QX6542 SRP: $8.95 **GBTru: $9**

Prize Topiary
Santa prunes bush into deer/clip on.
Handcrafted, Dated
E Seale
QX6675 SRP: $14.95 **GBTRu: $15**

PUPPY LOVE - 7TH
Puppy Love

Pup holds stocking, wears collar and tag.
Hndcr/Brass, Dated
A M Rogers

QX6222 SRP: $7.95 **GBTru: $15**

Santa's Ski Adventure

Santa & scared reindeer ride ski lift.
Handcrafted, Dated
R Chad

QX6422 SRP: $12.95 **GBTru: $18**

Snow Bowling

Bowling pin snowman.
Handcrafted, Dated
N Williams

QX6395 SRP: $6.95 **GBTru: $7**

Sailor Bear

Teddy holds sail boat.
Handcrafted, Dated
D Unruh

QX6765 SRP: $14.95 **GBTru: $18**

SCARLETT O'HARA - 1ST
Scarlett O'Hara

"Gone With The Wind" star in gown.
Handcrafted, Dated
P Andrews

QX6125 SRP: $14.95 **GBTru: $18**

Snowgirl

Child holds golden star.
Handcrafted, Dated
S Tague

QX6562 SRP: $7.95 **GBTru: $8**

Santa Mail

Boy mails letter/Santa reads letter.
Handcrafted, Dated
N Williams

QX6702 SRP: $10.95 **GBTru: $11**

Sister To Sister

Kittens share a moment of fun.
Handcrafted, Dated
S Pike

QX6635 SRP: $9.95 **GBTru: $14**

Son

Stocking with picture of Santa on rooftop.
Pressed Tin, Dated
K Bricker

QX6605 SRP: $7.95 **GBTru: $8**

Santa's Friend

Marjolein Bastin Art Design
Pup sits next to Santa/leash trims wreath.
Handcrafted, Dated
D Unruh

QX6685 SRP: $12.95 **GBTru: $16**

SKY'S THE LIMIT - 1ST
Flight At Kitty Hawk, The

Plane the Wright brothers flew.
Handcrafted, Dated
L Norton

QX5574 SRP: $14.95 **GBTru: $20**

Special Dog

Open gift box is photoholder frame.
Handcrafted, Dated
K Bricker

QX6632 SRP: $7.95 **GBTru: $10**

Spirit Of Christmas, The

Collector's Plate
Winter scene of church and sleigh/ displayer.
Handcrafted, Dated
T Larsen

QX6585 SRP: $9.95 **GBTru: $10**

STAR WARS - 1ST
Luke Skywalker
Special Issue
Luke prepares to fight Darth Vader.
Handcrafted, Dated
D Rhodus

QXI5484 SRP: $13.95 **GBTru: $18**

Sweet Dreamer

Bunny naps in Santa's hat.
Handcrafted, Dated
K Bricker

QX6732 SRP: $6.95 **GBTru: $7**

STAR TREK
Dr. Leonard H. McCoy
Special Issue
Dr. McCoy waits in the beam transporter.
Handcrafted, Stardated
A M Rogers

QXI6352 SRP: $24.00 **GBTru: $24**

Stealing A Kiss

African-American Mr & Mrs Claus.
Handcrafted, Dated
S Tague

QX6555 SRP: $14.95 **GBTru: $15**

Swinging In The Snow

Angel as bell clapper.
Handcrafted/Glass, Dated
S Tague

QX6775 SRP: $12.95 **GBTru: $13**

STAR TREK: THE NEXT GENERATION
Commander Data
Special Issue
Commander at control desk.
Handcrafted, Stardated
A M Rogers

QXI6345 SRP: $14.95 **GBTru: $20**

STOCK CAR CHAMPIONS - 1ST
Jeff Gordon

Stock car star driver: player card incl.
Handcrafted
E Seale

QXI6165 SRP: $15.95 **GBTru: $36**

TENDER TOUCHES
Perfect Tree, The
Ornament Premiere
Mother and child trim tree with berries.
Handcrafted, Dated
E Searle

QX6572 SRP: $15.00 **GBTru: $15**

STAR WARS
Yoda
Special Issue
Wise Alien Creature.
Handcrafted
K Bricker

QXI6355 SRP: $9.95 **GBTru: $30**

SUPER HEROES
Incredible Hulk, The

Transformed from man to super hero, hulk fights evil.
Handcrafted

QX5471 SRP: $12.95 **GBTru: $13**

THOMAS KINKADE, PAINTER OF LIGHT - 1ST
Victorian Christmas
Special Issue
Victorian evening street scene.
Porcelain, Dated

QXI6135 SRP: $10.95 **GBTru: $15**

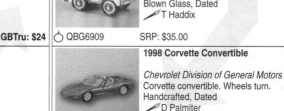

Tomorrow's Leader

Art by Norman Rockwell, honors Boy Scouts of America
Scout stands before Boy Scout Symbol.
Ceramic, Dated

QX6452 SRP: $9.95 **GBTru: $10**

Tonka Mighty Front Loader

Front bucket pivots and wheels turn on truck.
Cast Metal, Dated

QX6362 SRP: $13.95 **GBTru: $14**

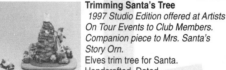

Trimming Santa's Tree
1997 Studio Edition offered at Artists On Tour Events to Club Members. Companion piece to Mrs. Santa's Story Orn.
Elves trim tree for Santa.
Handcrafted, Dated
19 Studio Artists

QXC5175 SRP: $60.00 **GBTru: $60**

TURN-OF-THE-CENTURY PARADE - 3RD AND FINAL
Santa Claus
Showcase Collection
Santa on wheeled horse with brass bell.
Die-cast Metal/Brass, Dated
KCrow

QX1215 SRP: $16.95 **GBTru: $18**

What A Deal!

Raccoon shuffles deck of cards.
Handcrafted, Dated
S Pike

QX6442 SRP: $8.95 **GBTru: $15**

WIZARD OF OZ, THE
Miss Gulch

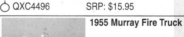

Miss Gulch rides off on bicycle with Toto in basket.
Handcrafted
J Lyle

QX6372 SRP: $13.95 **GBTru: $18**

YULETIDE CENTRAL - 4TH
Yuletide Central

Toy freight car.
Pressed Tin, Dated
L Sickman

QX5812 SRP: $18.95 **GBTru: $24**

1998

#1 Student

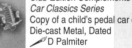

Inside view of snow covered school photo holder.
Handcrafted, Dated

QX6646 SRP: $7.95

1935 Steelcraft By Murray

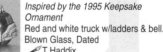

Club Edition Complements the Kiddie Car Classics Series
Copy of a child's pedal car design.
Die-cast Metal, Dated
D Palmiter

QXC4496 SRP: $15.95

1955 Murray Fire Truck

Inspired by the 1995 Keepsake Ornament
Red and white truck w/ladders & bell.
Blown Glass, Dated
T Haddix

QBG6909 SRP: $35.00

1998 Corvette Convertible

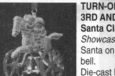

Chevrolet Division of General Motors
Corvette convertible. Wheels turn.
Handcrafted, Dated
D Palmiter

QX6416 SRP: $13.95

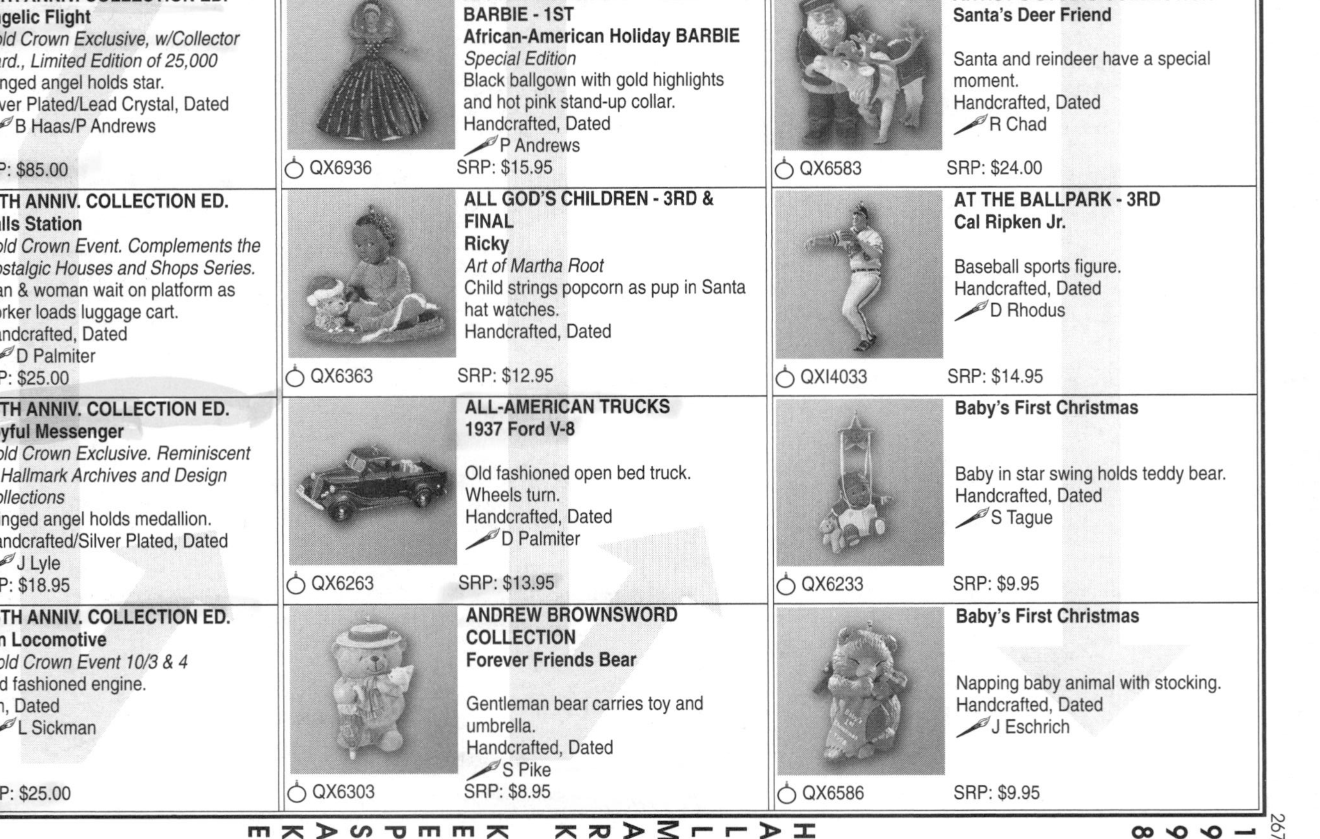

25TH ANNIV. COLLECTION ED.
Angelic Flight
Gold Crown Exclusive, w/Collector Card., Limited Edition of 25,000
Winged angel holds star.
Silver Plated/Lead Crystal, Dated
B Haas/P Andrews
QXI4146 SRP: $85.00

25TH ANNIV. COLLECTION ED.
Halls Station
Gold Crown Event. Complements the Nostalgic Houses and Shops Series.
Man & woman wait on platform as worker loads luggage cart.
Handcrafted, Dated
D Palmiter
QX6833 SRP: $25.00

25TH ANNIV. COLLECTION ED.
Joyful Messenger
Gold Crown Exclusive. Reminiscent of Hallmark Archives and Design Collections
Winged angel holds medallion.
Handcrafted/Silver Plated, Dated
J Lyle
QXI6733 SRP: $18.95

25TH ANNIV. COLLECTION ED.
Tin Locomotive
Gold Crown Event 10/3 & 4
Old fashioned engine.
Tin, Dated
L Sickman
QX6826 SRP: $25.00

AFRICAN-AMERICAN HOLIDAY BARBIE - 1ST
African-American Holiday BARBIE
Special Edition
Black ballgown with gold highlights and hot pink stand-up collar.
Handcrafted, Dated
P Andrews
QX6936 SRP: $15.95

ALL GOD'S CHILDREN - 3RD & FINAL
Ricky
Art of Martha Root
Child strings popcorn as pup in Santa hat watches.
Handcrafted, Dated
QX6363 SRP: $12.95

ALL-AMERICAN TRUCKS
1937 Ford V-8
Old fashioned open bed truck.
Wheels turn.
Handcrafted, Dated
D Palmiter
QX6263 SRP: $13.95

ANDREW BROWNSWORD COLLECTION
Forever Friends Bear
Gentleman bear carries toy and umbrella.
Handcrafted, Dated
S Pike
QX6303 SRP: $8.95

ARTIST'S STUDIO COLLECTION
Santa's Deer Friend
Santa and reindeer have a special moment.
Handcrafted, Dated
R Chad
QX6583 SRP: $24.00

AT THE BALLPARK - 3RD
Cal Ripken Jr.
Baseball sports figure.
Handcrafted, Dated
D Rhodus
QXI4033 SRP: $14.95

Baby's First Christmas
Baby in star swing holds teddy bear.
Handcrafted, Dated
S Tague
QX6233 SRP: $9.95

Baby's First Christmas
Napping baby animal with stocking.
Handcrafted, Dated
J Eschrich
QX6586 SRP: $9.95

Baby's First Christmas

Toy box photo holder.
Handcrafted, Dated
K Kline

QX6596 SRP: $8.95

BARBIE - 3RD
1990 Happy Holiday BARBIE Doll
Club Edition Complements Holiday BARBIE Series.
BARBIE wears a rose-pink ruffled ball gown.
Handcrafted, Dated
P Andrews

QXC4493 SRP: $15.95

BARBIE - 5TH
Silken Flame
Special Edition
Barbie wears party dress with red coat, hat, purse and shoes.
Handcrafted, Dated
P Andrews

QXI4043 SRP: $15.95

BLESSED NATIVITY COLLECTION
Holy Family, The
This set will be offered for 3 years and each year a new piece will be added.
Set of 3. The Holy Family.
Porcelain, Dated
J Lyle

QX6523 SRP: $25.00

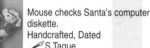

Bride And Groom - 1996 Madame Alexander
Gold Crown Ornament Premiere - Event Exclusive: Merry Miniature Figs.
Set of 2. Bride in wedding gown and groom in top hat and tails.
Handcrafted, Dated
J C Francis

QFM8486 SRP: $12.95

CAT NAPS - 5TH & FINAL
Cat Naps

Kitten naps in basket.
Handcrafted, Dated
K Bricker

QX6383 SRP: $8.95

Catch Of The Season

Santa braces his shoes on rowboat as he hooks big fish.
Handcrafted, Dated
E Seale

QX6786 SRP: $14.95

CELEBRATION OF ANGELS, A - 4TH & FINAL
Celebration of Angels, A

Winged Angel holds corn.
Handcrafted, Dated
P Andrews

QX6366 SRP: $13.95

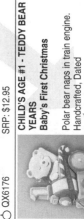

Chatty Chipmunk

Chipmunk chats on old fashioned wall phone.
Handcrafted, Dated
K Crow

QX6716 SRP: $9.95

Checking Santa's Files

Mouse checks Santa's computer diskette.
Handcrafted, Dated
S Tague

QX6806 SRP: $8.95

Child Is Born, A

The Holy Family.
Handcrafted, Dated
LD Votruba

QX6176 SRP: $12.95

CHILD'S AGE #1 - TEDDY BEAR YEARS
Baby's First Christmas

Polar bear naps in train engine.
Handcrafted, Dated
J C Francis

QX6603 SRP: $7.95

CHILD'S AGE #2 - TEDDY BEAR YEARS
Baby's Second Christmas

Teddy bear with cookie tree and stocking.
Handcrafted, Dated
K Crow
QX6606 SRP: $7.95

CHILD'S AGE #3 - TEDDY BEAR YEARS
Child's Third Christmas

Teddy bear with bell cookie and stocking.
Handcrafted, Dated
K Crow
QX6613 SRP: $7.95

CHILD'S AGE #4 - TEDDY BEAR YEARS
Child's Fourth Christmas

Panda bear with drum cookie and stocking.
Handcrafted, Dated
K Crow
QX6616 SRP: $7.95

CHILD'S AGE #5 - TEDDY BEAR YEARS
Child's Fifth Christmas

Teddy Bear with gift cookie and stocking.
Handcrafted, Dated
K Crow
QX6623 SRP: $7.95

Christmas Eve Story, A

Design by Becky Kelly
Child reads Christmas story. Miniature bulb from tree lights can create glow.
Handcrafted, Dated
S Tague
QX6873 SRP: $13.95

Christmas Request

Child whispers his wish list to Santa.
Handcrafted, Dated
J C Francis
QX6193 SRP: $14.95

Christmas Sleigh Ride

Reindeer pulls Santa's sleigh. Wheels turn.
Die-cast Metal, Dated
K Crow
QX6556 SRP: $12.95

CLASSIC AMERICAN CARS - 8TH
1970 Plymouth Hemi 'Cuda

Red sports car. Wheels turn.
Handcrafted, Dated
D Palmiter
QX6256 SRP: $13.95

CLAUSES ON VACATION, THE - 2ND
Clauses On Vacation, The

Santa and Mrs. Claus in inner tube.
Handcrafted, Dated
B Siedler
QX6276 SRP: $14.95

COLLEGIATE COLLECTION
Snowman displays logo of best known national schools. Sample ornament is Florida State.
Handcrafted, Dated
T Haddix

Florida State Seminoles
QSR2316 SRP: $9.95

Michigan Wolverines
QSR2323 SRP: $9.95

North Carolina Tar Heels
QSR2333 SRP: $9.95

Notre Dame Fighting Irish
QSR2313 SRP: $9.95

Penn State Nittany Lions
QSR2326 SRP: $9.95

Compact Skater

Girl figure skates on compact mirror.
Handcrafted, Dated
S Tague
QX6766 SRP: $9.95

CRAYOLA CRAYON - 10TH & FINAL
Bright Sledding Colors

Teddy on a crayon sled.
Handcrafted, Dated
S Tague

QX6166 SRP: $12.95

Cross Of Peace

Religious symbol in ornate design.
Metal, Dated
K Kline

QX6856 SRP: $9.95

CROWN REFLECTIONS - THREE KINGS COLLECTION
Frankincense: Gifts For A King

King carrying gift.
Blown Glass
T Larsen

QBG6896 SRP: $22.00

CROWN REFLECTIONS - THREE KINGS COLLECTION
Gold: Gifts For A King

King carrying gift.
Blown Glass
T Larsen

QBG6836 SRP: $22.00

CROWN REFLECTIONS - THREE KINGS COLLECTION
Myrrh: Gifts For A King

King carrying gift.
Blown Glass
T Larsen

QBG6893 SRP: $22.00

Cruising Into Christmas

Santa captains a paddlewheeler.
Handcrafted/Tin, Dated
K Crow

QX6196 SRP: $16.95

Dad

Dad bear paints holiday house trim.
Handcrafted, Dated
K Kline

QX6663 SRP: $8.95

Daughter

Nutcracker girl, opens and closes.
Handcrafted, Dated
N Aubé

QX6673 SRP: $8.95

DISNEY
Bouncy Baby-sitter
Winnie The Pooh & Friends
Roo sits atop Tigger's head.
Handcrafted, Dated

QXD4096 SRP: $12.95

DISNEY
Building A Snowman
Winnie The Pooh & Friends
Pooh and Piglet dress a snowman.
Handcrafted, Dated

QXD4133 SRP: $14.95

DISNEY
Buzz Lightyear
Movie: Toy Story
Buzz wears flying wings.
Handcrafted, Dated

QXD4066 SRP: $14.95

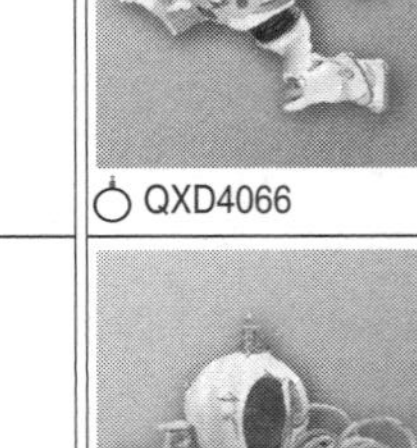

DISNEY
Cinderella's Coach
Movie: Cinderella
Pumpkin coach.
Handcrafted, Dated

QXD4083 SRP: $14.95

DISNEY
Daydreams
Movie: The Little Mermaid
Ariel and friends under the sea.
Handcrafted, Dated

QXD4136 SRP: $13.95

DISNEY
Princess Aurora
Movie: Sleeping Beauty
Set of 2. The three fairies and the Princess.
Handcrafted, Dated

QXD4126 SRP: $12.95

DISNEY: MICKEY & CO.
Make-Believe Boat

Mickey and Minnie as babies. Minnie sits in a boat pull-toy.
Handcrafted, Dated

QXD4113 SRP: $12.95

DISNEY
Flik
Movie: A Bug's Life
Flik races on leaf skis with acorn poles.
Handcrafted

QXD4153 SRP: $12.95

DISNEY
Simba & Nala
Movie: Simba's Pride
Simba as adult lion with his love, Nala.
Handcrafted, Dated

QXD4073 SRP: $13.95

DISNEY: MICKEY & CO.
Mickey And Minnie Handcar, The

Early design of Mickey and Minnie, with coiled spring legs, riding a handcar.
Handcrafted/Metal, Dated

QXD4116 SRP: $14.95

DISNEY
Iago, Abu and the Genie
Movie: Aladdin
Genie, parrot and monkey flying.
Handcrafted, Dated

QXD4076 SRP: $12.95

DISNEY
Woody The Sheriff
Movie: Toy Story
Woody swings lasso of tree lights.
Handcrafted, Dated

QXD4163 SRP: $14.95

DISNEY: MICKEY & CO.
Mickey's Favorite Reindeer

Pluto slurps a kiss on Mickey.
Handcrafted, Dated

QXD4013 SRP: $13.95

DISNEY
Mulan, Mushu and Cri-kee
Movie: Mulan
Set of 2. Asian girl disguised as a boy and her friends.
Handcrafted

QXD4156 SRP: $14.95

DISNEY: MICKEY & CO.
Goofy Soccer Star

Goofy balances soccer ball on foot.
Handcrafted, Dated

QXD4123 SRP: $10.95

DISNEY: MICKEY & CO.
Runaway Toboggan

Set of 2. Goofy falls off toboggan as Mickey and Donald race downhill.
Handcrafted, Dated

QXD4003 SRP: $16.95

DOLLS OF THE WORLD - 3RD
Mexican BARBIE

Barbie wears Mexican blouse and peasant skirt.
Handcrafted, Dated
A M Rogers

QX6356 SRP: $14.95

FABULOUS DECADE - 9TH
Fabulous Decade

Polar bear holds brass year date.
Handcrafted/Brass, Dated
S Pike

QX6393 SRP: $7.95

FOLK ART AMERICANA COLLECTION
Soaring With Angels

Winged Angel soars with eagle.
Handcrafted/Copper, Dated
L Sickman

QX6213 SRP: $16.95

Downhill Dash

Skiing Santa gives piggyback ride to three reindeer.
Handcrafted, Dated
K Crow

QX6776 SRP: $13.95

Fancy Footwork

Child dances with Snowman.
Handcrafted, Dated
LD Votruba

QX6536 SRP: $8.95

FOOTBALL LEGENDS - 4TH
Emmitt Smith

Football sports figure.
Handcrafted
D Rhodus

QXI4036 SRP: $14.95

DR. SEUSS
Grinch, The
Special Edition
Grinch in Santa suit holds “reindeer” dog.
Handcrafted, Dated
R Chad

QXI6466 SRP: $13.95

Feliz Navidad

Mouse paints lines on a chili pepper.
Handcrafted, Dated
R Chad

QX6173 SRP: $8.95

Friend Of My Heart

Set of 2. One mouse holds cookie cutter Other mouse has decorated cookie.
Handcrafted, Dated
E Seale

QX6723 SRP: $14.95

ENCHANTED MEMORIES COLLECTION - 2ND
Walt Disney's Snow White

Snow White in forest with bird and animals.
Handcrafted, Dated

QXD4056 SRP: $14.95

Festive Locomotive

Inspired by the 1982 Tin Locomotive Keepsake Ornament
Old fashioned steam engine.
Blown Glass, Dated
S Tague

QBG6903 SRP: $35.00

Frosty Friends
Inspired by the Frosty Friends Series Keepsake Ornaments
Set of 2. Eskimo child with tree and penguin with star.
Blown Glass, Dated
E Seale

QBG6907 SRP: $48.00

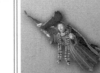

FROSTY FRIENDS - 19TH
Frosty Friends

Eskimo child leads penguins in caroling.
Handcrafted, Dated
E Seale

QX6226 SRP: $10.95

Good Luck Dice

Jack-in-the-dice holds a four leaf clover and horseshoe.
Handcrafted, Dated
T Haddix

QX6813 SRP: $9.95

Guardian Friend

Winged Angel hold baby animal.
Handcrafted, Dated
J Lyle

QX6543 SRP: $8.95

Future Ballerina

Kitten practices ballet steps.
Handcrafted, Dated
S Tague

QX6756 SRP: $7.95

Granddaughter

Granddaughter teddy in sailor outfit.
Handcrafted, Dated
J C Francis

QX6683 SRP: $7.95

HALLMARK ARCHIVES - 2ND
Ready For Christmas
Includes Collector's Card.
Mickey carries wrapped gifts.
Handcrafted, Dated

QXD4006 SRP: $12.95

Gifted Gardener

Gardener holds happy flower in flowerpot.
Handcrafted, Dated
R Chad

QX6736 SRP: $7.95

Grandma's Memories

Grandma Bear holds photo holder.
Handcrafted, Dated
K Kline

QX6686 SRP: $8.95

HALLMARK ARCHIVES COLLECTION
Heavenly Melody
Artwork by Bob Haas.. From Masterworks Archives.
Winged Angel plays harp.
Handcrafted, Dated
LD Votruba

QX6576 SRP: $18.95

Godchild

Teddy holds favorite stuffed animal toys.
Handcrafted, Dated
R Chad

QX6703 SRP: $7.95

Grandson

Grandson teddy in sailor outfit.
Handcrafted, Dated
J C Francis

QX6676 SRP: $7.95

HALLMARK ARCHIVES COLLECTION
Our First Christmas Together

Old fashioned portrait of a couple within gilt frame.
Porcelain/Brass, Dated
LD Votruba

QX6643 SRP: $18.95

HERE COMES SANTA - 20TH
Santa's Bumper Car

Santa drives amusement park bumper car.
Handcrafted, Dated
S Tague

QX6283 SRP: $14.95

HERSHEY'S - 2ND
Hershey's
Gold Crown Ornament Premiere - Event Exclusive: Merry Miniature Figurines
Set of 2. Mice with a Hersey kiss.
Handcrafted
K Bricker

QFM8493 SRP: $10.95

HERSHEY'S
Sweet Treat

Mice climb upon a chocolate kiss.
Handcrafted, Dated
K Kline

QX6433 SRP: $10.95

HOCKEY GREATS - 2ND
Mario Lemieux

Hockey sports figure.
Handcrafted, Dated
J C Francis

QXI6476 SRP: $15.95

HOLIDAY BARBIE - 6TH
Holiday BARBIE
Special Edition
Black ball gown with gold highlights and hot pink stand-up collar.
Handcrafted, Dated
P Andrews

QXI4023 SRP: $15.95

Holiday Camper

Backpacking raccoon holds working compass.
Handcrafted, Dated
E Seale

QX6783 SRP: $12.95

Holiday Decorator

Mouse peeks in window. Miniature bulb from tree lights can create glow.
Handcrafted, Dated
N Williams

QX6566 SRP: $13.95

HOLIDAY TRADITIONS - 1ST
Red Poinsettias

Christmas flower highlights ball ornament.
Glass Ball

QBG6906 SRP: $35.00

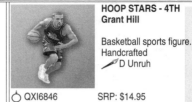

HOOP STARS - 4TH
Grant Hill

Basketball sports figure.
Handcrafted
D Unruh

QXI6846 SRP: $14.95

Hot Wheels

30th Anniversary of HOT WHEELS
Racer on a loop of racetrack.
Handcrafted, Dated
K Crow

QX6436 SRP: $13.95

Journey To Bethlehem

Madonna shelters newborn son within folds of robe.
Handcrafted, Dated
D Unruh

QX6223 SRP: $16.95

KIDDIE CAR CLASSICS - 5TH
1955 Murray Tractor and Trailer

Set of 2. Red farm tractor and trailer.
Wheels turn.
Handcrafted, Dated
D Palmiter

QX6376 SRP: $16.95

LANGUAGE OF FLOWERS, THE - 3RD
Iris Angel
Winged angel carrying basket of flowers.
Handcrafted/Silver Plated, Dated
S Tague
QX6156 SRP: $15.95

LEGEND OF THREE KINGS COLLECTION
King Kharoof - Second King
Collector's Card enclosed.
African King.
Handcrafted, Dated
P Andrews
QX6186 SRP: $12.95

LIONEL TRAIN - 3RD
Pennsylvania GG-1 Locomotive
Train wheels turn.
Replica of train engine.
Die-cast Metal, Dated
QX6346 SRP: $18.95

LOONEY TUNES
Bugs Bunny
Bugs spoofs Carmen Miranda.
Handcrafted
R Chad
QX6443 SRP: $13.95

MADAME ALEXANDER - 3RD
Mop Top Wendy
Red headed doll in dress and pinafore.
Handcrafted, Dated
J C Francis
QX6353 SRP: $14.95

MADAME ALEXANDER HOLIDAY ANGELS - 1ST
Glorious Angel
Winged angel with halo.
Handcrafted, Dated
J C Francis
QX6493 SRP: $14.95

Madonna And Child
Madonna holds son and a lamb.
Handcrafted, Dated
A M Rogers
QX6516 SRP: $12.95

MAJESTIC WILDERNESS - 2ND
Timber Wolves At Play
Art of Mark Newman
Adult wolf watches playing pups.
Handcrafted, Dated
QX6273 SRP: $12.95

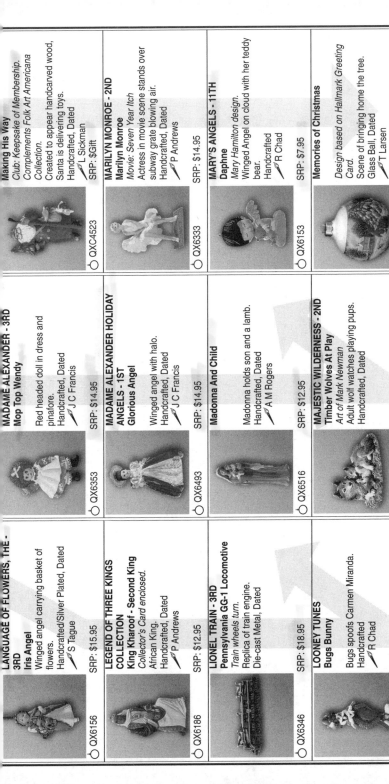

Making His Way
Club: Keepsake of Membership.
Complements Folk Art Americana Collection.
Created to appear handcarved wood, Santa is delivering toys.
Handcrafted, Dated
L Sickman
QXC4523 SRP: $Gift

MARILYN MONROE - 2ND
Marilyn Monroe
Movie: Seven Year Itch
Actress in movie scene stands over subway grate blowing air.
Handcrafted, Dated
P Andrews
QX6333 SRP: $14.95

MARY'S ANGELS - 11TH
Daphne
Mary Hamilton design.
Winged Angel on cloud with her teddy bear.
Handcrafted
R Chad
QX6153 SRP: $7.95

Memories of Christmas
Design based on Hallmark Greeting Card.
Scene of bringing home the tree.
Glass Ball, Dated
T Larsen
QX2406 SRP: $5.95

Merry Chime

Mouse dangles from candy cane wind chime. Will ring in breeze.
Handcrafted/Brass, Dated
K Crow

QX6692 SRP: $9.95

MERRY MINIATURE - MICKEY EXPRESS COLLECTION
Donald's Passenger Car - Week 3
*Gold Crown Reach Program - *w/any Hallmark purchase. Offered over a 3 week period beginning 11/14 & 15.*
Donald Duck rides on passenger car.
Handcrafted, Dated

QRP8513 SRP: $5.95*

MERRY MINIATURE - MICKEY EXPRESS COLLECTION
Goofy's Caboose - Week 3
*Gold Crown Reach Program - *w/any Hallmark purchase. Offered over a 3 week period beginning 11/14 & 15.*
Goofy the dog rides atop the caboose.
Handcrafted, Dated

QRP8516 SRP: $5.95*

MERRY MINIATURE - MICKEY EXPRESS COLLECTION
Mickey's Locomotive - Week 1
*Gold Crown Reach Program - *w/any Hallmark purchase. Offered over a 3 week period beginning 11/14 & 15.*
Mickey is engineer of special train.
Handcrafted, Dated

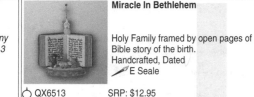

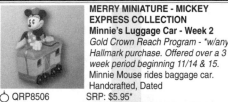

QRP8496 SRP: $5.95*

MERRY MINIATURE - MICKEY EXPRESS COLLECTION
Minnie's Luggage Car - Week 2
*Gold Crown Reach Program - *w/any Hallmark purchase. Offered over a 3 week period beginning 11/14 & 15.*
Minnie Mouse rides baggage car.
Handcrafted, Dated

QRP8506 SRP: $5.95*

MERRY MINIATURE - MICKEY EXPRESS COLLECTION
Pluto's Coal Car - Week 2
*Gold Crown Reach Program - *w/any Hallmark purchase. Offered over a 3 week period beginning 11/14 & 15.*
Pluto rides coal fuel car.
Handcrafted, Dated

QRP8503 SRP: $5.95*

MERRY OLDE SANTA - 9TH
Merry Olde Santa

Robed Santa has toys in pockets and hands.
Handcrafted, Dated
D Unruh

QX6386 SRP: $15.95

MICKEY'S HOLIDAY PARADE - 2ND
Minnie Plays The Flute

Minnie marches in band costume as she plays flute.
Handcrafted, Dated

QXD4106 SRP: $13.95

Miracle In Bethlehem

Holy Family framed by open pages of Bible story of the birth.
Handcrafted, Dated
E Seale

QX6513 SRP: $12.95

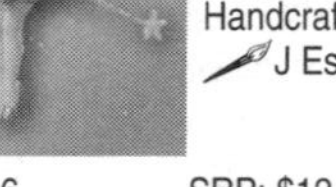

Mistletoe Fairy

Winged fairy holds sprig of mistletoe.
Handcrafted, Dated
J Eschrich

QX6216 SRP: $12.95

Mom

Teddy mom holds tray of Christmas cookies.
Handcrafted, Dated
K Kline

QX6656 SRP: $8.95

Mom And Dad

Mom and Dad beaver cut down perfect tree.
Handcrafted, Dated
K Kline

QX6653 SRP: $9.95

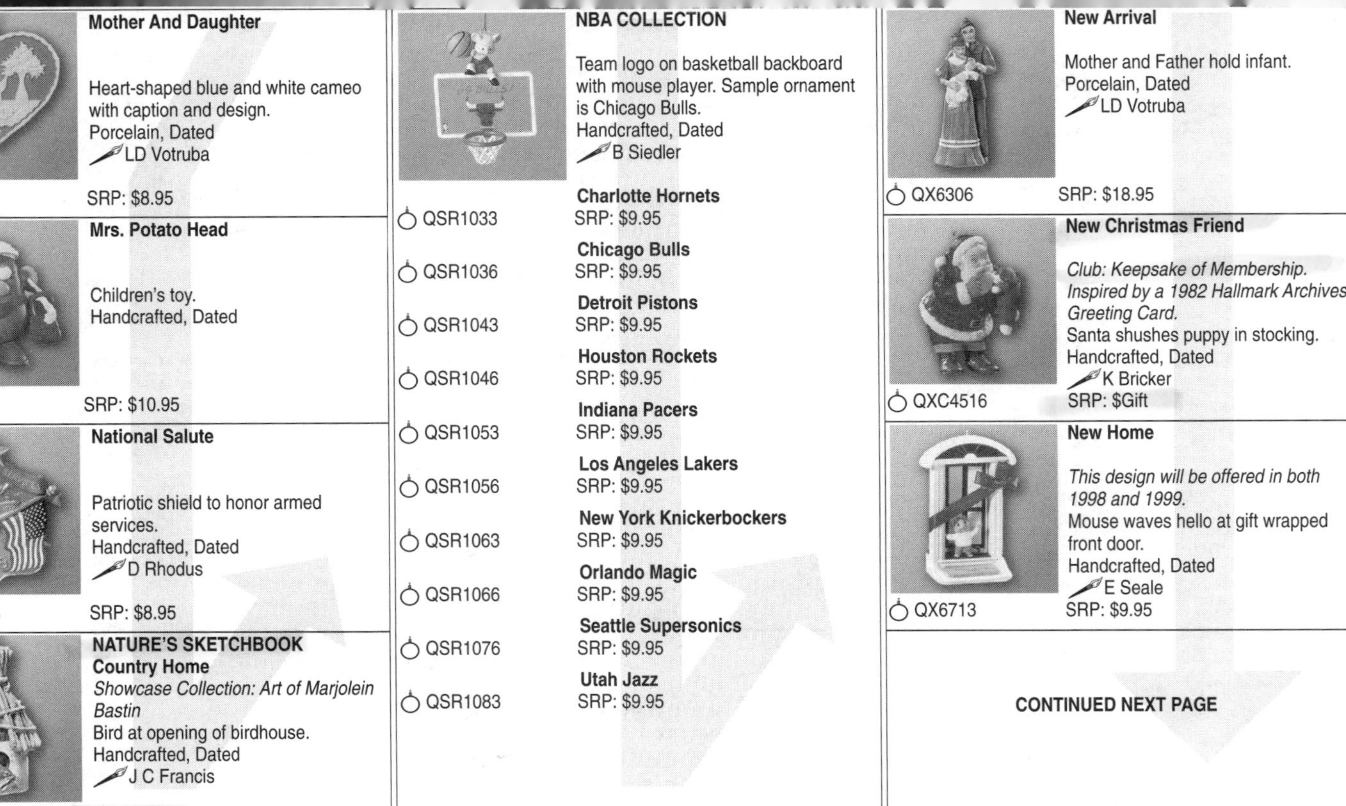

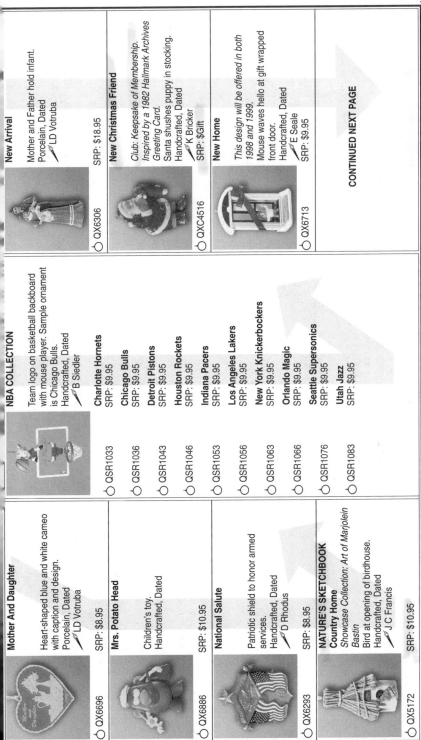

Mother And Daughter

Heart-shaped blue and white cameo with caption and design.
Porcelain, Dated
LD Votruba

QX6696 SRP: $8.95

Mrs. Potato Head

Children's toy.
Handcrafted, Dated

QX6886 SRP: $10.95

National Salute

Patriotic shield to honor armed services.
Handcrafted, Dated
D Rhodus

QX6293 SRP: $8.95

NATURE'S SKETCHBOOK
Country Home
Showcase Collection: Art of Marjolein Bastin
Bird at opening of birdhouse.
Handcrafted, Dated
J C Francis

QX5172 SRP: $10.95

NBA COLLECTION

Team logo on basketball backboard with mouse player. Sample ornament is Chicago Bulls.
Handcrafted, Dated
B Siedler

QSR1033 **Charlotte Hornets** SRP: $9.95

QSR1036 **Chicago Bulls** SRP: $9.95

QSR1043 **Detroit Pistons** SRP: $9.95

QSR1046 **Houston Rockets** SRP: $9.95

QSR1053 **Indiana Pacers** SRP: $9.95

QSR1056 **Los Angeles Lakers** SRP: $9.95

QSR1063 **New York Knickerbockers** SRP: $9.95

QSR1066 **Orlando Magic** SRP: $9.95

QSR1076 **Seattle Supersonics** SRP: $9.95

QSR1083 **Utah Jazz** SRP: $9.95

New Arrival

Mother and Father hold infant.
Porcelain, Dated
LD Votruba

QX6306 SRP: $18.95

New Christmas Friend

Club: Keepsake of Membership.
Inspired by a 1982 Hallmark Archives Greeting Card.
Santa shushes puppy in stocking.
Handcrafted, Dated
K Bricker

QXC4516 SRP: $Gift

New Home

This design will be offered in both 1998 and 1999.
Mouse waves hello at gift wrapped front door.
Handcrafted, Dated
E Seale

QX6713 SRP: $9.95

CONTINUED NEXT PAGE

NFL COLLECTION
Team logo on helmet with mouse referee. Sample shown is Green Bay Packers.
Handcrafted, Dated
J C Francis

QSR5026	**Carolina Panthers**	SRP: $9.95
QSR5033	**Chicago Bears**	SRP: $9.95
QSR5046	**Dallas Cowboys**	SRP: $9.95
QSR5053	**Denver Broncos**	SRP: $9.95
QSR5063	**Green Bay Packers**	SRP: $9.95
QSR5013	**Kansas City Chiefs**	SRP: $9.95
QSR5096	**Miami Dolphins**	SRP: $9.95
QSR5126	**Minnesota Vikings**	SRP: $9.95
QSR5143	**New York Giants**	SRP: $9.95
QSR5086	**Oakland Raiders**	SRP: $9.95
QSR5153	**Philadelphia Eagles**	SRP: $9.95
QSR5163	**Pittsburgh Steelers**	SRP: $9.95
QSR5173	**San Francisco 49ers**	SRP: $9.95
QSR5093	**St. Louis Rams**	SRP: $9.95
QSR5186	**Washington Redskins**	SRP: $9.95

Nick's Wish List
Santa checks his list.
Handcrafted, Dated
P Andrews
QX6863 SRP: $8.95

Night Watch
Mouse naps atop pocket watch.
Handcrafted, Dated
B Siedler
QX6725 SRP: $9.95

North Pole Reserve
Mouse with fire extinguisher on wheels.
Handcrafted, Dated
E Seale
QX6803 SRP: $10.95

NOSTALGIC HOUSES & SHOPS - 15TH
Grocery Store
Old fashioned grocery store.
Handcrafted, Dated
D Palmiter
QX6266 SRP: $16.95

OLD WEST, THE - 1ST
Pony Express Rider
Rider delivers mail and messages by horseback.
Handcrafted, Dated
D Unruh
QX6323 SRP: $13.95

Our First Christmas Together
Caption on acrylic oval disc.
Acrylic, Dated
LD Votruba
QX3193 SRP: $7.95

Our First Christmas Together
Penguins sit atop heart photo holder.
Handcrafted, Dated
S Tague
QX6636 SRP: $8.95

Our Song
Art of Brenda Joysmith
Depicts children in choir robes singing hymn. Display Stand included.
Ceramic, Dated
QX6183 SRP: $9.95

PEANUTS
Follow The Leader
Club Edition
Set of 2. Charlie Brown, Snoopy and friends ice skating.
Handcrafted, Dated
B Siedler
QXC4503 SRP: $16.95

Polar Bowler
Polar bear gets ready to release the bowling ball.
Handcrafted, Dated
J Eschrich
QX6746 SRP: $7.95

Puttin' Around
Mouse putts ball into swiss cheese hole.
Handcrafted, Dated
D Rhodus
QX6763 SRP: $8.95

Peekaboo Bears
Twirl to open tree and reveal three bears.
Handcrafted, Dated
K Crow
QX6563 SRP: $12.95

PONY FOR CHRISTMAS, A - 1ST
Pony For Christmas, A
Teddy bear atop pony pull-toy.
Handcrafted, Dated
L Sickman
QX6316 SRP: $10.95

Rocket To Success
Teacher pencil rocket has teddy bear pilot.
Handcrafted, Dated
S Pike
QX6793 SRP: $8.95

Perfect Match, A
Mouse couple sit in front of matchbox fireplace.
Handcrafted, Dated
D Rhodus
QX6633 SRP: $10.95

PUPPY LOVE - 8TH
Puppy Love
Pup with red bow is tangled in lights.
Handcrafted/Brass, Dated
A M Rogers
QX6163 SRP: $7.95

ROMANTIC VACATIONS - 1ST
Donald and Daisy in Venice
Donald as gondolier with Daisy as his passenger.
Handcrafted, Dated
QXD4103 SRP: $14.95

Pink Poinsettias
Complements Holiday Traditions Series
Band of pink flowers circles ball.
Glass Ball
QBG6926 SRP: $25.00

Purr-fect Little Deer
Kitten pretends to be reindeer.
Handcrafted, Dated
S Pike
QX6526 SRP: $7.95

Santa's Flying Machine
Santa tests his new sleighcopter.
Rotor blades and wheels turn.
Handcrafted/Tin, Dated
E Seale
QX6573 SRP: $16.95

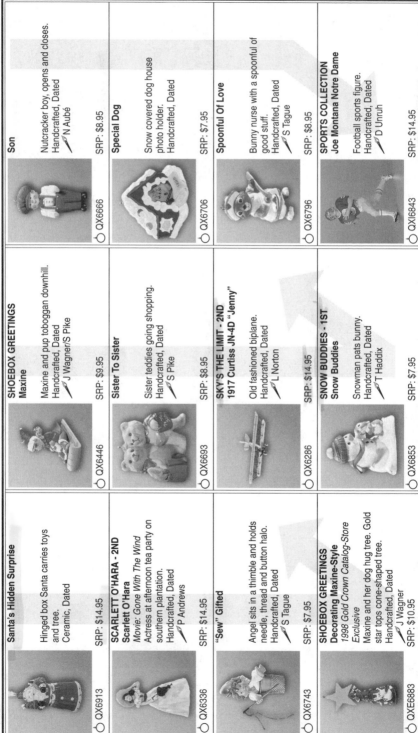

Santa's Hidden Surprise

Hinged box Santa carries toys and tree.
Ceramic, Dated

QX6913 SRP: $14.95

SHOEBOX GREETINGS
Maxine

Maxine and pup toboggan downhill.
Handcrafted, Dated
J Wagner/S Pike

QX6446 SRP: $9.95

Son

Nutcracker boy, opens and closes.
Handcrafted, Dated
N Aubé

QX6666 SRP: $8.95

SCARLETT O'HARA - 2ND
Scarlett O'Hara
Movie: Gone With The Wind
Actress at afternoon tea party on southern plantation.
Handcrafted, Dated
P Andrews

QX6336 SRP: $14.95

Sister To Sister

Sister teddies going shopping.
Handcrafted, Dated
S Pike

QX6693 SRP: $8.95

Special Dog

Snow covered dog house photo holder.
Handcrafted, Dated

QX6706 SRP: $7.95

"Sew" Gifted

Angel sits in a thimble and holds needle, thread and button halo.
Handcrafted, Dated
S Tague

QX6743 SRP: $7.95

SKY'S THE LIMIT - 2ND
1917 Curtiss JN-4D "Jenny"

Old fashioned biplane.
Handcrafted, Dated
L Norton

QX6286 SRP: $14.95

Spoonful Of Love

Bunny nurse with a spoonful of good stuff.
Handcrafted, Dated
S Tague

QX6796 SRP: $8.95

SHOEBOX GREETINGS
Decorating Maxine-Style
1998 Gold Crown Catalog-Store Exclusive
Maxine and her dog hug tree. Gold star tops cone-shaped tree.
Handcrafted, Dated
J Wagner

QXE6883 SRP: $10.95

SNOW BUDDIES - 1ST
Snow Buddies

Snowman pats bunny.
Handcrafted, Dated
T Haddix

QX6853 SRP: $7.95

SPORTS COLLECTION
Joe Montana Notre Dame

Football sports figure.
Handcrafted, Dated
D Unruh

QXI6843 SRP: $14.95

SPOTLIGHT ON SNOOPY - 1ST
Joe Cool

Cool Santa in shades with Woodstock atop pack.
Handcrafted, Dated
B Siedler

QX6453 SRP: $9.95

STOCK CAR CHAMPIONS - 2ND
Richard Petty

Race car sports figure.
Handcrafted
E Seale

QXI4143 SRP: $15.95

Sweet Memories

Set of 8
Stars,and old fashioned penny candies.
Blown Glass
K Kline

QBG6933 SRP: $45.00

STAR TREK: VOYAGER
Captain Kathryn Janeaway
Special Edition
Star Trek character.
Handcrafted, Dated
A M Rogers

QXI4046 SRP: $14.95

Sugarplum Cottage

Snow covered house with candy trim.
Blown Glass
T Haddix

QBG6917 SRP: $35.00

Sweet Rememberings

Girl holds gingerbread man and candy cane.
Handcrafted, Dated
S Tague

QX6876 SRP: $8.95

STAR WARS
Boba Fett
Special Edition
Star Wars character.
Handcrafted
D Rhodus

QXI4053 SRP: $14.95

SUPER HEROES
Superman
Commemorative Edition--
Lunchbox opens/closes, shows super hero.
Pressed Tin, Dated

QX6423 SRP: $12.95

THOMAS KINKADE, PAINTER OF LIGHT - 2ND
N. Victorian Christmas II

Scene of lighted and trimmed victorian mansion.
Ceramic, Dated

QX6343 SRP: $10.95

STAR WARS - 2ND
Princess Leia
Special Edition
Star Wars character.
Handcrafted, Dated
D Rhodus

QXI4026 SRP: $13.95

Surprise Catch

Ball lands in teddy bear's glove.
Handcrafted, Dated
J C Francis

QX6753 SRP: $7.95

THREE STOOGES, THE
Larry, Moe and Curly

Set of 3. The three stooges make music.
Handcrafted, Dated
T Larsen

QX6503 SRP: $27.00

Tonka Road Grader

Front section and grader pivots on road building vehicle.
Die-cast Metal, Dated

QX6483 SRP: $13.95

Watchful Shepherd

Shepherd holding lamb gazes at the star.
Handcrafted, Dated
K Kline

QX6496 SRP: $8.95

Writing To Santa

Baby chipmunk writes to Santa.
Handcrafted, Dated
N Aubé

QX6533 SRP: $7.95

Treetop Choir

Birds perched on birdhouse caroling.
Handcrafted
J C Francis

QX6506 SRP: $9.95

White Poinsettias

Compliments Holiday Traditions Series
White flowers highlighted on ball ornament.
Glass Ball

QBG6923 SRP: $25.00

YULETIDE CENTRAL - 5TH & FINAL
Yuletide Central

Red caboose car. Wheels turn.
Pressed Tin, Dated
L Sickman

QX6373 SRP: $18.95

UNFORGETTABLE VILLAINS - 1ST
Cruella de Vil
Movie: 101 Dalmatians
Fur coated villainess looking for pups.
Handcrafted, Dated

QXD4063 SRP: $14.95

WINNIE THE POOH - 1ST
Visit From Piglet, A

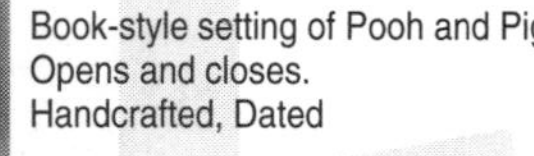

Book-style setting of Pooh and Piglet.
Opens and closes.
Handcrafted, Dated

QXD4086 SRP: $13.95

Warm And Cozy

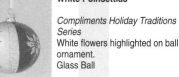

Bird wears fluffy muffler to keep warm.
Handcrafted, Dated
L Sickman

QX6866 SRP: $8.95

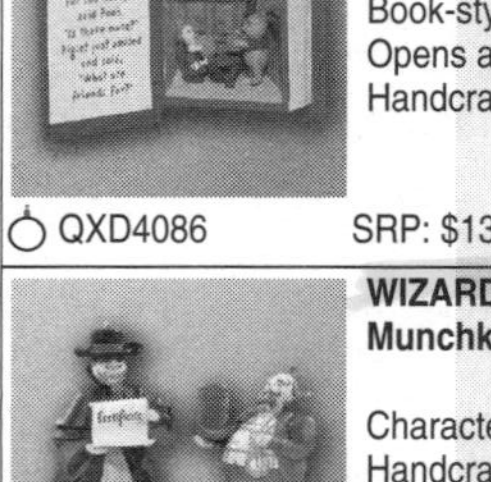

WIZARD OF OZ, THE
Munchkinland Mayor and Coroner

Characters from the movie.
Handcrafted, Dated
J Lyle

QX6463 SRP: $13.95

NOTES:

NOTES:

1984

City Lights

Santa and squirrel direct traffic atop light.
Handcrafted, 3.50",
B Siedler

QLX7014 | SRP: $10.00 | **GBTru: $50**

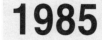

Stained Glass

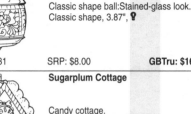

Classic shape ball:Stained-glass look.
Classic shape, 3.87",

QLX7031 | SRP: $8.00 | **GBTru: $16**

All Are Precious

Shepherd, lamb, donkey under star.
Acrylic, 4.00",

QLX7044 | SRP: $8.00 | **GBTru: $14**

Nativity

Panorama of Bethlehem/Three Kings.
Handcrafted, 3.50",
E Seale

QLX7001 | SRP: $12.00 | **GBTru: $20**

Sugarplum Cottage

Candy cottage.
Handcrafted, 3.00",

QLX7011 | SRP: $11.00 | **GBTru: $39**

Brass Carousel

Reindeer pulling Santa & sleigh.
Brass, 3.00",

QLX7071 | SRP: $9.00 | **GBTru: $68**

Santa's Arrival

Panorama of sleep'g tot, pup,
Santa with list.
Handcrafted, 3.50",
D Lee

QLX7024 | SRP: $13.00 | **GBTru: $59**

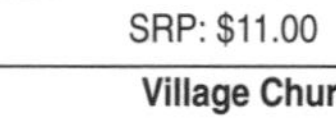

Village Church

Church door opens to carolers.
Handcrafted, 4.63",
D Lee

QLX7021 | SRP: $15.00 | **GBTru: $40**

Christmas In The Forest

Classic shape ball: Forest
night scene.
Classic shape, 3.87",

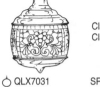

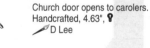

QLX7034 | SRP: $8.00 | **GBTru: $15**

Santa's Workshop

Santa shows toy bunny to real bunny.
Handcrafted, 3.50",

QLX7004 | SRP: $13.00 | **GBTru: $38**

1985

Baby's First Christmas

Carousel: Teddy bears ride ponies.
Handcrft/Acrylic, 4.00", Dated,
E Seale

QLX7005 SRP: $16.50 **GBTru: $36**

Little Red Schoolhouse

Parents watch school play.
Handcrafted, 2.63",
D Lee

QLX7112 SRP: $15.75 **GBTru: $70**

Swiss Cheese Lane

Mouse family in A-frame cheese home.
Handcrafted, 2.63", Dated,

QLX7065 SRP: $13.00 **GBTru: $30**

CHRIS MOUSE - 1ST
Chris Mouse

Mouse sits on candle base reading book.
Handcrafted, 3.88", Dated,
B Siedler

QLX7032 SRP: $12.50 **GBTru: $69**

Love Wreath

Wreath with caption.
Acrylic, 3.50",
L Votruba

QLX7025 SRP: $8.50 **GBTru: $10**

1986

Christmas Eve Visit

House with Santa and sleigh.
Brass, 2.00",

QLX7105 SRP: $12.00 **GBTru: $20**

Mr. & Mrs. Santa

The Kringles at home.
Handcrafted, 3.00",

QLX7052 SRP: $14.50 **GBTru: $50**

Baby's First Christmas

Panorama: Cat by tree sees sleigh/ shifting lights.
Handcrafted, 3.63", Dated,
K Crow

QLX7103 SRP: $19.50 **GBTru: $38**

Katybeth

Angel on rainbow and clouds.
Hndcr/Acryl, 3.62",

QLX7102 SRP: $10.75 **GBTru: $22**

Season Of Beauty

Classic shape ball: Winter scene.
Classic shape, 3.25",
J Lyle

QLX7122 SRP: $8.00 **GBTru: $14**

CHRIS MOUSE - 2ND
Chris Mouse Dreams

Mouse sleeps in pine cone bed.
Handcrafted, 3.25", Dated,
P Dutkin

QLX7056 SRP: $13.00 **GBTru: $70**

CHRISTMAS CLASSICS - 1ST
Nutcracker Ballet - Sugarplum Fairy

Dancing Nutcracker ballerina.
Handcrafted, 4.50", Dated,

QLX7043 SRP: $17.50 **GBTru: $62**

Gentle Blessing

Panorama of animals by manger.
Handcrafted, 3.63",
L Sickman

QLX7083 SRP: $15.00 **GBTru: $169**

Santa's On His Way

Hologram of Santa and sleigh over city.
Handcrafted, 3.63",
D Unruh

QLX7115 SRP: $15.00 **GBTru: $56**

Christmas Sleigh Ride

Couple in sleigh.
Handcrafted, 3.75", ,
E Seale

QLX7012 SRP: $24.50 **GBTru: $89**

Keep On Glowin'!

Elf on icicle.
Handcrafted, 2.44",
K Crow

QLX7076 SRP: $10.00 **GBTru: $25**

Santa's Snack

Santa with bedtime snack.
Handcrafted, 2.94",
K Crow

QLX7066 SRP: $10.00 **GBTru: $45**

First Christmas Together

Teddy bear couple in balloon.
Handcrafted, 5.25", Dated,
E Seale

QLX7073 SRP: $14.00 **GBTru: $35**

Merry Christmas Bell

Bell with caption.
Acrylic, 5.56",
L Votruba

QLX7093 SRP: $8.50 **GBTru: $12**

Sharing Friendship

Teardrop shape with friendship caption.
Acrylic, 5.31", Dated,
L Votruba

QLX7063 SRP: $8.50 **GBTru: $12**

General Store

Woman at store counter/ potbelly stove.
Handcrafted, 2.69",
D Lee

QLX7053 SRP: $15.75 **GBTru: $55**

SANTA & SPARKY - 1ST
Lighting The Tree

Santa and penguin pal by tree.
Handcrafted, 4.12", Dated, ,

QLX7033 SRP: $22.00 **GBTru: $45**

Village Express

Train circling village.
Handcrafted, 3.50", ,
L Sickman

QLX7072 SRP: $24.50 **GBTru: $60**

1987

Angelic Messengers

Panorama: Angels with shepherds/ changing lights.
Handcrafted, 3.63",
D Unruh

QLX7113 SRP: $18.75 **GBTru: $34**

Baby's First Christmas

Teddy painting window.
Handcrafted, 3.75", Dated,

QLX7049 SRP: $13.50 **GBTru: $29**

Bright Noel

"NOEL" star w/ look of neon lighting.
Acrylic, 5.50",
L Votruba

QLX7059 SRP: $7.00 **GBTru: $19**

CHRIS MOUSE - 3RD
Chris Mouse Glow

Mouse holds stained glass lamp pull.
Handcrafted, 4.13", Dated,
B Siedler

QLX7057 SRP: $11.00 **GBTru: $65**

CHRISTMAS CLASSICS - 2ND
Christmas Carol, A

Dickens scene: Scrooge and Cratchits.
Handcrafted, 4.25", Dated,

QLX7029 SRP: $16.00 **GBTru: $35**

Christmas Morning

Child slides down bannister.
Handcrafted, 4.31",
K Crow

QLX7013 SRP: $24.50 **GBTru: $30**

First Christmas Together

Polar bear couple in igloo.
Handcrafted, 2.62", Dated,

QLX7087 SRP: $11.50 **GBTru: $40**

Good Cheer Blimp

Santa in blimp.
Handcrafted, 3.06",
L Sickman

QLX7046 SRP: $16.00 **GBTru: $40**

Keeping Cozy

Santa at potbelly stove.
Handcrafted, 2.50",
K Crow

QLX7047 SRP: $11.75 **GBTru: $32**

Lacy Brass Snowflake

Brass snowflake.
Brass, 2.50",

QLX7097 SRP: $11.50 **GBTru: $14**

Loving Holiday

Clock: Couple in old fashioned glockenspiel.
Handcrafted, 3.63",
E Seale

QLX7016 SRP: $22.00 **GBTru: $38**

Memories Are Forever Photoholder

Photoholder with holly leaves.
Handcrafted, 3.88",
E Seale

QLX7067 SRP: $8.50 **GBTru: $16**

Train Station

Mother and child wait at station.
Handcrafted, 3.19",
D Lee

QLX7039 SRP: $12.75 **GBTru: $46**

CHRIS MOUSE - 4TH
Chris Mouse Star

Mouse polishes star.
Handcrafted, 2.50", Dated,
B Siedler

QLX7154 SRP: $8.75 **GBTru: $42**

Meowy Christmas!

Kittens play w/ribbon on heart.
Handcrafted, 2.50",
S Pike

QLX7089 SRP: $10.00 **GBTru: $38**

1988

CHRISTMAS CLASSICS - 3RD
Night Before Christmas
Ornament has no series symbol
Santa places toys by tree.
Handcrafted, 4.50", Dated,
D Lee

QLX7161 SRP: $15.00 **GBTru: $32**

SANTA & SPARKY - 2ND
Perfect Portrait

Penguin lights Santa's sculpture.
Handcrafted, 4.00", Dated,

QLX7019 SRP: $19.50 **GBTru: $30**

Baby's First Christmas

Horses prance on carousel.
Handcrafted, 4.00", Dated,
E Seale

QLX7184 SRP: $24.00 **GBTru: $40**

Christmas Is Magic

Santa makes shadow puppet for pup.
Handcrafted, 3.25",
K Crow

QLX7171 SRP: $12.00 **GBTru: $30**

Season For Friendship

Teardrop shape with caption.
Acrylic, 5.31",

QLX7069 SRP: $8.50 **GBTru: $15**

Bearly Reaching

Bear with candle/clip-on.
Handcrafted, 4.00",
L Sickman

QLX7151 SRP: $9.50 **GBTru: $28**

Circling The Globe

Santa plans global delivery.
Handcrafted, 2.75",
K Crow

QLX7124 SRP: $10.50 **GBTru: $30**

Country Express

Train circling old western town.
Handcrafted, 3.50",
L Sickman

QLX7211 SRP: $24.50 **GBTru: $50**

Festive Feeder

Bird feeder offers treats.
Handcrafted, 3.00",
L Sickman

QLX7204 SRP: $11.50 **GBTru: $30**

First Christmas Together

Two mice share candy wreath.
Handcrafted, 3.00", Dated,
L Sickman

QLX7027 SRP: $12.00 **GBTru: $25**

Heavenly Glow

Glowing angel.
Brass, 3.00",
M Pyda-Sevaik

QLX7114 SRP: $11.75 **GBTru: $18**

Kitty Capers

Kitten tangled in lights/clip-on.
Handcrafted, 1.50",
S Pike

QLX7164 SRP: $13.00 **GBTru: $38**

Last-Minute Hug

Swiss chalet glockenspiel design/
Santa hugs wife.
Handcrafted, 3.50",
D Unruh

QLX7181 SRP: $22.00 **GBTru: $35**

Moonlit Nap

Angel sleeps on moon.
Handcrafted, 2.75",
R Chad

QLX7134 SRP: $8.75 **GBTru: $14**

Parade Of Toys

Toys march around tree.
Handcrafted, 3.50",
L Sickman

QLX7194 SRP: $24.50 **GBTru: $35**

Radiant Tree

Glowing tree with cut-out designs.
Brass, 3.25",
J Lyle

QLX7121 SRP: $11.75 **GBTru: $15**

SANTA & SPARKY - 3RD & FINAL
On With The Show

MagicianSanta /penguin pops
out of hat.
Handcrafted, 4.00", Dated,

QLX7191 SRP: $19.50 **GBTru: $28**

Skater's Waltz

Couples skate around trees.
Handcrafted, 3.50",
D Unruh

QLX7201 SRP: $24.50 **GBTru: $38**

Song Of Christmas

Etched design of Cardinal on branch.
Acrylic, 3.50",

QLX7111 SRP: $8.50 **GBTru: $15**

Tree Of Friendship

Tree shape with etched caption.
Acrylic, 4.25", 💡

QLX7104 SRP: $8.50 **GBTru: $15**

1989

Angel Melody

Angel plays trumpet/baroque shape.
Acrylic, 5.44", 💡
L Votruba

QLX7202 SRP: $9.50 **GBTru: $15**

Animals Speak, The

Panorama: Angel listens to animals speak.
Handcrafted, 3.63", 💡
J Francis

QLX7232 SRP: $13.50 **GBTru: $60**

Baby's First Christmas

Mouse mom reads story and rocks cradle.
Handcrafted, 4.50", Dated, 💡, ⟲, ♪
E Seale
Tune: Brahms Lullaby

QLX7272 SRP: $30.00 **GBTru: $48**

Backstage Bear

Bear admires Santa cap in mirror.
Handcrafted, 3.38", 💡
B Siedler

QLX7215 SRP: $13.50 **GBTru: $25**

Busy Beaver

Beaver warming hands over fire.
Handcrafted, 2.88", 💡
D Lee

QLX7245 SRP: $17.50 **GBTru: $34**

CHRIS MOUSE - 5TH
Chris Mouse Cookout

Mouse toasting marshmallow.
Handcrafted, 4.50", Dated, 💡
A M Rogers

QLX7225 SRP: $9.50 **GBTru: $58**

CHRISTMAS CLASSICS - 4TH
Little Drummer Boy

Drummer boy at manger.
Handcrafted, 3.25", Dated, 💡
D Lee

QLX7242 SRP: $13.50 **GBTru: $22**

First Christmas Together

Flickering fireplace.
Handcrafted, 3.25", Dated, 💡
D Lee

QLX7342 SRP: $17.50 **GBTru: $24**

FOREST FROLICS - 1ST
Forest Frolics

Animals ski on candy cane trail.
Handcrafted, 4.44", Dated, 💡, ⟲
S Pike

QLX7282 SRP: $24.50 **GBTru: $62**

Holiday Bell

Faceted bell.
Crystal, 3.50", Dated, 💡

QLX7222 SRP: $17.50 **GBTru: $20**

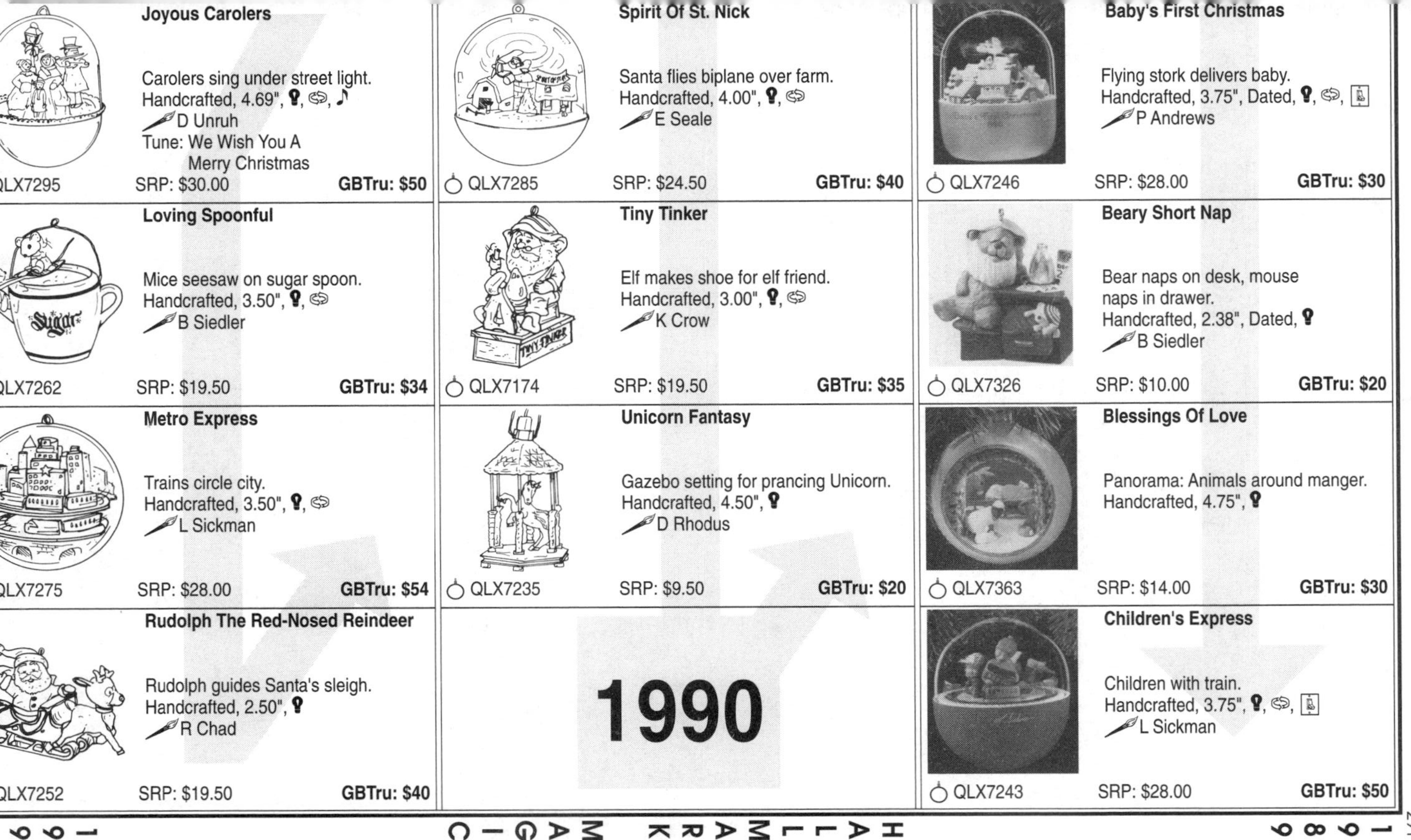

Joyous Carolers

Carolers sing under street light.
Handcrafted, 4.69", 💡, ♻, ♪
D Unruh
Tune: We Wish You A Merry Christmas

QLX7295 SRP: $30.00 **GBTru: $50**

Loving Spoonful

Mice seesaw on sugar spoon.
Handcrafted, 3.50", 💡, ♻
B Siedler

QLX7262 SRP: $19.50 **GBTru: $34**

Metro Express

Trains circle city.
Handcrafted, 3.50", 💡, ♻
L Sickman

QLX7275 SRP: $28.00 **GBTru: $54**

Rudolph The Red-Nosed Reindeer

Rudolph guides Santa's sleigh.
Handcrafted, 2.50", 💡
R Chad

QLX7252 SRP: $19.50 **GBTru: $40**

Spirit Of St. Nick

Santa flies biplane over farm.
Handcrafted, 4.00", 💡, ♻
E Seale

QLX7285 SRP: $24.50 **GBTru: $40**

Tiny Tinker

Elf makes shoe for elf friend.
Handcrafted, 3.00", 💡, ♻
K Crow

QLX7174 SRP: $19.50 **GBTru: $35**

Unicorn Fantasy

Gazebo setting for prancing Unicorn.
Handcrafted, 4.50", 💡
D Rhodus

QLX7235 SRP: $9.50 **GBTru: $20**

1990

Baby's First Christmas

Flying stork delivers baby.
Handcrafted, 3.75", Dated, 💡, ♻, ▣
P Andrews

QLX7246 SRP: $28.00 **GBTru: $30**

Beary Short Nap

Bear naps on desk, mouse naps in drawer.
Handcrafted, 2.38", Dated, 💡
B Siedler

QLX7326 SRP: $10.00 **GBTru: $20**

Blessings Of Love

Panorama: Animals around manger.
Handcrafted, 4.75", 💡

QLX7363 SRP: $14.00 **GBTru: $30**

Children's Express

Children with train.
Handcrafted, 3.75", 💡, ♻, ▣
L Sickman

QLX7243 SRP: $28.00 **GBTru: $50**

CHRIS MOUSE - 6TH
Chris Mouse Wreath

Mouse lighting candle in wreath.
Handcrafted, 4.50", Dated,
A M Rogers

QLX7296 SRP: $10.00 **GBTru: $35**

CHRISTMAS CLASSICS - 5TH & FINAL
Littlest Angel, The

Little angel watches gift become star.
Handcrafted, 4.50", Dated,
J Francis

QLX7303 SRP: $14.00 **GBTru: $38**

Christmas Memories

Clydesdale pulls sleigh/
Dad and kids with tree.
Handcrafted, 4.25", , ,
D Unruh

QLX7276 SRP: $25.00 **GBTru: $35**

Deer Crossing

Beaver with stop sign at
railroad crossing.
Handcrafted, 3.94",
B Siedler

QLX7213 SRP: $18.00 **GBTru: $25**

Elf Of The Year

Elf with "1990" sign.
Handcrafted, 2.94", Dated,
P Andrews

QLX7356 SRP: $10.00 **GBTru: $12**

Elfin Whittler

Elf sculpts Santa figure.
Handcrafted, 3.13", ,
K Crow

QLX7265 SRP: $20.00 **GBTru: $20**

FOREST FROLICS - 2ND
Forest Frolics

Animals playing in snow.
Handcrafted, 4.50", Dated, , ,
S Pike

QLX7236 SRP: $25.00 **GBTru: $30**

Holiday Flash

Elf with camera.
Handcrafted, 3.69",
R Chad

QLX7333 SRP: $18.00 **GBTru: $25**

Hop 'N Pop Popper

Teddy on popcorn popper.
Handcrafted, 3.44", ,
B Siedler

QLX7353 SRP: $20.00 **GBTru: $72**

Letter to Santa

Child at computer.
Handcrafted, 2.50",
A M Rogers

QLX7226 SRP: $14.00 **GBTru: $18**

Mrs. Santa's Kitchen

Mrs. Santa w/danc'g gingerbread men.
Handcrafted, 4.75", Dated, , ,
D Rhodus

QLX7263 SRP: $25.00 **GBTru: $50**

Our First Christmas Together

Changing scene: couple in house/
porch light.
Handcrafted, 3.63", Dated,
D Lee

QLX7255 SRP: $18.00 **GBTru: $36**

1991

Partridges In A Pear

Etched pear shaped partridge panels.
Brass, 3.75",
J Lyle

QLX7212 SRP: $14.00 **GBTru: $20**

Starship Christmas

Santa and reindeer in flying saucer ship.
Handcrafted, 2.25", Dated,
B Siedler

QLX7336 SRP: $18.00 **GBTru: $35**

Baby's First Christmas

Santa rocking baby by fireplace.
Hndcrafted, 4.50", Dated, , , ,
E Seale
Tune: Rock-A-Bye Baby

QLX7247 SRP: $30.00 **GBTru: $48**

Santa's Ho-Ho Hoedown

Santa calls square dance as reindeer twirl.
Handcrafted, 4.38", , ,
K Crow

QLX7256 SRP: $25.00 **GBTru: $78**

Beary Artistic

Club: Keepsake of Membership
Bear artist sculpting glowing ice.
Handcrafted, 2.50", Dated,
B Siedler

QXC7259 SRP: $10.00 **GBTru: $30**

Song And Dance

Handle turns, mice dance to record.
Handcrafted, 4.13", ,
A M Rogers
Tune: Jingle Bells

QLX7253 SRP: $20.00 **GBTru: $90**

Angel Of Light

2 years production
Angel with star tree topper.
Handcrafted,

QLT7239 SRP: $30.00 **GBTru: $40**

Bringing Home The Tree

Dad, child, pup bring home tree.
Handcrafted, 4.38", Dated, , ,
D Unruh

QLX7249 SRP: $28.00 **GBTru: $40**

Starlight Angel

Angel with bag of stars.
Handcrafted, 2.75",
A M Rogers

QLX7306 SRP: $14.00 **GBTru: $20**

Arctic Dome

Stadium with football game.
Handcrafted, 3.00", Dated, , ,
K Crow

QLX7117 SRP: $25.00 **GBTru: $36**

CHRIS MOUSE - 7TH
Chris Mouse Mail

Mouse reads by flashlight.
Handcrafted, 3.00", Dated,
B Siedler

QLX7207 SRP: $10.00 **GBTru: $25**

Elfin Engineer

Elf with train.
Handcrafted, 2.75",
R Chad

QLX7209 SRP: $10.00 **GBTru: $15**

Friendship Tree

Squirrel and owl in tree with gifts.
Handcrafted, 3.13", Dated,
P Dutkin

QLX7169 SRP: $10.00 **GBTru: $18**

Kringle's Bumper Cars

Santa, elf and deer drive cars.
Handcrafted, 3.75",
L Sickman

QLX7119 SRP: $25.00 **GBTru: $40**

Father Christmas

Santa with lantern, tree, and toys.
Handcrafted, 4.00", Dated,
D Unruh

QLX7147 SRP: $14.00 **GBTru: $35**

Holiday Glow

Panorama: Dog and cat gaze at tree.
Handcrafted, 3.75",
S Pike

QLX7177 SRP: $14.00 **GBTru: $28**

Mole Family Home

An underground peek at Mole family holiday.
Handcrafted, 3.38", Dated,
J Lee

QLX7149 SRP: $20.00 **GBTru: $26**

Festive Brass Church

Etched, dimensional Church.
Brass, 3.13",
D McGehee

QLX7179 SRP: $14.00 **GBTru: $15**

It's A Wonderful Life

Theatre showing Christmas movie.
Handcrafted, 3.19", Dated,
D Lee

QLX7237 SRP: $20.00 **GBTru: $54**

Our First Christmas Together

Bears in boat at Tunnel Of Love.
Handcrafted, 4.13", Dated,
L Sickman

QLX7137 SRP: $25.00 **GBTru: $25**

FOREST FROLICS - 3RD
Forest Frolics

Animals play and skate.
Handcrafted, 4.50", Dated,
S Pike

QLX7219 SRP: $25.00 **GBTru: $50**

Jingle Bears

Dad plays piano, Mom and baby sing.
Handcrafted, 4.38",
J Lee
Tune: Jingle Bells

QLX7323 SRP: $25.00 **GBTru: $38**

PEANUTS - 1ST
Snoopy And Woodstock

Snoopy and Woodstock in stocking on fireplace.
Handcrafted, 3.00", Dated,
D Rhodus

QLX7229 SRP: $18.00 **GBTru: $50**

Salvation Army Band

Portion of ornament price to Salvation Army
Band plays on street corner.
Handcrafted, 4.63"
D Unruh
Tune: Joy To The World

QLX7273 SRP: $30.00 **GBTru: $52**

Sparkling Angel

Angel with lighted garland.
Handcrafted, 3.81"
R Chad

QLX7157 SRP: $18.00 **GBTru: $30**

Baby's First Christmas

Baby sleeps in old fashioned crib.
Handcrafted, 3.44", Dated
K Crow
Tune: Silent Night

QLX7281 SRP: $22.00 **GBTru: $58**

Santa Special

Separate switches for motion & train sounds. 2 years production.
Santa as train engineer.
Handcrafted, 3.13"
E Seale

QLX7167 SRP: $40.00 **GBTru: $50**

STAR TREK
Starship Enterprise: NCC-1701
25th Anniversary Commemorative for TV Series
Space ship.
Handcrafted, 1.63", Dated
L Norton

QLX7199 SRP: $20.00 **GBTru: $349**

CHRIS MOUSE - 8TH
Chris Mouse Tales

Mouse looks out from his shoe house.
Handcrafted, 3.56", Dated
A M Rogers

QLX7074 SRP: $12.00 **GBTru: $28**

Santa's Hot Line

Elf on phone switchboard.
Handcrafted, 3.88", Dated
K Crow

QLX7159 SRP: $18.00 **GBTru: $25**

Toyland Tower

Castle with marching guards and Teddy drummer.
Handcrafted, 3.81"
K Crow

QLX7129 SRP: $20.00 **GBTru: $30**

Christmas Parade

Inflated toys in city parade.
Handcrafted, 3.38", Dated
L Sickman

QLX7271 SRP: $30.00 **GBTru: $52**

Ski Trip

Village with skiers and ski lift.
Handcrafted, 4.25"
E Seale

QLX7266 SRP: $28.00 **GBTru: $30**

1992

Continental Express

Two trains circle mountain village.
Handcrafted, 3.75", Dated
L Sickman

QLX7264 SRP: $32.00 **GBTru: $45**

Dancing Nutcracker, The

Nutcracker dances to ballet music.
Hndcrafted, 3.25", Dated,
L Votruba
Tune: Tchaikovsky: Overture to Nutcracker Ballet

QLX7261 SRP: $30.00 **GBTru: $34**

Enchanted Clock

Santa peeks out as toys circle base.
Handcrafted, 3.94", Dated,
K Crow

QLX7274 SRP: $30.00 **GBTru: $48**

Feathered Friends

Birds share food at feeding station.
Handcrafted, 1.94", Dated,
L Sickman

QLX7091 SRP: $14.00 **GBTru: $15**

FOREST FROLICS - 4TH
Forest Frolics

Forest animals enjoy seesaw.
Handcrafted, 4.13", Dated,
S Pike

QLX7254 SRP: $28.00 **GBTru: $32**

Good Sledding Ahead

Children sled around yard/dog follows.
Handcrafted, 3.56", Dated,
D Palmiter

QLX7244 SRP: $28.00 **GBTru: $42**

Lighting The Way

Winged Angel lights the way w/lamp.
Handcrafted, 3.69",
P Andrews

QLX7231 SRP: $18.00 **GBTru: $25**

Look! It's Santa

Children peek around tree see Santa's shadow.
Handcrafted, 4.06", Dated,
D Lee

QLX7094 SRP: $14.00 **GBTru: $30**

Nut Sweet Nut

Chipmunk trims acorn home with jelly bean lights.
Handcrafted, 2.06", Dated,
K Crow

QLX7081 SRP: $10.00 **GBTru: $20**

Our First Christmas Together

Panorama: Couple seated by lit fireplace.
Handcrafted, 3.63", Dated,
R Chad

QLX7221 SRP: $20.00 **GBTru: $20**

PEANUTS - 2ND
Snoopy and Woodstock

Pals cuddle on doghouse to wait for Santa.
Handcrafted, 3.94", Dated,
D Rhodus

QLX7214 SRP: $18.00 **GBTru: $44**

Santa Sub

Santa in submarine.
Handcrafted, 2.75", Dated,
K Crow

QLX7321 SRP: $18.00 **GBTru: $25**

Santa's Answering Machine

Button activates message
Mouse hears Santa message on answering machine.
Handcrafted, 1.88", Dated,
J Lee

QLX7241 SRP: $22.00 **GBTru: $20**

1993

STAR TREK
Shuttlecraft Galileo
Button activates message
Enterprise shuttlecraft/
Mr. Spock's voice.
Handcrafted, 1.13", Dated,
D Rhodus

QLX7331 SRP: $24.00 **GBTru: $40**

Under Construction

Beaver trims danger sign.
Handcrafted, 3.50", Dated,
D Palmiter

QLX7324 SRP: $18.00 **GBTru: $32**

Watch Owls

One owl watches for Santa/
one owl naps.
Porcelain, 2.25", Dated,
J Francis

QLX7084 SRP: $12.00 **GBTru: $20**

Yuletide Rider

Santa drives car w/gifts/tree/
country scene.
Handcrafted, 3.38", Dated,
E Seale

QLX7314 SRP: $28.00 **GBTru: $38**

Baby's First Christmas

Baby asleep in cradle.
Handcrafted, 3.88", Dated,
J Francis
Tune: Brahms Lullaby

QLX7365 SRP: $22.00 **GBTru: $38**

Bells Are Ringing

On/Off for motion and sound
Elf rings bell.
Hndcrfted, 4.19", Dated,
K Crow

QLX7402 SRP: $28.00 **GBTru: $56**

CHRIS MOUSE - 9TH
Chris Mouse Flight

Mouse rides tea cup hot air balloon.
Handcrafted, 4.00", Dated,
A M Rogers

QLX7152 SRP: $12.00 **GBTru: $22**

Dog's Best Friend

Dog decorates fire hydrant w/lights.
Handcrafted, 3.00", Dated,
J Lee

QLX7172 SRP: $12.00 **GBTru: $22**

Dollhouse Dreams

Child w/dollhouse/rooms light
in sequence.
Handcrafted, 3.31", Dated,
K Crow

QLX7372 SRP: $22.00 **GBTru: $46**

FOREST FROLICS - 5TH
Forest Frolics

Forest animals circle decorated tree.
Handcrafted, 4.06", Dated,
S Pike

QLX7165 SRP: $25.00 **GBTru: $30**

Home On The Range

Santa on rock'g horse lasso'g cactus.
Hndcrafted, 4.13", Dated,
L Sickman
Tune: Home On The Range

QLX7395 SRP: $32.00 **GBTru: $40**

Lamplighter, The

Victorian bear lights lamp post.
Handcrafted, 4.19", Dated,
D Palmiter

QLX7192 SRP: $18.00 **GBTru: $29**

North Pole Merrython

Reindeer/Santa run race 'round North Pole.
Handcrafted, 4.13", Dated, , ,
E Seale

QLX7392 SRP: $25.00 **GBTru: $48**

Raiding The Fridge

Santa checks refrigerator for snacks.
Handcrafted, 3.44", Dated,
A M Rogers

QLX7185 SRP: $16.00 **GBTru: $24**

Last-Minute Shopping

Shoppers move in/out of stores.
Handcrafted, 4.13", Dated, , ,
L Votruba

QLX7385 SRP: $28.00 **GBTru: $45**

Our First Christmas Together

Couple seated on sofa by fireplace.
Handcrafted, 2.75", Dated,
R Chad

QLX7355 SRP: $20.00 **GBTru: $25**

Santa's Snow-Getter

Santa on snowmobile delivers sports gear.
Handcrafted, 3.06", Dated,
K Crow

QLX7352 SRP: $18.00 **GBTru: $24**

LOONEY TUNES
Road Runner And Wile E. Coyote

Coyote & bird chase thru mine shaft.
Handcrafted, 4.13", Dated, ,
R Chad

QLX7415 SRP: $30.00 **GBTru: $40**

PEANUTS - 3RD
Snoopy and Woodstock

Friends stand near trimmed tree.
Handcrafted, 3.50", Dated,
D Rhodus

QLX7155 SRP: $18.00 **GBTru: $34**

Santa's Workshop

Toys on conveyer belt pass Santa's checkpoint.
Handcrafted, 4.06", Dated, , ,
B Siedler

QLX7375 SRP: $28.00 **GBTru: $45**

Messages Of Christmas

Record personal message
Chipmunk w/headphones atop radio.
Handcrafted, 4.50", Dated,
B Siedler

QLX7476 SRP: $35.00 **GBTru: $30**

Radio News Flash

Kitten listens to news of Santa.
Handcrafted, 3.19", Dated, , ,
D Lee

QLX7362 SRP: $22.00 **GBTru: $42**

Song Of The Chimes

On/off activates motion and sound
Candles flicker/chimes ring/doves/star.
Hndcrfted, 4.13", Dated, , , ,
P Andrews

QLX7405 SRP: $25.00 **GBTru: $35**

STAR TREK: THE NEXT GENERATION
U.S.S. Enterprise: NCC-1701-D

Space ship /TV Star Trek program.
Handcrafted, 1.19", Dated,
L Norton

QLX7412 SRP: $24.00 **GBTru: $50**

Baby's First Christmas

Mom, Dad chipmunk tuck baby in for nap.
Handcrafted, 2.69", Dated, ,
J Francis
Tune: Rock-A-Bye Baby

QLX7466 SRP: $20.00 **GBTru: $32**

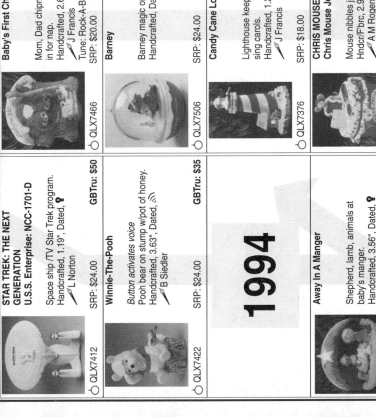

Conversations With Santa

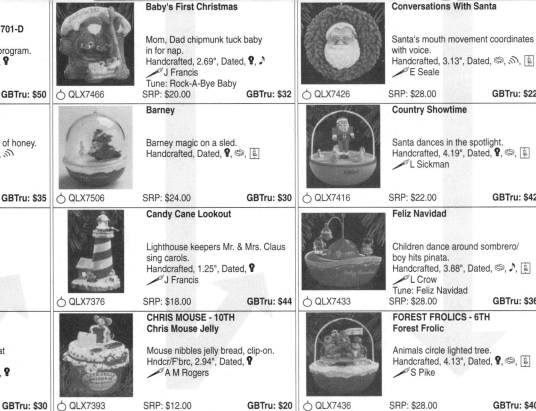

Santa's mouth movement coordinates with voice.
Handcrafted, 3.13", Dated, , ,
E Seale

QLX7426 SRP: $28.00 **GBTru: $22**

Winnie-The-Pooh

Button activates voice
Pooh bear on stump w/pot of honey.
Handcrafted, 3.63", Dated,
B Siedler

QLX7422 SRP: $24.00 **GBTru: $35**

Barney

Barney magic on a sled.
Handcrafted, Dated, , ,

QLX7506 SRP: $24.00 **GBTru: $30**

Country Showtime

Santa dances in the spotlight.
Handcrafted, 4.19", Dated, , ,
L Sickman

QLX7416 SRP: $22.00 **GBTru: $42**

1994

Candy Cane Lookout

Lighthouse keepers Mr. & Mrs. Claus sing carols.
Handcrafted, 1.25", Dated,
J Francis

QLX7376 SRP: $18.00 **GBTru: $44**

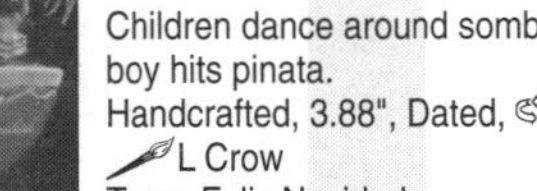

Feliz Navidad

Children dance around sombrero/ boy hits pinata.
Handcrafted, 3.88", Dated, , ,
L Crow
Tune: Feliz Navidad

QLX7433 SRP: $28.00 **GBTru: $36**

Away In A Manger

Shepherd, lamb, animals at baby's manger.
Handcrafted, 3.56", Dated,
J Lyle

QLX7383 SRP: $16.00 **GBTru: $30**

CHRIS MOUSE - 10TH
Chris Mouse Jelly

Mouse nibbles jelly bread, clip-on.
Hndcr/F'brc, 2.94", Dated,
A M Rogers

QLX7393 SRP: $12.00 **GBTru: $20**

FOREST FROLICS - 6TH
Forest Frolic

Animals circle lighted tree.
Handcrafted, 4.13", Dated, , ,
S Pike

QLX7436 SRP: $28.00 **GBTru: $40**

Gingerbread Fantasy

Gingerbread house.
Handcrafted, 4.25", 💡, ♪, P Andrews
Tune: Dance Of The Sugar Plum Fairies

QLX7382 SRP: $44.00 **GBTru: $82**

PEANUTS - 4TH
Snoopy And Woodstock

Snoopy and Woodstock ring bell and sing carol.
Handcrafted, 4.13", Dated, 💡
D Rhodus

QLX7406 SRP: $20.00 **GBTru: $32**

SHOEBOX GREETINGS
Maxine

Maxine holds treelights.
Handcrafted, 4.00", 💡
L Sickman

QLX7503 SRP: $20.00 **GBTru: $35**

Kringle Trolley

Santa drives penguin riders on trolley car.
Handcrafted, 3.56", Dated, 💡
K Crow

QLX7413 SRP: $20.00 **GBTru: $42**

Peekaboo Pup

Pup peeks in/out of basket.
Handcrafted, 3.88", Dated,
A M Rogers

QLX7423 SRP: $20.00 **GBTru: $32**

STAR TREK: THE NEXT GENERATION
Klingon Bird Of Prey

Star Trek space vehicle.
Handcrafted, Dated, 💡
L Norton

QLX7386 SRP: $24.00 **GBTru: $40**

LION KING, THE
Simba, Sarabi And Mufasa
Recalled: defective music box;
Reissued: see QLX7516
Simba, Sarabi and Mufasa.
Handcrafted, 💡, ♪
K Crow
Tune: Circle Of Life

QLX7513 SRP: $32.00 **GBTru: $60**

Rock Candy Miner

Hedgehog mines for rock candy.
Handcrafted, 3.50", Dated, 💡
B Siedler

QLX7403 SRP: $20.00 **GBTru: $28**

TOBIN FRALEY HOLIDAY CAROUSEL - 1ST
Tobin Fraley Holiday Carousel

Carousel horse on golden platform.
Handcrafted, 4.94", Dated, 💡, ♪
D Unruh
Tune: Skater's Waltz

QLX7496 SRP: $32.00 **GBTru: $45**

LION KING, THE
Simba, Sarabi And Mufasa
Reissued w/o music, see QLX7513
Simba, Sarabi and Mufasa.
Handcrafted, 💡
K Crow

QLX7516 SRP: $20.00 **GBTru: $38**

Santa's Sing-Along

Santa pedals and plays calliope.
Handcrafted, 3.94", Dated, 💡, ♪
K Crow
Tune: Santa Claus Is Coming To Town

QLX7473 SRP: $24.00 **GBTru: $46**

U.S. SPACE PROGRAM
Eagle Has Landed, The
Button activates message
25th Anniversary/1st lunar landing.
Handcrafted, 4.50", Dated, 💡
E Seale

QLX7486 SRP: $24.00 **GBTru: $30**

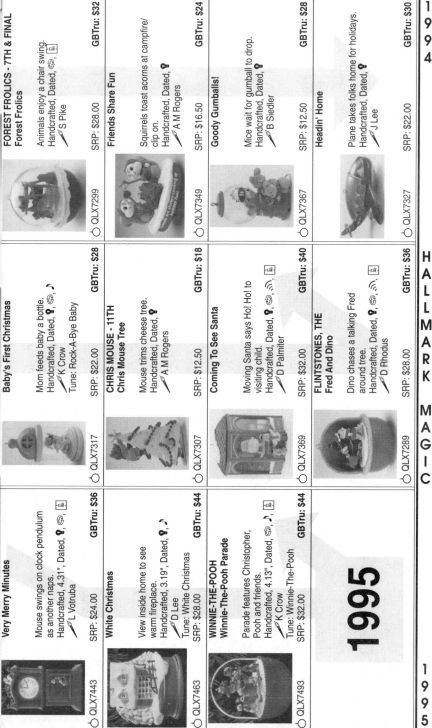

Very Merry Minutes

Mouse swings on clock pendulum as another naps.
Handcrafted, 4.31", Dated,
L Votruba

QLX7443 SRP: $24.00 **GBTru: $36**

Baby's First Christmas

Mom feeds baby a bottle.
Handcrafted, Dated,
K Crow
Tune: Rock-A-Bye Baby

QLX7317 SRP: $22.00 **GBTru: $28**

FOREST FROLICS - 7TH & FINAL
Forest Frolics

Animals enjoy a chair swing.
Handcrafted, Dated,
S Pike

QLX7299 SRP: $28.00 **GBTru: $32**

White Christmas

View inside home to see warm fireplace.
Handcrafted, 3.19", Dated,
D Lee
Tune: White Christmas

QLX7463 SRP: $28.00 **GBTru: $44**

CHRIS MOUSE - 11TH
Chris Mouse Tree

Mouse trims cheese tree.
Handcrafted, Dated,
A M Rogers

QLX7307 SRP: $12.50 **GBTru: $18**

Friends Share Fun

Squirrels toast acorns at campfire/clip on.
Handcrafted, Dated,
A M Rogers

QLX7349 SRP: $16.50 **GBTru: $24**

WINNIE-THE-POOH
Winnie-The-Pooh Parade

Parade features Christopher, Pooh and friends.
Handcrafted, 4.13", Dated,
K Crow
Tune: Winnie-The-Pooh

QLX7493 SRP: $32.00 **GBTru: $44**

Coming To See Santa

Moving Santa says Ho! Ho! to visiting child.
Handcrafted, Dated,
D Palmiter

QLX7369 SRP: $32.00 **GBTru: $40**

Goody Gumballs!

Mice wait for gumball to drop.
Handcrafted, Dated,
B Siedler

QLX7367 SRP: $12.50 **GBTru: $28**

1995

FLINTSTONES, THE
Fred And Dino

Dino chases a talking Fred around tree.
Handcrafted, Dated,
D Rhodus

QLX7289 SRP: $28.00 **GBTru: $36**

Headin' Home

Plane takes folks home for holidays.
Handcrafted, Dated,
J Lee

QLX7327 SRP: $22.00 **GBTru: $30**

Holiday Swim

Swimming fish wears Santa hat.
Handcrafted, Dated, 💡
A M Rogers

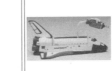

QLX7319 SRP: $18.50 **GBTru: $30**

Santa's Diner

Santa stands in doorway to greet diners.
Handcrafted, Dated, 💡
L Votruba

QLX7337 SRP: $24.50 **GBTru: $26**

U.S. SPACE PROGRAM
Space Shuttle - 30th Anniversary
US Spacewalk

Cargo door opens manually
Columbia shuttle/astronaut and satellite.
Handcrafted, Dated, 💡
K Crow

QLX7396 SRP: $24.50 **GBTru: $28**

Jumping For Joy

Tree and lamp light as mice jump barrels.
Handcrafted, Dated, 💡, ⟲, 🔋
J Francis

QLX7347 SRP: $28.00 **GBTru: $32**

STAR TREK
Romulan Warbird

Warship of outer space.
Handcrafted, Dated, 💡
L Norton

QLX7267 SRP: $24.00 **GBTru: $30**

Victorian Toy Box

Special Edition
Open chest w/toys/tree lights/toys move.
Handcrafted, 💡, ⟲, ♪, 🔋
J Lyle
Tune: Toyland

QLX7357 SRP: $42.00 **GBTru: $50**

My First HOT WHEELS

Kids play w/car & track by lighted tree.
Handcrafted, Dated, 💡, ⟲, 🔋
K Crow

QLX7279 SRP: $28.00 **GBTru: $36**

SUPER HEROES
Superman

Clark Kent becomes Superman in phone booth.
Handcrafted, Dated, 💡, ⟲, 🔋
R Chad

QLX7309 SRP: $28.00 **GBTru: $30**

Wee Little Christmas

Santa puts gifts by tree/scene behind wall.
Handcrafted, Dated, 💡
K Crow

QLX7329 SRP: $22.00 **GBTru: $28**

PEANUTS - 5TH & FINAL
Snoopy And Woodstock

Woodstock watches Snoopy skate .
Handcrafted, Dated, 💡, ⟲, 🔋
D Rhodus

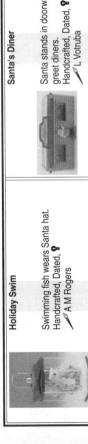

QLX7277 SRP: $24.50 **GBTru: $40**

TOBIN FRALEY HOLIDAY CAROUSEL - 2ND
Tobin Fraley Holiday Carousel

Carousel horse on platform.
Handcrafted, Dated, 💡, ♪
T Fraley
Tune: Over The Waves

QLX7269 SRP: $32.00 **GBTru: $38**

WINNIE-THE-POOH
Winne The Pooh: Too Much Hunny

Pals try push'g Pooh thru hole after too much honey.
Handcrafted, Dated, ⟲, 🔋
B Siedler

QLX7297 SRP: $24.50 **GBTru: $30**

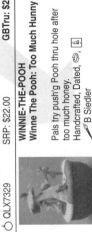

1996

Father Time

Watch battery included
Father Time holds working timepiece.
Handcrafted, Dated
R Chad

QLX7391 SRP: $24.50 **GBTru: $40**

Let Us Adore Him

The Holy Family and shepherds at manger.
Handcrafted, Dated,
J Lyle

QLX7381 SRP: $16.50 **GBTru: $24**

Baby's First Christmas

Angel holds star above sleep'g baby.
Handcrafted, Dated, ♪
J Francis
Tune: Brahms Lullaby

QLX7404 SRP: $22.00 **GBTru: $25**

JETSONS, THE

Jetson family out for a ride in bubble-car.
Handcrafted, Dated,
K Crow

QLX7411 SRP: $28.00 **GBTru: $36**

North Pole Volunteers

Special Edition, button activates sound
Santa fireman drives fire truck as dalmatian rides along.
Handcrafted, Dated,
E Seale

QLX7471 SRP: $42.00 **GBTru: $75**

Chicken Coop Chorus

Heads move manually
Bobbing hens sing Christmas songs.
Handcrafted, ♪
K Crow
Tune: Jingle Bells

QLX7491 SRP: $24.50 **GBTru: $32**

JOURNEY INTO SPACE - 1ST
Freedom 7

Button activates sound
Rocket celebrates 35th Anniv 1st manned flight.
Handcrafted, Dated,
E Seale

QLX7524 SRP: $24.00 **GBTru: $34**

OLYMPIC SPIRIT
Lighting The Flame

Athlete lights olympic torch.
Handcrafted, Dated, ♪
D Unruh
Tune: Bugler's Dream

QXE7444 SRP: $28.00 **GBTru: $30**

CHRIS MOUSE - 12TH
Chris Mouse Inn

Mouse house atop candlelight lantern.
Handcrafted, Dated,
B Siedler

QLX7371 SRP: $14.50 **GBTru: $20**

Jukebox Party

Jukebox plays popular Brenda Lee song.
Handcrafted, Dated, ♪
D Palmiter
Tune: Rockin' Around the Christmas Tree

QLX7339 SRP: $24.50 **GBTru: $38**

Over The Rooftops

Santa and sleigh, over the rooftops scene.
Handcrafted, Dated,
E Seale

QLX7374 SRP: $14.50 **GBTru: $24**

PEANUTS

Lucy leans on piano as Schroeder plays.
Handcrafted, Dated, ♪
R Chad
Tune: Linus and Lucy

QLX7394 SRP: $18.50 **GBTru: $28**

Pinball Wonder

Santa plays pinball game.
Handcrafted, Dated, 💡, ⟲, 〰, ▯
K Crow

QLX7451 SRP: $28.00 **GBTru: $34**

Sharing A Soda

Lights imitate bubbles
Boy & girl sit on stools at Santa's soda shop.
Handcrafted, Dated, 💡
K Crow

QLX7424 SRP: $24.50 **GBTru: $30**

STAR WARS
Millennium Falcon

Star Wars spacecraft from movie.
Handcrafted, Dated, 💡

QLX7474 SRP: $24.00 **GBTru: $40**

Statue of Liberty, The

Replica of Lady Liberty; Spec. Collector's Card.
Handcrafted, Dated, 💡, ♪
E Seale
Tune: The Star-Spangled Banner

QLX7421 SRP: $24.50 **GBTru: $28**

TOBIN FRALEY HOLIDAY CAROUSEL - 3RD & FINAL
Tobin Fraley Holiday Carousel

Carousel horse on platform.
Handcrafted, Dated, 💡, ♪
J Francis
Tune: On The Beautiful Blue Danube

QLX7461 SRP: $32.00 **GBTru: $35**

Treasured Memories

Santa brings gifts to tree in Jim Reid's home.
Handcrafted, Dated, 💡
L Sickman

QLX7384 SRP: $18.50 **GBTru: $20**

Video Party

Mice see video of snowman/ changing scene.
Handcrafted, Dated, 💡
B Siedler

QLX7431 SRP: $28.00 **GBTru: $32**

WINNIE-THE-POOH
Slippery Day

Pooh and friends skate on pond.
Handcrafted, ⟲, ▯
B Siedler

QLX7414 SRP: $24.50 **GBTru: $45**

WIZARD OF OZ, THE
Emerald City

Dorothy & friends on Yellow Brick road.
Handcrafted, 💡, ⟲, ♪, ▯
K Crow
Tune: We're Off to See the Wizard

QLX7454 SRP: $32.00 **GBTru: $50**

1997

ARTIST'S STUDIO COLLECTION
Night Before Christmas, The
Windup tor movement & music
Each side shows part of Moore's poem.
Handcrafted, Dated, ⟲, ♪
K Crow
Tune: Santa Claus Is Comin' To Town

QX5721 SRP: $24.00 **GBTru: $24**

CHRIS MOUSE - 13TH & FINAL
Chris Mouse Luminaria

Mouse lights candle in cut design bag.
Handcrafted, Dated,
B Siedler

QLX7525 SRP: $14.95 **GBTru: $20**

Joy To The World

Earth makes up letter 'O' in J O Y.
Handcrafted, Dated,
S Tague

QLX7512 SRP: $14.95 **GBTru: $15**

Madonna And Child

Cherubs watch Madonna And Child.
Handcrafted, Dated,
J Lyle

QLX7425 SRP: $18.95 **GBTru: $20**

Glowing Angel

Winged angel with halo.
Handcrafted, Dated,
L Votruba

QLX7435 SRP: $18.95 **GBTru: $19**

LIGHTHOUSE GREETINGS - 1ST
Lighthouse Greetings

The Clauses trim New England lighthouse tree.
Handcrafted, Dated,
J Francis

QLX7442 SRP: $24.00 **GBTru: $50**

Motorcycle Chums

Deer driver with Santa navigator in sidecar.
Handcrafted, Dated,
E Seale

QLX7495 SRP: $24.00 **GBTru: $30**

Holiday Serenade

Cardinals perch at birdhouse entry & sing.
Handcrafted, Dated, ,
J Francis

QLX7485 SRP: $24.00 **GBTru: $30**

Lincoln Memorial, The

Collector Card included
Seated Lincoln as in Wash. D.C. Memorial.
Handcrafted, Dated, , ♪
E Seale
Tune: America The Beautiful

QLX7522 SRP: $24.00 **GBTru: $26**

PEANUTS
SNOOPY Plays Santa

Snoopy drives sleigh doghouse/ Woodstock & friends are reindeer.
A M Rogers

QLX7475 SRP: $22.00 **GBTru: $22**

JOURNEYS INTO SPACE - 2ND
Friendship 7
Commemorates 1st US manned space flight. Activate msg w/button: plays original transmission
Astronauts spaceflight.
Handcrafted, Dated, ,
E Seale

QLX7532 SRP: $24.00 **GBTru: $25**

LOONEY TUNES
Decorator Taz

Taz spins about tree w/Daffy & Tweety caught in middle.
Handcrafted, Dated, ,
R Chad

QLX7502 SRP: $30.00 **GBTru: $30**

Santa's Secret Gift

Folk art Santa w/gift bag, can hold msg or gift.
Handcrafted, ♪
R Chad
Tune: Jolly Old St. Nicholas

QLX7455 SRP: $24.00 **GBTru: $24**

Santa's Showboat

Paddlewheel river boat.
Handcrafted, Dated, 💡, ⟲, ♪, [switch]
K Crow
Tune: Jingle Bells

QLX7465 SRP: $42.00 **GBTru: $50**

STAR TREK: DEEP SPACE NINE
U. S. S. Defiant
Special Issue: Stardated
Space craft with light and blinking lights.
Handcrafted, Dated, 💡
L Norton

QXI7481 SRP: $24.00 **GBTru: $35**

STAR WARS
Darth Vader
Button activates voice: Vader speaks to young Luke
Enemy invader ready to fight young Luke.
Handcrafted, 💡, [voice]
D Rhodus

QXI7531 SRP: $24.00 **GBTru: $30**

Teapot Party

Teddy and doll share afternoon tea.
Handcrafted, Dated, 💡
S Tague

QLX7482 SRP: $18.95 **GBTru: $19**

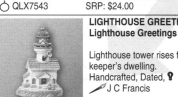

THOMAS KINKADE, PAINTER OF LIGHT
Warmth Of Home, The
Special Issue
Winter scene of mountain home.
Handcrafted, Dated, 💡
T Larsen

QXI7545 SRP: $18.95 **GBTru: $22**

1998

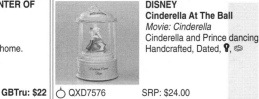

1998 Corvette
Chevrolet Division of General Motors
Red chase lights circle the turntable as car is spotlighted.
Handcrafted, Dated, 💡, ⟲
D Palmiter

QLX7605 SRP: $24.00

CANDLELIGHT SERVICES - 1ST
Stone Church, The
Tree-shaped symbol with number to identify place in the series.
Lighted church with stained glass windows.
Handcrafted, Dated, 💡
E Seale

QLX7636 SRP: $18.95

DISNEY
Cinderella At The Ball
Movie: Cinderella
Cinderella and Prince dancing.
Handcrafted, Dated, 💡, ⟲

QXD7576 SRP: $24.00

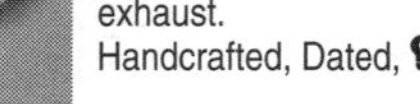

DISNEY: MICKEY & CO.
Mickey's Comet

Mickey hangs onto Goofy's shoe as he toasts marshmallow in comet's exhaust.
Handcrafted, Dated, 💡

QXD7586 SRP: $24.00

JOURNEYS INTO SPACE - 3RD
Apollo Lunar Module
Used to taxi astronauts to moon surface. Message from 1971 Apollo 14 mission.
Transport vehicle used by US astronauts to taxi to moon surface.
Handcrafted, Dated, N

QLX7543 SRP: $24.00

LIGHTHOUSE GREETINGS - 2ND
Lighthouse Greetings

Lighthouse tower rises from roof of keeper's dwelling.
Handcrafted, Dated, 💡
J C Francis

QLX7536 SRP: $24.00

Santa's Merry Workshop Musical Fig.
Gold Crown Ornament Premiere - Event Exclusive
Santa, Mrs. Claus, elf revolve in/out of workshop. Windup.
Handcrafted, Dated,
E Seale
Tune: Here Comes Santa Claus
QX6816 SRP: $32.00

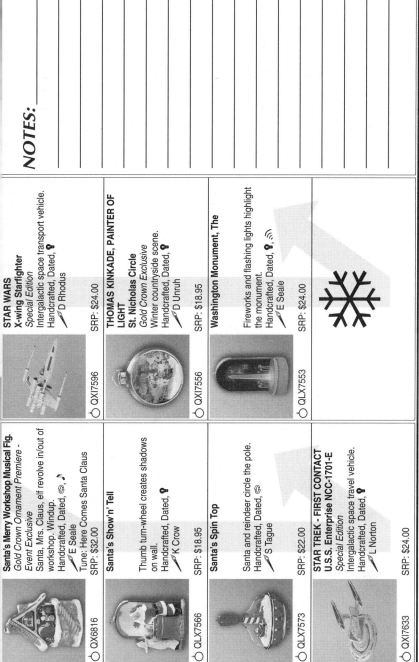

STAR WARS
X-wing Starfighter
Special Edition
Intergalactic space transport vehicle.
Handcrafted, Dated,
D Rhodus
QXI7596 SRP: $24.00

Santa's Show'n' Tell
Thumb turn-wheel creates shadows on wall.
Handcrafted, Dated,
K Crow
QLX7566 SRP: $18.95

THOMAS KINKADE, PAINTER OF LIGHT
St. Nicholas Circle
Gold Crown Exclusive
Winter countryside scene.
Handcrafted, Dated,
D Unruh
QXI7556 SRP: $18.95

Santa's Spin Top
Santa and reindeer circle the pole.
Handcrafted, Dated,
S Tague
QLX7573 SRP: $22.00

Washington Monument, The
Fireworks and flashing lights highlight the monument.
Handcrafted, Dated,
E Seale
QLX7553 SRP: $24.00

STAR TREK - FIRST CONTACT
U.S.S. Enterprise NCC-1701-E
Special Edition
Intergalactic space travel vehicle.
Handcrafted, Dated,
L Norton
QXI7633 SRP: $24.00

NOTES:

1988

Baby's First Christmas

Baby in swing.
Handcrafted, 2.50", Dated
D Lee

QXM5744 SRP: $6.00 GBTRU: **$10**

Brass Angel

Angel.
Brass, 1.25"
J Lyle

QXM5671 SRP: $1.50 **GBTru: $12**

Brass Star

Star.
Brass, 1.25"
J Lyle

QXM5664 SRP: $1.50 **GBTru: $12**

Brass Tree

Tree.
Brass, 1.25"
J Lyle

QXM5674 SRP: $1.50 **GBTru: $14**

Candy Cane Elf

Elf with candy cane.
Handcrafted,.88"
B Siedler

QXM5701 SRP: $3.00 **GBTru: $14**

Country Wreath

Two teddy bears on wreath.
Handcrafted, 1.50"
A M Rogers

QXM5731 SRP: $4.00 **GBTru: $8**

First Christmas Together

Country motif: Wreath with heart.
Wood/Straw, 1.75", Dated
D McGehee

QMX5741 SRP: $4.00 **GBTru: $6**

Folk Art Lamb

Lamb pull toy.
Wood, 1"
J Pattee

QXM5681 SRP: $2.75 **GBTru: $14**

Folk Art Reindeer

Reindeer pull toy.
Wood, 1.13"
J Pattee

QXM5684 SRP: $3.00 **GBTru: $12**

Friends Share Joy

"FRIENDS" caption.
Acrylic, 1.25"
J Pattee

QXM5764 SRP: $2.00 **GBTru: $8**

Gentle Angel

Angel.
Acrylic, 1.50"
L Votruba

QXM5771 SRP: $2.00 **GBTru: $12**

Happy Santa

Santa with bag.
Glass Ball,.75"
J Pattee

QXM5614 SRP: $4.50 **GBTru: $10**

KITTENS IN TOYLAND - 1ST
Kittens In Toyland

Kitten with train.
Handcrafted,.75"
K Crow

QXM5621 SRP: $5.00 **GBTru: $18**

OLD ENGLISH VILLAGE - 1ST
Family Home

Christmas decorated home.
Handcrafted, 1.25", Dated
D Lee

QXM5634 SRP: $8.50 **GBTru: $32**

Hold On Tight

Club: Early Renewal
Mouse on leaf/club logo.
Handcrafted,.94"
B Siedler

QXC5704 SRP: $0.00 **GBTru: $50**

Little Drummer Boy

Drummer boy.
Handcrafted, 1.25"
B Siedler

QXM5784 SRP: $4.50 **GBTru: $16**

PENGUIN PAL - 1ST
Penquin Pal

Penguin with gift.
Handcrafted, 1"
B Siedler

QXM5631 SRP: $3.75 **GBTru: $14**

Holy Family

Holy Family Nativity.
Handcrafted, 1.75"
D Unruh

QXM5611 SRP: $8.50 **GBTru: $15**

Love Is Forever

"Love" caption.
Acrylic, 1"
J Pattee

QXM5774 SRP: $2.00 **GBTru: $12**

ROCKING HORSE - 1ST
Rocking Horse
Adapted from Keepsake Series
Rocking horse.
Handcrafted, 1.13", Dated
L Sickman

QXM5624 SRP: $4.50 **GBTru: $30**

Jolly St. Nick

Replicates '86 Keepsake Special Edition
Santa with toys/ T. Nast art.
Handcrafted, 1.38"
D Unruh

QXM5721 SRP: $8.00 **GBTru: $30**

Mother

Puffed heart w/"Mother" caption.
Handcrafted, 1.25", Dated
S Pike

QXM5724 SRP: $3.00 **GBTru: $12**

Skater's Waltz

Adapted from Magic Orn
Skater's waltzing.
Handcrafted, 1.38"
D Unruh

QXM5601 SRP: $7.00 **GBTru: $15**

Sneaker Mouse

Adapted from Keepsake '83 Orn
Mouse in sneaker.
Handcrafted,.50"

QXM5711 SRP: $4.00 **GBTru: $15**

Snuggly Skater

Teddy sleeping in skates.
Handcrafted, 1.13"
B Siedler

QXM5714 SRP: $4.50 **GBTru: $18**

Sweet Dreams

Angel sleeping on moon.
Handcrafted, 1.50"

QXM5604 SRP: $7.00 **GBTru: $14**

Three Little Kittens

Three kittens in basket.
Handcrafted, 1"
S Pike

QXM5694 SRP: $6.00 **GBTru: $12**

TWIRL-ABOUT
Joyous Heart

"JOY" in heart.
Wood, 1.13"
D McGehee

QXM5691 SRP: $3.50 **GBTru: $28**

1989

Acorn Squirrel

Squirrel in acorn.
Handcrafted, 1.38"
S Pike

QXM5682 SRP: $4.50 **GBTru: $8**

Baby's First Christmas

Baby mobile.
Handcrafted, 1.38", Dated
S Pike

QXM5732 SRP: $6.00 **GBTru: $12**

Brass Partridge

Partridge.
Brass, 1.25"
J Lyle

QXM5725 SRP: $3.00 **GBTru: $6**

Brass Snowflake

Dimensional snowflake.
Brass, 1.38"
J Lyle

QXM5702 SRP: $4.50 **GBTru: $10**

Bunny Hug

Child hugging bunny.
Acrylic, 1.25"
L Votruba

QXM5775 SRP: $3.00 **GBTru: $6**

Cozy Skater

Mouse skating.
Handcrafted, 1.38"
J Lyle

QXM5735 SRP: $4.50 **GBTru: $10**

First Christmas Together

Wreath with caption.
Ceramic, 1.38", Dated
L Votruba

QXM5642 SRP: $8.50 **GBTru: $9**

KITTENS IN TOYLAND - 2ND
Kittens In Toyland

Kitten rides on scooter.
Handcrafted, 1"
K Crow

QXM5612 SRP: $4.50 **GBTru: $10**

Little Star Bringer

Angel with stars.
Handcrafted, 1.25", Dated
J Lyle

QXM5622 SRP: $6.00 **GBTru: $12**

Folk Art Bunny

Bunny with heart.
Handcrafted, 1"
J Pattee

QXM5692 SRP: $4.50 **GBTru: $8**

Kitty Cart

Kitty on pullcart.
Wood, 1.13"
J Pattee

QXM5722 SRP: $3.00 **GBTru: $7**

Load Of Cheer

Elf hanging from ornament.
Handcrafted,.88", Dated
D Rhodus

QXM5745 SRP: $6.00 **GBTru: $22**

Happy Bluebird

Bluebird with Santa cap.
Handcrafted,.88"
A M Rogers

QXM5662 SRP: $4.50 **GBTru: $12**

KRINGLES, THE - 1ST
Kringles, The

Santa hides gift from Mrs. Claus.
Handcrafted, 1.13"
A M Rogers

QXM5625 SRP: $6.00 **GBTru: $22**

Merry Seal

Seal.
Porcelain,.88"
J Francis

QXM5755 SRP: $6.00 **GBTru: $10**

Holiday Deer

Deer.
Acrylic, 1.50"
L Votruba

QXM5772 SRP: $3.00 **GBTru: $8**

Little Soldier

Soldier with drum.
Handcrafted, 1.38"
L Sickman

QXM5675 SRP: $4.50 **GBTru: $9**

Mother

Swan.
Cameo, 1.25", Dated

QXM5645 SRP: $6.00 **GBTru: $8**

NOEL R.R. - 1ST
Locomotive

Locomotive.
Handcrafted, 1", Dated
L Sickman

QXM5762 SRP: $8.50 **GBTru: $35**

Pinecone Basket

Pine cones in basket.
Handcrafted,.88"
D Rhodus

QXM5734 SRP: $4.50 **GBTru: $6**

Roly-Poly Pig

Spotted Poland Pig.
Handcrafted,.88"
S Pike

QXM5712 SRP: $3.00 **GBTru: $10**

OLD ENGLISH VILLAGE - 2ND
Sweet Shop

Sweet shop.
Handcrafted, 1.25", Dated
J Lee

QXM5615 SRP: $8.50 **GBTru: $20**

Puppy Cart

Puppy rides on pullcart.
Wood, 1.25"
L Sickman

QXM5715 SRP: $3.00 **GBTru: $5**

Roly-Poly Ram

Ram.
Handcrafted,.88"

QXM5705 SRP: $3.00 **GBTru: $8**

Old-World Santa

Santa with tree.
Handcrafted, 1.38"
B Siedler

QXM5695 SRP: $3.00 **GBTru: $7**

Rejoice

“REJOICE”.
Acrylic, 1"
L Votruba

QXM5782 SRP: $3.00 **GBTru: $5**

Santa's Magic Ride

Special Edition
Santa rides on unicorn.
Handcrafted, 1.19"
A M Rogers

QXM5632 SRP: $8.50 **GBTru: $10**

PENGUIN PAL - 2ND
Penguin Pal

Penguin with candy cane.
Handcrafted, 1.38"

QXM5602 SRP: $4.50 **GBTru: $9**

ROCKING HORSE - 2ND
Rocking Horse

Palomino Rocking horse.
Handcrafted, 1.13", Dated
L Sickman

QXM5605 SRP: $4.50 **GBTru: $22**

Santa's Roadster

Santa in car.
Handcrafted, 1", Dated
K Crow

QXM5665 SRP: $6.00 **GBTru: $12**

Scrimshaw Reindeer

Reindeer.
Handcrafted, 1"
L Votruba

QXM5685 SRP: $4.50 **GBTru: $8**

Special Friend

Wreath with tree.
Handcrft/Willow, 1.38", Dated

QXM5652 SRP: $4.50 **GBTru: $6**

TWIRL-ABOUT Lovebirds

Heart with brass birds.
Handcrft/Brass, 1.13", Dated
S Pike

QXM5635 SRP: $6.00 **GBTru: $10**

Sharing A Ride

Elf with teddy on swing.
Handcrafted, 1.25"
P Dutkin

QXM5765 SRP: $8.50 **GBTru: $12**

Starlit Mouse

Mouse on star.
Handcrafted, 1.19", Dated
D Rhodus

QXM5655 SRP: $4.50 **GBTru: $12**

1990

Sitting Purrty

Club: Keepsake of Membership
Kitten in HM Club mug.
Handcrafted, 1.25", Dated
P Dutkin

QXC5812 **GBTru: $22**

Stocking Pal

Teddy in stocking.
Handcrafted, 1"
J Lee

QXM5672 SRP: $4.50 **GBTru: $8**

Acorn Wreath

Squirrel in wreath holds acorn.
Handcrafted, 1.25"
K Crow

QXM5686 SRP: $6.00 **GBTru: $9**

Slow Motion

Chipmunk on turtle.
Handcrafted, 1"
B Siedler

QXM5752 SRP: $6.00 **GBTru: $12**

Strollin' Snowman

Snowman.
Porcelain, 1.25"
B Siedler

QXM5742 SRP: $4.50 **GBTru: $10**

Air Santa

Santa in plane.
Handcrafted,.50", Dated

QXM5656 SRP: $4.50 **GBTru: $10**

Baby's First Christmas

Baby in cradle with mobile.
Handcrafted, 1.13", Dated
J Francis

QXM5703 SRP: $8.50 **GBTru: $12**

Basket Buddy

Spaniel puppy in basket.
Hndcr/Wickr,.81"
A M Rogers

QXM5696 SRP: $6.00 **GBTru: $10**

Bear Hug

Girl hugging teddy bear.
Handcrafted, 1"
D Palmiter

QXM5633 SRP: $6.00 **GBTru: $9**

Brass Bouquet

Poinsettia holly bouquet medallion.
Brass, 1.25"
J Lyle

QXM5776 SRP: $6.00 **GBTru: $6**

Brass Horn

Hunting horn.
Brass,.75", Dated

QXM5793 SRP: $3.00 **GBTru: $6**

Brass Peace

"PEACE" filigree design.
Brass, 1.25"

QXM5796 SRP: $3.00 **GBTru: $6**

Brass Santa

Santa moon.
Brass, 1.25", Dated
J Pattee

QXM5786 SRP: $3.00 **GBTru: $6**

Brass Year

"1990" filigree design.
Brass,.25", Dated

QXM5833 SRP: $3.00 **GBTru: $5**

Busy Carver

Beaver with carved tree.
Handcrafted, .75", Dated
K Crow

QXM5673 SRP: $4.50 **GBTru: $8**

Christmas Dove

White dove.
Handcrafted, .69"
B Siedler

QXM5636 SRP: $4.50 **GBTru: $8**

Country Heart

Heart-shaped folk-art wreath.
Handcrafted, 1.38"
A M Rogers

QXM5693 SRP: $4.50 **GBTru: $6**

Crown Prince

Club: Bonus Ornament
Bear w/HM Crown/Club logo t-shirt.
Handcrafted, 1.38", Dated
A M Rogers

QXC5603 SRP: $0.00 **GBTru: $18**

First Christmas Together

Two doves in nest.
Porcelain, 1", Dated
P Andrews

QXM5536 SRP: $6.00 **GBTru: $7**

Going Sledding

Bear on sled.
Handcrafted,.81"
J Lee

QXM5683 SRP: $4.50 **GBTru: $10**

Grandchild's First Christmas

Teddy in high chair.
Handcrafted, 1.25", Dated
B Siedler

QXM5723 SRP: $6.00 **GBTru: $6**

Holiday Cardinal

Cardinal on branch.
Acrylic, 1.50"
J Francis

QXM5526 SRP: $3.00 **GBTru: $6**

KITTENS IN TOYLAND - 3RD
Kittens In Toyland

Kitten in sailboat.
Handcrafted, .81"
K Crow

QXM5736 SRP: $4.50 **GBTru: $10**

KRINGLES, THE - 2ND
Kringles, The

Mrs. Claus kisses Santa good-bye.
Handcrafted, 1", Dated
A M Rogers

QXM5753 SRP: $6.00 **GBTru: $20**

Lion And Lamb

Lion and lamb in pull-toy cart.
Wood, 1.13"
L Sickman

QXM5676 SRP: $4.50 **GBTru: $8**

LITTLE FROSTY FRIENDS
Memory Wreath
*Gold Crown Reach Program - *w/any HM purchase*
Wreath with 4 Brass hooks, Brass plate with name, date.
Hndcr/Acryl, 5.00", Dated
D Lee

XPR9724 SRP: $2.95* **GBTru: $6**

LITTLE FROSTY FRIENDS - 1ST
Little Frosty
*Gold Crown Reach Program - * per wk for 4 wks w/any HM purchase*
Eskimo on ice floe ringing in season.
Hndcr/Acryl, 1.06", Dated
B Siedler

XPR9720 SRP: $2.95* **GBTru: $8**

LITTLE FROSTY FRIENDS - 2ND
Little Seal
*Gold Crown Reach Program- * per wk for 4 wks w/any HM purchase*
Flocked seal w/satin ribbon & star.
Hndcr/Acryl, 1.13", Dated
J Lee

XPR9721 SRP: $2.95* **GBTru: $8**

LITTLE FROSTY FRIENDS - 3RD
Little Husky
*Gold Crown Reach Program- * per wk for 4 wks w/any HM purchase*
Husky pup w/package tied on back.
Hndcr/Acryl, 1.13", Dated
E Seale

XPR9722 SRP: $2.95* **GBTru: $8**

LITTLE FROSTY FRIENDS - 4TH
Little Bear
*Gold Crown Reach Program- * per wk for 4 wks w/any HM purchase*
Seated polar teddy holding stocking.
Hndcr/Acryl, 1.00", Dated
B Siedler

XPR9723 SRP: $2.95* **GBTru: $8**

Loving Hearts

"Two Hearts One Love".
Acrylic, 1.25"

QXM5523 SRP: $3.00 **GBTru: $7**

Madonna And Child

Madonna and Child.
Handcrafted, 1.25"
A M Rogers

QXM5643 SRP: $6.00 **GBTru: $9**

Mother

Bas-relief flowers, brass bezel medallion.
Cameo, 1.13", Dated
J Lyle

QXM5716 SRP: $4.50 **GBTru: $10**

Nativity

Nativity scene.
Handcrafted, 1.38", Dated
D Unruh

QXM5706 SRP: $4.50 **GBTru: $12**

NATURE'S ANGELS - 1ST
Nature's Angel

Bunny angel.
Handcrafted, 1.25"
E Seale

QXM5733 SRP: $4.50 **GBTru: $22**

NOEL R.R. - 2ND
Coal Car

Train car with toys.
Handcrafted, .75", Dated
L Sickman

QXM5756 SRP: $8.50 **GBTru: $22**

OLD ENGLISH VILLAGE - 3RD
School

Snow-covered schoolhouse.
Handcrafted, 1.13", Dated
J Lee

QXM5763 SRP: $8.50 **GBTru: $20**

Panda's Surprise

Panda with jack-in-the-box.
Handcrafted, .88", Dated
J Francis

QXM5616 SRP: $4.50 **GBTru: $9**

PENGUIN PAL - 3RD
Penguin Pal

Penguin on skis.
Handcrafted, .88"

QXM5746 SRP: $4.50 **GBTru: $12**

Perfect Fit

Santa in chimney.
Handcrafted, 1", Dated
R Chad

QXM5516 SRP: $4.50 **GBTru: $8**

PRECIOUS EDITION - 1ST
Cloisonné Poinsettia

Poinsettia.
Cloisonné, 1"
L Votruba

QXM5533 SRP: $10.50 **GBTru: $15**

Puppy Love

Boy hugging puppy.
Handcrafted, 1"
D Palmiter

QXM5666 SRP: $6.00 **GBTru: $10**

ROCKING HORSE - 3RD
Rocking Horse

Pinto rocking horse.
Handcrafted, 1.13", Dated
L Sickman

QXM5743 SRP: $4.50 **GBTru: $20**

Ruby Reindeer

Reindeer leaping.
Glass, 1"
J Pattee

QXM5816 SRP: $6.00 **GBTru: $9**

Santa's Journey

Santa in sleigh filled with toys.
Hndcr/Brass, 1", Dated
L Sickman

QXM5826 SRP: $8.50 **GBTru: $12**

Santa's Streetcar

Santa standing at rear of streetcar.
Handcrafted, 1.25", Dated
D Lee

QXM5766 SRP: $8.50 **GBTru: $9**

Snow Angel

Girl making angel in snow.
Handcrafted, 1.13"
J Lee

QXM5773 SRP: $6.00 **GBTru: $10**

Special Friends

Two kittens on wagon.
Handcrafted, 1.31"
S Pike

QXM5726 SRP: $6.00 **GBTru: $12**

Stamp Collector

Chipmunk checks stamp with magnifying glass.
Handcrafted, .88", Dated
K Crow

QXM5623 SRP: $4.50 **GBTru: $6**

Stringing Along

Elf with string of gold garland.
Handcrafted, 1.13"
E Seale

QXM5606 SRP: $8.50 **GBTru: $14**

Sweet Slumber

Mouse sleeping in matchbox.
Handcrafted, .56"
B Siedler

QXM5663 SRP: $4.50 **GBTru: $8**

Teacher

Owl with pencil.
Handcrafted, .88", Dated
S Pike

QXM5653 SRP: $4.50 **GBTru: $7**

THIMBLE BELLS - 1ST
Thimble Bell

Winter scene with bunnies.
Porcelain, 1.13", Dated
M Pyda-Sevaik

QXM5543 SRP: $6.00 **GBTru: $15**

Type Of Joy

Mouse at typewriter.
Handcrafted,.69"
R Chad

QXM5646 SRP: $4.50 **GBTru: $8**

Warm Memories

Fireplace with stockings.
Handcrafted, 1.13", Dated
E Seale

QXM5713 SRP: $4.50 **GBTru: $8**

Wee Nutcracker

Nutcracker musician.
Handcrafted, 1.25", Dated
B Siedler

QXM5843 SRP: $8.50 **GBTru: $10**

1991

All Aboard

Beaver engineer on train.
Handcrafted, 1", Dated
R Chad

QXM5869 SRP: $4.50 **GBTru: $8**

Baby's First Christmas

Baby mouse in carriage.
Handcrafted, 1", Dated
J Francis

QXM5799 SRP: $6.00 **GBTru: $7**

Brass Bells

Bells with ribbon.
Brass, 1.25", Dated
P Andrews

QXM5977 SRP: $3.00 **GBTru: $7**

Brass Church

Church.
Brass, 1.25", Dated

QXM5979 SRP: $3.00 **GBTru: $7**

Brass Soldier

Soldier.
Brass, 1.25", Dated

QXM5987 SRP: $3.00 **GBTru: $5**

Bright Boxers

Santa in shorts.
Handcrafted, 1", Dated
D Rhodus

QXM5877 SRP: $4.50 **GBTru: $12**

Busy Bear

Bear.
Wood, 1.44"
D Rhodus

QXM5939 SRP: $4.50 **GBTru: $7**

Cardinal Cameo

Cardinal with Holly leaves.
Cameo, 1.44", Dated
J Lyle

QXM5957 SRP: $6.00 **GBTru: $10**

Caring Shepherd

Shepherd carrying lamb.
Porc/Brass, 1.06"
J Francis

QXM5949 SRP: $6.00 **GBTru: $12**

Cool 'N' Sweet

Snowman with candy cane.
Porcelain, 1.19", Dated
S Pike

QXM5867 SRP: $4.50 **GBTru: $16**

Country Sleigh

Sleigh.
Enamel, 1", Dated
L Votruba

QXM5999 SRP: $4.50 **GBTru: $8**

Courier Turtle

Turtle trims his shell with red bow.
Handcrafted, 1.13"
S Pike

QXM5857 SRP: $4.50 **GBTru: $12**

Fancy Wreath

Wreath with baby's breath.
Handcrafted, 1.06"
J Lyle

QXM5917 SRP: $4.50 **GBTru: $6**

Feliz Navidad

Bunny in straw sombrero.
Hndcr/Straw, 1", Dated
A M Rogers

QXM5887 SRP: $6.00 **GBTru: $10**

First Christmas Together

Couple in victorian sleigh.
Hndcr/Brass, 1.13", Dated
D Unruh

QXM5819 SRP: $6.00 **GBTru: $10**

Fly By

Elf on 'paper' glider plane.
Handcrafted,.88", Dated
K Crow

QXM5859 SRP: $4.50 **GBTru: $8**

Friendly Fawn

Reindeer with wreath and bow.
Handcrafted, 1.13", Dated
J Lee

QXM5947 SRP: $6.00 **GBTru: $10**

Grandchild's First Christmas

Baby rattle.
Porcelain, 1.06", Dated
A M Rogers

QXM5697 SRP: $4.50 **GBTru: $6**

Heavenly Minstrel

Designed like1980 Special Edition, Keepsake Orn
Winged Angel with lute.
Handcrafted, 1.81"
D Lee

QXM5687 SRP: $9.75 **GBTru: $12**

Holiday Snowflake

Snowflake on faceted teardrop shape.
Acrylic, 1.50", Dated
D Rhodus

QXM5997 SRP: $3.00 **GBTru: $7**

Key To Love

Bunny opening heart lock with key.
Handcrafted, 1", Dated
K Crow

QXM5689 SRP: $4.50 **GBTru: $9**

KITTENS IN TOYLAND - 4TH
Kittens In Toyland

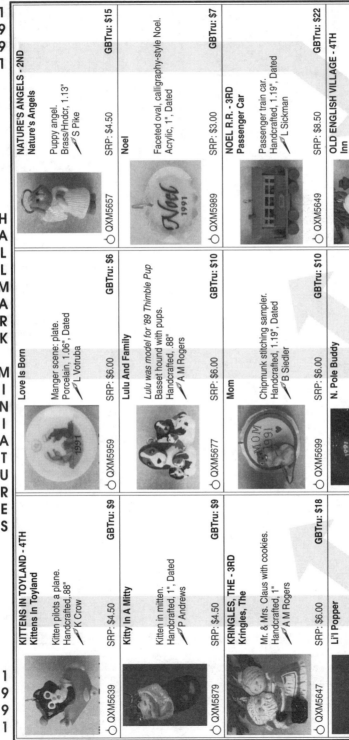

Kitten pilots a plane.
Handcrafted,.88"
K Crow

QXM5639 SRP: $4.50 **GBTru: $9**

Love Is Born

Manger scene: plate.
Porcelain, 1.06", Dated
L Votruba

QXM5959 SRP: $6.00 **GBTru: $6**

NATURE'S ANGELS - 2ND
Nature's Angels

Puppy angel.
Brass/Hndcr, 1.13"
S Pike

QXM5657 SRP: $4.50 **GBTru: $15**

Kitty In A Mitty

Kitten in mitten.
Handcrafted, 1", Dated
P Andrews

QXM5879 SRP: $4.50 **GBTru: $9**

Lulu And Family

Lulu was model for '89 Thimble Pup
Basset hound with pups.
Handcrafted, .88"
A M Rogers

QXM5677 SRP: $6.00 **GBTru: $10**

Noel

Faceted oval, calligraphy-style Noel.
Acrylic, 1", Dated

QXM5989 SRP: $3.00 **GBTru: $7**

KRINGLES, THE - 3RD
Kringles, The

Mr. & Mrs. Claus with cookies.
Handcrafted, 1"
A M Rogers

QXM5647 SRP: $6.00 **GBTru: $18**

Mom

Chipmunk stitching sampler.
Handcrafted, 1.19", Dated
B Siedler

QXM5699 SRP: $6.00 **GBTru: $10**

NOEL R.R. - 3RD
Passenger Car

Passenger train car.
Handcrafted, 1.19", Dated
L Sickman

QXM5649 SRP: $8.50 **GBTru: $22**

Li'l Popper

Mouse swings from popcorn,
stringer orn.
Handcrafted, 1.75"
L Sickman

QXM5897 SRP: $4.50 **GBTru: $10**

N. Pole Buddy

Flocked Polar bear in cap.
Handcrafted, 1", Dated
D Palmiter

QXM5927 SRP: $4.50 **GBTru: $12**

OLD ENGLISH VILLAGE - 4TH
Inn

Country inn.
Handcrafted, 1.13", Dated
J Lee

QXM5627 SRP: $8.50 **GBTru: $17**

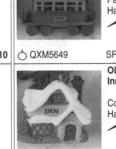

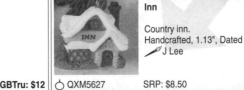

PENGUIN PAL - 4TH & FINAL
Penquin Pal

Penguin on skates.
Handcrafted, .75"
B Siedler

QXM5629 SRP: $4.50 **GBTru: $8**

PRECIOUS EDITION - 2ND
Silvery Santa

Old fashioned Santa.
Silver Plated, 1.13", Dated
J Lee

QXM5679 SRP: $9.75 **GBTru: $12**

Ring-A-Ding Elf

Elf on bell.
Brass/Hndcr, 1.25", Dated
R Chad

QXM5669 SRP: $8.50 **GBTru: $10**

ROCKING HORSE - 4TH
Rocking Horse

Arabian rocking horse.
Handcrafted, 1.13", Dated
L Sickman

QXM5637 SRP: $4.50 **GBTru: $18**

Seaside Otter

Otter on seashell sled.
Handcrafted,.88"
B Siedler

QXM5909 SRP: $4.50 **GBTru: $9**

Special Friends

Pup and kitten nap in basket.
Hndcr/Wckr, .81", Dated
J Lee

QXM5797 SRP: $8.50 **GBTru: $10**

THIMBLE BELLS - 2ND
Thimble Bells

Holly branches/berries trim bell.
Porcelain, 1.13", Dated
M Pyda-Sevaik

QXM5659 SRP: $6.00 **GBTru: $12**

Tiny Tea Party

Mice with tea and cookies, Set/6.
Porc/Handcrft, .63-1.19", Dated
E Seale

QXM5827 SRP: $29.00 **GBTru: $150**

Top Hatter

Bunny w/gift pops from magic hat.
Handcrafted, 1", Dated
E Seale

QXM5889 SRP: $6.00 **GBTru: $8**

Treeland Trio

Animals in victorian finery, caroling.
Handcrafted, .88", Dated
R Chad

QXM5899 SRP: $8.50 **GBTru: $10**

Upbeat Bear

Drum Major bear on drum.
Hndcr/Metal, 1.06", Dated
J Francis

QXM5907 SRP: $6.00 **GBTru: $12**

Vision Of Santa

Wood-look Santa with candy cane.
Handcrafted, 1.06", Dated
R Chad

QXM5937 SRP: $4.50 **GBTru: $9**

Wee Toymaker

Designed similar to Toymaker Grouping
Santa paints toy plane.
Handcrafted, 1", Dated
R Bishop

QXM5967 SRP: $8.50 **GBTru: $10**

WOODLAND BABIES - 1ST
Woodland Babies

Squirrel in nutshell cradle.
Handcrafted, 1"
K Crow

QXM5667 SRP: $6.00 **GBTru: $12**

1992

A+ Teacher

Raccoon with chalk and slate.
Handcrafted, 1.13", Dated
D Unruh

QXM5511 SRP: $3.75 **GBTru: $6**

Angelic Harpist

Angel plays harp.
Handcrafted, 1.75"
J Lyle

QXM5524 SRP: $4.50 **GBTru: $10**

Baby's First Christmas

Baby shoes hang from brass tag.
Hndcr/Brass, 1.25", Dated
J Lyle

QXM5494 SRP: $4.50 **GBTru: $5**

BEARYMORES, THE - 1ST
Bearymores, The

Polar bears trim tree.
Hndcr/Acryl, 1.13", Dated
A M Rogers

QXM5544 SRP: $5.75 **GBTru: $15**

Black-Capped Chickadee

Chickadee on wreath.
Handcrafted, 1.38", Dated
J Francis

QXM5484 SRP: $3.00 **GBTru: $9**

Bright Stringers

Bluebirds hold tree lights.
Handcrafted, 1.13"
E Seale

QXM5841 SRP: $3.75 **GBTru: $5**

Buck-A-Roo

Santa rides rocking reindeer.
Handcrafted, 1.13", Dated
K Crow

QXM5814 SRP: $4.50 **GBTru: $6**

Chipmunk Parcel Service

Club: Early Renewal
Chipmunk with package.
Handcrafted, 1.19", Dated
E Seale

QXC5194 **GBTru: $20**

Christmas Bonus

Bunny holds holiday bonus.
Handcrafted, 1.19", Dated
D Palmiter

QXM5811 SRP: $3.00 **GBTru: $5**

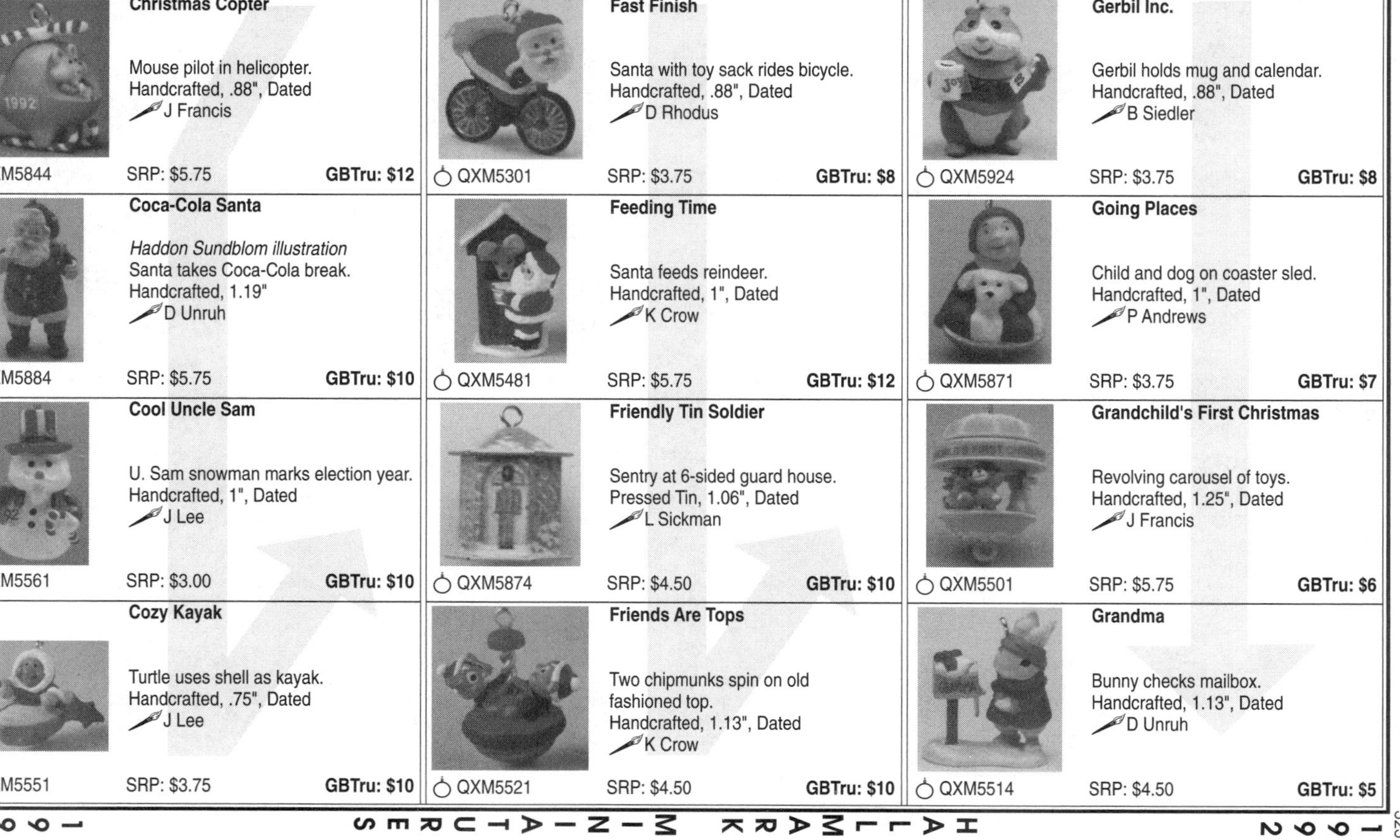

Christmas Copter

Mouse pilot in helicopter.
Handcrafted, .88", Dated
J Francis

QXM5844 SRP: $5.75 **GBTru: $12**

Coca-Cola Santa

Haddon Sundblom illustration
Santa takes Coca-Cola break.
Handcrafted, 1.19"
D Unruh

QXM5884 SRP: $5.75 **GBTru: $10**

Cool Uncle Sam

U. Sam snowman marks election year.
Handcrafted, 1", Dated
J Lee

QXM5561 SRP: $3.00 **GBTru: $10**

Cozy Kayak

Turtle uses shell as kayak.
Handcrafted, .75", Dated
J Lee

QXM5551 SRP: $3.75 **GBTru: $10**

Fast Finish

Santa with toy sack rides bicycle.
Handcrafted, .88", Dated
D Rhodus

QXM5301 SRP: $3.75 **GBTru: $8**

Feeding Time

Santa feeds reindeer.
Handcrafted, 1", Dated
K Crow

QXM5481 SRP: $5.75 **GBTru: $12**

Friendly Tin Soldier

Sentry at 6-sided guard house.
Pressed Tin, 1.06", Dated
L Sickman

QXM5874 SRP: $4.50 **GBTru: $10**

Friends Are Tops

Two chipmunks spin on old fashioned top.
Handcrafted, 1.13", Dated
K Crow

QXM5521 SRP: $4.50 **GBTru: $10**

Gerbil Inc.

Gerbil holds mug and calendar.
Handcrafted, .88", Dated
B Siedler

QXM5924 SRP: $3.75 **GBTru: $8**

Going Places

Child and dog on coaster sled.
Handcrafted, 1", Dated
P Andrews

QXM5871 SRP: $3.75 **GBTru: $7**

Grandchild's First Christmas

Revolving carousel of toys.
Handcrafted, 1.25", Dated
J Francis

QXM5501 SRP: $5.75 **GBTru: $6**

Grandma

Bunny checks mailbox.
Handcrafted, 1.13", Dated
D Unruh

QXM5514 SRP: $4.50 **GBTru: $5**

Harmony Trio

Fox, bunny, & pig play music, Set/3.
Handcrafted, 1.13" ea, Dated
L Votruba

QXM5471 SRP: $11.75 **GBTru: $14**

Inside Story

Santa & sleigh inside corked bottle.
Handcrafted, .75", Dated
E Seale

QXM5881 SRP: $7.25 **GBTru: $12**

Minted For Santa

Bas-relief Santa penny.
Copper, 1", Dated
D Unruh

QXM5854 SRP: $3.75 **GBTru: $5**

Hickory, Dickory, Dock

Mouse naps on clock.
Handcrafted, 1.19", Dated
R Chad

QXM5861 SRP: $3.75 **GBTru: $10**

KITTENS IN TOYLAND - 5TH & FINAL
Kittens In Toyland

Kitten on pogo stick.
Handcrafted, 1.19"
K Crow

QXM5391 SRP: $4.50 **GBTru: $12**

Mom

Beaming mom cat puts on gift bonnet.
Handcrafted, 1.19", Dated
P Andrews

QXM5504 SRP: $4.50 **GBTru: $6**

Holiday Splash

Gold fish & fishbowl.
Handcrafted, 1", Dated
J Francis

QXM5834 SRP: $5.75 **GBTru: $10**

KRINGLES, THE - 4TH
Kringles, The

Mr. & Mrs. Claus sing carols.
Handcrafted, 1"
A M Rogers

QXM5381 SRP: $6.00 **GBTru: $12**

NATURE'S ANGELS - 3RD
Nature's Angels

Koala bear angel w/wreath.
Handcrafted, 1"
S Pike

QXM5451 SRP: $4.50 **GBTru: $12**

Hoop It Up

Elf with hula hoop.
Handcrafted, 1", Dated
K Crow

QXM5831 SRP: $4.50 **GBTru: $9**

Little Town Of Bethlehem

Scene of Bethlehem within wreath.
Handcrafted, 1", Dated
L Sickman

QXM5864 SRP: $3.00 **GBTru: $10**

NIGHT BEFORE CHRISTMAS, THE - 1ST
Night Before Christmas, The
Display house, undated;
rocker with mouse, dated.
Hndcr/Tin, 8", 1.13", Dated
D Unruh/L Votruba

QXM5541 SRP: $13.75 **GBTru: $25**

NOEL R.R. - 4TH
Box Car

Stock car - door slides open to reveal toys.
Handcrafted, .81", Dated
L Sickman

QXM5441 SRP: $7.00 **GBTru: $18**

PRECIOUS EDITION - 3RD
Holiday Holly

22-Karat gld-plat'd Holly leaves w/bow.
Gold Plated, 1.13", Dated

QXM5364 SRP: $9.75 **GBTru: $12**

Ski For Two

Dog & cat share skis.
Handcrafted, .94", Dated
P Andrews

QXM5821 SRP: $4.50 **GBTru: $10**

OLD ENGLISH VILLAGE - 5TH
Church

Old English village church.
Handcrafted, 1.31", Dated
J Lee

QXM5384 SRP: $7.00 **GBTru: $18**

Puppet Show

Bear holds hand puppet.
Handcrafted, 1", Dated
B Siedler

QXM5574 SRP: $3.00 **GBTru: $10**

Snowshoe Bunny

Bunny wears snowshoes.
Handcrafted, 1.06"
L Votruba

QXM5564 SRP: $3.75 **GBTru: $10**

Perfect Balance

Seal balances on ball ornament.
Handcrafted, 1.25", Dated
A M Rogers

QXM5571 SRP: $3.00 **GBTru: $10**

ROCKING HORSE - 5TH
Rocking Horse

Brown rocking horse.
Handcrafted, 1.13", Dated
L Sickman

QXM5454 SRP: $4.50 **GBTru: $12**

Snug Kitty

Kitten naps in dresser drawer.
Handcrafted, 1", Dated
S Pike

QXM5554 SRP: $3.75 **GBTru: $8**

Polar Polka

Polar bears dance on ice cube.
Hndcr/Brass, 1.81", Dated
E Seale

QXM5534 SRP: $4.50 **GBTru: $12**

Sew, Sew Tiny

Mice with sewing basket implements, Set/6.
Handcrafted, .81"-1.25", Dated
E Seale

QXM5794 SRP: $29.00 **GBTru: $39**

Spunky Monkey

Monkey munches banana.
Handcrafted, 1.38", Dated
R Chad

QXM5921 SRP: $3.00 **GBTru: $10**

1993

THIMBLE BELLS - 3RD
Thimble Bells

Teddy bear & gift.
Porcelain, 1.13", Dated
J Lyle

QXM5461 SRP: $6.00 **GBTru: $10**

Visions Of Acorns

Squirrel Santa puts acorns in stock'g.
Handcrafted, 1.19", Dated
P Andrews

QXM5851 SRP: $4.50 **GBTru: $8**

Wee Three Kings

Three Kings on a camel.
Handcrafted, 1.19", Dated
D Palmiter

QXM5531 SRP: $5.75 **GBTru: $12**

WOODLAND BABIES - 2ND
Woodland Babies

Skunk naps in holly leaf cradle.
Handcrafted, 1", Dated
D Palmiter

QXM5444 SRP: $6.00 **GBTru: $14**

Baby's First Christmas

Teddy bear jack-in-the-box.
Handcrafted, 1.06", Dated
L Votruba

QXM5145 SRP: $5.75 **GBTru: $8**

BEARYMORES, THE - 2ND
Bearymores, The

Polar bear family sing carols.
Handcrafted, 1.13", Dated
A M Rogers

QXM5125 SRP: $5.75 **GBTru: $10**

Cheese Please

Mouse writes wish list.
Handcrafted, 1.25", Dated
B Siedler

QXM4072 SRP: $3.75 **GBTru: $9**

Christmas Castle

Castle, turrets, towers, moat.
Handcrafted, 1.13", Dated
E Seale

QXM4085 SRP: $5.75 **GBTru: $9**

Country Fiddling

Bird listens to fiddler kitten.
Handcrafted, 1", Dated
J Francis

QXM4062 SRP: $3.75 **GBTru: $8**

Ears To Pals

Bunny delivers gift with bluebird pal.
Handcrafted, 1.19", Dated
P Andrews

QXM4075 SRP: $3.75 **GBTru: $6**

Forty Winks

Club: Keepsake of Membership
Mouse naps on holly leaf/bottle-cap.
Handcrafted, 1.19"
J Francis

QXC5294 **GBTru: $15**

Grandma

Chipmunk takes cookie from acorn jar.
Handcrafted, 1", Dated
E Seale

QXM5162 SRP: $4.50 **GBTru: $6**

I Dream Of Santa

Santa as genie from magic lamp.
Handcrafted, 1.13", Dated
L Sickman

QXM4055 SRP: $3.75 **GBTru: $8**

Into The Woods

Elf chops tree for holiday.
Handcrafted, 1", Dated
E Seale

QXM4045 SRP: $3.75 **GBTru: $9**

KRINGLES, THE - 5TH & FINAL
Kringles, The

Santa & Mrs. Claus hold wreath.
Handcrafted, 1"
A M Rogers

QXM5135 SRP: $5.75 **GBTru: $12**

Learning To Skate

Elf ice skates.
Handcrafted, 1.13"
R Chad

QXM4122 SRP: $3.00 **GBTru: $8**

Lighting A Path

Elf holds lantern to light the way.
Handcrafted, 1.06"
R Chad

QXM4115 SRP: $3.00 **GBTru: $9**

MARCH OF THE TEDDY BEARS - 1ST
March Of The Teddy Bears

Drum Major bear leads parade.
Handcrafted, 1.44", Dated
D Unruh

QXM4005 SRP: $4.50 **GBTru: $12**

Merry Mascot

Dalmatian pup slides down fire pole.
Handcrafted, 1.38", Dated
B Siedler

QXM4042 SRP: $3.75 **GBTru: $7**

Mom

Mouse mom w/poinsettia parasol.
Handcrafted, 1.13", Dated
P Andrews

QXM5155 SRP: $4.50 **GBTru: $6**

Monkey Melody

Santa, organ grinder; monkey w/gift: stringer orn.
Handcrafted, .94" - 1", Dated
L Sickman

QXM4092 SRP: $5.75 **GBTru: $10**

NATURE'S ANGELS - 4TH
Nature's Angels

Cat angel carries stars.
Handcrafted, 1.13"
P Andrews

QXM5122 SRP: $4.50 **GBTru: $9**

NIGHT BEFORE CHRISTMAS, THE
Night Before Christmas Display House, The
Displayer available separately in '93, not dated.
Tin, 8"
L Votruba

QXM5185 SRP: $8.75 **GBTru: $8.75**

NIGHT BEFORE CHRISTMAS, THE - 2ND
Night Before Christmas, The

Children nestled asleep in their bed.
Handcrafted, 1.13", Dated
D Unruh

QXM5115 SRP: $4.50 **GBTru: $18**

ON THE ROAD - 1ST
On The Road

Family heads home in station wagon.
Pressed Tin, .44", Dated
L Sickman

QXM4002 SRP: $5.75 **GBTru: $12**

Pull Out A Plum

Raccoon & squirrel w/plum pudding.
Handcrafted, .63", Dated
J Francis

QXM4095 SRP: $5.75 **GBTru: $10**

NOEL R.R. - 5TH
Flatbed Car

Flatbed rail car carries sleigh w/gifts.
Handcrafted, .88", Dated
L Sickman

QXM5105 SRP: $7.00 **GBTru: $10**

Pear-Shaped Tones

Partridge plays pear-shaped cello.
Handcrafted, 1", Dated
J Lyle

QXM4052 SRP: $3.75 **GBTru: $6**

Refreshing Flight

Santa astride a Coke bottle.
Handcrafted, .88"
R Chad

QXM4112 SRP: $5.75 **GBTru: $10**

North Pole Fire Truck

Hook & ladder fire truck.
Handcrafted, .63", Dated
D Palmiter

QXM4105 SRP: $4.75 **GBTru: $6**

PRECIOUS EDITION - 4TH
Cloisonné Snowflake

Enameled snowflake design on pendant.
Cloisonné/Brass, 1"
L Votruba

QXM4012 SRP: $9.75 **GBTru: $18**

ROCKING HORSE - 6TH
Rocking Horse

Blanket Appaloosa rocking horse.
Handcrafted, 1.13", Dated
L Sickman

QXM5112 SRP: $4.50 **GBTru: $10**

OLD ENGLISH VILLAGE - 6TH
Toy Shop

English tudor toy shop.
Handcrafted, 1.44", Dated
J Lee

QXM5132 SRP: $7.00 **GBTru: $12**

PRECIOUS EDITION - 5TH
Crystal Angel
See '96 collection for another Crystal Angel
Crystal topped by gold-plated winged angel.
Crystal/Gold Pltd, 1", Dated
D Palmiter

QXM4015 SRP: $9.75 **GBTru: $60**

'Round The Mountain

Train goes through tunnel.
Handcrafted, 1.69", Dated
K Crow

QXM4025 SRP: $7.25 **GBTru: $14**

Secret Pal

Mouse peeks out of Christmas stocking.
Handcrafted, 1", Dated
A M Rogers

QXM5172 SRP: $3.75 **GBTru: $6**

Tiny Green Thumbs

Mice tend garden, Set/6.
Handcrafted, 1.25"- .69", Dated
E Seale

QXM4032 SRP: $29.00 **GBTru: $42**

Baby's First Christmas

Bear on decorated rocking horse.
Handcrafted, 1.25", Dated
J Lyle

QXM4003 SRP: $5.75 **GBTru: $7**

Snuggle Birds

Bird couple share home/stocking.
Handcrafted, 1.56", Dated
P Andrews

QXM5182 SRP: $5.75 **GBTru: $6**

Visions Of Sugarplums

Bas-relief designed spoon of child dreaming.
Pewter, 1.38", Dated
D Palmiter

QXM4022 SRP: $7.25 **GBTru: $7**

Baking Tiny Treats

Mice bake holiday treats, Set/6.
Handcrafted, .56-1.25", Dated
E Seale

QXM4033 SRP: $29.00 **GBTru: $52**

Special Friends

Moose and cardinal friends.
Handcrafted, 1", Dated
J Francis

QXM5165 SRP: $4.50 **GBTru: $8**

WOODLAND BABIES - 3RD & FINAL
Woodland Babies

Woodchuck clings to branch.
Handcrafted, 1.13", Dated
J Francis

QXM5102 SRP: $5.75 **GBTru: $9**

Beary Perfect Tree

Bear carries home a perfect tree.
Handcrafted, 1.19", Dated
R Bishop

QXM4076 SRP: $4.75 **GBTru: $8**

THIMBLE BELLS - 4TH & FINAL
Thimble Bells

Poinsettia design decorates bell.
Porcelain, 1.13", Dated
L Votruba

QXM5142 SRP: $5.75 **GBTru: $10**

1994

BEARYMORES, THE - 3RD & FINAL
Bearymores, The

Bears build a snowman.
Handcrafted, 1.13", Dated
A M Rogers

QXM5133 SRP: $5.75 **GBTru: $10**

CENTURIES OF SANTA - 1ST
Centuries Of Santa

Old fashioned Santa with tree.
Handcrafted, 1.25", Dated
L Sickman

QXM5153 SRP: $6.00 **GBTru: $14**

Friends Need Hugs

Seated bear & rabbit ready to hug.
Handcrafted, 1", Dated
J Lyle

QXM4016 SRP: $4.50 **GBTru: $10**

Jolly Visitor

Santa Claus.
Handcrafted, 1", Dated
L Sickman

QXM4053 SRP: $5.75 **GBTru: $10**

COCA COLA
Pour Some More
("Enjoy Coca Cola")

Elf pours Coke for friend.
Handcrafted, 1.56"
R Chad

QXM5156 SRP: $5.75 **GBTru: $8**

Graceful Carousel Horse

Carousel horse.
Pewter, 1.38", Dated

QXM4056 SRP: $7.75 **GBTru: $10**

Jolly Wolly Snowman

Roly poly snowman.
Handcrafted, 1", Dated
L Votruba

QXM4093 SRP: $3.75 **GBTru: $9**

Corny Elf

Elf strings popcorn for garland.
Handcrafted, 1"
D Rhodus

QXM4063 SRP: $4.50 **GBTru: $8**

Have A Cookie

Cookies in a cookie jar.
Handcrafted, 1.13", Dated
D Lee

QXM5166 SRP: $5.75 **GBTru: $9**

Journey To Bethlehem

Holy Family enroute to Bethlehem.
Handcrafted, 1.25"
J Lyle

QXM4036 SRP: $5.75 **GBTru: $10**

Cute As A Button

Mouse on a button holds a gift.
Handcrafted, 1", Dated
K Crow

QXM4103 SRP: $3.75 **GBTru: $8**

Hearts A-Sail

Bears sail with gift on
heart-shaped boat.
Handcrafted, .94", Dated
R Bishop

QXM4006 SRP: $5.75 **GBTru: $10**

Just My Size

Beaver cuts Christmas tree to his size.
Handcrafted, 1.61", Dated
R Bishop

QXM4086 SRP: $3.75 **GBTru: $8**

Love Was Born

Star suspends baby in cradle.
Handcrafted, 1.19", Dated
L Sickman

QXM4043 SRP: $4.50 **GBTru: $10**

Mom

Swan carries holly and ribbon.
Handcrafted, 1.13", Dated
A M Rogers

QXM4013 SRP: $4.50 **GBTru: $5**

NOEL R.R - 6TH
Stock Car

Stock railroad car.
Handcrafted, 1.31", Dated
L Sickman

QXM5113 SRP: $7.00 **GBTru: $14**

MARCH OF THE TEDDY BEARS - 2ND
March Of The Teddy Bears

Teddy bear drummer.
Handcrafted, 1.19", Dated
D Unruh

QXM5106 SRP: $4.50 **GBTru: $10**

NATURE'S ANGELS - 5TH
Nature's Angels

Skunk as winged angel.
Hndcr/Brass, 1.19"
L Votruba

QXM5126 SRP: $4.50 **GBTru: $9**

NUTCRACKER GUILD - 1ST
Nutcracker Guild

Baker nutcracker.
Handcrafted, 1.19", Dated
L Sickman

QXM5146 SRP: $5.75 **GBTru: $12**

Melodic Cherub

Winged cherub plays lute.
Handcrafted, 1.31", Dated
A M Rogers

QXM4066 SRP: $3.75 **GBTru: $8**

NIGHT BEFORE CHRISTMAS, THE - 3RD
Night Before Christmas, The

Dad from Christmas poem.
Handcrafted, 1.81", Dated
D Unruh

QXM5123 SRP: $4.50 **GBTru: $10**

OLD ENGLISH VILLAGE - 7TH
Hat Shop

English cottage hat shop.
Handcrafted, 1.31", Dated
P Andrews

QXM5143 SRP: $7.00 **GBTru: $14**

Merry Flight, A

Santa in sleigh circles village.
Handcrafted, 1.13", Dated
K Crow

QXM4073 SRP: $5.75 **GBTru: $9**

NOAH'S ARK
Noah's Ark
Special Edition: Ark displayer deck lifts off.
Noah and wife on Ark, 2 bears, 2 seals, Set/3.
Handcrafted, 4.31"
L Sickman

QXM4106 SRP: $24.50 **GBTru: $50**

ON THE ROAD - 2ND
On The Road

Taxi delivers presents.
Pressed Tin, 1.25", Dated
L Sickman

QXM5103 SRP: $5.75 **GBTru: $12**

PRECIOUS EDITION - 6TH
Dazzling Reindeer

Leaping deer in red/green harness/bridle.
Handcrafted, 1.38"
L Votruba

QXM4026 SRP: $9.75 **GBTru: $16**

ROCKING HORSE - 7TH
Rocking Horse

White rocking horse.
Handcrafted, 1.38", Dated
L Sickman

QXM5116 SRP: $4.50 **GBTru: $8**

Scooting Along

Bears rides a scooter.
Handcrafted, 1.19", Dated
J Francis

QXM5173 SRP: $6.75 **GBTru: $10**

Sweet Bouquet

Club: Early Renewal
Skunk w/poinsettia in bottlecap.
Handcrafted

QXC4806 **GBTru: $15**

Sweet Dreams

Mouse naps in a nutshell.
Handcrafted,.88"
K Crow

QXM4096 SRP: $3.00 **GBTru: $8**

Tea With Teddy

Child has tea party with teddy.
Handcrafted,.94", Dated
A M Rogers

QXM4046 SRP: $7.25 **GBTru: $8**

TINY TOON ADVENTURES
Babs Bunny

Skating girl rabbit.
Handcrafted, 1.31"
D Palmiter

QXM4116 SRP: $5.75 **GBTru: $9**

TINY TOON ADVENTURES
Buster Bunny

Skating boy rabbit.
Handcrafted, 1.31"
D Palmiter

QXM5163 SRP: $5.75 **GBTru: $9**

TINY TOON ADVENTURES
Dizzy Devil

Devil gets ready to mail note to Santa.
Handcrafted, 1"
D Palmiter

QXM4133 SRP: $5.75 **GBTru: $10**

TINY TOON ADVENTURES
Hamton

Pig lights way to bed with candle.
Handcrafted, 1.06"
D Palmiter

QXM4126 SRP: $5.75 **GBTru: $9**

TINY TOON ADVENTURES
Plucky Duck

Duck checks bag of gifts.
Handcrafted, 1.13"
D Palmiter

QXM4123 SRP: $5.75 **GBTru: $9**

1995

ALICE IN WONDERLAND - 1ST
Alice In Wonderland

Alice sits on a thimble.
Handcrafted, 1.44", Dated
P Andrews

QXM4777 SRP: $6.75 **GBTru: $15**

Christmas Wishes

Mouse on candlestick base, checks list.
Handcrafted, 1.06", Dated
E Seale

QXM4087 SRP: $3.75 **GBTru: $8**

FLINTSTONES, THE
Pebbles And Bamm-Bamm

Kids build snowdinosaur.
Handcrafted, 1.13"
D Rhodus

QXM4757 SRP: $9.75 **GBTru: $12**

Baby's First Christmas

Mouse baby naps in walnut shell.
Handcrafted, 1.06", Dated
E Seale

QXM4027 SRP: $4.75 **GBTru: $10**

COCA COLA
Cool Santa
Club: Keepsake of Membership
Santa takes Coke from a cooler.
Handcrafted
J Francis

QXM4457 **GBTru: $10**

Friendship Duet

Squirrel & mouse share songbook.
Handcrafted, 1.25", Dated
D Unruh

QXM4019 SRP: $4.75 **GBTru: $5**

CENTURIES OF SANTA - 2ND
Centuries Of Santa

Santa holds open filled toy bag.
Handcrafted, 1.25", Dated
L Sickman

QXM4789 SRP: $5.75 **GBTru: $12**

Cozy Christmas

Club: Early Renewal
Deer with holly in bottlecap.
Handcrafted
J Francis

QXC4119 **GBTru: $15**

Gift From Rodney, A

Club: Keepsake of Membership
Rodney ice skates holding a gift.
Handcrafted, Dated
L Sickman

QXC4129 **GBTru: $12**

CHRISTMAS BELLS - 1ST
Christmas Bells

Angel jingle bell.
Hndcr/Metal, 1.25", Dated
E Seale

QXM4007 SRP: $4.75 **GBTru: $12**

Downhill Double

Bears bellyflop together on sled.
Handcrafted, .63", Dated
D Palmiter

QXM4837 SRP: $4.75 **GBTru: $6**

Grandpa's Gift

Bear sits on rocking chair.
Handcrafted, 1.00", Dated
A M Rogers

QXM4829 SRP: $5.75 **GBTru: $8**

Heavenly Praises

Winged Angel.
Handcrafted, 1.31", Dated
P Andrews

QXM4037 SRP: $5.75 **GBTru: $10**

MINIATURE KIDDIE CAR CLASSICS - 1ST
Murray 'Champion'

Blue kiddie car.
Cast Metal, .56", Dated
D Palmiter

QXM4079 SRP: $5.75 **GBTru: $14**

NOAH'S ARK: COMPLEMENTS SPECIAL EDITION SET
Merry Walruses

Two walruses.
Handcrafted, .56"
L Sickman

QXM4057 SRP: $5.75 **GBTru: $10**

Joyful Santa

Santa.
Handcrafted, 1.13", Dated
D Unruh

QXM4089 SRP: $4.75 **GBTru: $10**

Moustershire Christmas, A

Special Edition
Dated house displayer: Robin, Violet, Dunne, Set/4.
Handcrafted, 2.63"- .81", Dated
D Rhodus

QXM4839 SRP: $24.50 **GBTru: $35**

NOAH'S ARK: COMPLEMENTS SPECIAL EDITION SET
Playful Penguins

Two penguins.
Handcrafted, .69"
L Sickman

QXM4059 SRP: $5.75 **GBTru: $15**

MARCH OF THE TEDDY BEARS - 3RD
March Of The Teddy Bears

Bear with red bow plays a horn.
Handcrafted, 1.31", Dated
D Unruh

QXM4799 SRP: $4.75 **GBTru: $9**

NATURE'S ANGELS - 6TH
Nature's Angels

Bear angel with harp.
Hndcr/Brass, 1.13"
P Andrews

QXM4809 SRP: $4.75 **GBTru: $9**

NOEL R.R. - 7TH
Milk Tank Car

Milk tank car.
Handcrafted, .69", Dated
L Sickman

QXM4817 SRP: $6.75 **GBTru: $9**

MINIATURE CLOTHESPIN SOLDIER - 1ST
Miniature Clothespin Soldier

Drum Major in flocked hat.
Handcrafted, 1.13"
L Sickman

QXM4097 SRP: $3.75 **GBTru: $10**

NIGHT BEFORE CHRISTMAS, THE - 4TH
Night Before Christmas, The

Santa and toy bag.
Handcrafted, 1.25", Dated
D Unruh

QXM4807 SRP: $4.75 **GBTru: $12**

NUTCRACKER GUILD - 2ND
Nutcracker Guild

Postman nutcracker with gift.
Handcrafted, 1.13", Dated
L Sickman

QXM4787 SRP: $5.75 **GBTru: $8**

OLD ENGLISH VILLAGE - 8TH
Tudor House

Period English home.
Handcrafted, 1.00", Dated
J Lee

QXM4819 SRP: $6.75 **GBTru: $12**

ROCKING HORSE - 8TH
Rocking Horse

Child's rocking horse.
Handcrafted, 1.13", Dated
L Sickman

QXM4827 SRP: $4.75 **GBTru: $12**

Sugarplum dreams

Sleep'g child dreams of toys/treats.
Handcrafted, .94", Dated
K Crow

QXM4099 SRP: $4.75 **GBTru: $8**

ON THE ROAD - 3RD
On The Road

Red van carries gifts.
Pressed Tin, .44", Dated
L Sickman

QXM4797 SRP: $5.75 **GBTru: $10**

SANTA'S LITTLE BIG TOP - 1ST
Santa's Little Big Top

Ringmaster Santa with performing animals.
Handcrafted, 1.63", Dated
K Crow

QXM4779 SRP: $6.75 **GBTru: $12**

TINY TOON ADVENTURES
Calamity Coyote

Cartoon coyote as downhill skier.
Handcrafted, 1.44"
A M Rogers

QXM4467 SRP: $6.75 **GBTru: $12**

Precious Creations

Sea, earth & sky animals balance on globe.
Handcrafted, 1.25", Dated
L Sickman

QXM4077 SRP: $9.75 **GBTru: $12**

Santa's Visit

Batteries are included to light house
Santa on house chimney.
Handcrafted, 1.44", Dated,
K Crow

QXM4047 SRP: $7.75 **GBTru: $12**

TINY TOON ADVENTURES
Furball

Cartoon cat with sardine can gift.
Handcrafted, .88"
A M Rogers

QXM4459 SRP: $5.75 **GBTru: $12**

PRECIOUS EDITION - 7TH
Cloisonné Partridge

Partridge on a pear tree branch.
Enamel/Metal, 1.00"
L Votruba

QXM4017 SRP: $9.75 **GBTru: $16**

Starlight Nativity

Batteries are included to light creche
Holy Family.
Handcrafted, 1.44", Dated,
D Unruh

QXM4039 SRP: $7.75 **GBTru: $14**

TINY TOON ADVENTURES
Little Beeper

Cartoon rooster snow surfs.
Handcrafted, .75"
A M Rogers

QXM4469 SRP: $5.75 **GBTru: $12**

COCA-COLA
Cool Delivery Coca-Cola

Santa & toy bag on Coke bottle sleigh.
Handcrafted
S Pike

QXM4021 SRP: $5.75 **GBTru: $10**

GONE WITH THE WIND - 60TH ANNIV.
Gone With The Wind
Collector's Classics:
Margaret Mitchell's Novel
Tara plantation displayer; Scarlet & Rhett Butler, Set/3.
Handcrafted, Dated
P Andrews

QXM4211 SRP: $19.95 **GBTru: $35**

Holiday Bunny

Club: Early Renewal
Bunny peeks out/bottlecap mini orn.
Handcrafted

QXC4191 **GBTru: $** **GBTru: $12**

Joyous Angel

Winged angel in 'south of the border' colorful dress.
Handcrafted, Dated
P Andrews

QXM4231 SRP: $4.75 **GBTru: $8**

Tiny Treasures

Lady mice primp for party, Set/6.
Handcrafted, .63"-1.38", Dated
E Seale

QXM4009 SRP: $29.00 **GBTru: $40**

Tunnel Of Love

Mouse couple on swan boat ride.
Handcrafted, .81", Dated
K Crow

QXM4029 SRP: $4.75 **GBTru: $8**

1996

ALICE IN WONDERLAND - 2ND
Mad Hatter

Mad Hatter sits on thimble drink'g tea.
Handcrafted, Dated
P Andrews

QXM4074 SRP: $6.75 **GBTru: $12**

CENTURIES OF SANTA - 3RD
Centuries Of Santa

Old fashined Santa w/lantern & staff.
Handcrafted, Dated
L Sickman

QXM4091 SRP: $5.75 **GBTru: $10**

Child's Gifts, A

Little girl carries gifts.
Handcrafted, Dated
P Andrews

QXM4234 SRP: $6.75 **GBTru: $7**

Christmas Bear

Bear in red bow tie holds candy cane.
Handcrafted
E Seale

QXM4241 SRP: $4.75 **GBTru: $10**

CHRISTMAS BELLS - 2ND
Christmas Bells

Santa Claus jingle bell.
Hndcr/Metal, Dated
E Seale

QXM4071 SRP: $4.75 **GBTru: $8**

Long Winter's Nap

Mouse naps in sardine can.
Handcrafted, Dated
P Andrews

QXM4244 SRP: $5.75 **GBTru: $8**

Message For Santa

Bear steers bottle sailboat to North Pole.
Handcrafted, Dated
E Seale

QXM4254 SRP: $6.75 **GBTru: $7**

NATURE'S ANGELS - 7TH & FINAL
Nature's Angels

Angel squirrel with halo, carries a gift.
Brass
S Pike

QXM4111 SRP: $4.75 **GBTru: $7**

LOONEY TUNES LOVABLES
Baby Sylvester

Baby cat with toy.
Handcrafted
D Palmiter

QXM4154 SRP: $5.75 **GBTru: $10**

MINIATURE CLOTHESPIN SOLDIER - 2ND
Miniature Clothespin Soldier

Colonial soldier drummer.
Handcrafted
L Sickman

QXM4144 SRP: $4.75 **GBTru: $9**

NIGHT BEFORE CHRISTMAS, THE - 5TH & FINAL
Night Before Christmas, The
Santa waves goodbye from sleigh.
Handcrafted, Dated
D Unruh

QXM4104 SRP: $5.75 **GBTru: $12**

LOONEY TUNES LOVABLES
Baby Tweety

Baby bird with toy.
Handcrafted
D Palmiter

QXM4014 SRP: $5.75 **GBTru: $10**

MINIATURE KIDDIE CAR CLASSICS - 2ND
Murray "Fire Truck"

Mini Kiddie Car fire truck.
Cast metal, Dated
D Palmiter

QXM4031 SRP: $6.75 **GBTru: $10**

NOAH'S ARK: COMPLEMENTS SPECIAL EDITION SET
African Elephants

Two african elephants.
Handcrafted
L Sickman

QXM4224 SRP: $5.75 **GBTru: $15**

MARCH OF THE TEDDY BEARS - 4TH & FINAL
March Of The Teddy Bears
Teddy with red bow marches, plays horn.
Handcrafted, Dated
D Unruh

QXM4094 SRP: $4.75 **GBTru: $7**

MOUSTERSHIRE CHRISTMAS, A: COMPLEMENTS '95 SPECIAL EDITION
Hattie Chapeau
Mouse wears hat & coat & carries gift.
Handcrafted, Dated
D Rhodus

QXM4251 SRP: $4.75 **GBTru: $8**

NOEL R.R. - 8TH
Cookie Car

Stock car carries cookies.
Handcrafted, Dated
L Sickman

QXM4114 SRP: $6.75 **GBTru: $10**

NUTCRACKER BALLET, THE - 1ST
Nutcracker Ballet, The
Displayer only available in 1996
Figure of Clara and display stage of house.
Handcrafted, Dated
L Votruba
QXM4064 SRP: $14.95 **GBTru: $20**

OLYMPIC SPIRIT
Cloisonné Medallion
Medallion of Olympic torch.
Cloisonné, Dated
D McGehee
QXE4041 SRP: $9.75 **GBTru: $15**

PRECIOUS EDITION - 8TH
Sparkling Crystal Angel
See '93 collection for another Crystal Angel
Lead crystal, silver plated Angel.
Lead Crystal/Silver Pltd, Dated
L Votruba
QXM4264 SRP: $9.75 **GBTru: $20**

NUTCRACKER GUILD - 3RD
Nutcracker Guild
Fisherman with pole and fish catch.
Handcrafted, Dated
L Sickman
QXM4084 SRP: $5.75 **GBTru: $7**

ON THE ROAD - 4TH
On The Road
Pressed tin delivery vehicle.
Pressed Tin
L Sickman
QXM4101 SRP: $5.75 **GBTru: $10**

ROCKING HORSE - 9TH
Rocking Horse
Rocking horse.
Handcrafted, Dated
L Sickman
QXM4121 SRP: $4.75 **GBTru: $10**

O Holy Night
Special Edition
Holy Family [undated], dated stable display, Set/4.
Handcrafted, Dated
D Rhodus
QXM4204 SRP: $24.50 **GBTru: $26**

Peaceful Christmas
Lion cub & lamb rest together.
Handcrafted, Dated
D Unruh
QXM4214 SRP: $4.75 **GBTru: $7**

Rudolph's Helper
Club: Keepsake of Membership
Elf carries reindeer treats.
Handcrafted, Dated
B Siedler
QXC4171 **GBTru: $9**

OLD ENGLISH VILLAGE - 9TH
Village Mill
Water wheel mill grinds grains.
Handcrafted, Dated
D Rhodus
QXM4124 SRP: $6.75 **GBTru: $10**

PEANUTS
Tree For Woodstock, A
Complements '96 PEANUTS: A Tree For Snoopy QX5507
Woodstock pulls tree on sled.
Handcrafted, Dated
B Siedler
QXM4767 SRP: $5.75 **GBTru: $12**

SANTA'S LITTLE BIG TOP - 2ND
Santa's Little Big Top
Ringmaster Santa & clowns perform in circus.
Handcrafted, Dated
K Crow
QXM4081 SRP: $6.75 **GBTru: $10**

STAR WARS
Vehicles of STAR WARS, The

Space vehicles, Set/3.
Handcrafted, Dated
D Rhodus

QXM4024 SRP: $19.95 **GBTru: $25**

ALICE IN WONDERLAND - 3RD
White Rabbit

Rabbit holds pocket-watch.
Handcrafted, Dated
P Andrews

QXM4142 SRP: $6.95 **GBTru: $10**

CHRISTMAS BELLS - 3RD
Christmas Bells

Snowman jingle bell.
Hndcr/Metal, Dated
E Seale

QXM4162 SRP: $4.95 **GBTru: $9**

Tiny Christmas Helpers

Mice trim tree & wrap gifts, Set/6.
Handcrafted, Dated
E Seale

QXM4261 SRP: $29.00 **GBTru: $35**

ANTIQUE TRACTORS - 1ST
Antique Tractors

Wheels turn & front cross bar pivots on red tractor.
Die-Cast Metal, Dated
L Sickman

QXM4185 SRP: $6.95 **GBTru: $15**

COCA-COLA
Ice Cold Coca-Cola

Santa sculpts ice coke bottle.
Handcrafted
R Chad

QXM4252 SRP: $6.95 **GBTru: $10**

WINNIE-THE-POOH
Winnie-The-Pooh And Tigger

Balloons carry Pooh & Tigger aloft.
Handcrafted, Dated
B Siedler

QXM4044 SRP: $9.75 **GBTru: $18**

Casablanca

1942 Film Classic: Winner of 3 Oscars
Stars Bogart & Bergman and Film ad poster, Set/3.
Handcrafted, Dated
P Andrews

QXM4272 SRP: $19.95 **GBTru: $20**

DISNEY - WINNIE THE POOH
Honey Of A Gift

Winnie the Pooh hugs his 'hunny' pot.
Handcrafted

QXD4255 SRP: $6.95 **GBTru: $10**

1997

CENTURIES OF SANTA - 4TH
Centuries of Santa

Old world Santa with staff and gold crown.
Handcrafted, Dated
L Sickman

QXM4295 SRP: $5.95 **GBTru: $8**

Future Star

Ballerina on ballet toe shoe.
Handcrafted, Dated
S Pike

QXM4232 SRP: $5.95 **GBTru: $6**

Gentle Giraffes

Complements the 1994 "Noah's Ark" Special Edition Set
Two giraffes.
Handcrafted
L Sickman

QXM4221 SRP: $5.95 **GBTru: $8**

Miniature 1997 Corvette

Special Issue
Red Sports car.
Handcrafted, Dated
D Palmiter

QXI4322 SRP: $6.95 **GBTru: $10**

NIGHT BEFORE CHRISTMAS, THE - 175TH ANNIVERSARY MOORE'S POEM
Ready For Santa
Club: Keepsake of Membership
Fireplace with stockings, watched by a mouse.
Handcrafted, Dated

QXC5142 **GBTru: $10**

He Is Born

Angel appears over Holy Family Manger scene.
Handcrafted, Dated
L Votruba

QXM4235 SRP: $7.95 **GBTru: $8**

MINIATURE CLOTHESPIN SOLDIER - 3RD
Miniature Clothespin Soldier

Royal Canadian soldier.
Handcrafted
L Sickman

QXM4155 SRP: $4.95 **GBTru: $7**

NOEL R. R. - 9TH
Candy Car

Open stock car filled w/candy.
Handcrafted, Dated
L Sickman

QXM4175 SRP: $6.95 **GBTru: $10**

Heavenly Music

Winged angel with halo carries a heart.
Handcrafted, Dated
S Tague

QXM4292 SRP: $5.95 **GBTru: $6**

MINIATURE KIDDIE CAR CLASSICS - 3RD
Murray Inc. "Pursuit" Airplane

Propeller plane.
Die-cast Metal, Dated
D Palmiter

QXM4132 SRP: $6.95 **GBTru: $10**

NUTCRACKER BALLET, THE - 2ND
Herr Drosselmeyer

Gentleman brings gift to Clara.
Handcrafted, Dated
L Votruba

QXM4135 SRP: $5.95 **GBTru: $8**

Home Sweet Home

Gingerbread House with Gingerbread man.
Handcrafted, Dated
E Seale

QXM4222 SRP: $5.95 **GBTru: $6**

NIGHT BEFORE CHRISTMAS, THE - 175TH ANNIVERSARY MOORE'S POEM
Jolly Old Santa
Club: Keepsake of Membership
Santa laughing, watched by a mouse.
Handcrafted, Dated

QXC5145 **GBTru: $10**

NUTCRACKER GUILD - 4TH
Nutcracker Guild

Nutcracker gardener w/plant and trowel, opens/closes.
Handcrafted, Dated
L Sickman

QXM4165 SRP: $6.95 **GBTru: $8**

OLD ENGLISH VILLAGE - 10TH & FINAL
Village Depot

Depot with clock tower.
Handcrafted, Dated
T Larsen

QXM4182 SRP: $6.95 **GBTru: $8**

PRECIOUS EDITION - 9TH
Our Lady Of Guadalupe

Religious figure.
Pewter, Dated
R Chad

QXM4275 SRP: $8.95 **GBTru: $9**

Sew Talented

Miss Mouse holds needle/spool of thread/button.
Handcrafted, Dated
E Seale

QXM4195 SRP: $5.95 **GBTru: $9**

ON THE ROAD - 5TH
On The Road

Pressed Tin, Dated
L Sickman

QXM4172 SRP: $5.95 **GBTru: $9**

ROCKING HORSE - 10TH & FINAL
Rocking Horse

Grey horse with red trim.
Handcrafted, Dated
L Sickman

QXM4302 SRP: $4.95 **GBTru: $9**

Shutterbug

Bug photographer.
Handcrafted, Dated
S Tague

QXM4212 SRP: $5.95 **GBTru: $8**

Peppermint Painter

Squirrel paints stripes on candy cane.
Handcrafted, Dated
S Tague

QXM4312 SRP: $4.95 **GBTru: $6**

SANTA'S LITTLE BIG TOP - 3RD & FINAL
Santa's Little Big Top

Santa directs balancing elephants.
Handcrafted, Dated
K Crow

QXM4152 SRP: $6.95 **GBTru: $9**

Snowboard Bunny

Downhill snowboard racer.
Handcrafted, Dated
S Tague

QXM4315 SRP: $4.95 **GBTru: $9**

Polar Buddies

Penguin rides on skating Polar Bear's leg.
Handcrafted, Dated
J Francis

QXM4332 SRP: $4.95 **GBTru: $6**

Seeds Of Joy

Angel plants flower seed in flower pot.
Handcrafted, Dated
S Tague

QXM4242 SRP: $6.95 **GBTru: $7**

SNOWFLAKE BALLET - 1ST
Snowflake Ballet

Ballerina in snowflake costume.
Handcrafted, Dated
P Andrews

QXM4192 SRP: $5.95 **GBTru: $8**

STAR WARS
C-3PO And R2-D2
Special Issue
Robot friends of Luke Skywalker, Set/2.
Handcrafted, Dated
D Rhodus

QXI4265 SRP: $12.95 **GBTru: $20**

TEDDY-BEAR STYLE - 1ST
Teddy-Bear Style

Bear in hat, vest, has movable arms & legs.
Handcrafted, Dated
D Unruh

QXM4215 SRP: $5.95 **GBTru: $8**

Tiny Home Improvers

Mice renovators and interior designers, Set/6.
Handcrafted, Dated
E Seale

QXM4282 SRP: $29.00 **GBTru: $30**

Victorian Skater

Skater in winter coat with fur hat and muff.
Handcrafted, Dated
D Unruh

QXM4305 SRP: $5.95 **GBTru: $6**

WELCOME FRIENDS - 1ST
Welcome Friends

Birds & squirrel at feeder.
Handcrafted, Dated
S Pike

QXM4205 SRP: $6.95 **GBTru: $8**

WIZARD OF OZ, THE
King Of The Forest

Dorothy, Tin Man, & Scarecrow salute King Lion,Set/4.
Handcrafted
A M Rogers

QXM4262 SRP: $24.00 **GBTru: $29**

1998

ALICE IN WONDERLAND - 4TH & FINAL
Cheshire Cat

Grinning cat atop a thimble.
Handcrafted, Dated
P Andrews

QXM4186 SRP: $6.95

Angel Chime

Precious Edition
Winged Angel with bell.
Handcrafted, Dated
S Tague

QXM4283 SRP: $8.95

ANTIQUE TRACTORS - 2ND
Antique Tractors

Old style farm tractor.
Die-Cast Metal, Dated
L Sickman

QXM4166 SRP: $6.95

BETSEY CLARK
Betsey's Prayer

Child says bedtime prayers.
Handcrafted, Dated
K Kline

QXM4263 SRP: $4.95

CENTURIES OF SANTA - 5TH
Centuries Of Santa

Santa holds toy bag and polar bear pull-toy.
Handcrafted, Dated
L Sickman

QXM4206 SRP: $5.95

CHRISTMAS BELLS - 4TH
Christmas Bells

Teddy bear jinglebell.
Handcrafted/Metal, Dated
E Seale

QXM4196 SRP: $4.95

Holly-Jolly Jig

Santa in his red suit. Legs dangle.
Handcrafted, Dated
S Tague

QXM4266 SRP: $6.95

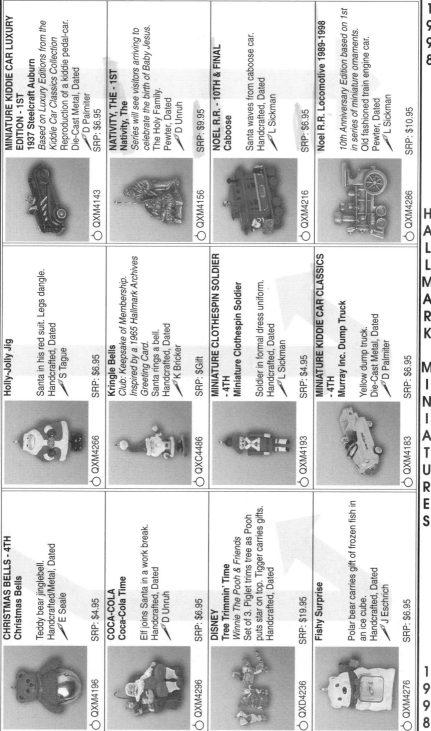

MINIATURE KIDDIE CAR LUXURY EDITION - 1ST
1937 Steelcraft Auburn
Based on Luxury Editions from the Kiddie Car Classics Collection
Reproduction of a kiddie pedal-car.
Die-Cast Metal, Dated
D Palmiter

QXM4143 SRP: $6.95

COCA-COLA
Coca-Cola Time

Elf joins Santa in a work break.
Handcrafted, Dated
D Unruh

QXM4296 SRP: $6.95

Kringle Bells
Club: Keepsake of Membership.
Inspired by a 1965 Hallmark Archives Greeting Card.
Santa rings a bell.
Handcrafted, Dated
K Bricker

QXC4486 SRP: $Gift

NATIVITY, THE - 1ST
Nativity, The
Series will see visitors arriving to celebrate the birth of Baby Jesus.
The Holy Family.
Pewter, Dated
D Unruh

QXM4156 SRP: $9.95

DISNEY
Tree Trimmin' Time
Winnie The Pooh & Friends
Set of 3. Piglet trims tree as Pooh puts star on top. Tigger carries gifts.
Handcrafted, Dated

QXD4236 SRP: $19.95

MINIATURE CLOTHESPIN SOLDIER - 4TH
Miniature Clothespin Soldier

Soldier in formal dress uniform.
Handcrafted, Dated
L Sickman

QXM4193 SRP: $4.95

NOEL R.R. - 10TH & FINAL
Caboose

Santa waves from caboose car.
Handcrafted, Dated
L Sickman

QXM4216 SRP: $6.95

Fishy Surprise

Polar bear carries gift of frozen fish in an ice cube.
Handcrafted, Dated
J Eschrich

QXM4276 SRP: $6.95

MINIATURE KIDDIE CAR CLASSICS - 4TH
Murray Inc. Dump Truck

Yellow dump truck.
Die-Cast Metal, Dated
D Palmiter

QXM4183 SRP: $6.95

Noel R.R. Locomotive 1989-1998

10th Anniversary Edition based on 1st in series of miniature ornaments.
Old fashioned train engine car.
Pewter, Dated
L Sickman

QXM4286 SRP: $10.95

NUTCRACKER BALLET, THE - 3RD
Nutcracker

Nutcracker character from the ballet.
Handcrafted, Dated
LD Votruba

QXM4146 SRP: $5.95

NUTCRACKER GUILD - 5TH
Nutcracker Guild

Nutcracker ready to head to the ski slopes.
Handcrafted, Dated
L Sickman

QXM4203 SRP: $6.95

ON THE ROAD - 6TH & FINAL
On The Road

Mail truck delivers mail and packages.
Pressed Tin, Dated
L Sickman

QXM4213 SRP: $5.95

Peaceful Pandas

Complements the 1994 "Noah's Ark" Special Edition Set.
Pandas with bamboo shoots.
Handcrafted
L Sickman

QXM4253 SRP: $5.95

Pixie Parachute

Pixie holds onto spring of mistletoe.
Handcrafted, Dated
J Eschrich

QXM4256 SRP: $4.95

Sharing Joy

Rodney reindeer cuts out JOY streamer.
Handcrafted, Dated

QXM4273 SRP: $4.95

Singin' In The Rain
Features Gene Kelly and copy of original 1952 movie poster.
Set of 2. Gene Kelly in famous street scene plus ad poster.
Handcrafted, Dated
P Andrews

QXM4303 SRP: $10.95

SNOWFLAKE BALLET - 2ND
Snowflake Ballet

Snowflake ballerina.
Handcrafted, Dated
P Andrews

QXM4173 SRP: $5.95

STAR WARS
Ewoks
Special Edition
Set of 3. Animal form alien creatures.
Handcrafted
K Bricker

QXI4223 SRP: $16.95

SUPER HEROES
Superman
Commemorates Man of Steel's career. W/copy of Action Comics #1.
Superman plus reproduction of comic book.
Handcrafted, Dated
R Chad

QXM4313 SRP: $10.95

TEDDY-BEAR STYLE - 2ND
Teddy-Bear Style

Lady bear wears fancy chapeau and collar. Arms and legs move.
Handcrafted, Dated
D Unruh

QXM4176 SRP: $5.95

WELCOME FRIENDS - 2ND
Welcome Friends

Cardinals perch outside birdhouse.
Handcrafted, Dated
S Pike

QXM4153 SRP: $6.95

WINTER FUN WITH SNOOPY - 1ST
Winter Fun With Snoopy

Snoopy and Woodstock share icy activities.
Handcrafted, Dated
T Larsen

QXM4243 SRP: $6.95

WIZARD OF OZ, THE
Glinda The Good Witch & Wicked Witch Of The West
Set of 2. Glinda in pink gown w/crown and star scepter. Glinda in witches black w/broom.
Handcrafted, Dated
J Lyle

QXM4233 SRP: $14.95

NOTES:

1991

Baby's First Easter

Quilt covered bunny in basket.
Handcrafted, 1.50", Dated

QEO5189 SRP: $8.75 GBTRU: **$26**

Daughter

Bunny holding carrot with pink bow.
Handcrafted, 1.50"

QEO5179 SRP: $5.75 **GBTru: $28**

Easter Memories Photoholder

Egg shape photohold'r w/spring flwrs.
Fabric, 2.50", Dated

QEO5137 SRP: $7.75 **GBTru: $12**

Full Of Love

Bunny & chick in easter basket.
Handcrafted, 2.00", Dated

QEO5149 SRP: $7.75 **GBTru: $36**

Gentle Lamb

Lamb in necklace of flowers and bell.
Handcrafted, 2.00", Dated

QEO5159 SRP: $6.75 **GBTru: $14**

Grandchild

Cowboy bunny on tan rocking horse.
Handcrafted, 2.50", Dated

QEO5177 SRP: $6.75 **GBTru: $12**

L'il Dipper

Bunny in metal egg dipper.
Handcrft/Metal, 2.50"

QEO5147 SRP: $6.75 **GBTru: $18**

Lily Egg

Easter lilies decorate pale yellow egg.
Porcelain, 2.00", Dated
D Unruh

QEO5139 SRP: $9.75 **GBTru: $18**

Son

Bunny holding carrot with blue ribbon.
Handcrafted, 1.50"

QEO5187 SRP: $5.75 **GBTru: $12**

Spirit Of Easter

Bunny in airplane delivering eggs.
Handcrafted, 2.00", Dated

QEO5169 SRP: $7.75 **GBTru: $30**

Springtime Stroll

Gentleman bunny with walking stick.
Handcrafted, 2.50", Dated

QEO5167 SRP: $6.75 **GBTru: $18**

1992

Baby's First Easter

Chick pops out of egg.
Handcrafted, 3.00", Dated
J Francis

QEO9271 SRP: $6.75 **GBTru: $20**

Belle Bunny

Bunny dressed in ballgown bell.
Porcelain, 3.00", Dated
L Votruba

QEO9354 SRP: $9.75 **GBTru: $15**

Bless You

Bunny naps holding plush bunny toy.
Handcrafted, 3.00"
J Francis

QEO9291 SRP: $6.75 **GBTru: $15**

Cosmic Rabbit

Astronaut bunny delivers Easter basket.
Handcrafted, 3.00", Dated
B Siedler

QEO9364 SRP: $7.75 **GBTru: $15**

CRAYOLA CRAYON
Crayola Bunny

Artist bunny colors easter egg.
Handcrafted, 3.00", Dated
A M Rogers

QEO9304 SRP: $7.75 **GBTru: $26**

Cultivated Gardener

Farmer bunny w/seeds/hoe/carrots.
Handcrafted, 3.00", Dated
B Siedler

QEO9351 SRP: $5.75 **GBTru: $12**

Daughter

Girl bunny holding easter egg balloon.
Handcrafted, 3.00", Dated
A M Rogers

QEO9284 SRP: $5.75 **GBTru: $15**

EASTER PARADE - 1ST
Easter Parade

Drum Major bunny leads parade.
Handcrafted, 3.00", Dated
K Crow

QEO9301 SRP: $6.75 **GBTru: $22**

EGGS IN SPORTS - 1ST
Grade A's '92

Baseball player egg w/bat.
Handcrafted, 3.00", Dated
B Siedler

QEO9341 SRP: $6.75 **GBTru: $24**

Eggspert Painter

Bunny seated on scaffold painting egg.
Handcrafted, 3.00", Dated
B Siedler

QEO9361 SRP: $6.75 **GBTru: $16**

Everything's Ducky!

Duck playing in spring puddle.
Handcrafted, 3.00", Dated
SPike

QEO9331 SRP: $6.75 **GBTru: $15**

Grandchild

Bunny on carrot pogo stick/basket.
Handcrafted, 3.00", Dated
K Crow

QEO9274 SRP: $6.75 **GBTru: $12**

Somebunny Loves You

Bunny hugs a chocolate bunny.
Handcrafted, 3.00"
J Francis

QEO9294 SRP: $6.75 **GBTru: $24**

Warm Memories

Embroidered tulips on photo holder.
Fabric, 4.00", Dated
L Votruba

QEO9311 SRP: $7.75 **GBTru: $12**

Joy Bearer

Girl bunny in bonnet/Easter egg basket.
Handcrafted, 3.00", Dated
D Palmiter

QEO9334 SRP: $8.75 **GBTru: $24**

Son

Boy bunny holding Easter egg balloon.
Handcrafted, 3.00", Dated
A M Rogers

QEO9281 SRP: $5.75 **GBTru: $14**

1993

Promise Of Easter

Lamb resting in heart-shaped holder.
Prlcn/Metal, 3.00", Dated
J Lyle

QEO9314 SRP: $8.75 **GBTru: $14**

Springtime Egg

Egg with raised floral design.
Handcrafted, 3.00", Dated
J Lee

QEO9321 SRP: $8.75 **GBTru: $15**

Baby's First Easter

Bunny pull toy with yellow ribbon.
Handcrafted, 1.25", Dated
D Palmiter

QEO8345 SRP: $6.75 **GBTru: $12**

Rocking Bunny

Bunny as a "rocking-horse".
Prlcn/Metal, 3.00", Dated
L Votruba

QEO9324 SRP: $9.75 **GBTru: $20**

Sunny Wisher

Songbird sings Easter wishes.
Handcrafted, 3.00"
S Pike

QEO9344 SRP: $5.75 **GBTru: $12**

Backyard Bunny

Bunny in tulip decorated watering can.
Handcrafted, 2.00", Dated
L Sickman

QEO8405 SRP: $6.75 **GBTru: $14**

Barrow Of Giggles

Two bunnies take ride in wheelbarrow.
Handcrafted, 1.88", Dated
P Andrews

QEO8402 SRP: $8.75 **GBTru: $12**

Beautiful Memories Photoholder

Spring flowers trim photo holder.
Handcrafted, 2.50", Dated
D Unruh

QEO8362 SRP: $6.75 **GBTru: $8**

Best Dressed Turtle

Turtle with striped Easter egg colors shell.
Handcrafted, 1.88"
J Lee

QEO8392 SRP: $5.75 **GBTru: $10**

Daughter

Lamb in pink overalls jumps rope.
Handcrafted, 2.50", Dated
P Andrews

QEO8342 SRP: $5.75 **GBTru: $10**

EASTER PARADE - 2ND
Easter Parade

Bunny marches playing glockenspiel.
Handcrafted, 2.88", Dated
J Lee

QEO8325 SRP: $6.75 **GBTru: $15**

EGGS IN SPORT - 2ND
Tennis Ace '93

Egg tennis player holds racket.
Handcrafted, 2.00", Dated
B Siedler

QEO8332 SRP: $6.75 **GBTru: $12**

Grandchild

Bunny rides in a wagon.
Handcrafted, 1.88", Dated
B Seidler

QEO8352 SRP: $6.75 **GBTru: $10**

Li'l Peeper

Chick w/Easter eggs/basket/clip on.
Handcrafted, 1.88"
J Lee

QEO8312 SRP: $7.75 **GBTru: $12**

Lop-eared Bunny

Droopy eared bunny/orchid bow.
Handcrafted,.88"
L Sickman

QEO8315 SRP: $5.75 **GBTru: $12**

Lovely Lamb

Lady lamb in a ball gown bell.
Porcelain, 3.00", Dated
L Votruba

QEO8372 SRP: $9.75 **GBTru: $12**

Maypole Stroll

3 orns dance 'round may-pole/basket.
Hndcrf/Wckr, 4.25"
J Francis & R Chad

QEO8395 SRP: $28.00 **GBTru: $28**

Nutty Eggs

Squirrel carries pink easter basket.
Handcrafted, 1.88"
J Lee

QEO8382 SRP: $6.75 **GBTru: $10**

Radiant Window

Two bluebirds on gothic window/cross.
Handcrafted, 3.25"
D Unruh

QEO8365 SRP: $7.75 **GBTru: $12**

Son

Boy lamb/overalls/juggles eggs.
Handcrafted, 2.50", Dated
P Andrews

QEO8335 SRP: $5.75 **GBTru: $10**

SPRINGTIME BONNETS - 1ST
Springtime Bonnets

Bunny shows off easter outfit.
Handcrafted, 2.25", Dated
D Lee

QEO8322 SRP: $7.75 **GBTru: $22**

Time For Easter

Cuckoo clock w/bunnies, flowers, eggs.
Handcrafted, 3.25", Dated
R Chad

QEO8385 SRP: $8.75 **GBTru: $12**

TWIRL-ABOUT
Chicks-On-A-Twirl

Two chicks twirl in egg shape.
Handcrafted, 3.00", Dated
J Lyle

QEO8375 SRP: $7.75 **GBTru: $10**

1994

Baby's First Easter

Bunny naps in easter basket.
Handcrafted, Dated
J Francis

QEO8153 SRP: $6.75 **GBTru: $10**

COLLECTOR'S PLATE - 1ST
Gathering Sunny Memories 1994

Bunny boy & girl gather flowers.
Porcelain, Dated
L Votruba

QEO8233 SRP: $7.75 **GBTru: $20**

CRAYOLA CRAYON
Colorful Spring

Bunny holds carrot on crayon swing.
Handcrafted, Dated
K Crow

QEO8166 SRP: $7.75 **GBTru: $30**

Daughter

Bunny in pinafore & pantaloons.
Handcrafted, Dated
P Andrews

QEO8156 SRP: $5.75 **GBTru: $6**

Divine Duet

Bunny & chick sing hymns.
Handcrafted
L Votruba

QEO8183 SRP: $6.75 **GBTru: $7**

Easter Art Show

Kitten strings eggs on garland.
Handcrafted
L Votruba

QEO8193 SRP: $7.75 **GBTru: $8**

EASTER PARADE - 3RD & FINAL
Easter Parade '94

Bunny band horn player.
Handcrafted, Dated
D Rhodus

QEO8136 SRP: $6.75 **GBTru: $15**

EGGS IN SPORT - 3RD & FINAL
Golf Club '94

Egg golfer.
Handcrafted, Dated
B Siedler

QEO8133 SRP: $6.75 **GBTru: $12**

First Hello

Club: Member Get Member
Bunny holds chick in eggshell.
Handcrafted, Dated

QXC4846 **GBTru: $38**

HERE COMES EASTER - 1ST
HOP-N-GO 1994

Bunny drives Easter egg car.
Handcrafted, Dated
K Crow

QEO8093 SRP: $7.75 **GBTru: $35**

Joyful Lamb

Prancing lamb with baskets.
Handcrafted
D Unruh

QEO8206 SRP: $5.75 **GBTru: $8**

PEANUTS
Peanuts

Snoopy draws on
Charlie Brown's head.
Handcrafted, Dated
D Unruh

QEO8176 SRP: $7.75 **GBTru: $25**

Peeping Out

Bunny meets newly hatched chick.
Handcrafted
D Unruh

QEO8203 SRP: $6.75 **GBTru: $12**

Riding A Breeze

Rabbit flies a kite.
Handcrafted, Dated
D Palmiter

QEO8213 SRP: $5.75 **GBTru: $10**

Son

Bunny in cap & overalls.
Handcrafted, Dated
P Andrews

QEO8163 SRP: $5.75 **GBTru: $6**

SPRINGTIME BONNETS - 2ND
Springtime Bonnets

Girl bunny in Easter finery.
Handcrafted, Dated
R Bishop

QEO8096 SRP: $7.75 **GBTru: $18**

Sunny Bunny Garden
Daisies' friends: Top Carrot, Prize Posey
Bunnies tend spring garden, Set/3.
Handcrafted, Dated
E Seale

QEO8146 SRP: $15.00 **GBTru: $20**

Sweet As Sugar

View inside egg reveals lamb.
Handcrafted, Dated
A M Rogers

QEO8086 SRP: $8.75 **GBTru: $14**

TENDER TOUCHES
Sweet Easter Wishes

Seated rabbit holds toy bunny.
Handcrafted, Dated
E Seale

QEO8196 SRP: $8.75 **GBTru: $20**

Tilling Time

Club: Keepsake Easter Sidekick Gift. Complements Sunny Bunny Garden Orn.
Bunny tills the garden.
Handcrafted, Dated

QXC8256 **GBTru: $28**

Treetop Cottage

Bird house.
Handcrafted, Dated
L Sickman

QEO8186 SRP: $9.75 **GBTru: $15**

Yummy Recipe

Carrot Cake recipe included
Mouse bakes carrot cake.
Handcrafted, Dated
A M Rogers

QEO8143 SRP: $7.75 **GBTru: $12**

1995

APPLE BLOSSOM LANE - 1ST
Apple Blossom Lane

Mouse greets spring with flowers.
Handcrafted, Dated
J Francis

QEO8207 SRP: $8.95 **GBTru: $16**

April Shower

Club: Easter Sidekick Gift. Complements the May Flower Orn.
Bunny with watering can.
Handcrafted, Dated

QEO8253 SRP: $6.95 **GBTru: $10**

Baby's First Easter

Baby chick in egg carriage.
Handcrafted, Dated
D Palmiter

QEO8237 SRP: $7.95 **GBTru: $9**

COLLECTOR'S PLATE - 2ND
Catching The Breeze

Bunnies fly kite in meadow.
Porcelain, Dated
L Votruba

QEO8219 SRP: $7.95 **GBTru: $12**

CRAYOLA CRAYON
Picture Perfect

Bunny crayons Easter art.
Handcrafted, Dated
K Crow

QEO8249 SRP: $7.95 **GBTru: $16**

Daughter

Girl duck in Easter dress and hat.
Handcrafted, Dated
A M Rogers

QEO8239 SRP: $5.95 **GBTru: $8**

Easter Eggspress

Bunny engineer on train.
Handcrafted, Dated
B Siedler

QEO8269 SRP: $4.95 **GBTru: $12**

Elegant Lily

Easter lily medallion.
Brass
L Votruba

QEO8267 SRP: $6.95 **GBTru: $10**

HERE COMES EASTER - 2ND
Here Comes Easter

Bunny and chick in eggcopter.
Handcrafted, Dated
K Crow

QEO8217 SRP: $7.95 **GBTru: $18**

Son

Boy duck in sailor suit.
Handcrafted, Dated
A M Rogers

QEO8247 SRP: $5.95 **GBTru: $15**

Flowerpot Friends

Lamb, bunny, chicks in flowerpots/ window box.
Handcrafted, Dated
P Andrews

QEO8229 SRP: $14.95 **GBTru: $20**

LOONEY TUNES
Bugs Bunny

Artist Bugs paints carrot.
Handcrafted
R Chad

QEO8279 SRP: $8.95 **GBTru: $18**

SPRINGTIME BARBIE - 1ST
Springtime BARBIE
Only available at Gold Crown Retailers with Reach Program
BARBIE in floral gown, hat/flwr basket.
Handcrafted, Dated
P Andrews

QEO8069 SRP: $12.95 **GBTru: $28**

GARDEN CLUB - 1ST
Garden Club

Chipmunk with tulips.
Handcrafted, Dated
L Sickman

QEO8209 SRP: $7.95 **GBTru: $18**

May Flower

Club: Keepsake Easter Sidekick Gift, Purchase with Coupon
Duck holds flower petal umbrella.
Handcrafted, Dated
B Siedler

QXC8246 SRP: $4.95 **GBTru: $39**

SPRINGTIME BONNETS - 3RD
Springtime Bonnets

Plumed floral hat tops bunny's dress.
Handcrafted, Dated
D Unruh

QEO8227 SRP: $7.95 **GBTru: $15**

Ham 'n Eggs

Pig in overalls holds basket of eggs.
Handcrafted, Dated
R Chad

QEO8277 SRP: $7.95 **GBTru: $12**

PEANUTS
Snoopy & Woodstock

Snoopy in bunny ears/ Woodstock in basket.
Handcrafted, Dated
D Rhodus

QEO8257 SRP: $7.95 **GBTru: $22**

TENDER TOUCHES
High Hopes

Bunny carries seedpacket tray.
Handcrafted, Dated
E Seale

QEO8259 SRP: $8.95 **GBTru: $15**

1996

COTTONTAIL EXPRESS - 1ST
Locomotive

Bunny engineer in egg train.
Handcrafted, Dated
K Crow

QEO8074 SRP: $8.95 **GBTru: $30**

INSPIRATIONAL
Easter Morning

Flower decorated cross with butterfly.
Handcrafted, Dated
D Unruh

QEO8164 SRP: $7.95 **GBTru: $10**

APPLE BLOSSOM LANE - 2ND
Apple Blossom Lane

Bunny greets friends at cottage.
Handcrafted, Dated
J Francis

QEO8084 SRP: $8.95 **GBTru: $12**

CRAYOLA CRAYON
Hippity- Hop Delivery

Bunny with jelly bean filled wheelbarrow.
Handcrafted, Dated
K Crow

QEO8144 SRP: $7.95 **GBTru: $12**

JOYFUL ANGELS - 1ST
Joyful Angels

Winged angels carries flowers.
Handcrafted, Dated
J Lyle

QEO8184 SRP: $9.95 **GBTru: $20**

BEATRIX POTTER - 1ST
Peter Rabbit

bunny dressed in Easter finery.
Handcrafted, Dated
L Votruba

QEO8071 SRP: $8.95 **GBTru: $84**

GARDEN CLUB - 2ND
Garden Club

Skunk with bouquet of lilacs.
Handcrafted, Dated
D Palmiter

QEO8091 SRP: $7.95 **GBTru: $12**

LOONEY TUNES
Daffy Duck

Daffy dresses up as Easter Bunny.
Handcrafted
A M Rogers

QEO8154 SRP: $8.95 **GBTru: $15**

COLLECTOR'S PLATE - 3RD
Keeping A Secret

Bunny picks flowers with duck and butterfly.
Porcelain, Dated
L Votruba

QEO8221 SRP: $7.95 **GBTru: $12**

HERE COMES EASTER - 3RD
Here Comes Easter

Bunny drives truck transporting chick in egg.
Handcrafted, Dated
K Crow

QEO8094 SRP: $7.95 **GBTru: $12**

PEANUTS
Parade Pals

Snoopy balances Woodstock in jelly bean nest.
Handcrafted, Dated
D Rhodus

QEO8151 SRP: $7.95 **GBTru: $16**

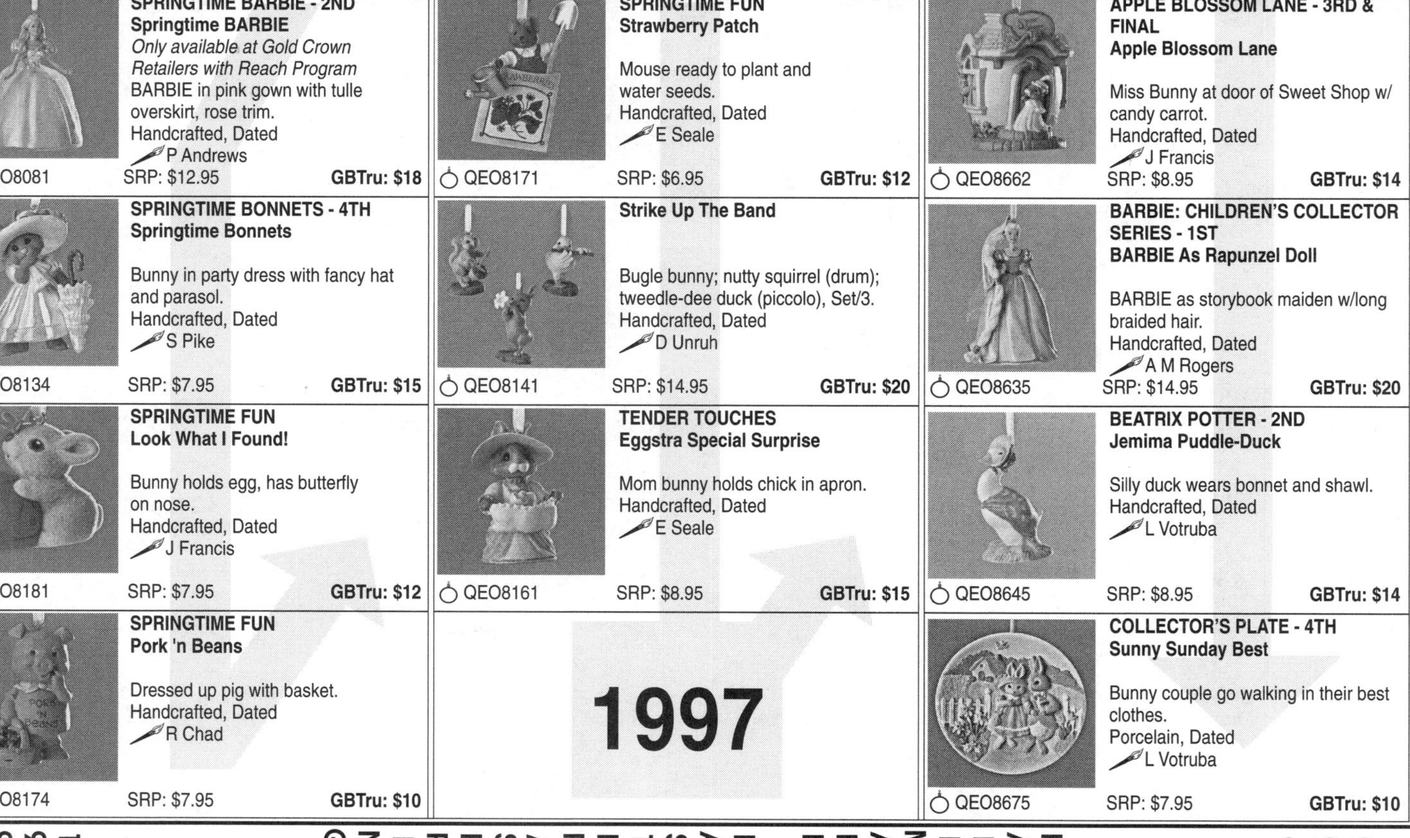

SPRINGTIME BARBIE - 2ND
Springtime BARBIE
Only available at Gold Crown Retailers with Reach Program
BARBIE in pink gown with tulle overskirt, rose trim.
Handcrafted, Dated
P Andrews
QEO8081 SRP: $12.95 **GBTru: $18**

SPRINGTIME FUN
Strawberry Patch

Mouse ready to plant and water seeds.
Handcrafted, Dated
E Seale
QEO8171 SRP: $6.95 **GBTru: $12**

APPLE BLOSSOM LANE - 3RD & FINAL
Apple Blossom Lane

Miss Bunny at door of Sweet Shop w/ candy carrot.
Handcrafted, Dated
J Francis
QEO8662 SRP: $8.95 **GBTru: $14**

SPRINGTIME BONNETS - 4TH
Springtime Bonnets

Bunny in party dress with fancy hat and parasol.
Handcrafted, Dated
S Pike
QEO8134 SRP: $7.95 **GBTru: $15**

Strike Up The Band

Bugle bunny; nutty squirrel (drum); tweedle-dee duck (piccolo), Set/3.
Handcrafted, Dated
D Unruh
QEO8141 SRP: $14.95 **GBTru: $20**

BARBIE: CHILDREN'S COLLECTOR SERIES - 1ST
BARBIE As Rapunzel Doll

BARBIE as storybook maiden w/long braided hair.
Handcrafted, Dated
A M Rogers
QEO8635 SRP: $14.95 **GBTru: $20**

SPRINGTIME FUN
Look What I Found!

Bunny holds egg, has butterfly on nose.
Handcrafted, Dated
J Francis
QEO8181 SRP: $7.95 **GBTru: $12**

TENDER TOUCHES
Eggstra Special Surprise

Mom bunny holds chick in apron.
Handcrafted, Dated
E Seale
QEO8161 SRP: $8.95 **GBTru: $15**

BEATRIX POTTER - 2ND
Jemima Puddle-Duck

Silly duck wears bonnet and shawl.
Handcrafted, Dated
L Votruba
QEO8645 SRP: $8.95 **GBTru: $14**

SPRINGTIME FUN
Pork 'n Beans

Dressed up pig with basket.
Handcrafted, Dated
R Chad
QEO8174 SRP: $7.95 **GBTru: $10**

1997

COLLECTOR'S PLATE - 4TH
Sunny Sunday Best

Bunny couple go walking in their best clothes.
Porcelain, Dated
L Votruba
QEO8675 SRP: $7.95 **GBTru: $10**

COTTONTAIL EXPRESS - 2ND
Colorful Coal Car

Chick conductor w/ Easter egg filled car.
Handcrafted, Dated
K Crow

QEO8652 SRP: $8.95 **GBTru: $15**

CRAYOLA CRAYON
Eggs-pert Artist

Bunny colors Easter Egg.
Handcrafted, Dated
S Tague

QEO8695 SRP: $8.95 **GBTru: $14**

Digging In

Mouse plants seeds for herb Rosemary.
Handcrafted, Dated
E Seale/L Votruba

QEO8712 SRP: $7.95 **GBTru: $12**

GARDEN CLUB - 3RD
Garden Club

Squirrel holds spring bouquet.
Handcrafted, Dated
K Bricker

QEO8665 SRP: $7.95 **GBTru: $14**

Gentle Guardian

Art by Scott Freeman
Angel holds lamb.
Handcrafted
T Larsen

QEO8732 SRP: $6.95 **GBTru: $8**

HERE COMES EASTER - 4TH & FINAL
Here Comes Easter

Duck captains a tugboat.
Handcrafted, Dated
K Crow

QEO8682 SRP: $7.95 **GBTru: $10**

JOYFUL ANGELS - 2ND
Joyful Angels

Winged Angel carries roses.
Handcrafted, Dated
J Lyle

QEO8655 SRP: $10.95 **GBTru: $15**

NATURE'S SKETCHBOOK
Garden Bunnies
Art by Marjolein Bastin
Bunnies nibbling in garden patch.
Handcrafted, Dated
D Unruh

QEO8702 SRP: $14.95 **GBTru: $20**

Purr-fect Princess, A

Angel Cat with star scepter.
Handcrafted, Dated
S Pike

QEO8715 SRP: $7.95 **GBTru: $10**

SIDEWALK CRUISERS - 1ST
1935 Steelcraft Streamline Velocipede By Murray

Tricycle with sporty wheel fenders.
Die-cast Metal, Dated
D Rhodus

QEO8632 SRP: $12.95 **GBTru: $25**

SPRINGTIME BARBIE - 3RD & FINAL
Springtime BARBIE

BARBIE in rose-trimmed lawn party gown.
Handcrafted, Dated
P Andrews

QEO8642 SRP: $12.95 **GBTru: $25**

SPRINGTIME BONNETS - 5TH & FINAL
Springtime Bonnets

Miss Bunny in bonnet that matches dress.
Handcrafted, Dated
S Pike

QEO8672 SRP: $7.95 **GBTru: $14**

Swing-Time

Little girl takes kitten for ride on swing.
Handcrafted, Dated
S Tague

QEO8705 SRP: $7.95 **GBTru: $12**

TENDER TOUCHES
Bumper Crop: 24-Carrot Dreams, Grade A Packer, First Taster, Set/3

Bunnies nap, taste and pack carrots for road stand.
Handcrafted, Dated
E Seale

QEO8735 SRP: $14.95 **GBTru: $19**

TENDER TOUCHES SPRING 1997 "BUMPER CROP" COMPLEMENT
Farmer's Market
Club Edition
Bunny farmer by roadside veggie stand.
Handcrafted, Dated
E. Searle

QXC5182 SRP: $15.00 **GBTru: $15**

Victorian Cross

Scroll design cross.
Pewter

QEO8725 SRP: $8.95 **GBTru: $9**

1998

ANDREW BROWNSWORD COLLECTION
Forever Friends

Bear boosts friend up so that card can be mailed at postal box.
Handcrafted, Dated
S Pike

QEO8423 SRP: $9.95

BARBIE
Midge - 35th Anniversary

Girl friend to BARBIE.
Handcrafted, Dated
P Andrews

QEO8413 SRP: $14.95

BARBIE: CHILDREN'S COLLECTOR SERIES - 2ND
BARBIE as Little Bo Peep Doll

BARBIE as a nursery rhyme character.
Handcrafted, Dated
A M Rogers

QEO8373 SRP: $14.95

Bashful Gift

Set of 2. Bashful boy gives bunny to bashful girl.
Handcrafted, Dated
N Aubé

QEO8446 SRP: $11.95

BEATRIX POTTER - 3RD
Benjamin Bunny

Bunny from English children's story
Handcrafted, Dated
LD Votruba

QEO8383 SRP: $8.95

Bouquet Of Memories

Girl in spring finery carries bouquet of flowers.
Handcrafted, Dated
S Tague

QEO8456 SRP: $7.95

COTTONTAIL EXPRESS - 3RD
Passenger Car

Chick waves from passenger car.
Handcrafted, Dated
K Crow

QEO8376 SRP: $9.95

DISNEY
Practice Swing - Donald Duck

Donald attacks the golf ball.
Handcrafted, Dated

QEO8396 SRP: $10.95

Happy Diploma Day!

Pup holds class of 1998 diploma.
Handcrafted, Dated
T Haddix

QEO8476 SRP: $7.95

SIDEWALK CRUISERS - 2ND
1939 Mobo Horse

Old fashioned child's moveable horse.
Handcrafted, Dated

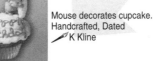

QEO8393 SRP: $12.95

DISNEY
The Garden Of Piglet And Pooh

Set of 2. Pooh and friend Piglet enjoy spring flowers.
Handcrafted, Dated

QEO8403 SRP: $10.95

JOYFUL ANGELS - 3RD & FINAL
Joyful Angels

Winged Angel.
Handcrafted, Dated
J Lyle

QEO8386 SRP: $10.95

Special Friends - Spoonful Of Stars

Art of Becky Kelly
Two friends share a spring day.
Caption on ornament.
Handcrafted, Dated
LD Votruba

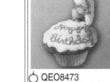

QEO8523 SRP: $12.95

DISNEY
Tigger In The Garden
Available only 3/28/98, Spring Preview Event. Coordinates with The Garden of Piglet and Pooh set.
Tigger plays among the flowers.
Handcrafted, Dated

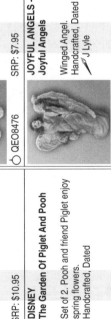

QEO8436 SRP: $9.95

PEANUTS
Going Up? - Charlie Brown

Charlie Brown runs with kite to make it fly.
Handcrafted, Dated
S Pike

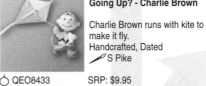

QEO8433 SRP: $9.95

STAR WARS
STAR WARS

Space vehicle. Lunchbox opens and closes.
Pressed Tin, Dated

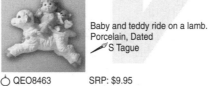

QEO8406 SRP: $12.95

GARDEN CLUB - 4TH & FINAL
Garden Club

Butterfly visits a blossom in Bunny's bouquet.
Handcrafted, Dated
S Pike

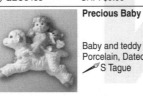

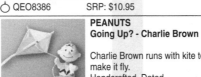

QEO8426 SRP: $7.95

Precious Baby

Baby and teddy ride on a lamb.
Porcelain, Dated
S Tague

QEO8463 SRP: $9.95

Sweet Birthday

Mouse decorates cupcake.
Handcrafted, Dated
K Kline

QEO8473 SRP: $7.95

Victorian Cross

Religious symbol.
Pewter, Dated
D Unruh

QEO8453 SRP: $8.95

VINTAGE ROADSTER - 1ST
1931 Ford Model A Roadster

Old fashioned touring car.
Die-Cast Metal, Dated
D Palmiter

QEO8416 SRP: $14.95

Wedding Memories

Bride and groom on a balcony. Flat ornament with caption.
Porcelain, Dated
LD Votruba

QEO8466 SRP: $9.95

What's Your Name?

Kitten and bird on spring wreath meet each other.
Handcrafted, Dated
K Kline

QEO8443 SRP: $7.95

NOTES:

ALL GOD'S CHILDREN		*Series of 3*	*Dated*	page
1996	QX5564	Christy - All God's Children		239
1997	QX6142	Nikki - All God's Children		253
1998	QX6363	Ricky - All God's Children		267

ART MASTERPIECE		*Series of 3*	*Not Dated*	
1984	QX3494	Madonna And Child And St. John		96
1985	QX3772	Madonna Of The Pomegranate		105
1986	QX3506	Madonna And Child With The Infant St. John		114

BASEBALL HEROES		*Series of 4*	*Dated*	
1994	QX5323	Babe Ruth		207
1995	QX5029	Lou Gehrig		223
1996	QX5304	Satchel Paige		239
1997	QX6202	Jackie Robinson		254

BELLRINGERS, THE		*Series of 6*	*Dated*	
1979	QX1479	The Bellswinger		59
1980	QX1574	The Bellringers		64
1981	QX4415	Swingin' Bellringer		71
1982	QX4556	Angel Bellringer		79
1983	QX4039	Teddy Bellringer		88
1984	QX4384	Elfin Artist		97

BETSEY CLARK		*Series of 13*	*Dated*	
1973	XHD1102	Christmas 1973		42
1974	QX1081	Musicians		43
1975	QX1331	Caroling Trio		45
1976	QX1951	Christmas 1976		48
1977	QX2642	Truest Joys Of Christmas		51
1978	QX2016	Christmas Spirit		55
1979	QX2019	Holiday Fun		60
1980	QX2154	Joy-In-The-Air		65
1981	QX8022	Christmas 1981		71
1982	QX2156	Joys Of Christmas		79
1983	QX2119	Christmas Happiness		88
1984	QX2494	Days Are Merry		97
1985	QX2632	Special Kind Of Feeling		106

BETSEY CLARK: HOME FOR CHRISTMAS		*Series of 6*	*Dated*	
1986	QX2776	Home For Christmas		115
1987	QX2727	Home For Christmas		125
1988	QX2714	Home For Christmas		135
1989	QX2302	Home For Christmas		145
1990	QX2033	Home For Christmas		156
1991	QX2109	Home For Christmas		167

BETSEY'S COUNTRY CHRISTMAS		*Series of 3*	*Dated*	
1992	QX2104	Betsey's Country Christmas		179
1993	QX2062	Betsey's Country Christmas		192
1994	QX2403	Betsey's Country Christmas		207

CARROUSEL		*Series of 6*	*Dated*	page
1978	QX1463	Antique Toys		55
1979	QX1467	Christmas Carrousel		60
1980	QX1414	Merry Carrousel		65
1981	QX4275	Skaters' Carrousel		72
1982	QX4783	Snowman Carrousel		79
1983	QX4019	Santa And Friends		88

CAT NAPS		*Series of 5*	*Dated*	
1994	QX5313	Cat Naps		207
1995	QX5097	Cat Naps		223
1996	QX5641	Cat Naps		240
1997	QX6205	Cat Naps		254
1998	QX6383	Cat Naps		268

CELEBRATION OF ANGELS, A		*Series of 4*	*Dated*	
1995	QX5077	Celebration Of Angels, A		224
1996	QX5634	Celebration Of Angels, A		240
1997	QX6175	Celebration Of Angels, A		254
1998	QX6366	Celebration Of Angels, A		268

CHRISTMAS KITTY		*Series of 3*	*Not Dated*	
1989	QX5445	Christmas Kitty		146
1990	QX4506	Christmas Kitty		157
1991	QX4377	Christmas Kitty		168

CHRISTMAS VISITORS		*Series of 3*	*Dated*	
1995	QX5087	St. Nicholas		225
1996	QX5631	Christkindl		241
1997	QX6172	Kolyada		255

CLOTHESPIN SOLDIER		*Series of 6*	*Not Dated*	
1982	QX4583	British		80
1983	QX4029	Early American		89
1984	QX4471	Canadian Mountie		98
1985	QX4715	Scottish Highlander		107
1986	QX4063	French Officer		116
1987	QX4807	Sailor		126

COLLECTOR'S PLATE		*Series of 6*	*Dated*	
1987	QX4817	Light Shines At Christmas		126
1988	QX4061	Waiting For Santa		136
1989	QX4612	Morning Of Wonder		147
1990	QX4436	Cookies For Santa		157
1991	QX4369	Let It Snow!		169
1992	QX4461	Sweet Holiday Harmony		180

CRAYOLA CRAYON		Series of 10	Dated	page
1989	QX4352	Bright Journey		147
1990	QX4586	Bright Moving Colors		158
1991	QX4219	Bright Vibrant Carols		169
1992	QX4264	Bright Blazing Colors		180
1993	QX4422	Bright Shining Castle		193
1994	QX5273	Bright Playful Colors		209
1995	QX5247	Bright 'N' Sunny Tepee		225
1996	QX5391	Bright Flying Colors		241
1997	QX6235	Bright Rocking Colors		256
1998	QX6166	Bright Sledding Colors		270

GIFT BRINGERS, THE		Series of 5	Dated	
1989	QX2795	St. Nicholas		149
1990	QX2803	St. Lucia		159
1991	QX2117	Christkindl		171
1992	QX2124	Kolyada		182
1993	QX2065	The Magi		194

GREATEST STORY		Series of 3	Dated	
1990	QX4656	Greatest Story		160
1991	QX4129	Greatest Story		172
1992	QX4251	Greatest Story		183

HARK! IT'S HERALD		Series of 4	Dated	
1989	QX4555	Hark! It's Herald		150
1990	QX4463	Hark! It's Herald		161
1991	QX4379	Hark! It's Herald		172
1992	QX4464	Hark! It's Herald		183

HEART OF CHRISTMAS		Series of 5	Dated	
1990	QX4726	Heart Of Christmas		161
1991	QX4357	Heart Of Christmas		172
1992	QX4411	Heart Of Christmas		183
1993	QX4482	Heart Of Christmas		195
1994	QX5266	Heart Of Christmas		211

HEAVENLY ANGELS		Series of 3	Dated	
1991	QX4367	Heavenly Angels		172
1992	QX4454	Heavenly Angels		183
1993	QX4945	Heavenly Angels		195

HOLIDAY HEIRLOOM		Series of 3	Dated	Ltd. Ed. of 34,600
1987	QX4857	Holiday Heirloom	Keepsake Collection	129
1988	QX4064	Holiday Heirloom	Collector's Club	138
1989	QXC4605	Holiday Heirloom	Collector's Club	150

HOLIDAY WILDLIFE		Series of 7	Dated	
1982	QX3133	Cardinalis Cardinalis		83
1983	QX3099	Black-Capped Chickadees		92
1984	QX3474	Ring-Necked Pheasant		100
1985	QX3765	California Quail		110
1986	QX3216	Cedar Waxwing		119
1987	QX3717	Snow Goose		129
1988	QX3711	Purple Finch		138

MINIATURE CRECHE		*Series of 5*	*Not Dated*	**page**
1985	QX4825	Wood And Woven Straw		111
1986	QX4076	Fine Porcelain		120
1987	QX4819	Multi-Plated Brass		130
1988	QX4034	Acrylic		139
1989	QX4592	Handcrafted		151

MOTHER GOOSE		*Series of 5*	*Dated*	
1993	QX5282	Humpty-Dumpty		198
1994	QX5213	Hey Diddle, Diddle		215
1995	QX5099	Jack & Jill		230
1996	QX5644	Mary Had A Little Lamb		246
1997	QX6215	Little Boy Blue		261

MR. AND MRS. CLAUS		*Series of 10*	*Dated*	
1986	QX4026	Merry Mistletoe Time		120
1987	QX4837	Home Cooking		130
1988	QX4011	Shall We Dance		140
1989	QX4575	Holiday Duet		151
1990	QX4393	Popcorn Party		162
1991	QX4339	Checking His List		173
1992	QX4294	Gift Exchange		185
1993	QX4202	Fitting Moment, A		198
1994	QX5283	Handwarming Present, A		215
1995	QX5157	Christmas Eve Kiss		230

NORMAN ROCKWELL		*Series of 9*	*Dated*	
1980	QX3061	Santa's Visitors		69
1981	QX5115	Carolers,The		76
1982	QX3053	Filling The Stockings		85
1983	QX3007	Dress Rehearsal		93
1984	QX3411	Caught Napping		102
1985	QX3745	Jolly Postman		111
1986	QX3213	Checking Up		121
1987	QX3707	Christmas Dance, The		131
1988	QX3704	And To All A Good Night		140

OWLIVER		*Series of 3*	*Dated*	
1992	QX4544	Owliver		186
1993	QX5425	Owliver		199
1994	QX5226	Owliver		216

PEACE ON EARTH		*Series of 3*	*Dated*	
1991	QX5129	Peace On Earth - Italy		175
1992	QX5174	Peace On Earth - Spain		186
1993	QX5242	Peace On Earth - Poland		199

PEANUTS GANG		*Series of 4*	*Dated*	
1993	QX5315	Peanuts: Charlie Brown and Snowman		199
1994	QX5203	Peanuts Gang, The: Lucy		216
1995	QX5059	Peanuts Gang, The: Linus		232
1996	QX5381	Peanuts Gang, The: Sally		248

PORCELAIN BEAR		*Series of 8*	*Not Dated*	page
1983	QX4289	Cinnamon Teddy		94
1984	QX4541	Cinnamon Bear		103
1985	QX4792	Cinnamon Bear		112
1986	QX4056	Cinnamon Bear		121
1987	QX4427	Cinnamon Bear		132
1988	QX4044	Cinnamon Bear		141
1989	QX4615	Cinnamon Bear		153
1990	QX4426	Cinnamon Bear		164

REINDEER CHAMPS		*Series of 8*	*Dated*	
1986	QX4223	Dasher		122
1987	QX4809	Dancer		132
1988	QX4051	Prancer		141
1989	QX4562	Vixen		153
1990	QX4433	Comet		164
1991	QX4347	Cupid		175
1992	QX5284	Donder		187
1993	QX4331	Blitzen		201

ROCKING HORSE		*Series of 16*	*Dated*	
1981	QX4222	Dappled		76
1982	QX5023	Black		85
1983	QX4177	Russet		94
1984	QX4354	Appaloosa		103
1985	QX4932	Pinto		112
1986	QX4016	Palomino		122
1987	QX4829	White		132
1988	QX4024	Dappled Gray		141
1989	QX4622	Bay		153
1990	QX4646	Appaloosa		164
1991	QX4147	Buckskin		175
1992	QX4261	Rocking Horse		187
1993	QX4162	Rocking Horse		201
1994	QX5016	Rocking Horse		218
1995	QX5167	Rocking Horse		233
Anniv. Ed.	QX6167	Pewter Rocking Horse		234
1996	QX5674	Rocking Horse		249

SHOWCASE: TURN-OF-THE-CENTURY PARADE		*Series of 3*	*Dated*	
1995	QK1027	Fireman, The		237
1996	QK1084	Uncle Sam		252
1997	QK1215	Santa Claus		266

SNOOPY AND FRIENDS		*Series of 5*	*Dated*	
1979	QX1419	Ice-Hockey Holiday		63
1980	QX1541	Ski Holiday		69
1981	QX4362	Snoopy And Friends		77
1982	QX4803	Snoopy And Friends		86
1983	QX4169	Santa Snoopy		95

THIMBLE		*Series of 12*	*Not Dated*	**page**
1978	QX1336	Mouse In A Thimble		58
1979, 80	QX1319	Christmas Salute, A		64
1980	QX1321	Thimble Elf		70
1981	QX4135	Thimble Angel		78
1982	QX4513	Thimble Mouse		86
1983	QX4017	Thimble Elf		95
1984	QX4304	Thimble Angel		104
1985	QX4725	Thimble Santa		114
1986	QX4066	Thimble Partridge		123
1987	QX4419	Thimble Drummer		133
1988	QX4054	Thimble Snowman		143
1989	QX4552	Thimble Puppy		154

TIN LOCOMOTIVE		*Series of 8*	*Dated*	
1982	QX4603	Tin Locomotive		86
1983	QX4049	Tin Locomotive		96
1984	QX4404	Tin Locomotive		104
1985	QX4972	Tin Locomotive		114
1986	QX4036	Tin Locomotive		123
1987	QX4849	Tin Locomotive		133
1988	QX4004	Tin Locomotive		143
1989	QX4602	Tin Locomotive		154
Anniv. Ed.	QX6826	Tin Locomotive		267

TOBIN FRALEY CAROUSEL		*Series of 4*	*Dated*	
1992	QX4891	Tobin Fraley Carousel		189
1993	QX5502	Tobin Fraley Carousel		204
1994	QX5223	Tobin Fraley Carousel		221
1995	QX5069	Tobin Fraley Carousel		237

TWELVE DAYS OF CHRISTMAS		*Series of 12*	*Dated*	
1984	QX3484	Partridge In A Pear Tree		104
1985	QX3712	Two Turtle Dove		114
1986	QX3786	Three French Hens		124
1987	QX3709	Four Colly Birds		133
1988	QX3714	Five Golden Rings		143
1989	QX3812	Six Geese A-Laying		154
1990	QX3033	Seven Swans A-Swimming		166
1991	QX3089	Eight Maids A-Milking		177
1992	QX3031	Nine Ladies Dancing		189
1993	QX3012	Ten Lords A-Leaping		205
1994	QX3183	Eleven Pipers Piping		221
1995	QX3009	Twelve Drummers Drumming		237

U.S. CHRISTMAS STAMPS		*Series of 3*	*Dated*	
1993	QX5292	U.S. Christmas Stamps		205
1994	QX5206	U.S. Christmas Stamps		221
1995	QX5067	U.S. Christmas Stamps		238

WINDOWS OF THE WORLD		*Series of 6*	*Dated*	
1985	QX4902	Mexico: Feliz Navidad		114
1986	QX4083	Holland: Vrolyk Kerstfeest		124
1987	QX4827	Polynesia: Mele Kalikimaka		134
1988	QX4021	France: Joyeux Noel		144
1989	QX4625	German: Frohliche Weihnachten		155
1990	QX4636	Ireland: Nollaig Shona		166

WINTER SURPRISE		*Series of 4*	*Dated*	**page**
1989	QX4272	Winter Surprise		155
1990	QX4443	Winter Surprise		166
1991	QX4277	Winter Surprise		178
1992	QX4271	Winter Surprise		189

WOOD CHILDHOOD ORNAMENTS		*Series of 6*	*Dated*	
1984	QX4394	Wooden Lamb		105
1985	QX4722	Wooden Train		114
1986	QX4073	Wooden Reindeer		124
1987	QX4417	Wooden Horse		134
1988	QX4041	Wooden Airplane		144
1989	QX4595	Wooden Truck		155

YULETIDE CENTRAL		*Series of 5*	*Dated*	
1994	QX5316	Yuletide Central - Engine		222
1995	QX5079	Yuletide Central - Candy Car		238
1996	QX5011	Yuletide Central - Mail Car		252
1997	QX5812	Yuletide Central - Toy Car		266
1998	QX6373	Yuletide Central - Caboose		282

AFRICAN-AMERICAN HOLIDAY BARBIE				**page**
1998	QX6936	African-American Holiday BARBIE		267

ALL-AMERICAN TRUCKS			*Dated*	
1995	QX5527	1956 Ford Truck		222
1996	QX5241	1955 Chevrolet Cameo		239
1997	QX6105	1953 GMC		253
1998	QX6263	1937 Ford V-8		267

AT THE BALLPARK			*Dated*	
1996	QXI5711	Nolan Ryan		239
1997	QXI6152	Hank Aaron		253
1998	QX14033	Cal Ripken, Jr.		267

BARBIE ORNAMENT SERIES, THE			*Dated*	
1994	QX5006	Debut - 1959; 35th Anniversary Keepsake Ornament		206
1995	QXI5049	Solo In The Spotlight		223
1996	QXI6541	Enchanted Evening BARBIE Doll		239
1997	QXI6812	Wedding Day 1959-1962		254
1998	QX14043	Silken Flame		268

CLASSIC AMERICAN CARS			*Dated*	
1991	QX4319	1957 Corvette		168
1992	QX4284	1966 Mustang		180
1993	QX5275	1956 Ford Thunderbird		193
1994	QX5422	1957 Chevrolet Bel Air		208
1995	QX5239	1969 Chevrolet Camaro		225
1996	QX5384	1959 Cadillac De Ville		241
1997	QX6102	1969 Hurst Oldsmobile 442		255
1998	QX6256	1970 Plymouth Hemi 'Cuda		269

CLAUSES ON VACATION, THE			*Dated*	
1997	QX6112	Clauses On Vacation, The		255
1998	QX6276	Clauses On Vacation, The		269

DOLLS OF THE WORLD			*Dated*	
1996	QX5561	Native American BARBIE		241
1997	QX6162	Chinese BARBIE		257
1998	QX6356	Mexican BARBIE		272

ENCHANTED MEMORIES				
1997	QXD4045	Cinderella		255
1998	QXD4056	Snow White		272

FABULOUS DECADE			*Dated*	
1990	QX4466	Fabulous Decade		159
1991	QX4119	Fabulous Decade		170
1992	QX4244	Fabulous Decade		181
1993	QX4475	Fabulous Decade		194
1994	QX5263	Fabulous Decade		209
1995	QX5147	Fabulous Decade		226
1996	QX5661	Fabulous Decade		241
1997	QX6232	Fabulous Decade		257
1998	QX6393	Fabulous Decade		272

FOOTBALL LEGENDS				**page**
1995	QXI5759	Joe Montana, San Francisco		226
1995	QXI6207	Complementary Special Issue:		
		Joe Montana, K C Chiefs		226
1996	QXI5021	Troy Aikman		242
1997	QXI6182	Joe Namath		258
1998	QXI4036	Emmitt Smith		272

FROSTY FRIENDS			*Dated*	
1980	QX1374	A Cool Yule		67
1981	QX4335	Frosty Friends		73
1982	QX4523	Frosty Friends		81
1983	QX4007	Frosty Friends		90
1984	QX4371	Frosty Friends		99
1985	QX4822	Frosty Friends		108
1986	QX4053	Frosty Friends		118
1987	QX4409	Frosty Friends		128
1988	QX4031	Frosty Friends		137
1989	QX4572	Frosty Friends		148
1990	QX4396	Frosty Friends		159
1991	QX4327	Frosty Friends		171
1992	QX4291	Frosty Friends		182
Anniv. Ed.	QX5682	Frosty Friends		190
1993	QX4142	Frosty Friends		194
1994	QX5293	Frosty Friends		210
1995	QX5169	Frosty Friends		227
1996	QX5681	Frosty Friends		242
1997	QX6255	Frosty Friends		258
1998	QX6226	Frosty Friends		273

HALLMARK ARCHIVES - MICKEY & CO.			*Dated*	
1997	QXD4025	Donald's Surprising Gift		258
1998	QXD4006	Ready For Christmas		273

HERE COMES SANTA			*Dated*	
1979	QX1559	Santa's Motorcar		61
1980	QX1434	Santa's Express		67
1981	QX4382	Rooftop Deliveries		74
1982	QX4643	Jolly Trolley		82
1983	QX4037	Santa Express		91
1984	QX4324	Santa's Deliveries		100
1985	QX4965	Santa's Fire Engine		110
1986	QX4043	Kringle's Kool Treats		119
1987	QX4847	Santa's Woody		129
1988	QX4001	Kringle Koach		138
1989	QX4585	Christmas Caboose		150
1990	QX4923	Festive Surrey		161
1991	QX4349	Santa's Antique Car		172
1992	QX4341	Kringle Tours		184
Anniv. Ed.	QX5675	Shopping With Santa		190
1993	QX4102	Happy Haul-idays		195
1994	QX5296	Makin' Tractor Tracks		211
1995	QX5179	Santa's Roadster		228
1996	QX5684	Santa's 4 x 4		243
1997	QX6262	Claus-Mobile, The		259
1998	QX6283	Santa's Bumper Car		274

HOCKEY GREATS			Dated	page
1997	QXI6275	Wayne Gretzky		259
1998	QXI6476	Mario Lemieux		274
HOLIDAY BARBIE			*Dated*	
1993	QX5725	Holiday BARBIE		196
1994	QX5216	Holiday BARBIE		212
1995	QXI5057	Holiday BARBIE		228
1996	QXI5371	Holiday BARBIE		243
1997	QXI6212	Holiday BARBIE		259
1998	QXI4023	Holiday BARBIE		274
HOLIDAY TRADITIONS				
1998	QBG6906	Red Poinsettias		274
HOOP STARS				
1995	QXI5517	Shaquille O'Neal		228
1996	QXI5014	Larry Bird		243
1997	QXI6832	Magic Johnson		259
1998	QXI6846	Grant Hill		274
KIDDIE CAR CLASSICS			*Dated*	
1994	QX5426	Murray "Champion"		213
1995	QX5027	Murray Fire Truck		228
1996	QX5364	Murray Airplane		244
1997	QX6195	Murray Dump Truck		259
1998	QX6376	Murray Tractor And Trailer		274
LIONEL TRAIN			*Dated*	
1996	QX5531	700E Hudson Steam Locomotive		244
1997	QX6145	1950 Sante Fe F3 Diesel Locomotive		260
1998	QX6346	Pennsylvania GG-I Locomotive		275
MADAME ALEXANDER				
1996	QX6311	Cinderella - 1955		245
1997	QX6155	Little Red Riding Hood - 1991		260
1998	QX6353	Mop Top Wendy		275
MADAME ALEXANDER HOLIDAY ANGELS				
1998	QX6493	Glorious Angel		275
MAJESTIC WILDERNESS			*Dated*	
1997	QX5694	Snowshoe Rabbits in Winter		260
1998	QX6273	Timberwolves At Play		275
MARILYN MONROE			*Dated*	
1997	QX5704	Marilyn Monroe		260
1998	QX6333	Marilyn Monroe		275

MARY'S ANGELS			page
1988	QX4074	Buttercup	139
1989	QX4545	Bluebell	151
1990	QX4423	Rosebud	162
1991	QX4279	Iris	173
1992	QX4274	Lily	184
1993	QX4282	Ivy	197
1994	QX5276	Jasmine	214
1995	QX5149	Camellia	229
1996	QX5664	Violet	245
1997	QX6242	Daisey	261
1998	QX6153	Daphne	275

MERRY OLDE SANTA		*Dated*	
1990	QX4736	Merry Olde Santa	162
1991	QX4359	Merry Olde Santa	173
1992	QX4414	Merry Olde Santa	184
1993	QX4842	Merry Olde Santa	197
1994	QX5256	Merry Olde Santa	214
1995	QX5139	Merry Olde Santa	229
1996	QX5654	Merry Olde Santa	245
1997	QX6225	Merry Olde Santa	261
1998	QX6386	Merry Olde Santa	276

MICKEY'S HOLIDAY PARADE - MICKEY & CO.		*Dated*	
1997	QXD4022	Bandleader Mickey	261
1998	QXD4106	Minnie Plays The Flute	276

NOSTALGIC			
1998	QX6316	A Pony For Christmas	279

NOSTALGIC HOUSES AND SHOPS		*Dated*	
1984	QX4481	Victorian Dollhouse	102
1985	QX4975	Old-Fashioned Toy Shop	112
1986	QX4033	Christmas Candy Shoppe	121
1987	QX4839	House On Main St.	131
1988	QX4014	Hall Bro's Card Shop	140
1989	QX4582	U. S. Post Office	151
1990	QX4696	Holiday Home	163
1991	QX4139	Fire Station	174
1992	QX4254	Five-And-Ten-Cent Store	186
Anniv. Ed.	QX5612	Tannenbaum's Dept. Store	190
1993	QX4175	Cozy Home	198
1994	QX5286	Neighborhood Drugstore	215
1995	QX5159	Town Church	231
Accessory	QX5089	Accessories For Nostalgic Houses And Shops	231
1996	QX5671	Victorian Painted Lady	247
1997	QX6245	Cafe	263
1998	QX6266	Grocery Store	278

OLD WEST, THE			
1998	QX6323	Pony Express Rider	278

PUPPY LOVE			Dated	page
1991	QX5379	Puppy Love		175
1992	QX4484	Puppy Love		187
1993	QX5045	Puppy Love		201
1994	QX5253	Puppy Love		217
1995	QX5137	Puppy Love		233
1996	QX5651	Puppy Love		248
1997	QX6222	Puppy Love		264
1998	QX6163	Puppy Love		279
ROMANTIC VACATIONS				
1998	QXD4103	Donald And Daisy In Venice		279
SCARLETT O'HARA			*Dated*	
1997	QX6125	Scarlett O'Hara		264
1998	QX6336	Scarlett O'Hara		280
SHOWCASE: LANGUAGE OF FLOWERS			*Dated*	
1996	QK1171	Pansy		244
1997	QX1095	Snowdrop Angel		260
1998	QX6156	Iris Angel		275
SKY'S THE LIMIT			*Dated*	
1997	QX5574	Flight At Kitty Hawk, The		264
1998	QX6286	1917 Curtiss JN-4D "Jenny"		280
SNOW BUDDIES				
1998	QX6853	Snow Buddies		280
SPOTLIGHT ON SNOOPY				
1998	QX6453	Joe Cool		281
STAR WARS			*Dated*	
1997	QXI5484	Luke Skywalker		265
1998	QX14026	Princess Leia		281
STOCK CAR CHAMPIONS				
1997	QXI6165	Jeff Gordon		265
1998	QXI4143	Richard Petty		281
THOMAS KINKADE, Painter Of Light			*Dated*	
1997	QXI6135	Victorian Christmas		265
1998	QXI6343	Victorian Christmas II		281
UNFORGETTABLE VILLIANS				
1998	QXD4063	101 Dalmatians		282
WINNIE THE POOH				
1998	QXD4086	A Visit From Piglet		282

RETIRED:

CHRIS MOUSE		*Series of 13*	*Dated*	page
1985	QLX7032	Chris Mouse		285
1986	QLX7056	Chris Mouse Dreams		285
1987	QLX7057	Chris Mouse Glow		287
1988	QLX7154	Chris Mouse Star		288
1989	QLX7225	Chris Mouse Cookout		290
1990	QLX7296	Chris Mouse Wreath		292
1991	QLX7207	Chris Mouse Mail		293
1992	QLX7074	Chris Mouse Tales		295
1993	QLX7152	Chris Mouse Flight		297
1994	QLX7393	Chris Mouse Jelly		299
1995	QLX7307	Chris Mouse Tree		301
1996	QLX7371	Chris Mouse Inn		303
1997	QLX7525	Chris Mouse Luminaria		305

CHRISTMAS CLASSICS		*Series of 5*	*Dated*	
1986	QLX7043	Nutcracker Ballet, The - Sugarplum Fairy		286
1987	QLX7029	Christmas Carol, A		287
1988	QLX7161	Night Before Christmas		288
1989	QLX7242	Little Drummer Boy		290
1990	QLX7303	Littlest Angel, The		292

FOREST FROLICS		*Series of 7*	*Dated*	
1989	QLX7282	Forest Frolics		290
1990	QLX7236	Forest Frolics		292
1991	QLX7219	Forest Frolics		294
1992	QLX7254	Forest Frolics		296
1993	QLX7165	Forest Frolics		297
1994	QLX7436	Forest Frolics		299
1995	QLX7299	Forest Frolics		301

PEANUTS		*Series of 5*	*Dated*	
1991	QLX7229	Peanuts		294
1992	QLX7214	Peanuts		296
1993	QLX7155	Peanuts		298
1994	QLX7406	Peanuts		300
1995	QLX7277	Peanuts		302

SANTA AND SPARKY		*Series of 3*	*Dated*	
1986	QLX7033	Lighting The Tree		286
1987	QLX7019	Perfect Portrait		288
1988	QLX7191	On With The Show		289

TOBIN FRALEY HOLIDAY CAROUSEL		*Series of 3*	*Dated*	
1994	QLX7496	Tobin Fraley Holiday Carousel		300
1995	QLX7269	Tobin Fraley Holiday Carousel		302
1996	QLX7461	Tobin Fraley Holiday Carousel		304

ONGOING:

CANDLELIGHT SERVICES			page
1998	QLX7636	The Stone Church	306

JOURNEYS INTO SPACE		*Dated*	
1996	QLX7524	Freedom 7: 35th Anniv. 1st Amer. Manned Flight	303
1997	QLX7532	Friendship 7	305
1998	QLX7543	Apollo Lunar Module	306

LIGHTHOUSE GREETINGS		*Dated*	
1997	QLX7442	Lighthouse Greetings	305
1998	QLX7536	Lighthouse Greetings	306

RETIRED:

ALICE IN WONDERLAND		*Series of 4*	*Dated*	**page**
1995	QXM4777	Alice In Wonderland		333
1996	QXM4074	Mad Hatter		336
1997	QXM4142	White Rabbit		339
1998	QXM4186	Cheshire Cat		342

BEARYMORES,THE		*Series of 3*	*Dated*	
1992	QXM5544	Bearymores, The		322
1993	QXM5125	Bearymores, The		326
1994	QXM5133	Bearymores, The		329

KITTENS IN TOYLAND		*Series of 5*	*Not Dated*	
1988	QXM5621	Kittens In Toyland		309
1989	QXM5612	Kittens In Toyland		311
1990	QXM5736	Kittens In Toyland		315
1991	QXM5639	Kittens In Toyland		320
1992	QXM5391	Kittens In Toyland		324

KRINGLES , THE		*Series of 5*	*Not Dated*	
1989	QXM5625	Kringles, The		311
1990	QXM5753	Kringles, The		315
1991	QXM5647	Kringles, The		320
1992	QXM5381	Kringles, The		324
1993	QXM5135	Kringles, The		327

MARCH OF THE TEDDY BEARS		*Series of 4*	*Dated*	
1993	QXM4005	March Of The Teddy Bears		327
1994	QXM5106	March Of The Teddy Bears		331
1995	QXM4799	March Of The Teddy Bears		334
1996	QXM4094	March Of The Teddy Bears		337

NATURE'S ANGELS		*Series of 7*	*Not Dated*	
1990	QXM5733	Nature's Angels - Bunny		316
1991	QXM5657	Nature's Angels - Dog		320
1992	QXM5451	Nature's Angels - Koala Bear		324
1993	QXM5122	Nature's Angels - Cat		327
1994	QXM5126	Nature's Angels - Skunk		331
1995	QXM4809	Nature's Angels - Bear		334
1996	QXM4111	Nature's Angels - Squirrel		337

NIGHT BEFORE CHRISTMAS, THE		*Series of 5*	*Dated*	
1992	QXM5541	Night Before Christmas, The - Mouse, House		324
1993	QXM5185	Display House available separately in 1993		327
1993	QXM5115	Night Before Christmas, The - Children		328
1994	QXM5123	Night Before Christmas, The - Dad		331
1995	QXM4807	Night Before Christmas, The - Santa and Toys		334
1996	QXM4104	Night Before Christmas, The - Santa in Sleigh		337

NOEL R. R.			*Series of 10*	*Dated*	**page**
1989	QXM5762	Locomotive			312
1990	QXM5756	Coal Car			316
1991	QXM5649	Passenger Car			320
1992	QXM5441	Box Car			325
1993	QXM5105	Flatbed Car			328
1994	QXM5113	Stock Car			331
1995	QXM4817	Milk Tank Car			334
1996	QXM4114	Cookie Car			337
1997	QXM4175	Candy Car			340
1998	QXM4216	Caboose			343

OLD ENGLISH VILLAGE			*Series of 10*	*Dated*	
1988	QXM5634	Family Home			309
1989	QXM5615	Sweet Shop			312
1990	QXM5763	School			316
1991	QXM5627	Inn			320
1992	QXM5384	Church			325
1993	QXM5132	Toy Shop			328
1994	QXM5143	Hat Shop			331
1995	QXM4819	Tudor House			335
1996	QXM4124	Village Mill			338
1997	QXM4182	Village Depot			341

ON THE ROAD					
1993	QXM4002	On The Road			328
1994	QXM5103	On The Road			331
1995	QXM4797	On The Road			335
1996	QXM4101	On The Road			338
1997	QXM4172	On The Road			341
1998	QXM4213	On The Road			344

PENGUIN PAL			*Series of 4*	*Not Dated*	
1988	QXM5631	Penguin Pal			309
1989	QXM5602	Penguin Pal			312
1990	QXM5746	Penguin Pal			316
1991	QXM5629	Penguin Pal			321

ROCKING HORSE			*Series of 10*	*Dated*	
1988	QXM5624	Dappled			309
1989	QXM5605	Palomino			312
1990	QXM5743	Pinto			317
1991	QXM5637	Arabian			321
1992	QXM5454	Rocking Horse			325
1993	QXM5112	Rocking Horse			328
1994	QXM5116	Rocking Horse			332
1995	QXM4827	Rocking Horse			335
1996	QXM4121	Rocking Horse			338
1997	QXM4302	Rocking Horse			341

SANTA'S LITTLE BIG TOP			*Series of 3*	*Dated*	
1995	QXM4779	Santa's Little Big Top			335
1996	QXM4081	Santa's Little Big Top			338
1997	QXM4152	Santa's Little Big Top			341

THIMBLE BELLS		*Series of 4*	*Dated*	**page**
1990	QXM5543	Thimble Bell		317
1991	QXM5659	Thimble Bell		321
1992	QXM5461	Thimble Bell		326
1993	QXM5142	Thimble Bell		329

WOODLAND BABIES		*Series of 3*	*Not Dated*	
1991	QXM5667	Woodland Babies		322
1992	QXM5444	Woodland Babies		326
1993	QXM5102	Woodland Babies		329

ONGOING:

ANTIQUE TRACTORS			*Dated*	
1997	QXM4185	Antique Tractors		339
1998	QXM4166	Antique Tractors		342

CENTURIES OF SANTA			*Dated*	
1994	QXM5153	Centuries Of Santa		330
1995	QXM4789	Centuries Of Santa		333
1996	QXM4091	Centuries Of Santa		336
1997	QXM4295	Centuries Of Santa		339
1998	QXM4206	Centuries Of Santa		342

CHRISTMAS BELLS			*Dated*	
1995	QXM4007	Christmas Bells		333
1996	QXM4071	Christmas Bells		336
1997	QXM4162	Christmas Bells		339
1998	QXM4196	Christmas Bells		343

MINIATURE CLOTHESPIN SOLDIER				
1995	QXM4097	Miniature Clothespin Soldier		334
1996	QXM4144	Miniature Clothespin Soldier		337
1997	QXM4155	Miniature Clothespin Soldier		340
1998	QXM4193	Miniature Clothespin Soldier		343

MINIATURE KIDDIE CAR CLASSICS			*Dated*	
1995	QXM4079	Murray "Champion"		334
1996	QXM4031	Murray "Fire Truck"		337
1997	QXM4132	Murray Inc. "Pursuit" Airplane		340
1998	QXM4183	Murray Inc. Dump Truck		343

MINIATURE KIDDIE CAR LUXURY EDITION				
1998	QXM4143	1937 Steelcraft Auburn		343

NATIVITY, THE				
1998	QXM4156	The Nativity		343

NUTCRACKER BALLET, THE		*Series of 5*	*Dated*	page
1996	QXM4064	Nutcracker Ballet, The: Clara and Stage Set/2		338
1997	QXM4135	Herr Drosselmeyer		340
1998	QXM4146	Nutcracker		344

NUTCRACKER GUILD			*Dated*	
1994	QXM5146	Nutcracker Guild - Baker		331
1995	QXM4787	Nutcracker Guild - Postman		334
1996	QXM4084	Nutcracker Guild - Fisherman		338
1997	QXM4165	Nutcracker Guild - Gardener		340
1998	QXM4203	Nutcracker Guild - Skier		344

SNOWFLAKE BALLET			*Dated*	
1997	QXM4192	Snowflake Ballet		341
1998	QXM4173	Snowflake Ballet		344

TEDDY-BEAR STYLE			*Dated*	
1997	QXM4215	Teddy-Bear Style		342
1998	QXM4176	Teddy-Bear Style		344

WELCOME FRIENDS			*Dated*	
1997	QXM4205	Welcome Friends		342
1998	QXM4153	Welcome Friends		344

WINTER FUN WITH SNOOPY				
1998	QXM4243	Winter Fun With Snoopy		345

KEEPSAKE OF MEMBERSHIP

			page
1987	QCX5809	Wreath Of Memories	134
1988	QXC5804	Our Clubhouse	140
1988	QXC5704	Hold On Tight, Miniature	309
1989	QXC5802	Visit From Santa	154
1989	QXC5812	Sitting Purrty, Miniature	313
1990	QXC4456	Club Hollow	157
1990	QXC5603	Crown Prince, Miniature	314
1991	QXC4769	Hidden Treasure, L'il Keeper	172
1992	QXC5081	Rodney Takes Flight	187
1992	QXC5194	Chipmunk Parcel Service, Miniature	322
1993	QXC5272	It's In The Mail	196
1993	QXC5294	Forty Winks, Miniature	326
1994	QXC4823	Holiday Pursuit	212
1994	QXC480-6	Sweet Bouquet, Miniature	332
1995	QXC4117	Collecting Memories	225
1995	QXC5207	Fishing For Fun	226
1995	QXC4129	A Gift From Rodney, Miniature	333
1995	QXM4457	Cool Santa, Miniature	333
1996	QXC4164	Santa	249
1996	QXC7341	Rudolph The Red-Nosed Reindeer	249
1996	QXC4171	Rudolph's Helper, Miniature	338
1997	QXC5132	Happy Christmas To All	263
1997	QXC5135	Away To The Window	263
1997	QXC5142	Ready For Santa, Miniature	340
1997	QXC5145	Jolly Old Santa, Miniature	340
1998	QXC4486	Kringle Bells, Miniature	343
1998	QXC4516	New Christmas Friend	277
1998	QXC4523	Making His Way	275

MEMBERS ONLY ORNAMENTS

1987	QXC5817	Carousel Reindeer	125
1988	QXC5801	Sleighful Of Dreams	142
1989	QXC4285	Collect A Dream	147
1990	QXC4453	Armful Of Joy	155
1991	QXC7259	Beary Artistic, Magic	293
1992	QXC7291	Santa's Club List	187
1993	QXC5432	Trimmed With Memories: Anniversary Ed	205
1994	QXC4853	On Cloud Nine	215
1995	QXC4167	1958 Ford Edsel Citation Convertible	225
1995	QXC5397	Brunette Debut - 1959 BARBIE	223
1995	QXC1059	Home From The Woods	235
1996	QXC4181	BARBIE - 1988 Happy Holidays	239
1996	QXC4174	1937 Steelcraft Auburn By Murray	244
1996	QXC4161	Wizard Of Oz, The	252
1997	QXC5162	BARBIE - 1989 Happy Holidays	254
1997	QXC5182	Tender Touches - Farmer's Market	339
1997	QXC5185	1937 Steelcraft Airflow by Murray	260
1998	QXC4493	BARBIE - 1990 Happy Holidays	268
1998	QXC4496	1935 Steelcraft by Murray	266
1998	QXC4503	Follow The Leader	279

CLUB EDITION ONGOING SERIES: COLLECTORS CLUB BARBIE DOLL SERIES

1996	QXC4181	1988 Happy Holidays BARBIE Doll	239
1997	QXC5162	1989 Happy Holidays BARBIE Doll	254
1998	QXC4493	1990 Happy Holdiays BARBIE Doll	268

CHARTER MEMBER ORNAMENT

			page
1991	QXC3159	Five Years Together	170

RENEWAL BONUS

1988	QXC5104	Merry Miniature: Seal Of Friendship	139
1994	QXC4803	Merry Miniature: Happy Collecting	214
1995	QXC4119	Cozy Christmas: Unofficial "Bottlecap," Mini.	333
1996	QXC4191	Holiday Bunny, Miniature	336

MEMBERS ONLY LIMITED EDITIONS

1988	QX4084	Angelic Minstrel	49,900 pcs	134
1988	QX4071	Christmas Is Sharing	49,900 pcs	135
1988	QX4064	Holiday Heirloom	34,600 pcs	138
1989	QXC4512	Christmas Is Peaceful	49,900 pcs	146
1989	QXC4605	Holiday Heirloom	34,600 pcs	150
1989	QXC4483	Noelle	49,900 pcs	151
1990	QXC4766	Christmas Limited	38,700 pcs	157
1990	QXC4476	Dove Of Peace	25,400 pcs	159
1990	QXC4473	Sugar Plum Fairy	25,400 pcs	165
1991	QXC4779	Galloping Into Christmas	28,400 pcs	171
1991	QXC4797	Secrets For Santa	28,700 pcs	175
1992	QXC5464	Christmas Treasures	15,500 pcs	180
1992	QXC4067	Victorian Skater	14,700 pcs	189
1993	QXC5442	Gentle Tidings	17,500 pcs	194
1993	QXC5435	Sharing Christmas	16,500 pcs	201
1994	QXC4833	Jolly Holly Santa	16,398 pcs	212
1994	QXC4836	Majestic Deer	27,180 pcs	214

MEMBER GET MEMBER GIFT

1993	QXC2112	Circle Of Friendship, Ball Ornament	193
1994	QXC4846	First Hello	351
1995	QXC4159	Merry Miniature: Cinderella's Stepsisters	229
1996	QXC4194	Airmail For Santa	238

KEEPSAKE EASTER SIDEKICK GIFT

1994	QXC8256	Tilling Time *[Gift]*	352
1995	QXC8246	May Flower *[Purchase with Coupon]*	353

EXCLUSIVE PREMIERE ORNAMENTS *available for purchase in limited quantities only at the Ornament Premieres*

1993	QX5692	Tender Touches: You're Always Welcome	204
1994	QX5336	Tender Touches: Eager For Christmas	221
1995	QX5859	Tender Touches: Wish List	237
1996	QFM8054	Merry Miniature: Bashful Mistletoe	245
1997	QX6572	Tender Touches: Perfect Tree, The	265

EXCLUSIVE PREMIERE FIGURINES *available for purchase in limited quantities only at the Ornament Premieres* — **page**

			page
1997	QFM8602	Merry Miniatures: Snowbear Season, Set/3	261
1998	QX6816	Santa's Merry Workshop Musical Figurine, Magic	307
1998	QFM8486	Bride And Groom–1996 Madame Alexander	268
1998	QFM8493	Hershey's Merry Miniatures	274

SIGNATURE COLLECTION *available at Artist Tours Events only, one per collector*

1993	QXC4125	Santa's Favorite Stop	203
1994	QXC4843	Mrs. Claus' Cupboard	220
1995	QXC4049	Christmas Eve Bake-Off	236
1996	QXC4201	Santa's Toy Shop	250
1996		Toy Shop Santa: Companion piece to Toy Shop, only available at Event	250

STUDIO EDITIONS *Dated*

available at Artist Tour Events only, one per Club Member

1997	QXC5175	Trimming Santa's Tree	266
1997	QXC5175	Mrs. Claus' Story: Companion piece to Trimming Santa's Tree, only available at Event.	261

"UNOFFICIAL" BOTTLECAP SERIES *gift for Early Membership Renewal*

1993	QXC5294	Forty Winks, Miniature	326
1994	QXC4806	Sweet Bouquet, Miniature	332
1995	QXC4119	Cozy Christmas, Miniature	333
1996	QXC4191	Holiday Bunny, Miniature	336

APPLE BLOSSOM LANE		*Series of 3*	*Dated*	**page**
1995	QEO8207	Apple Blossom Lane		352
1996	QEO8084	Apple Blossom Lane		354
1997	QEO8662	Apple Blossom Lane		355
COLLECTOR'S PLATE		*Series of 4*	*Dated*	
1994	QEO8233	Gathering Sunny Memories 1994		350
1995	QEO8219	Catching The Breeze		352
1996	QEO8221	Keeping A Secret		354
1997	QEO8675	Sunny Sunday Best		355
EASTER PARADE		*Series of 3*	*Dated*	
1992	QEO9301	Easter Parade		347
1993	QEO8325	Easter Parade		349
1994	QEO8136	Easter Parade		351
EGGS IN SPORTS		*Series of 3*	*Dated*	
1992	QEO9341	Grade A's 92		347
1993	QEO8332	Tennis Ace 93		349
1994	QEO8133	Golf Club 94		351
GARDEN CLUB		*Series of 4*	*Dated*	
1995	QEO8209	Garden Club		353
1996	QEO8091	Garden Club		354
1997	QEO8665	Garden Club		356
1998	QEO8426	Garden Club		358
HERE COMES EASTER		*Series of 4*	*Dated*	
1994	QEO8093	Hop-N-Go 1994		351
1995	QEO8217	Here Comes Easter		353
1996	QEO8094	Here Comes Easter		354
1997	QEO8682	Here Comes Easter		356
JOYFUL ANGELS		*Series of 3*	*Dated*	
1996	QEO8184	Joyful Angels		354
1997	QEO8655	Joyful Angels		356
1998	QEO8386	Joyful Angels		358
SPRINGTIME BARBIE		*Series of 3*	*Dated*	
	Series only available at Gold Crown Retailers with REACH Program			
1995	QEO8069	Springtime BARBIE		353
1996	QEO8081	Springtime BARBIE		355
1997	QEO8642	Springtime BARBIE		356
SPRINGTIME BONNETS		*Series of 5*	*Dated*	
1993	QEO8322	Springtime Bonnets		350
1994	QEO8096	Springtime Bonnets		351
1995	QEO8134	Springtime Bonnets		353
1996	QEO8227	Springtime Bonnets		355
1997	QEO8672	Springtime Bonnets		356

BEATRIX POTTER			*Dated*	**page**
1996	QEO8071	Peter Rabbit		354
1997	QEO8645	Jemima Puddle-duck		355
1998	QEO8383	Benjamin Bunny		357
CHILDREN'S COLLECTOR SERIES			*Dated*	
1997	QEO8635	BARBIE as Rapunzel Doll		355
1998	QEO8373	BARBIE as Little Bo Beep		357
COTTONTAIL EXPRESS			*Dated*	
1996	QEO8074	Locomotive		354
1997	QEO8652	Colorful Coal Car		356
1998	QEO8376	Passenger Car		357
SIDEWALK CRUISERS			*Dated*	
1997	QEO8632	1935 Steelcraft Streamline Velocipede by Murray		356
1998	QEO8393	1939 Mobo Horse		358
VINTAGE ROADSTERS				
1998	QEO8416	1931 Ford Model A Roadster		359

◆ FINAL EDITION IN SERIES

◆ FINAL EDITION IN SERIES

◆ FINAL EDITION IN SERIES

♦ FINAL EDITION IN SERIES

◆ FINAL EDITION IN SERIES

E

F

G

♦ FINAL EDITION IN SERIES

H

♦ FINAL EDITION IN SERIES

♦ FINAL EDITION IN SERIES

♦ FINAL EDITION IN SERIES

♦ FINAL EDITION IN SERIES

♦ FINAL EDITION IN SERIES

N

♦ FINAL EDITION IN SERIES

♦ FINAL EDITION IN SERIES

◆ FINAL EDITION IN SERIES

Q

◆ FINAL EDITION IN SERIES

◆ FINAL EDITION IN SERIES

♦ FINAL EDITION IN SERIES

♦ FINAL EDITION IN SERIES

◆ FINAL EDITION IN SERIES

U

V

W

♦ FINAL EDITION IN SERIES

NOTES:

♦ FINAL EDITION IN SERIES

MAGIC INDEX

◆ FINAL EDITION IN SERIES

◆ FINAL EDITION IN SERIES

NOTES:

◆ FINAL EDITION IN SERIES

♦ FINAL EDITION IN SERIES

◆ FINAL EDITION IN SERIES

◆ FINAL EDITION IN SERIES

NOTES:

◆ FINAL EDITION IN SERIES

◆ FINAL EDITION IN SERIES

NOTES:

NOTES:

OTHER GUIDES FROM GREENBOOK

GREENBOOK Guide to
Ty BEANIE BABIES™

GREENBOOK Guide to
The Enesco PRECIOUS MOMENTS Collection

GREENBOOK Guide to
Hallmark KIDDIE CAR CLASSICS

GREENBOOK Guide to
DEPARTMENT 56® Villages including
The Original Snow Village and
The Heritage Village Collections

GREENBOOK Guide to
DEPARTMENT 56® Snowbabies™

GREENBOOK Guide to
the WALT DISNEY Classics Collection

GREENBOOK Guide to
Enesco's CHERISHED TEDDIES

GREENBOOK Guide to
Precious Moments Company Dolls

GREENBOOK Guide to
Harbour Lights

GREENBOOK Guide to
Boyds Bears

GREENBOOK Guide to
Charming Tails